An Introduction to Semiconductor Devices

An Introduction to Semiconductor Devices

Donald A. Neamen

AN INTRODUCTION TO SEMICONDUCTOR DEVICES
International Edition 2006

10 09 08 07
20 19
SLP

When ordering this title, use ISBN 007-125447-1

www.mhhe.com

To the many students I've had the privilege of teaching over the years who have contributed in many ways to the broad field of electrical engineering, and to future students who will contribute in ways we cannot now imagine.

ABOUT THE AUTHOR

Donald A. Neamen is a professor emeritus in the Department of Electrical and Computer Engineering at the University of New Mexico where he taught for more than 25 years. He received his Ph.D. from the University of New Mexico and then became an electronics engineer at the Solid State Sciences Laboratory at Hanscom Air Force Base. In 1976, he joined the faculty in the ECE department at the University of New Mexico, where he specialized in teaching semiconductor physics and devices courses and electronic circuits courses. He is still a part-time instructor in the department.

In 1980, Professor Neamen received the Outstanding Teacher Award for the University of New Mexico. In 1983 and 1985, he was recognized as Outstanding Teacher in the College of Engineering by Tau Beta Pi. In 1990, and each year from 1994 through 2001, he received the Faculty Recognition Award, presented by graduating ECE students. He was also honored with the Teaching Excellence Award in the College of Engineering in 1994.

In addition to his teaching, Professor Neamen served as Associate Chair of the ECE department for several years and has also worked in industry with Martin Marietta, Sandia National Laboratories, and Raytheon Company. He has published many papers and is the author of *Electronic Circuit Analysis and Design,* Second Edition and *Semiconductor Physics and Devices: Basic Principles,* Third Edition.

CONTENTS IN BRIEF

CONTENTS

PREFACE

PHILOSOPHY AND GOALS

The purpose of this text is to provide a basis for understanding the characteristics, operation, and limitations of semiconductor devices. In order to gain this understanding, it is essential to have a thorough knowledge of the physics of the semiconductor material. The goal of this book is to bring together the fundamental physics of the semiconductor material and the semiconductor device physics.

Since the objective of this text is to provide an introduction to the theory of semiconductor devices, there is a great deal of advanced theory that is not considered. This material is found in more advanced texts. There are occasions in the text where equations and relationships are simply stated with no or very little derivation. Again, the details are found in more advanced texts. However, the author feels that there is enough mathematics included to provide a good foundation for the basic understanding of semiconductor devices in this first course.

PREREQUISITES

This text is intended for junior and senior undergraduates in electrical engineering. The prerequisites for understanding the material are college mathematics, up to and including differential equations, and college physics, including an introduction to modern physics and electrostatics. Prior completion of an introductory course in electronic circuits is helpful, but not essential.

ORDER OF PRESENTATION

Each instructor has a personal preference for the order in which the course material is presented. The order of presentation of topics in this text is somewhat different compared to many semiconductor textbooks. Chapters 1–4 cover the basic physics of the semiconductor material and contain topics normally covered initially in any semiconductor device course. Chapter 5 discusses the electrostatics of the pn and Schottky junctions. This material is necessary and sufficient for the understanding of the MOS transistor presented in Chapters 6 and 7. There are two reasons for discussing the MOS transistor at this point. First, since the MOS transistor is fundamental to integrated circuits, this material is presented early enough in the course so that it doesn't get "short changed," as it might when covered at the end of a course. Second, since a "real" semiconductor device is discussed fairly early in the course, the reader may have more motivation to continue studying this course material.

After the MOS transistor is presented, the nonequilibrium characteristics of the semiconductor material is presented in Chapter 8 and then the forward-biased pn junction and Schottky diodes are discussed in Chapter 9. The bipolar transistor is presented in Chapter 10. Chapter 11 covers additional devices such as junction field-effect transistors and thyristors. Finally, optical devices are discussed in Chapter 12.

One possible disadvantage to this order of presentation is that the discussion of the pn junction is "interrupted." However, the author feels that a "just-in-time" approach is justified. Some discussion of the pn junction is necessary before presenting the MOS transistor. However, if the entire discussion of the pn junction, including the discussion of nonequilibrium excess carriers, took place before the MOS transistor, then much of the knowledge gained of forward-biased pn junctions would be lost by the reader by the time the bipolar transistor is discussed.

The following table lists the textbook approach to the order of presentation of topics. Unfortunately, because of time constraints, every topic in every chapter cannot be covered in a one-semester course.

Textbook Approach	
Chapter 1	Crystal structure
Chapter 2	Selected topics from quantum mechanics and theory of solids
Chapter 3	Semiconductor material physics
Chapter 4	Transport phenomena
Chapter 5	Electrostatics of the pn junction
Chapter 6	The MOS transistor
Chapter 7	Selected topics for advanced MOSFETs
Chapter 8	Selected topics from nonequilibrium semiconductor physics
Chapter 9	The pn junction diode
Chapter 10	The bipolar transistor
Chapter 11	Selected topics from other devices
Chapter 12	Selected topics from optical devices

For those instructors who prefer the classical approach and wish to cover the bipolar transistor before the MOS transistor, the following table lists the order of presentation. The chapters are written so that this order of presentation is very plausible.

Classical Approach	
Chapter 1	Crystal structure
Chapter 2	Selected topics from quantum mechanics and theory of solids
Chapter 3	Semiconductor material physics
Chapter 4	Transport phenomena
Chapter 8	Selected topics from Nonequilibrium semiconductor physics
Chapter 5	Electrostatics of the pn junction
Chapter 9	The pn junction diode
Chapter 10	The bipolar transistor
Chapter 6	The MOS transistor
Chapter 7	Selected topics from advanced MOSFETs
Chapter 11	Selected topics from other devices
Chapter 12	Selected topics from optical devices

USE OF THE BOOK

The text is intended for a one-semester course at the junior or senior level. As with most textbooks, there is more material than can be conveniently covered in one semester; this enables each instructor some flexibility in designing the course to his or her own specific needs.

At the end of several chapters, there is a section dealing with fabrication technology. In Chapter 1, this topic deals with the growth of semiconductor materials and the oxidation process. In Chapter 3, this topic deals with the introduction of specific impurities into the semiconductor by either diffusion or ion implantation. In later chapters, this topic deals with the fabrication of specific devices. In each case, the fabrication discussion is relatively short and intended only to give the reader a basic understanding of the fabrication technology. These sections, as well as a few other sections in the text, are denoted by the symbol Σ in front of the section heading. The symbol Σ shows that reading these sections will aid in the total summation of the understanding of semiconductor devices. However, a basic understanding of semiconductor device physics can be accomplished without studying these sections in detail during this first introductory course.

FEATURES OF THE BOOK

■*Preview section:*   A preview section introduces each chapter. This preview links the chapter to previous chapters and states the chapter's goals, that is, what the reader should gain from the chapter.

■*Historical and Present-Day Insights:*   A Historical Insight section relates the chapter material to a few historical events and a Present-Day Insight section relates the chapter material to current research and manufacturing events.

■*Icon:* Σ, indicates sections that are to be read for understanding to increase the total summation of knowledge of semiconductor devices. However, a detailed study of these sections is not required during this first introductory course.

■*Key terms in the margin:*   Key terms are listed in the margin of the text. Quickly finding a key term adjacent to the text in which the material is discussed should aid the student in reviewing the material.

■*Examples:*   There are a liberal number of examples given in the text to reinforce the theoretical concepts being developed. These examples contain all the details of the analysis or design, so the reader does not have to fill in missing steps.

■*Exercise problems:*   An exercise problem is given after each example. These exercises are similar in scope to the preceding example. The ability to solve these exercise problems should be an indication as to whether the student has mastered the previous material. Answers to these problems are given.

■*Test Your Understanding exercises:*   At the end of major sections, additional exercise problems are given. These exercise problems tend to be more comprehensive than the exercise problems given after each example. Answers to these problems are also given.

■*Summary:*   A summary section follows the text of each chapter. This section summarizes the overall results derived in the chapter and reviews the basic concepts developed.

■*Checkpoint:*   A checkpoint section follows the Summary section. This section states the goals that should have been met and states the abilities the reader should have gained. The Checkpoints will help assess progress before moving to the next chapter.

■*Review questions:*   A list of review questions is included at the end of each chapter. These questions serve as a self-test to help the reader determine how well the concepts developed in the chapter have been mastered.

■*End-of-chapter problems:*   A substantial number of problems are provided at the end of each chapter, organized according to the subject of each section. An asterisk in front of a problem indicates a more difficult problem. Answers to a selected number are provided in Appendix F.

■*Reading list:*   A reading list finishes up each chapter. The references indicated by an asterisk are at a more advanced level compared with this text.

■*Answers to selected problems:*   Answers to selected problems are given in Appendix F. Knowing the answer to a problem can aid and reinforce the problem solving.

SUPPLEMENTS

ACKNOWLEDGMENTS

Peter John Burke, *University of California, Irvine*

Chris S. Ferekides, *University of South Florida*

Ashok K. Goel, *Michigan Technological University*

Lili He, *San Jose State University*

Erin Jones, *Oregon State University*

Yaroslav Koshka, *Mississippi State University*

Shrinivas G. Joshi, *Marquette University*

Gregory B. Lush, *University of Texas, El Paso*

A. James Mallmann, *Milwaukee School of Engineering*

Donald C. Malocha, *University of Central Florida*

Shmuel Mardix, *University of Rhode Island*

An Introduction to Semiconductor Devices

1

The Crystal Structure of Solids

This text deals with the electrical properties and characteristics of semiconductor materials and devices. The electrical properties of solids are therefore of primary interest. Since the semiconductor is in general a single-crystal material and since the electrical properties of a single-crystal material are determined not only by the chemical composition but also by the arrangement of atoms in the solid, a brief study of the crystal structure of solids is warranted. This introductory chapter provides the necessary background in single-crystal materials and crystal growth for a basic understanding of the electrical properties of semiconductor materials and devices.

1.0 | PREVIEW

In this chapter, we will

1. List and describe semiconductor materials.
2. Describe three classifications of solids: amorphous, polycrystalline, and single crystal.
3. Describe basic crystal structures, crystal planes, and the diamond structure.
4. Discuss differences in atomic bonding between various solids.
5. Describe various single-crystal imperfections and impurities in solids.
6. Describe processes that are used to create single-crystal semiconductor materials.
7. Describe the formation of an oxide on silicon.

Historical Insight

Materials have always been an integral part of electrical engineering, from finding good conductors of electricity that can handle hundreds of amperes to finding good insulators that can handle thousands of volts. Dielectric properties of materials are fundamental in the design of capacitors and magnetic properties of materials are fundamental in the design of electromagnets or permanent magnets. Creating high-purity single-crystal semiconductor materials has been crucial to the development of the vast semiconductor industry.

Present-Day Insight

Materials continue to be a fundamental component of electrical engineering. Creating single-crystal silicon semiconductor wafers that are 12 inches in diameter and, at the other end of the scale, creating layers of different semiconductor materials that are on the order of tens of angstroms thick are continuing topics of research. The properties of high-purity single-crystal materials are fundamental to the design of the vast number of semiconductor devices.

1.1 | SEMICONDUCTOR MATERIALS

Objective: List and describe semiconductor materials.

Semiconductors are a group of materials having conductivities between those of metals and insulators. One fundamental characteristic of a semiconductor material is that the conductivity can be varied over several orders of magnitude by adding controlled amounts of impurity atoms. The ability to control and change the conductivity of a semiconductor material allows for the design of the vast number of semiconductor devices.

Two general classifications of semiconductors are the elemental semiconductor materials, found in group IV of the periodic table, and the compound semiconductor materials, most of which are formed from special combinations of group III and group V elements. Table 1.1 shows a portion of the periodic table in which the more common semiconductors are found, and Table 1.2 lists a few of the semiconductor materials. (Semiconductors can also be formed from combinations of group II and group VI elements, but in general these will not be considered in this text.)

Elemental semiconductor

The elemental materials, those that are composed of single species of atoms, are silicon and germanium. Silicon dominates the semiconductor commercial market. The vast majority of integrated circuits (ICs) are fabricated in silicon, so silicon will be emphasized to a great extent in this text.

Binary semiconductor

The two-element, or *binary,* compounds such as gallium arsenide or gallium phosphide are formed by combining one group III and one group V element. Gallium arsenide is one of the more common of the compound semiconductors. It is used to make light-emitting diodes and laser diodes. GaAs is also used in specialized applications in which, for example, very high speed is required.

Ternary semiconductor

We can also form a three-element, or *ternary,* compound semiconductor. An example is $Al_x Ga_{1-x} As$, in which the subscript x indicates the fraction of the lower atomic number element component. More complex semiconductors can also be formed that provide flexibility when choosing material properties.

Table 1.1 | A portion of the periodic table showing elements used in semiconductor materials

Period \ Group	II	III	IV	V	VI
2		B Boron	C Carbon	N Nitrogen	O Oxygen
3		Al Aluminum	Si Silicon	P Phosphorus	S Sulfur
4	Zn Zinc	Ga Gallium	Ge Germanium	As Arsenic	Se Selenium
5	Cd Cadmium	In Indium	Sn Tin	Sb Antimony	Te Tellurium
6	Hg Mercury				

Table 1.2 | A partial list of semiconductor materials

Elemental Semiconductors		**IV Compound Semiconductors**	
Si	Silicon	SiC	Silicon carbide
Ge	Germanium	SiGe	Silicon germanium

Binary III–V Compounds		**Binary II–VI Compounds**	
AlAs	Aluminum arsenide	CdS	Cadmium sulfide
AlP	Aluminum phosphide	CdTe	Cadmium telluride
AlSb	Aluminum antimonide	HgS	Mercury sulfide
GaAs	Gallium arsenide	ZnS	Zinc sulfide
GaP	Gallium phosphide	ZnTe	Zinc telluride
GaSb	Gallium antimonide		
InAs	Indium arsenide		
InP	Indium phosphide		

Ternary Compounds		**Quaternary Compounds**	
$Al_xGa_{1-x}As$	Aluminum gallium arsenide	$Al_xGa_{1-x}As_ySb_{1-y}$	Aluminum gallium arsenic atimonide
$GaAs_{1-x}P_x$	Gallium arsenic phosphide	$Ga_xIn_{1-x}As_{1-y}P_y$	Gallium indium arsenic phosphide

1.2 | TYPES OF SOLIDS

Objective: Describe three classifications of solids: amorphous, polycrystalline, and single crystal.

In Section 1.1, we simply listed various semiconductor materials. Since semiconductors used in discrete device or IC fabrication are generally single-crystal materials, it is worth while discussing various types of crystalline structures. We will describe the spatial arrangement of atoms in crystals and attempt to visualize the three-dimensional configurations. The arrangement of atoms, as well as the chemical composition, affect the electrical properties of the material.

Amorphous, polycrystalline, and single crystal are the three general types of solids. Each type is characterized by the size of an ordered region within the material.

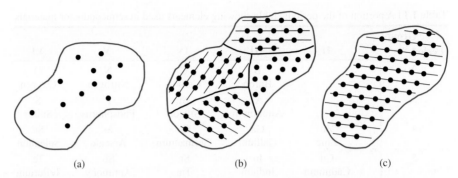

Figure 1.1 | Two-dimensional schematics of three general types of solids: (a) amorphous, (b) polycrystalline, and (c) single crystal.

An ordered region is a spatial volume in which atoms or molecules have a regular geometric arrangement or periodicity. Amorphous materials have order only within a few atomic or molecular dimensions, while polycrystalline materials have a high degree of order over many atomic or molecular dimensions. These ordered regions, or single-crystal regions, vary in size and orientation with respect to one another. The single-crystal regions are called grains and are separated from one another by grain boundaries. Single-crystal materials, ideally, have a high degree of order, or regular geometric periodicity, throughout the entire volume of the material. The advantage of a single-crystal material is that, in general, its electrical properties are superior to those of a nonsingle-crystal material, since grain boundaries tend to degrade the electrical characteristics. Two-dimensional representations of amorphous, polycrystalline, and single-crystal materials are shown in Figure 1.1.

1.3 | SPACE LATTICES

Objective: Describe basic crystal structures, crystal planes, and the diamond structure.

Our primary concern will be the single crystal with its regular geometric periodicity in the atomic arrangement. A representative unit, or group of atoms, is repeated at regular intervals in each of the three dimensions to form the single crystal. The periodic arrangement of atoms in the crystal is called the *lattice*.

Lattice

1.3.1   Primitive and Unit Cell

Lattice point

We can represent a particular atomic array by a dot that is called a *lattice point*. Figure 1.2 shows part of an infinite two-dimensional array of lattice points. The simplest means of repeating an atomic array is by translation. Each lattice point in Figure 1.2 can be translated a distance a_1 in one direction and a distance b_1 in a second noncolinear direction to generate the two-dimensional lattice. A third noncolinear translation will produce the three-dimensional lattice. The translation directions need not be perpendicular.

Since the three-dimensional lattice is a periodic repetition of a group of atoms, we do not need to consider the entire lattice, but only a fundamental unit that is being

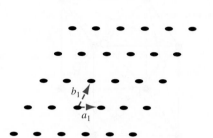

Figure 1.2 | Two-dimensional representation of a single-crystal lattice.

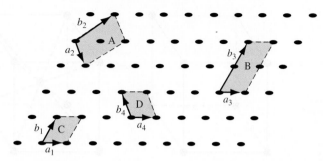

Figure 1.3 | Two-dimensional representation of a single-crystal lattice showing various possible unit cells.

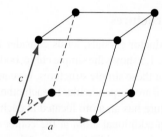

Figure 1.4 | A generalized primitive unit cell.

repeated. A *unit cell* is a small volume of the crystal that can be used to reproduce the entire crystal. A unit cell is not a unique entity. Figure 1.3 shows several possible unit cells in a two-dimensional lattice.

    The unit cell A can be translated in directions a_2 and b_2, the unit cell B can be translated in directions a_3 and b_3, and the entire two-dimensional lattice can be constructed by the translations of either of these unit cells. The unit cells C and D in Figure 1.3 can also be used to construct the entire lattice by using the appropriate translations. This discussion of two-dimensional unit cells can easily be extended to three dimensions to describe a real single-crystal material.

    A *primitive cell* is the smallest unit cell that can be repeated to form the lattice. In many cases, it is more convenient to use a unit cell that is not a primitive cell. Unit cells may be chosen that have orthogonal sides, for example, whereas the sides of a primitive cell may be nonorthogonal.

    A generalized three-dimensional unit cell is shown in Figure 1.4. The relationship between this cell and the lattice is characterized by three vectors $\bar{a}$, $\bar{b}$, and $\bar{c}$, which need not be perpendicular and which may or may not be equal in length. Every equivalent lattice point in the three-dimensional crystal can be found using the vector

$$\bar{r} = p\bar{a} + q\bar{b} + s\bar{c} \qquad (1.1)$$

where p, q, and s are integers. Since the location of the origin is arbitrary, we will let p, q, and s be positive integers for simplicity.

Unit cell

Primitive cell

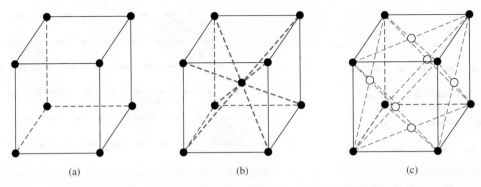

Figure 1.5 | Three lattice types: (a) simple cubic, (b) body-centered cubic, and (c) face-centered cubic.

1.3.2   Basic Crystal Structures

Before we discuss semiconductor crystals, let us consider the characteristics of three basic cubic structures. Figure 1.5 shows the simple cubic, body-centered cubic, and face-centered cubic structures. For these simple structures, we can choose unit cells such that the general vectors $\bar{a}$, $\bar{b}$, and $\bar{c}$ are perpendicular to each other and the lengths are equal. The *simple cubic* (sc) structure has an atom located at each corner; the *body-centered cubic* (bcc) structure has an additional atom at the center of the cube; and the *face-centered cubic* (fcc) structure has an additional atom at the center of each face plane.

Simple cubic
Body-centered cubic
Face-centered cubic

By knowing the crystal structure of a material and its lattice dimensions, we can determine several characteristics of the crystal. For example, we can determine the volume density of atoms.

EXAMPLE 1.1

OBJECTIVE
Determine the volume density of atoms in a crystal.

Consider a single-crystal material that is a face-centered cubic with a lattice constant $a_0 = 5\text{Å} = 5 \times 10^{-8}$ cm. Each corner atom is shared by eight unit cells that meet at the corner, so each corner atom effectively contributes one-eighth of its volume to each unit cell. The eight corner atoms then contribute an equivalent of one atom to the unit cell. Each face atom is shared by two unit cells that meet at each side, so each face atom effectively contributes one-half of its volume to each unit cell. The six face atoms then contribute an equivalent of three atoms to the unit cell. Each unit cell of a face-centered cubic then effectively contains four atoms.

■ **Solution**
The volume density of atoms is then found by dividing the number of unit cell atoms by the unit cell volume, or

$$\text{Volume density} = \frac{4 \text{ atoms}}{a_0^3} = \frac{4}{(5 \times 10^{-8})^3}$$

or

$$\text{Volume density} = 3.2 \times 10^{22} \text{ atoms per cm}^3$$

■ **Comment**

This value of the volume density of atoms in a crystal represents the order of magnitude of density for most materials. The actual density is a function of the crystal type and crystal structure since the packing density—number of atoms per unit cell—depends on crystal structure.

EX1.1 The lattice constant of a body-centered cubic structure is $a_0 = 4.75$Å. Determine the volume density of atoms. (Ans. 1.87×10^{22} cm^{-3})

1.3.3 Crystal Planes and Miller Indices

Since real crystals are not infinitely large, they eventually terminate at a surface. Semiconductor devices are fabricated at or near a surface, so the surface properties may influence the device characteristics. We would like to be able to describe these surfaces in terms of the lattice. Surfaces, or planes through the crystal, can be described by first considering the intercepts of the plane along the $\bar{a}$, $\bar{b}$, and $\bar{c}$ axes used to describe the lattice.

Figure 1.6 shows a general plane intercepting the $\bar{a}$, $\bar{b}$, and $\bar{c}$ axes at points pa, qb, and sc, where p, q, and s are integers. To describe the plane, we write the reciprocals of the intercepts as

$$\left(\frac{1}{p}, \frac{1}{q}, \frac{1}{s}\right) \tag{1.2}$$

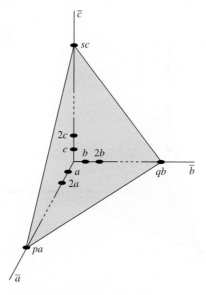

Figure 1.6 | General lattice plane intercepting the $\bar{a}$, $\bar{b}$, and $\bar{c}$ axes at p, q, and s, respectively.

Miller indices

Multiplying by the lowest common denominator, we obtain a set of numbers such as (hkl). The plane is then referred to as the (hkl) plane. The parameters h, k, and l are referred to as the Miller indices.

EXAMPLE 1.2

OBJECTIVE
Describe the plane shown in Figure 1.7.

The lattice points in Figure 1.7 are shown along the $\bar{a}$, $\bar{b}$, and $\bar{c}$ axes only.

■ Solution
From Equation (1.1), the intercepts of the plane correspond to $p = 2$, $q = 3$, and $s = 2$. Write the reciprocals of the intercepts, from Equation (1.2), as

$$\left(\frac{1}{2}, \frac{1}{3}, \frac{1}{2}\right)$$

Now multiply by the lowest common denominator, which in this case is 6, to obtain (3, 2, 3). The plane in Figure 1.7 is then referred to as the (323) plane. The integers are referred to as the Miller indices. We will refer to a general plane as the (hkl) plane.

■ Comment
We can show that the same three Miller indices are obtained for any plane that is parallel to the one shown in Figure 1.7. Any parallel plane is entirely equivalent to any other.

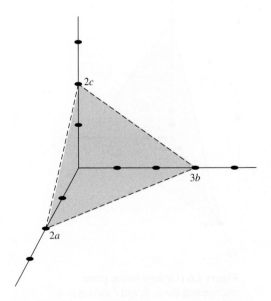

Figure 1.7 | A crystal-lattice plane for Example 1.2.

Exercise Problem

EX1.2 A plane in a simple cubic crystal is described as a (132) plane. (*a*) What are the intercepts on the $\bar{a}$, $\bar{b}$, and $\bar{c}$ axes. (*b*) Sketch the plane. [Ans. (*a*) $p = 6$, $q = 2$, $s = 3$]

Three planes that are commonly considered in a cubic crystal are shown shaded in Figure 1.8. The plane in Figure 1.8a is parallel to the $\bar{b}$ and $\bar{c}$ axes so the intercepts are given as $p = 1$, $q = \infty$, and $s = \infty$. Taking the reciprocal, we obtain the Miller indices as (1, 0, 0), so the plane shown in Figure 1.8a is referred to as the (100) plane. Again, any plane parallel to the one shown in Figure 1.8a and separated by an integral number of lattice constants is equivalent and is referred to as the (100) plane. One advantage to taking the reciprocal of the intercepts to obtain the Miller indices is that the use of infinity is avoided when describing a plane that is parallel to an axis. If we were to describe a plane passing through the origin of our system, we would obtain infinity as one or more of the Miller indices after taking the reciprocal of the intercepts. However, the location of the origin of our system is entirely arbitrary and so, by translating the origin to another equivalent lattice point, we can avoid the use of infinity in the set of Miller indices.

For the simple cubic structure, the body-centered cubic, and the face-centered cubic, there is a high degree of symmetry. The axes can be rotated by 90° in each of the three dimensions and each lattice point can again be described by Equation (1.1) as

$$\bar{r} = p\bar{a} + q\bar{b} + s\bar{c} \tag{1.1}$$

Each face plane of the cubic structure shown in Figure 1.8a is entirely equivalent. These planes are grouped together and are referred to as the {100} set of planes.

We may also consider the planes shown in Figures 1.8b and 1.8c. The intercepts of the plane shown in Figure 1.8b are $p = 1$, $q = 1$, and $s = \infty$. The Miller indices

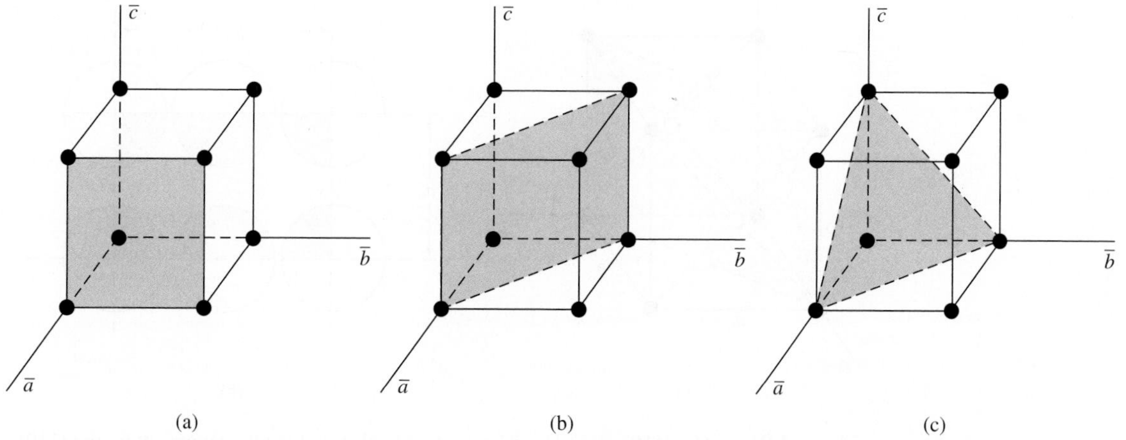

Figure 1.8 | Three lattice planes in a simple cubic lattice: (a) (100) plane, (b) (110) plane, and (c) (111) plane.

are found by taking the reciprocal of these intercepts and, as a result, this plane is referred to as the (110) plane. In a similar way, the plane shown in Figure 1.8c is referred to as the (111) plane.

One characteristic of a crystal that can be determined is the distance between nearest equivalent parallel planes. Another characteristic is the surface concentration of atoms, number per square centimeter (#/cm^2), that are cut by a particular plane. Again, a single-crystal semiconductor is not infinitely large and must terminate at some surface. The surface density of atoms may be important, for example, in determining how another material, such as an insulator, will "fit" on the surface of a semiconductor material.

EXAMPLE 1.3

OBJECTIVE
Calculate the surface density of atoms on a particular plane in a crystal.

Consider the face-centered cubic structure and the (110) plane shown in Figure 1.9a. Assume the atoms can be represented as hard spheres with the closest atoms touching each other and that the lattice constant is $a_0 = 4.5 \text{ Å} = 4.5 \times 10^{-8}$ cm. Figure 1.9b shows how the atoms are cut by the (110) plane.

The atom at each corner is shared by four similar equivalent lattice planes, so each corner atom effectively contributes one-fourth of its area to this lattice plane, as indicated in the figure. The four corner atoms then effectively contribute one atom to this lattice plane. The atom on each face plane is shared by two similar equivalent lattice planes, so each face atom effectively contributes one-half of its area to this lattice plane as indicated in the figure. The two face atoms then effectively contribute one atom to this lattice plane. The lattice plane in Figure 1.9b, then, contains two atoms.

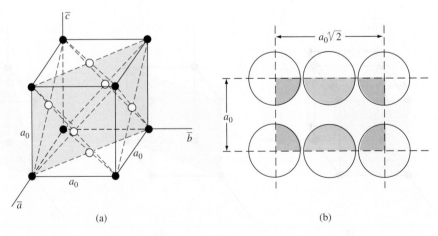

(a)   (b)

Figure 1.9 | (a) The (110) plane in a face-centered cubic and (b) the atoms cut by the (110) plane in a face-centered cubic.

■ **Solution**

We find the surface density by dividing the number of lattice atoms by the surface area, or in this case

$$\text{Surface density} = \frac{2 \text{ atoms}}{(a_0)(a_0\sqrt{2})} = \frac{2}{(4.5 \times 10^{-8})^2(\sqrt{2})}$$

or

$$\text{Surface density} = 6.98 \times 10^{14} \text{ atoms/cm}^2$$

■ **Comment**

The surface density of atoms is a function of the particular crystal plane in the lattice and generally varies from one crystal plane to another.

Exercise Problem

EX1.3 The lattice constant of a body-centered cubic structure is $a_0 = 4.75 \text{ Å} = 4.75 \times 10^{-8}$ cm. Calculate the surface density of atoms for (a) a (100) plane and (b) a (110) plane. [Ans. (a) 4.43×10^{14} cm^{-2}, (b) 6.27×10^{14} cm^{-2}]

In addition to describing crystal planes in a lattice, we may want to describe a particular direction in the crystal. The direction can be expressed as a set of three integers which are the components of a vector in that direction. For example, the body diagonal in a simple cubic lattice is composed of vector components 1, 1, 1. The body diagonal is then described as the [111] direction. The brackets are used to designate direction as distinct from the parentheses used for the crystal planes. The three basic directions and the associated crystal planes for the simple cubic structure are shown in Figure 1.10. Note that in the simple cubic lattices, the [*hkl*] direction is perpendicular to the (*hkl*) plane. This perpendicularity may not be true in noncubic lattices.

Lattice direction

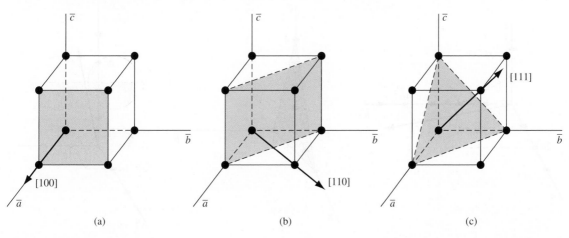

Figure 1.10 | Three lattice planes and directions in a simple cubic lattice: (a) (100) plane and [100] direction, (b) (110) plane and [110] direction, and (c) (111) plane and [111] direction.

EXAMPLE 1.4

OBJECTIVE

Describe a direction in a lattice and the corresponding lattice plane.

Consider the lattice direction shown in Figure 1.11. Describe this lattice direction and the corresponding lattice plane that is perpendicular to this direction.

■ Solution

The direction of the vector shown is described by the components of the vector, or $p = 2$, $q = 4$, and $s = 1$ or [241] direction.

The plane perpendicular to this direction is also described as the (241) plane. The intercepts of the plane are then found by taking the reciprocal of (241) and multiplying by the least common denominator. We find

$$\left(\frac{1}{2}, \frac{1}{4}, \frac{1}{1}\right) \rightarrow (2, 1, 4)$$

or $p = 2$, $q = 1$, and $s = 4$. This plane is shown in Figure 1.12 and is perpendicular to the vector shown in Figure 1.11.

■ Comment

As mentioned, for a simple cubic structure, the direction in the lattice is perpendicular to the corresponding plane.

Exercise Problem

EX1.4 Describe the lattice direction shown in Figure 1.13 and the corresponding lattice plane perpendicular to this direction.

[Ans. [113] direction, (113) plane with intercepts $p = 3$, $q = 3$, and $s = 1$]

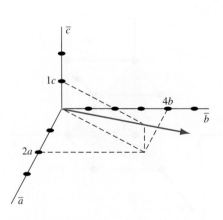

Figure 1.11 | Lattice direction for Example 1.4.

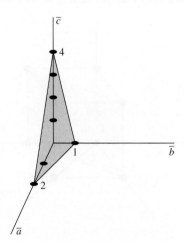

Figure 1.12 | Plane perpendicular to the direction shown in Figure 1.11.

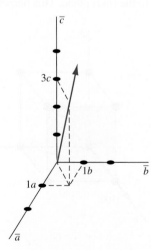

Figure 1.13 | Lattice direction for Exercise Problem EX1.4.

1.3.4 The Diamond Structure

As already stated, silicon is the most common semiconductor material. Silicon is referred to as a group IV element and has a diamond crystal structure. Germanium is also a group IV element and has the same diamond structure. A unit cell of the diamond structure, shown in Figure 1.14, is more complicated than the simple cubic structures that we have considered up to this point.

Diamond lattice

We can begin to understand the diamond lattice by considering the tetrahedral structure shown in Figure 1.15. This structure is basically a body-centered cubic with four of the corner atoms missing. Every atom in the tetrahedral structure has four nearest neighbors and it is this structure that is the basic building block of the diamond lattice.

There are several ways to visualize the diamond structure. One way to gain a further understanding of the diamond lattice is by considering Figure 1.16. Figure 1.16a shows two body-centered cubic, or tetrahedral, structures diagonally adjacent to each

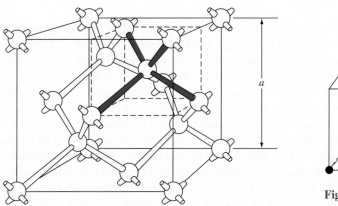

Figure 1.14 | The diamond structure.

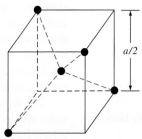

Figure 1.15 | The tetrahedral structure of closest neighbors in the diamond lattice.

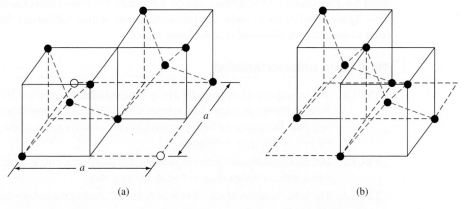

(a)   (b)

Figure 1.16 | Portions of the diamond lattice: (a) bottom half and (b) top half.

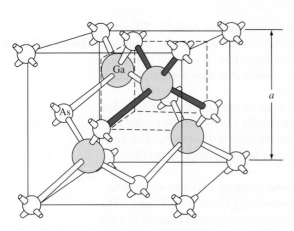

Figure 1.17 | The zincblende (spalerite) lattice of GaAs.

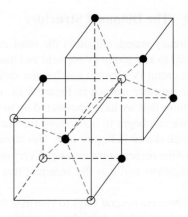

Figure 1.18 | The tetrahedral structure of closest neighbors in the zincblende lattice.

other. The open circles represent atoms in the lattice that are generated when the structure is translated to the right or left, one lattice constant, a. Figure 1.16b represents the top half of the diamond structure. The top half again consists of two tetrahedral structures joined diagonally, but which are at 90° with respect to the bottom-half diagonal. An important characteristic of the diamond lattice is that any atom within the diamond structure will have four nearest neighboring atoms. We will note this characteristic again in our discussion of atomic bonding in Section 1.4.

Zincblende lattice

The diamond structure refers to the particular lattice in which all atoms are of the same species, such as silicon or germanium. The zincblende (sphalerite) structure differs from the diamond structure only in that there are two different types of atoms in the lattice. Compound semiconductors, such as gallium arsenide, have the zincblende structure shown in Figure 1.17. The important feature of both the diamond and the zincblende structures is that the atoms are joined together to form a tetrahedron. Figure 1.18 shows the basic tetrahedral structure of GaAs in which each Ga atom has four nearest As neighbors and each As atom has four nearest Ga neighbors. This figure also begins to show the interpenetration of two sublattices that can be used to generate the diamond or zincblende lattice.

TEST YOUR UNDERSTANDING

TYU1.1 The volume density of atoms for a body-centered cubic lattice is 5×10^{22} cm^{-3}. Assume that the atoms are hard spheres with each atom touching its nearest neighbor. Determine the lattice constant and the effective radius of the atom.
(Ans. $a_0 = 3.42$ Å, $r = 1.48$ Å)

TYU1.2 Determine the distance between nearest (110) planes in a simple cubic lattice with a lattice constant of $a_0 = 4.83$ Å. (Ans. 3.42 Å)

TYU1.3 The lattice constant of silicon is $a_0 = 5.43$ Å. Calculate the volume density of silicon atoms. (Ans. 5×10^{22} cm^{-3})

1.4 | ATOMIC BONDING

Objective: Discuss differences in atomic bonding between various solids.

We have been considering various single-crystal structures. The question arises as to why one particular crystal structure is favored over another for a particular assembly of atoms. A fundamental law of nature is that the total energy of a system in thermal equilibrium tends to reach a minimum value. The interaction that occurs between atoms to form a solid and to reach the minimum total energy depends on the type of atom or atoms involved. The type of bond, or interaction, between atoms, then, depends on the particular atom or atoms in the crystal. If there is not a strong bond between atoms, they will not "stick together" to create a solid.

   The interaction between atoms can be described by quantum mechanics. Although an introduction to quantum mechanics is presented in Chapter 2, the quantum-mechanical description of the atomic bonding interaction is still beyond the scope of this text. We can nevertheless obtain a qualitative understanding of how various atoms interact by considering the valence, or outermost, electrons of an atom.

   The atoms at the two extremes of the periodic table (excepting the inert elements) tend to lose or gain valence electrons, thus forming ions. These ions then essentially have complete outer energy shells. The elements in group I of the periodic table tend to lose their one electron and become positively charged, while the elements in group VII tend to gain an electron and become negatively charged. These oppositely charged ions then experience a coulomb attraction and form a bond referred to as an *ionic bond*. If the ions were to get too close, a repulsive force would become dominant, so an equilibrium distance results between these two ions. In a crystal, negatively charged ions tend to be surrounded by positively charged ions and positively charged ions tend to be surrounded by negatively charged ions, so a periodic array of the atoms is formed to create the lattice. A classic example of ionic bonding is sodium chloride. **Ionic bonding**

   The interaction of atoms tends to form closed valence shells such as we see in ionic bonding. Another atomic bond that tends to achieve closed-valence energy shells is *covalent bonding,* an example of which is found in the hydrogen molecule. A hydrogen atom has one electron and needs one more electron to complete the lowest energy shell. A schematic of two noninteracting hydrogen atoms, and the hydrogen molecule with the covalent bonding, are shown in Figure 1.19. Covalent bonding results in electrons being shared between atoms, so that in effect the valence energy shell of each atom is full. **Covalent bonding**

   Atoms in group IV of the periodic table, such as silicon and germanium, also tend to form covalent bonds. Each of these elements has four valence electrons and needs four more electrons to complete the valence energy shell. If a silicon atom, for example, has four nearest neighbors, with each neighbor atom contributing one valence electron to be shared, then the center atom will in effect have eight electrons in its outer shell. Figure 1.20a schematically shows five noninteracting silicon atoms with the four valence electrons around each atom. A two-dimensional representation of the covalent bonding in silicon is shown in Figure 1.20b. The center atom has eight shared valence electrons.

   Figure 1.20b shows a two-dimensional representation of the covalent bonding of silicon atoms. In the actual three-dimensional structure, the atoms are arranged in a

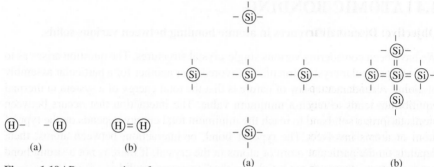

Figure 1.19 | Representation of (a) hydrogen valence electrons and (b) covalent bonding in a hydrogen molecule.

Figure 1.20 | Two-dimensional representation of (a) silicon valence electrons and (b) covalent bonding in the silicon crystal.

tetrahedral configuration, as was shown in Figure 1.15. However, the two-dimensional representation will be useful in much of the discussion of semiconductor behavior.

A significant difference between the covalent bonding of hydrogen and of silicon is that, when the hydrogen molecule is formed, it has no additional electrons to form additional covalent bonds, while the outer silicon atoms always have valence electrons available for additional covalent bonding. The silicon array may then be formed into an infinite crystal, with each silicon atom having four nearest neighbors and eight shared electrons. The four nearest neighbors in silicon forming the covalent bond correspond to the tetrahedral structure and the diamond lattice, which were shown in Figures 1.15 and 1.14, respectively. Atomic bonding and crystal structure are obviously directly related.

Metallic bonding
The third major atomic bonding scheme is referred to as *metallic bonding*. Group I elements have one valence electron. If two sodium atoms ($Z = 11$), for example, are brought into close proximity, the valence electrons interact in a way similar to that in covalent bonding. When a third sodium atom is brought into close proximity with the first two, the valence electrons can also interact and continue to form a bond. Solid sodium has a body-centered cubic structure, so each atom has eight nearest neighbors with each atom sharing many valence electrons. We can think of the positive metallic ions as being surrounded by a sea of negative electrons, the solid being held together by the electrostatic forces. This description gives a qualitative picture of the metallic bond.

A fourth type of atomic bond, called the *Van der Waals* bond, is the weakest of the chemical bonds. A hydrogen fluoride (HF) molecule, for example, is formed by an ionic bond. The effective center of the positive charge of the molecule is not the same as the effective center of the negative charge. This nonsymmetry in the charge distribution results in a small electric dipole that can interact with the dipoles of other HF molecules. With these weak interactions, solids formed by the Van der Waals bonds have a relatively low melting temperature—in fact, most of these materials are in gaseous form at room temperature.

1.5 | IMPERFECTIONS AND IMPURITIES IN SOLIDS

Objective: Describe various single-crystal imperfections and impurities in solids.

Up to this point, we have been considering an ideal single-crystal structure. In a real crystal, the lattice is not perfect, but contains imperfections or defects; that is, the perfect geometric periodicity is disrupted in some manner. Imperfections tend to alter the electrical properties of a material and, in some cases, electrical parameters can be dominated by these defects or impurities. We will see in Chapter 3 that, by adding small, controlled concentrations of a specific impurity atom in a semiconductor, the conductivity of the material can be significantly changed in a favorable manner.

1.5.1 Imperfections in Solids

One type of imperfection that all crystals have in common is atomic thermal vibration. A perfect single crystal contains atoms at particular lattice sites, the atoms separated from each other by a distance we have assumed to be constant. The atoms in a crystal, however, have a certain thermal energy, which is a function of temperature. The thermal energy causes the atoms to vibrate in a random manner about an equilibrium lattice point. This random thermal motion causes the distance between atoms to randomly fluctuate, slightly disrupting the perfect geometric arrangement of atoms. This imperfection, called *lattice vibrations,* affects some electrical parameters, as we will see later in our discussion of semiconductor material characteristics.

Another type of defect is called a *point defect.* There are several of this type that we need to consider. Again, in an ideal single-crystal lattice, the atoms are arranged in a perfect periodic arrangement. However, in a real crystal, an atom may be missing from a particular lattice site. This defect is referred to as a *vacancy;* it is schematically **Vacancy defect** shown in Figure 1.21a. In another situation, an atom may be located between lattice sites. This defect is referred to as an *interstitial* and is schematically shown in **Interstitial defect** Figure 1.21b. In the case of vacancy and interstitial defects, not only is the perfect geometric arrangement of atoms broken, but also the ideal chemical bonding between atoms is disrupted, which tends to change the electrical properties of the material. A

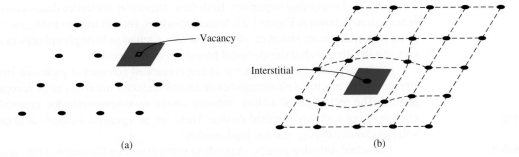

Figure 1.21 | Two-dimensional representation of a single-crystal lattice showing (a) a vacancy defect and (b) an interstitial defect.

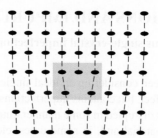

Figure 1.22 | Two-dimensional representation of a line dislocation.

vacancy and interstitial may be in close enough proximity to exhibit an interaction between the two point defects. This vacancy-interstitial defect, also known as a *Frenkel defect,* produces different effects than the simple vacancy or interstitial.

The point defects involve single atoms or single-atom locations. In forming single-crystal materials, more complex defects may occur. A line defect, for example, occurs when an entire row of atoms is missing from its normal lattice site. This defect is referred to as a *line dislocation* and is shown in Figure 1.22. As with a point defect, a line dislocation disrupts both the normal geometric periodicity of the lattice and the ideal atomic bonds in the crystal. This dislocation can also alter the electrical properties of the material, usually in a less predictable manner than the simple point defects.

Other complex dislocations can also occur in a crystal lattice. However, this introductory discussion is intended only to present a few of the basic types of defects, and to show that a real crystal is not necessarily a perfect lattice structure. The effect of these imperfections on the electrical properties of a semiconductor will be considered in Chapter 8.

1.5.2   Impurities in Solids

Substitutional impurity

Foreign atoms, or impurity atoms, may be present in a crystal lattice. Impurity atoms may be located at normal lattice sites, in which case they are called *substitutional* impurities. Impurity atoms may also be located between normal sites, in which case they are called *interstitial* impurities. Both these impurities are lattice defects and are schematically shown in Figure 1.23. Some impurities, such as oxygen in silicon, tend to be essentially inert; however, other impurities, such as gold or phosphorus in silicon, can drastically alter the electrical properties of the material.

Doping

Diffusion

In Chapter 3 we will see that, by adding controlled amounts of particular impurity atoms, the electrical characteristics of a semiconductor material can be favorably altered. The technique of adding impurity atoms to a semiconductor material to change its conductivity is called *doping*. There are two general methods of doping: solid/gas source doping and ion implantation.

The actual diffusion process depends to some extent on the material but, in general, impurity diffusion occurs when a semiconductor crystal is placed in a high-temperature ($\approx 1000°C$) gaseous atmosphere containing the desired impurity atom.

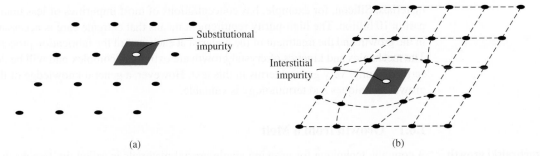

Figure 1.23 | Two-dimensional representation of a single-crystal lattice showing (a) a substitutional impurity and (b) an interstitial impurity.

At this high temperature, many of the crystal atoms can randomly move in and out of their single-crystal lattice sites. Vacancies may be created by this random motion so that impurity atoms can move through the lattice by hopping from one vacancy to another. Impurity diffusion is the process by which impurity particles move from a region of high concentration near the surface to a region of lower concentration within the crystal. When the temperature decreases, the impurity atoms become permanently frozen into the substitutional lattice sites. Diffusion of various impurities into selected regions of a semiconductor enables us to fabricate complex electronic circuits in a single semiconductor crystal.

Ion implantation generally takes place at a lower temperature than diffusion. A collimated beam of impurity ions is accelerated to kinetic energies in the range of 50 keV or greater and then directed to the surface of the semiconductor. The high-energy impurity ions enter the crystal and come to rest at some average depth from the surface. One advantage of ion implantation is that controlled numbers of impurity atoms can be introduced into specific regions of the crystal. A disadvantage of this technique is that the incident impurity atoms collide with the crystal atoms, causing lattice-displacement damage. However, most of the lattice damage can be removed by thermal annealing, in which the temperature of the crystal is raised for a short time. Thermal annealing is a required step after implantation.

Ion implantation

Σ^1 1.6 | GROWTH OF SEMICONDUCTOR MATERIALS

Objective: Describe processes that are used to create single-crystal semiconductor materials.

The success in fabricating very large scale integrated (VLSI) circuits is a result, to a large extent, of the development of and improvement in the formation or growth of pure single-crystal semiconductor materials. Semiconductors are some of the purest

---

[1]Σ Indicates those sections that will aid in the total summation of understanding of semiconductor devices, but may be skipped the first time through the text.

materials. Silicon, for example, has concentrations of most impurities of less than 1 part in 10 billion. The high-purity requirement means that extreme care is necessary in the growth and the treatment of the material at each step of the fabrication process. The mechanics and kinetics of crystal growth are extremely complex and will be described in only very general terms in this text. However, a general knowledge of the growth techniques and terminology is valuable.

1.6.1   Growth from a Melt

Czochralski growth method

A common technique for growing single-crystal materials is called the *Czochralski method*. In this technique, a small piece of single-crystal material, known as a *seed*, is brought into contact with the surface of the same material in liquid phase, and then slowly pulled from the melt. As the seed is slowly pulled, solidification occurs along the plane between the solid–liquid interface. Usually the crystal is also rotated slowly as it is being pulled, to provide a slight stirring action to the melt, resulting in a more uniform temperature. Controlled amounts of specific impurity atoms, such as boron or phosphorus, may be added to the melt so that the grown semiconductor crystal is intentionally doped with the impurity atom. Figure 1.24a shows a schematic of the Czochralski growth process and a silicon ingot or boule grown by this process.

Some impurities may be present in the ingot that are undesirable. Zone refining is a common technique for purifying material. A high-temperature coil, or r-f induction coil, is slowly passed along the length of the boule. The temperature induced by the coil is high enough so that a thin layer of liquid is formed. At the solid–liquid interface is a distribution of impurities between the two phases. The parameter that describes this distribution is called the *segregation coefficient:* the ratio of the concentration of impurities in the solid to the concentration in the liquid. If the segregation coefficient is 0.1, for example, the concentration of impurities in the liquid is a factor of 10 greater than that in the solid. As the liquid zone moves through the material, the impurities are driven along with the liquid. After several passes of the r-f coil, most impurities are at the end of the bar, which can then be cut off. The moving molten zone, or the zone-refining technique, can result in considerable purification.

After the semiconductor is grown, the boule is mechanically trimmed to the proper diameter and a flat is ground over the entire length of the boule to denote the crystal orientation. The flat is perpendicular to the [110] direction or indicates the (110) plane. (See Figure 1.24b.) This then enables the individual chips to be fabricated along given crystal planes so that the chips can be sawed apart more easily. The boule is then sliced into wafers. The wafer must be thick enough to mechanically support itself. A mechanical two-sided lapping operation produces a flat wafer of uniform thickness. Since the lapping procedure can leave a surface damaged and contaminated by the mechanical operation, the surface must be removed by chemical etching. The final step is polishing. This provides a smooth surface on which devices may be fabricated or further growth processes may be carried out. This final semiconductor wafer is called the substrate material.

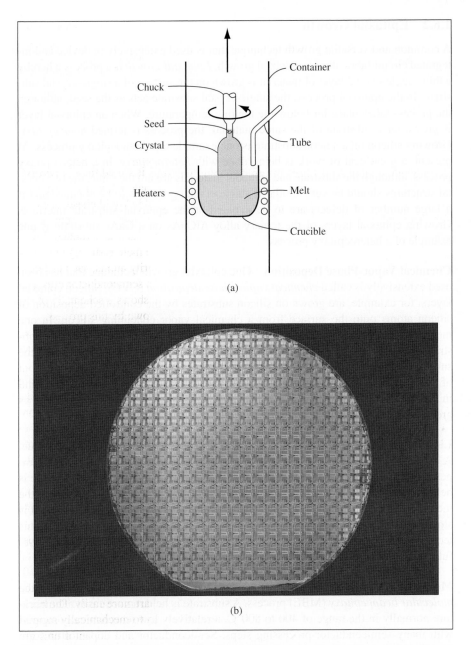

(a)

(b)

Figure 1.24 (a) Schematic of a crystal puller and (b) photograph of a silicon wafer with an array of integrated circuits. The circuits are tested on the wafer then sawed apart into chips that are mounted into packages. The flat at the bottom of the photograph is perpendicular to the [110] direction. (Photo courtesy of Intel Corporation.)

1.6.2   Epitaxial Growth

Epitaxial growth

A common and versatile growth technique that is used extensively in device and integrated circuit fabrication is epitaxial growth. *Epitaxial growth* is a process whereby a thin, single-crystal layer of material is grown on the surface of a single-crystal substrate. In the epitaxial process, the single-crystal substrate acts as the seed, although the process takes place far below the melting temperature. When an epitaxial layer is grown on a substrate of the same material, the process is termed *homoepitaxy*. Growing silicon on a silicon substrate is one example of a homoepitaxy process. At present, a great deal of work is being done with *heteroepitaxy*. In a heteroepitaxy process, although the substrate and epitaxial materials are not the same, the two crystal structures should be very similar if single-crystal growth is to be obtained and if a large number of defects are to be avoided at the epitaxial–substrate interface. Growing epitaxial layers of the ternary alloy AlGaAs on a GaAs substrate is one example of a heteroepitaxy process.

Chemical Vapor-Phase Deposition   One epitaxial growth technique that has been used extensively is called *chemical vapor-phase deposition* (CVD). Silicon epitaxial layers, for example, are grown on silicon substrates by the controlled deposition of silicon atoms onto the surface from a chemical vapor containing silicon. In one method, silicon tetrachloride reacts with hydrogen at the surface of a heated substrate. The silicon atoms are released in the reaction and can be deposited onto the substrate, while the other chemical reactant, HCl, is in gaseous form and is swept out of the reactor. A sharp demarcation between the impurity doping in the substrate and in the epitaxial layer can be achieved using the CVD process. This technique allows great flexibility in the fabrication of semiconductor devices.

Liquid-Phase Epitaxy   *Liquid-phase epitaxy* is another epitaxial growth technique. A compound of the semiconductor with another element may have a melting temperature lower than that of the semiconductor itself. The semiconductor substrate is held in the liquid compound and, since the temperature of the melt is lower than the melting temperature of the substrate, the substrate does not melt. As the solution is slowly cooled, a single-crystal semiconductor layer grows on the seed crystal. This technique, which occurs at a lower temperature than the Czochralski method, is useful in growing group III–V compound semiconductors.

Molecular Beam Epitaxy   A versatile technique for growing epitaxial layers is the *molecular beam epitaxy* (MBE) process. A substrate is held in vacuum at a temperature normally in the range of 400 to 800°C, a relatively low temperature compared with many semiconductor-processing steps. Semiconductor and dopant atoms are then evaporated onto the surface of the substrate. In this technique, the doping can be precisely controlled, resulting in very complex doping profiles. Complex ternary compounds, such as AlGaAs, can be grown on substrates, such as GaAs, where abrupt changes in the crystal composition are desired. Many layers of various types of epitaxial compositions can be grown on a substrate in this manner. These structures are extremely beneficial in optical devices such as laser diodes.

Σ 1.7 | DEVICE FABRICATION TECHNIQUES: OXIDATION

Objective: Describe the formation of an oxide on silicon.

The integrated circuit is a direct result of the development of various processing techniques needed to fabricate the transistor and interconnect lines on the single chip. The total collection of these processes for making an IC is called a *technology*. Introductions to basic fabrication processes are given throughout the text where appropriate. Here, we discuss one such process—thermal oxidation.

A major reason for the success of silicon ICs is the fact that an excellent native oxide, silicon dioxide (SiO_2), can be formed on the surface of silicon. This oxide is used as a gate insulator in the metal–oxide–semiconductor field-effect transistor (MOSFET). As we will see in Chapter 6, the oxide is an integral part of this electronic device. Most other semiconductors do not form native oxides that are of sufficient quality to be used in device fabrication.

Silicon dioxide is an important material in the fabrication process for devices, as we will see throughout the text. In addition, the oxide is used as an insulator, known as the field oxide, between devices. Metal interconnect lines that electrically connect various electronic devices on the chip can be placed on top of the field oxide. The thermal oxidation of silicon in an atmosphere of oxygen proceeds according to the reaction

$$Si(solid) + O_2(gas) \rightarrow SiO_2(solid)$$

This process is called a *dry oxidation* since oxygen is present without any water vapor.   **Dry oxidation**

After an oxide layer forms on the surface of the silicon, oxygen molecules must diffuse through the existing oxide to reach the silicon surface where the reaction occurs. This process is shown in Figure 1.25. The probability of Si diffusing through the

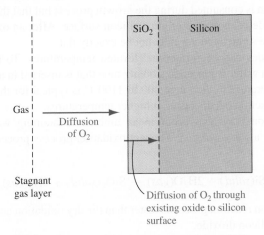

Figure 1.25 | Schematic of the oxidation process indicating the diffusion of oxygen through the existing silicon dioxide.

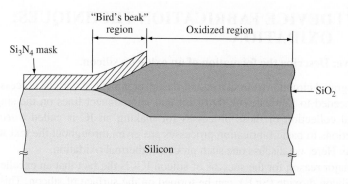

Figure 1.26 | Silicon dioxide grows over bare silicon. However, there will be some lateral growth under the silicon nitride mask. Since the silicon dioxide both consumes silicon and grows in thickness, a "bird's beak" region forms as shown.

SiO_2 is many orders of magnitude smaller than the probability of O_2 diffusing through SiO_2. For this reason, the chemical reaction occurs at the Si–SiO_2 interface. The amount of silicon consumed during the chemical reaction is about 44 percent of the thickness of the final oxide.

A native oxide forms on the surface of silicon at room temperature. However, when the oxide thickness reaches approximately 25 Å, the reaction effectively stops since the diffusion coefficient of O_2 in SiO_2 at room temperature is extremely small.

Figure 1.26 shows an example of a finished oxidation process. The silicon dioxide only grows on bare silicon. Silicon nitride (Si_3N_4) acts as a mask so SiO_2 will not grow over this region. However, the SiO_2 will tend to grow laterally under the edge of the Si_3N_4 to form a "bird's beak" region, as shown in the figure. The figure also shows that silicon is consumed during the growth process but that the final surface of the silicon dioxide is above the original silicon surface. After an oxidation process, the surface of the semiconductor may not be exactly flat.

Thicker oxides can be formed at elevated temperatures. To create a thermal oxide, the silicon wafer is placed in a quartz tube that is inserted in a resistive-heated furnace. A temperature in the range 800 to 1100°C is typical for thermal oxidation. The chemical reaction occurs faster at higher temperatures.

Wet oxidation
The oxidation may also occur in an ambient containing water vapor. This process is called a *wet oxidation*. The wet oxidation process proceeds according to the reaction

$$Si(solid) + 2H_2O(gas) \rightarrow SiO_2(solid) + 2H_2(gas)$$

This wet oxidation reaction proceeds faster than the dry oxidation and is used to form thick layers of silicon dioxide.

As the silicon dioxide forms, the oxygen or water molecules diffuse through the previously created oxide, as mentioned, to form additional SiO_2. For very thin oxides, the oxide thickness is directly proportional to the oxidation time, whereas for thicker

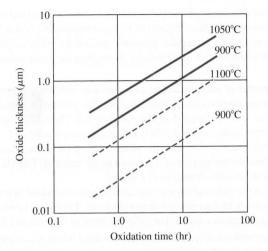

Figure 1.27 | A few curves showing silicon dioxide thickness as a function of oxidation time and temperature for (111) oriented silicon. Solid lines, wet oxidation: dotted lines, dry oxidation.

oxides, the oxide thickness is approximately proportional to the square root of the oxidation time. The oxide thickness versus oxidation time for dry and wet oxidation processes for a couple of oxidation temperatures are shown in Figure 1.27. The oxide thickness is a strong function of temperature, but is also a function of the silicon surface orientation.

Silicon dioxide layers can also be formed by deposition. However, thermally grown oxides are generally higher-quality oxides than deposited oxides. Thermally grown oxides are strongly bonded to the silicon surface, and the interface between the Si and SiO_2, in general, has stable and controlled electrical characteristics. The quality of the $Si–SiO_2$ interface is an important characteristic in the fabrication of the MOSFET, as we will see in Chapter 6.

This discussion presents the basic concepts of thermal oxidation. There are several finer details that are usually incorporated in the oxidation process. For example, chlorine may be incorporated in the oxygen atmosphere. Chlorine reacts with metallic contaminants so Cl has the effect of cleaning the gas ambient. Chlorine also produces better $Si–SiO_2$ interface characteristics.

Additional oxidation details can be found in the various fabrication references found at the end of the chapter.

1.8 | SUMMARY

1. A list of some common semiconductor materials was presented. The conductivity of a semiconductor can be varied by orders of magnitude, as we will see in Chapter 3. Silicon is the most common semiconductor material, but other semiconductor materials are useful in specialized applications.

2. The characteristics of amorphous, polycrystalline, and single-crystal materials are defined in terms of the ordered regions of atoms or molecules. Atoms in an amorphous material have essentially no regular geometric periodicity, while single-crystal materials have a high degree of periodicity throughout the entire volume of material.

3. A. The properties of semiconductors and other materials are determined to a large extent by the single-crystal lattice structure. The unit cell is a small volume of the crystal that is used to reproduce the entire crystal. Three basic unit cells are the simple cubic, body-centered cubic, and face-centered cubic.

   B. Miller indices are used to describe planes in a crystal lattice. These planes can be used to describe the surface of a semiconductor material. The Miller indices are also used to describe directions in a crystal.

   C. Silicon has the diamond crystal structure. Atoms are formed in a tetrahedral configuration with four nearest-neighbor atoms. The binary semiconductors have a zincblende lattice, which is basically the same as the diamond lattice.

4. The interaction between silicon atoms forms covalent bonds. Covalent bonding results in electrons being shared between atoms.

5. Imperfections do exist in semiconductor materials. A few of these imperfections are vacancies, substitutional impurities, and interstitial impurities. Small amounts of controlled substitutional impurities can favorably alter semiconductor properties as we will see in Chapter 3.

6. A brief description of semiconductor growth methods was given. Bulk growth, using the Czochralski method, for example, produces the starting semiconductor material or substrate. Epitaxial growth can be used to control the surface properties of a semiconductor. Most semiconductor devices are fabricated in the epitaxial layer.

7. The thermal oxidation of the silicon surface was described. The oxidation process is used extensively in semiconductor device fabrication as we will see throughout the text.

CHECKPOINT

After studying this chapter, the reader should have the ability to

1. List two elemental semiconductor materials and several compound semiconductor materials.

2. Describe the differences between amorphous, polycrystalline, and single-crystal materials.

3. A. Determine the volume density of atoms for various lattice structures.

   B. Determine the Miller indices of a crystal-lattice plane and sketch a lattice plane given the Miller indices.

   C. Determine the surface density of atoms on a given crystal-lattice plane.

   D. Describe the diamond lattice.

4. Describe what is meant by covalent bonding.

5. Understand and describe various defects in a single-crystal lattice.

6. Describe the basic epitaxial growth process.

7. Describe the thermal oxidation process of silicon.

REVIEW QUESTIONS

1. List two elemental semiconductor materials and two compound semiconductor materials.
2. Describe the primary characteristic that differentiates an amorphous material from a single-crystal material.
3. A. Sketch three lattice structures: (*a*) simple cubic, (*b*) body-centered cubic, and (*c*) face-centered cubic.
   B. Describe the procedure for finding the volume density of atoms in a crystal.
   C. Describe the procedure for obtaining the Miller indices that describe a plane in the crystal.
   D. Describe the procedure for finding the surface density of atoms in a crystal plane.
4. Sketch a two-dimensional representation of a single-crystal silicon lattice showing the valence electrons. What is covalent bonding?
5. What is meant by a substitutional impurity in a crystal? What is meant by an interstitial impurity?
6. What is meant by epitaxial growth?
7. Why does the thermal oxidation of silicon occur at the Si–SiO$_2$ interface even after an oxide has formed?

PROBLEMS

Section 1.3   Space Lattices

1.1   Determine the number of atoms per unit cell in a (*a*) face-centered cubic, (*b*) body-centered cubic, and (*c*) diamond lattice.

1.2   The lattice constant of GaAs is 5.65 Å. Determine the number of Ga atoms and As atoms per cm^3.

1.3   Determine the volume density of germanium atoms in a germanium semiconductor. The lattice constant of germanium is 5.65 Å.

1.4   Assume that each atom is a hard sphere with the surface of each atom in contact with the surface of its nearest neighbor. Determine the percentage of total unit cell volume that is occupied in (*a*) a simple cubic lattice, (*b*) a face-centered cubic lattice, (*c*) a body-centered cubic lattice, and (*d*) a diamond lattice.

1.5   Consider GaAs. What is the distance (center-to-center) between nearest Ga and As atoms?

1.6   A material, with a volume of 1 cm^3, is composed of an fcc lattice with a lattice constant of 2.5 mm. The "atoms" in this material are actually coffee beans. Assume the coffee beans are hard spheres with each bean touching its nearest neighbor. Determine the volume of coffee after the coffee beans have been ground. (Assume 100 percent packing density of the ground coffee.)

1.7   If the lattice constant of silicon is 5.43 Å, calculate (*a*) the distance from the center of one silicon atom to the center of its nearest neighbor, (*b*) the number density of silicon atoms (#/cm^3), and (*c*) the mass density (grams/cm^3) of silicon.

1.8   A crystal is composed of two elements, A and B. The basic crystal structure is a face-centered cubic with element A at each of the corners and element B in the face plane. The effective radius of element A is 1.02 Å. Assume the elements are hard spheres with the surface of each A-type atom in contact with the surface of its nearest A-type neighbor. Calculate (*a*) the maximum radius of the B-type atom that will fit into this structure and (*b*) the volume density (#/cm^3) of both A-type atoms and B-type atoms.

1.9   Assume the radius of an atom is $r = 2.1$ Å and can be represented as a hard sphere. The atom is placed in simple cubic, bcc, fcc, and diamond lattices. What is the lattice constant of each lattice?

1.10 The crystal structure of sodium chloride (NaCl) is a simple cubic lattice with the Na and Cl atoms alternating positions. Each Na atom is surrounded by six Cl atoms, and likewise each Cl atom is surrounded by six Na atoms. (*a*) Sketch the atoms in a (100) plane. (*b*) Assume the atoms are hard spheres with nearest neighbors touching. The effective radius of Na is 1.0 Å and the effective radius of Cl is 1.8 Å. Determine the lattice constant. (*c*) Calculate the volume density of Na and Cl atoms. (*d*) Calculate the mass density of NaCl.

1.11 (*a*) A material is composed of two types of atoms. Atom A has an effective radius of 2.2 Å and atom B has an effective radius of 1.8 Å. The lattice is a bcc with atoms A at the corners and atom B in the center. Determine the lattice constant and the volume densities of A atoms and B atoms. (*b*) Repeat part (*a*) with atoms B at the corners and atom A in the center. (*c*) What comparison can be made of the materials in parts (*a*) and (*b*)?

1.12 Consider the materials described in Problem 1.11 in parts (*a*) and (*b*). For each case, calculate the surface density of A atoms and B atoms in the (110) plane. What comparison can be made of the two materials?

1.13 (*a*) A simple cubic structure consists of a single atom in the center of the cube. The lattice constant is a_0 and the diameter of the atom is a_0. Determine the volume density of atoms and the surface density of atoms in the (110) plane. (*b*) Compare the results of part (*a*) to the results for the case of the simple cubic structure shown in Figure 1.5a with the same lattice constant.

1.14 Consider the (100), (110), and (111) planes in silicon. (*a*) Which plane has the highest surface density of atoms? What is that density? (*b*) Which plane has the smallest surface density of atoms? What is that density?

1.15 Consider a three-dimensional cubic lattice with a lattice constant equal to a_0. (*a*) Sketch the following planes: (*i*) (100), (*ii*) (130), and (*iii*) (203). (*b*) Sketch the following directions: (*i*) [110], (*ii*) [311], and (*iii*) [123].

1.16 For a simple cubic lattice, determine the Miller indices for the planes shown in Figure P1.16.

1.17 The lattice constant of a simple cubic cell is 5.25 Å. Calculate the distance between the nearest parallel (*a*) (100), (*b*) (110), and (*c*) (111) planes.

1.18 The lattice constant of a simple cubic cell is 5.20 Å. Calculate the distance between the nearest parallel (*a*) (100), (*b*) (110), and (*c*) (111) planes.

1.19 Consider a body-centered cubic lattice. Assume the atoms are hard spheres with the surfaces of the nearest neighbors touching. Assume the radius of the atom is 2.25 Å. (*a*) Calculate the volume density of atoms in the crystal. (*b*) Calculate the distance between nearest (110) planes. (*c*) Calculate the surface density of atoms on the (110) plane.

Section 1.4   Atomic Bonding

1.20 Calculate the density of valence electrons in silicon.

1.21 The structure of GaAs is the zincblende lattice. The lattice constant is 5.65 Å. Calculate the density of valence electrons in GaAs.

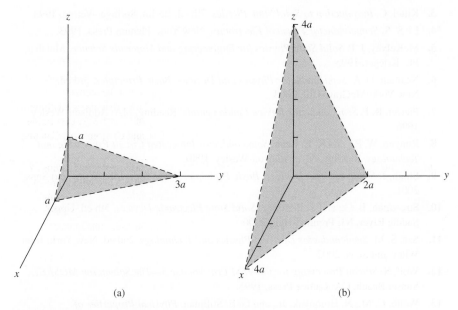

(a)   (b)

Figure P1.16 | Figure for Problem 1.16.

1.22 Determine the density of valence electrons in silver. Assume silver is a simple cubic structure.

1.23 Determine the angle between the tetrahedral bonds of a silicon lattice.

Section 1.5   Imperfections and Impurities in Solids

1.24 (*a*) If 4×10^{16} arsenic atoms per cm^3 are added to intrinsic silicon as a substitutional impurity, determine what percentage of the silicon atoms are displaced in the single crystal lattice. (*b*) Repeat part (*a*) if 2×10^{15} boron atoms per cm^3 are added to intrinsic silicon.

1.25 (*a*) Phosphorus atoms, at a concentration of 5×10^{16} cm^{-3}, are added to a pure sample of intrinsic silicon. Assume the phosphorus atoms are distributed homogeneously throughout the silicon sample. What is the fraction by weight of phosphorus? (*b*) If boron atoms, at a concentration of 10^{18} cm^{-3}, are added to the material in part (*a*), determine the fraction by weight of boron.

1.26 If 2×10^{15} gold atoms per cm^3 are added to intrinsic silicon as a substitutional impurity and are distributed uniformly throughout the semiconductor, determine the distance between gold atoms in terms of the silicon lattice constant. (Assume the gold atoms are distributed in a rectangular or cubic array.)

READING LIST

  1. Azaroll, L. V., and J. J. Brophy. *Electronic Processes in Materials.* New York: McGraw-Hill, 1963.

  2. Campbell, S. A. *The Science and Engineering of Microelectronic Fabrication.* New York: Oxford University Press, 1996.

3. Kittel, C. *Introduction to Solid State Physics,* 7th ed. Berlin: Springer-Verlag, 1993.

*4. Li, S. S. *Semiconductor Physical Electronics.* New York: Plenum Press, 1993.

5. McKelvey, J. P. *Solid State Physics for Engineering and Materials Science.* Malabar, FL: Krieger, 1993.

6. Neamen, D. A. *Semiconductor Physics and Devices: Basic Principles,* 3rd ed. New York: McGraw-Hill, 2003.

7. Pierret, R. F. *Semiconductor Device Fundamentals.* Reading, MA: Addison-Wesley, 1996.

8. Runyan, W. R., and K. E. Bean. *Semiconductor Integrated Circuit Processing and Technology.* Reading, MA: Addison-Wesley, 1990.

9. Singh, J. *Semiconductor Devices: Basic Principles.* New York: John Wiley and Sons, 2001.

10. Streetman, B. G., and S. Banerjee. *Solid State Electronic Devices,* 5th ed. Upper Saddle River, NJ: Prentice-Hall, 2000.

11. Sze, S. M. *Semiconductor Devices: Physics and Technology,* 2nd ed. New York: John Wiley and Sons, 2002.

12. Wolf, S. *Silicon Processing for the VLSI Era: Volume 3—The Submicron MOSFET.* Sunset Beach, CA: Lattice Press, 1995.

*13. Wolfe, C. M., N. Holonyak, Jr., and G. E. Stillman. *Physical Properties of Semiconductors.* Englewood Cliffs, NJ: Prentice-Hall, 1989.

2

Theory of Solids

I deally, we would like to begin discussing the operation and characteristics of
semiconductor devices immediately. However, to understand the current–voltage
characteristics of semiconductor devices, we need some knowledge of the electron
behavior in a crystal when the electron is subjected to various potential functions.
Toward this end, we have two tasks in this chapter: to determine the properties of
electrons in a crystal lattice, and to determine the statistical characteristics of a very
large number of electrons in a crystal. We will, therefore, consider a brief introduction to quantum mechanics, which is used to predict the behavior of electrons in
solids.

2.0 | PREVIEW

In this chapter, we will

1. Discuss a few basic principles of quantum mechanics that apply to
   semiconductor material and device physics.
2. List a few results of quantum mechanics, including energy quantization and
   probability concepts, in order to make understandable some properties of
   electrons in crystals.
3. Develop the energy-band theory of semiconductors and the two types of
   charged carriers in semiconductors.
4. Discuss and develop the density of quantum states as a function of electron
   energy.
5. Develop the Fermi–Dirac distribution function, which describes the probability
   of an electron occupying a quantum state as a function of electron energy.

Historical Insight

The motion of large objects, such as planets and satellites, can be predicted to a high degree of accuracy using classical theoretical physics based on Newton's laws of motion. Beginning around 1895, certain experimental results that involved electrons and high-frequency electromagnetic waves (x-rays) appeared to be inconsistent with results predicted by classical physics. In 1923, Arthur Compton established that x-rays behave like particles with well-defined energy quanta when they scatter from metals. These new experimental results can be predicted and described using the principles of quantum mechanics, which were developed during the 1920s. The quantum mechanical wave theory is the basis for the theory of semiconductor physics.

Present-Day Insight

Quantum mechanical wave theory is still the basis for describing and predicting the behavior of semiconductor devices and materials. Quantum mechanics is especially important in analyzing heterojunction devices such as the heterojunction field-effect device (Chapter 11) and heterojunction lasers (Chapter 12).

2.1 | PRINCIPLES OF QUANTUM MECHANICS

Objective: Discuss a few basic principles of quantum mechanics that apply to semiconductor material and device physics.

Wave mechanics

We are ultimately interested in semiconductor materials whose electrical properties are directly related to the behavior of electrons in the crystal lattice. The behavior and characteristics of these electrons can be described by the formulation of quantum mechanics called *wave mechanics*. We first describe two principles of quantum mechanics. We then briefly introduce Schrodinger's wave equation and consider a few basic results that are derived from applying this equation to specific problems.

2.1.1 Energy Quanta

One experiment that demonstrates an inconsistency between experimental results and the classical theory of light is called the photoelectric effect. If monochromatic light is incident on a clean surface of a material, then under certain conditions, electrons (photoelectrons) are emitted from the surface. The experimental setup is shown in Figure 2.1a. According to classical physics, if the intensity of the light is large enough, the work function (the energy required to pull an electron away from the surface) of the material will be overcome and an electron will be emitted from the surface independent of the incident frequency. This predicted result is not observed. The observed effect is that, at a constant incident intensity, the maximum kinetic energy of the photoelectron varies linearly with frequency with a limiting frequency $\nu = \nu_0$, below which no photoelectron is produced. This result is shown in Figure 2.1b. If the incident intensity varies at a constant frequency, the rate of photoelectron emission changes, but the maximum kinetic energy remains constant.

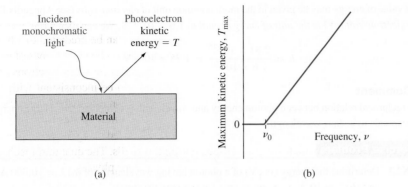

Figure 2.1 | (a) The photoelectric effect and (b) the maximum kinetic energy of the photoelectron as a function of incident frequency.

Planck postulated in 1900 that thermal radiation is emitted from a heated surface in discrete packets of energy called *quanta*. The energy of these quanta is given by $E = h\nu$, where ν is the frequency of the radiation and h is a constant now known as Planck's constant ($h = 6.625 \times 10^{-34}$ J-s). Then in 1905, Einstein interpreted the photoelectric results by suggesting that the energy in a light wave is also contained in discrete packets or bundles. The particle-like packet of energy is called a *photon,*   **Photon** whose energy is also given by $E = h\nu$. A photon with sufficient energy, then, can knock an electron from the surface of the material. The minimum energy required to remove an electron is called the *work function* of the material and any excess photon   **Work function** energy goes into the kinetic energy of the photoelectron. This result was confirmed experimentally as demonstrated in Figure 2.1b. The photoelectric effect shows the discrete nature of the photon and demonstrates the particle-like behavior of the light wave.

The maximum kinetic energy of the photoelectron can be written as

$$T = \frac{1}{2}mv^2 = h\nu - h\nu_0 \text{(for } \nu > \nu_0) \tag{2.1}$$

where $h\nu$ is the incident photon energy and $h\nu_0$ is the minimum energy, or work function, required to remove an electron from the surface.

EXAMPLE 2.1

OBJECTIVE

Calculate the photon energy corresponding to a particular wavelength.

Consider an x-ray with a wavelength of $\lambda = 0.708 \times 10^{-8}$ cm.

■ **Solution**

The energy is

$$E = h\nu = \frac{hc}{\lambda} = \frac{(6.625 \times 10^{-34})(3 \times 10^{10})}{0.708 \times 10^{-8}} = 2.81 \times 10^{-15} \text{ J}$$

This value of energy may be given in the more common unit of *electron-volts* (see Appendix D). *The electron-volt (eV) is the unit of energy equal to* 1.6×10^{-19} J. We can then write

$$E = \frac{2.81 \times 10^{-15}}{1.6 \times 10^{-19}} = 1.75 \times 10^4 \text{ eV}$$

■ Comment

The reciprocal relation between photon energy and wavelength is demonstrated: a large energy corresponds to a short wavelength.

Exercise Problem

EX2.1 Determine the energy (in eV) of a photon having wavelengths of (a) $\lambda = 10,000$ Å and (b) $\lambda = 10$ Å. [Ans. (a) 1.24 eV, (b) 1.24 × 10³ eV.]

2.1.2   Wave–Particle Duality Principle

Wave–particle duality principle

We have seen in the previous paragraphs that light waves, in the photoelectric effect, behave as if they are particles. In 1924, de Broglie postulated the existence of matter waves. He suggested that since waves exhibit particle-like behavior, then particles should be expected to show wave-like properties. The hypothesis of de Broglie is the existence of a *wave–particle duality principle*. The momentum of a photon is given by

$$p = \frac{h}{\lambda} \tag{2.2}$$

where λ is the wavelength of the light wave. Then, de Broglie hypothesized that the wavelength of a particle can be expressed as

$$\lambda = \frac{h}{p} \tag{2.3}$$

de Broglie wavelength

where p is the momentum of the particle and λ is known as the *de Broglie wavelength* of the matter wave.

EXAMPLE 2.2

OBJECTIVE

Determine the de Broglie wavelength of a particle.

Consider an electron traveling at a velocity of 10^7 cm/s = 10^5 m/s.

■ Solution

The momentum is given by

$$p = mv = (9.11 \times 10^{-31})(10^5) = 9.11 \times 10^{-26} \text{ kg-m/s}$$

Then the de Broglie wavelength is

$$\lambda = \frac{h}{p} = \frac{6.625 \times 10^{-34}}{9.11 \times 10^{-26}} = 7.27 \times 10^{-9} \text{ m}$$

or

$$\lambda = 72.7 \text{ Å}$$

■ **Comment**

This calculation shows the order of magnitude of the de Broglie wavelength for a "typical" electron.

Exercise Problem

EX2.2 (a) Find the momentum and energy of a particle with mass 5×10^{-31} kg and a de Broglie wavelength of 180 Å. (b) An electron has a kinetic energy of 20 meV. Determine the de Broglie wavelength. [Ans. (a) $p = 3.68 \times 10^{-26}$ kg-m/s, $E = 4.65 \times 10^{-3}$ eV; (b) $p = 7.64 \times 10^{-26}$ kg-m/s, $\lambda = 86.8$ Å]

To gain some appreciation of the frequencies and wavelengths involved in the wave–particle duality principle, Figure 2.2 shows the electromagnetic frequency spectrum. We see that a wavelength of 72.7 Å obtained in Example 2.2 is in the ultraviolet range. Typically, we will be considering wavelengths in the ultraviolet and visible range. These wavelengths are very short compared with the usual radio spectrum range.

In some cases, electromagnetic waves behave as if they are particles (photons) and, in some cases, particles behave as if they are waves. This wave–particle duality principle of quantum mechanics applies primarily to small particles such as electrons, but it has also been shown to apply to protons and neutrons. For very large particles,

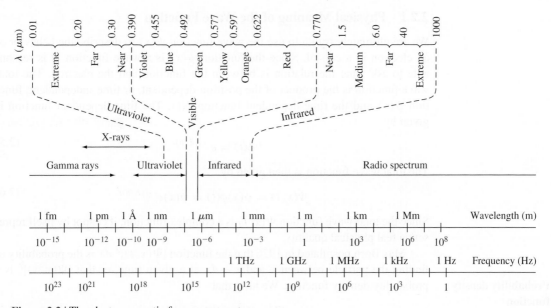

Figure 2.2 | The electromagnetic frequency spectrum.

we can show that the relevant equations reduce to those of classical mechanics. *The wave–particle duality principle is the basis on which we use wave theory to describe the motion and behavior of electrons in a crystal.*

2.2 | ENERGY QUANTIZATION AND PROBABILITY CONCEPTS

Objective: List a few results of quantum mechanics, including energy quantization and probability concepts.

The various experimental results involving electromagnetic waves and particles that could not be explained by classical laws of physics showed that a revised formulation of mechanics was required. Schrödinger, in 1926, provided a formulation called *wave mechanics,* that incorporated the principles of quanta introduced by Planck, and the wave–particle duality principle introduced by de Broglie. Based on the wave–particle duality principle, we can describe the motion of electrons in a crystal by wave theory. This wave theory is described by Schrödinger's wave equation.

Time-independent Schrödinger's wave equation

The time-independent Schrödinger's wave equation is given by

$$\frac{d^2\psi(x)}{dx^2} + \frac{2m}{\hbar^2}[E - V(x)]\psi(x) = 0 \qquad (2.4)$$

Modified Planck's constant

where E is the total energy of the particle and is assumed to be a constant, $V(x)$ is the potential energy of the particle, m is the mass of the particle, and $\hbar$ is called a modified Planck's constant defined as $\hbar = h/2\pi$.

2.2.1   Physical Meaning of the Wave Function

We are ultimately trying to use the wave function $\psi(x)$ to describe the behavior of an electron in a crystal. Since the function $\psi(x)$ is a wave function, it is reasonable to ask what the relation is between the function and the electron. The total wave function is the product of the position-dependent, or time-independent, function $\psi(x)$ and the time-dependent function $\phi(t)$. The time-dependent function is given by

$$\phi(t) = e^{-j(E/\hbar)t} \qquad (2.5)$$

The total wave function is then given by

$$\Psi(x, t) = \psi(x)\phi(t) = \psi(x)e^{-j(E/\hbar)t} \qquad (2.6)$$

Since the total wave function $\Psi(x, t)$ is a complex function, it cannot by itself represent a real physical quantity.

Max Born postulated in 1926 that the function $|\Psi(x, t)|^2 \, dx$ is the probability of finding the particle between x and $x + dx$ at a given time, or that $|\Psi(x, y)|^2$ is a probability density function. We have that

Probability density function

$$|\Psi(x, t)|^2 = \Psi(x, t)\Psi^*(x, t) \qquad (2.7)$$

where $\Psi^*(x, t)$ is the complex conjugate function. Therefore

$$\Psi^*(x, t) = \psi^*(x)e^{+j(E/\hbar)t} \tag{2.8}$$

Then the product of the total wave function and its complex conjugate is given by

$$\Psi(x, t)\Psi^*(x, t) = \left[\psi(x)e^{-j(E/\hbar)t}\right]\left[\psi^*(x)e^{+j(E/\hbar)t}\right]$$
$$= \psi(x)\psi^*(x) = |\psi(x)|^2 \tag{2.9}$$

Therefore, we have that $|\psi(x)|^2$ is the probability density function and is independent of time. One major difference between classical physics and quantum mechanics is that in classical mechanics, the position and energy of a particle or body can be determined precisely, whereas in quantum mechanics, the position and energy of a particle are found in terms of a probability. *We will, therefore, be concerned with finding the probability of an electron having a particular energy.*

2.2.2 The One-Electron Atom[1]

We now consider the one-electron, or hydrogen, atom potential problem. The nucleus is a heavy, positively charged proton and the electron is a light, negatively charged particle that, in the classical Bohr theory, revolves around the nucleus. The potential energy $V(r)$ is due to the coulomb attraction between the proton and electron and is given by

$$V(r) = \frac{-e^2}{4\pi\epsilon_0 r} \tag{2.10}$$

where e is the magnitude of the electronic charge,[2] ϵ_0 is the permittivity of free space, and r is the radial distance from the proton to the electron. The potential function, although spherically symmetric, leads to a three-dimensional problem in spherical coordinates.

Quantized Energies One particular result from the rather complex analysis required for this problem is that the total energy of the electron is given by

$$E_n = \frac{-m_0 e^4}{(4\pi\epsilon_0)^2 2\hbar^2 n^2} \tag{2.11}$$

where n is a positive constant called the principal quantum number and m_0 is the mass of the electron. The negative energy indicates that the electron is bound to the nucleus. Since n is an integer, the energy of the bound electron can take on only discrete values or the energy is said to be *quantized*.

Discrete energy values for the hydrogen atom

---

[1]The application of Schrödinger's wave equation to a few specific potential energy functions is given in Appendix E.

[2]Throughout the text, we will use the symbol e as the magnitude of the electronic charge. The symbol q will be used for any arbitrary charge that might be either positive or negative.

EXAMPLE 2.3

OBJECTIVE

Determine the first three allowed electron energies in the hydrogen atom.

■ Solution

The mass of an electron is $m_0 = 9.11 \times 10^{-31}$ kg and the permittivity of free space is $\epsilon_o = 8.85 \times 10^{-12}$ F/m. The modified Planck's constant is

$$\hbar = \frac{h}{2\pi} = \frac{6.625 \times 10^{-34}}{2\pi} = 1.054 \times 10^{-34} \text{ J-s}$$

The first energy level, from Equation (2.11) for $n = 1$, is

$$E_1 = -\frac{(9.11 \times 10^{-31})(1.6 \times 10^{-19})^4}{[4\pi(8.85 \times 10^{-12})]^2 \, 2\,(1.054 \times 10^{-34})^2 (1)^2}$$

$$= -2.17 \times 10^{-18} \text{ J} \rightarrow -13.6 \text{ eV}$$

The second and third allowed energy levels are determined by setting $n = 2$ and $n = 3$. We find

$$E_2 = -3.39 \text{ eV} \qquad \text{and} \qquad E_3 = -1.51 \text{ eV}$$

■ Comment

The first allowed energy level corresponds to the given value of ionization energy of hydrogen. The classical representation of the first three energy levels is shown in Figure 2.3. The energy of the electron increases (becomes less negative) as the orbit of the electron becomes larger.

Exercise Problem

EX2.3   For the one-electron atom, determine the value of n such that the difference in energies $E_{n+1} - E_n$ is less than 0.20 eV. [Ans. $n = 5$]

Quantum Numbers   Another result derived from the analysis of this potential problem (one-electron atom) is that two additional quantum numbers emerge as a result

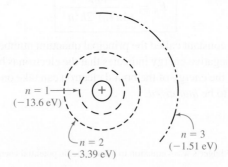

Figure 2.3 | Classical representation of the first three allowed energy levels of the one-electron atom.

of the multidimensional aspect of this problem. These quantum numbers are the magnetic quantum number m (not to be confused with the electron mass m_0) and the azimuthal quantum number l. These quantum numbers are not independent, but are related by

$$\begin{aligned}
n &= 1, 2, 3, \ldots \\
l &= n - 1, n - 2, n - 3, \ldots, 0 \\
|m| &= l, l - 1, l - 2, \ldots, 0
\end{aligned} \tag{2.12}$$

Quantum numbers

Each set of quantum numbers corresponds to a quantum state that the electron may occupy.

The solution of Schrödinger's wave equation for the one-electron potential function can be designated by ψ_{nlm} where $n, l,$ and m are the quantum numbers. For the lowest energy state, $n = 1, l = 0,$ and $m = 0$, the wave function is given by

$$\psi_{100} = \frac{1}{\sqrt{\pi}} \left(\frac{1}{a_0} \right)^{3/2} e^{-r/a_0} \tag{2.13}$$

This function is spherically symmetric, and the parameter a_0 is given by

$$a_0 = \frac{4\pi \epsilon_0 \hbar^2}{m_0 e^2} = 0.529 \text{ Å} \tag{2.14}$$

and is equal to the Bohr radius (from the classical Bohr theory of the atom).

The radial probability density function, or the probability of finding the electron at a particular distance from the nucleus, is proportional to the product $\psi_{100} \cdot \psi_{100}^*$ and also to the differential volume of the shell around the nucleus. The probability density function for the lowest energy state is plotted in Figure 2.4a. The most probable distance from the nucleus is at $r = a_0$, which is the same as the Bohr theory. Considering this spherically symmetric probability function, we can now begin to conceive the concept of an electron cloud, or energy shell, surrounding the nucleus rather than a discrete particle orbiting around the nucleus.

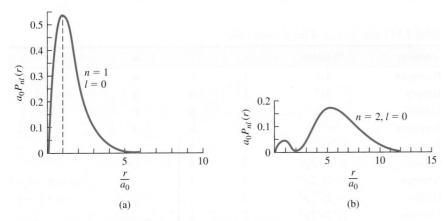

(a)   (b)

Figure 2.4 | The radial probability density function for the one-electron atom in the (a) lowest energy state and (b) next higher energy state.
(From Eisberg and Resnick [4].)

The radial probability density function for the next higher spherically symmetric wave function, corresponding to $n = 2$, $l = 0$, and $m = 0$, is shown in Figure 2.4b. This figure shows the idea of the next higher energy shell of the electron. The second energy shell is at a greater distance from the nucleus than the first energy shell. As indicated in the figure, though, there is still a small probability that the electron will exist at the smaller radius.

2.2.3 Periodic Table

Electron spin

Basic quantum numbers

Pauli exclusion principle

The initial portion of the periodic table of elements can be determined using the results of the one-electron atom plus two additional concepts. The first concept needed is that of *electron spin*. The electron has an intrinsic angular momentum, or spin, that is quantized and may take on one of two possible values. The spin is designated by a quantum number s, that has a value of $s = +\frac{1}{2}$ or $s = -\frac{1}{2}$. We now have four basic quantum numbers: n, l, m, and s.

The second concept needed is the *Pauli exclusion principle*. The Pauli exclusion principle states that, in any given system (an atom, molecule, or crystal), no two electrons can occupy the same quantum state. In an atom, the exclusion principle means that no two electrons can have the same set of quantum numbers. We will see that the exclusion principle is also an important factor in determining the distribution of electrons among available energy states in a crystal.

Table 2.1 shows the first few elements of the periodic table. For the first element, hydrogen, we have one electron in the lowest energy state corresponding to $n = 1$. From Equation (2.12), both quantum numbers l and m must be zero. However, the electron can take on either spin factor, $+\frac{1}{2}$ or $-\frac{1}{2}$. For helium, two electrons can exist in the lowest energy state. For this case, $l = m = 0$, so now both electron spin states are occupied and the lowest energy shell is full. The chemical activity of an element is determined primarily by the valence, or outermost, electrons. Since the valence energy shell of helium is full, helium does not react with other elements and is an inert element.

Table 2.1 | Initial portion of the periodic table

Element	Notation	n	l	m	s
Hydrogen	$1s^1$	1	0	0	$+\frac{1}{2}$ or $-\frac{1}{2}$
Helium	$1s^2$	1	0	0	$+\frac{1}{2}$ and $-\frac{1}{2}$
Lithium	$1s^2 2s^1$	2	0	0	$+\frac{1}{2}$ or $-\frac{1}{2}$
Beryllium	$1s^2 2s^2$	2	0	0	$+\frac{1}{2}$ and $-\frac{1}{2}$
Boron	$1s^2 2s^2 2p^1$	2	1		
Carbon	$1s^2 2s^2 2p^2$	2	1		
Nitrogen	$1s^2 2s^2 2p^3$	2	1	$m = 0, -1, +1$	
Oxygen	$1s^2 2s^2 2p^4$	2	1	$s = +\frac{1}{2}, -\frac{1}{2}$	
Fluorine	$1s^2 2s^2 2p^5$	2	1		
Neon	$1s^2 2s^2 2p^6$	2	1		

The third element, lithium, has three electrons. The third electron must go into the second energy shell corresponding to $n = 2$. When $n = 2$, the quantum number l may be 0 or 1, and when $l = 1$, the quantum number m may be $-1, 0$, or $+1$. In each case, the electron spin factor may be $+\frac{1}{2}$ or $-\frac{1}{2}$. For $n = 2$, then, there are eight possible quantum states. Neon has 10 electrons. Two electrons are in the $n = 1$ energy shell and 8 electrons are in the $n = 2$ energy shell. The second energy shell is now also full, which means that neon is also an inert element.

From the solution of Schrödinger's wave equation for the one-electron atom, plus the concepts of electron spin and the Pauli exclusion principle, we can begin to build up the periodic table of elements. *These results, then, should give us some confidence that the solution to Schrödinger's wave equation can predict the behavior of electrons in a crystal.* As the atomic numbers of the elements increase, electrons will begin to interact with each other, so that the buildup of the periodic table will deviate somewhat from this simple method.

2.3 | ENERGY-BAND THEORY

Objective: Develop the energy-band theory of semiconductors and the two types of charged carriers in semiconductors.

In Section 2.2, we considered the one-electron, or hydrogen, atom. That discussion indicated that the energy of the bound electron is quantized; only discrete values of electron energy are allowed. The radial probability density for the electron was also discussed. This function gives the probability of finding the electron at a particular distance from the nucleus and shows that the electron is not localized at a given radius. We can now begin to extrapolate these single-atom results to a crystal and qualitatively derive the concepts of allowed and forbidden energy bands. We will find that the energy states for electrons occur in bands of allowed states and are separated by forbidden energy bands.

2.3.1 Formation of Energy Bands

Figure 2.5a shows the radial probability density function for the lowest electron energy state of a single, noninteracting hydrogen atom, and Figure 2.5b shows the same probability curves for two atoms that are in close proximity to each other. The wave functions of the two atoms overlap, which means that the two electrons will interact. This interaction or perturbation results in the discrete quantized energy level splitting into two discrete energy levels, schematically shown in Figure 2.5c. The splitting of the discrete states into two states is consistent with the Pauli exclusion principle.

A simple analogy of the splitting of energy levels by interacting particles is the following. Consider two identical race cars driven far apart on a race track. There is no interaction between the cars, so they both must provide the same power to achieve a given speed. However, if one car pulls up close behind the other car, there is an interaction called *draft*. The second car will be pulled to an extent by the lead car. The lead car will therefore require more power to achieve the same speed, since it is pulling the second car, and the second car will require less power, since it is being

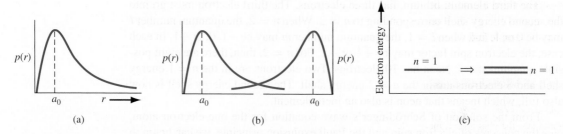

Figure 2.5 | (a) Probability density function of an isolated hydrogen atom. (b) Overlapping probability density functions of two adjacent hydrogen atoms. (c) Splitting of the $n = 1$ state.

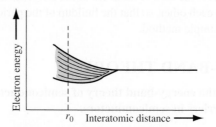

Figure 2.6 | The splitting of an energy state into a band of allowed energies.

pulled by the lead car. So there is a "splitting" of power (energy) of the two interacting race cars. (Keep in mind not to take analogies too literally.)

Now, if we somehow start with a regular periodic arrangement of hydrogen-type atoms that are initially very far apart, and begin pushing the atoms together, the initial quantized energy level will split into a band of discrete energy levels. This effect is shown schematically in Figure 2.6, where the parameter r_0 represents the equilibrium interatomic distance in the crystal. At the equilibrium interatomic distance, there is a band of allowed energies, but within the allowed band, the energies are at discrete levels. The Pauli exclusion principle states that the joining of atoms to form a system (crystal) does not alter the total number of quantum states regardless of size. However, since no two electrons can have the same quantum number, the discrete energy must split into a band of energies in order that each electron can occupy a distinct quantum state.

We have seen previously that, at any energy level, the number of allowed quantum states is relatively small. To accommodate all of the electrons in a crystal, then, we must have many energy levels within the allowed band. As an example, suppose that we have a system with 10^{19} one-electron atoms and also suppose that at the equilibrium interatomic distance, the width of the allowed energy band is 1 eV. For simplicity, we assume that each electron in the system occupies a different energy level, and if the discrete energy states are equidistant, then the energy levels are separated by 10^{-19} eV. This energy difference is extremely small, so that for all practical purposes,

Allowed energy bands

we have a quasi-continuous energy distribution through the allowed energy band. The fact that 10^{-19} eV is a very small difference between two energy states can be seen from Example 2.4.

EXAMPLE 2.4

OBJECTIVE

Calculate the change in kinetic energy of an electron when the velocity changes by a small amount.

Consider an electron traveling at a velocity of 10^7 cm/s. Assume the velocity increases by a value of 1 cm/s. The increase in kinetic energy is given by

$$\Delta E = \frac{1}{2}mv_2^2 - \frac{1}{2}mv_1^2$$

Let $v_2 = v_1 + \Delta v$. Then,

$$v_2^2 = (v_1 + \Delta v)^2 = v_1^2 + 2v_1\Delta v + (\Delta v)^2$$

But $\Delta v \ll v_1$, so we have

$$\Delta E \approx \frac{1}{2}m(2v_1\Delta v) = mv_1\Delta v$$

■ **Solution**

Substituting the numbers into this equation (using mks values), we obtain

$$\Delta E = (9.11 \times 10^{-31})(10^5)(0.01) = 9.11 \times 10^{-28} \text{ J}$$

which can be converted to units of electron volts as

$$\Delta E = \frac{9.11 \times 10^{-28}}{1.6 \times 10^{-19}} = 5.7 \times 10^{-9} \text{ eV}$$

■ **Comment**

A change in velocity of 1 cm/s compared with 10^7 cm/s results in a change in kinetic energy of 5.7×10^{-9} eV, which is orders of magnitude larger than the change in energy of 10^{-19} eV between energy states in the allowed energy band. This example serves to demonstrate that a difference in adjacent energy states of 10^{-19} eV is indeed very small, so that the discrete energies within an allowed band can be treated as a quasi-continuous distribution.

Exercise Problem

EX2.4 An electron is traveling at a speed of $v_0 = 2 \times 10^7$ cm/s. The speed is increased such that the increase in energy is $\Delta E = 10^{-8}$ eV. Determine the increase in electron speed. [Ans. $\Delta v = 0.878$ cm/s]

Consider again a regular periodic arrangement of atoms, in which each atom now contains more than one electron. Suppose the atom in this imaginary crystal

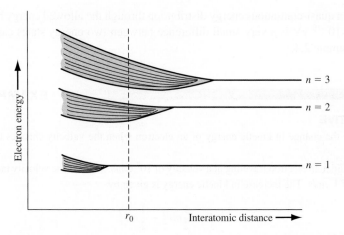

Figure 2.7 | Schematic showing the splitting of three energy states into allowed bands of energies.

Allowed energy bands

Forbidden energy bands

Energy band splitting in silicon

contains electrons up through the $n = 3$ energy level. If the atoms are initially very far apart, the electrons in adjacent atoms will not interact and will occupy the discrete energy levels. If these atoms are brought closer together, the outermost electrons in the $n = 3$ energy shell will begin to interact initially, so that this discrete energy level will split into a band of allowed energies. If the atoms continue to move closer together, the electrons in the $n = 2$ shell may begin to interact and will also split into a band of allowed energies. Finally, if the atoms become sufficiently close together, the innermost electrons in the $n = 1$ level may interact, so that this energy level may also split into a band of allowed energies. The splitting of these discrete energy levels is qualitatively shown in Figure 2.7. If the equilibrium interatomic distance is r_0, then we have bands of allowed energies that the electrons may occupy separated by bands of forbidden energies. The energy-band splitting and the formation of allowed and forbidden bands is the energy-band theory of single-crystal materials.

The actual band splitting in a crystal is much more complicated than indicated in Figure 2.7. A schematic representation of an isolated silicon atom is shown in Figure 2.8a. Ten of the fourteen silicon atom electrons occupy deep-lying energy levels close to the nucleus. The four remaining valence electrons are relatively weakly bound and are the electrons involved in chemical reactions. Figure 2.8b shows the band splitting of silicon. We need to consider the $n = 3$ level for the valence electrons, since the first two energy shells are completely full and are tightly bound to the nucleus. The $3s$ state corresponds to $n = 3$ and $l = 0$, and contains two quantum states per atom. This state will contain two electrons at $T = 0$ K. The $3p$ state corresponds to $n = 3$ and $l = 1$, and contains six quantum states per atom. This state will contain the remaining two electrons in the individual silicon atoms.

As the interatomic distance decreases, the $3s$ and $3p$ states interact and overlap. At the equilibrium interatomic distance, the bands have again split, but now four quantum states per atom are in the lower band and four quantum states per atom are

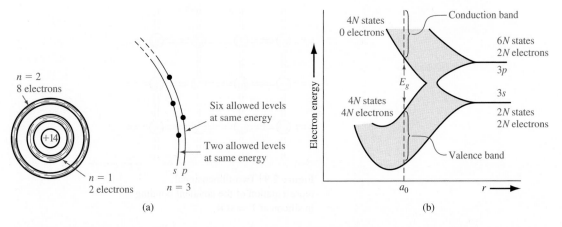

Figure 2.8 | (a) Schematic of an isolated silicon atom. (b) The splitting of the $3s$ and $3p$ states of silicon into the allowed and forbidden bands.
(From Shockley [10].)

in the upper band. At absolute zero degrees, electrons are in the lowest energy state, so that all states in the lower band (the valence band) will be full, and all states in the upper band (the conduction band) will be empty. The *bandgap energy E_g* between   **Bandgap energy**
the top of the valence band and the bottom of the conduction band is the width of the *forbidden energy band.*

We have discussed qualitatively how and why bands of allowed and forbidden energies are formed in a crystal. The formation of these energy bands is directly related to the electrical characteristics of the crystal, as we will see later in our discussion.

2.3.2 The Energy Band and the Bond Model

Again, we are eventually interested in determining the current–voltage characteristics of semiconductor devices. We will need to consider electrical conduction in solids as it relates to the band theory we have just discussed. Let us begin to consider the motion of electrons in the various allowed energy bands.

In Chapter 1, we discussed the covalent bonding of silicon. Figure 2.9 shows a two-dimensional representation of the covalent bonding in a single-crystal silicon lattice. This figure represents silicon at $T = 0 \, \text{K}$ in which each silicon atom is surrounded by eight valence electrons that are in their lowest energy state and are directly involved in the covalent bonding. Figure 2.8b represented the splitting of the discrete silicon energy states into bands of allowed energies as the crystal is formed. At $T = 0 \, \text{K}$, the $4N$ states in the lower band, the valence band, are filled with the va-   **Valence band**
lence electrons. All of the valence electrons schematically shown in Figure 2.9 are in the valence band. The upper band, the conduction band, is completely empty at   **Conduction band**
$T = 0 \, \text{K}$.

As the temperature increases above 0 K, a few valence band electrons may gain enough thermal energy to break the covalent bond and jump into the conduction band. Figure 2.10a shows a two-dimensional representation of this bond-breaking

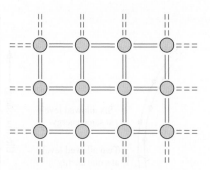

Figure 2.9 | Two-dimensional
representation of the covalent bonding
in silicon at $T = 0$ K.

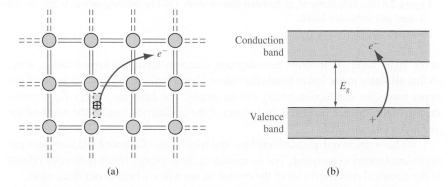

(a)   (b)

Figure 2.10 | (a) Two-dimensional representation of the breaking of a covalent bond.
(b) Corresponding line representation of the energy band and the generation of a
negative and a positive charge with the breaking of a covalent bond.

effect and Figure 2.10b shows a simple line representation of the energy-band model
showing the same bond-breaking effect.

We will be considering the energy-band diagram shown in Figure 2.10b a great
deal throughout the text. The vertical axis is electron energy and, in many cases, the
horizontal axis will be distance in a semiconductor material. Keep in mind that there
are discrete energy levels in both the valence band and conduction band. The minimum energy of the conduction band is designated as E_c and the maximum energy of
the valence band is designated as E_v. We will be interested in the distribution of electrons among the energy states in the valence and conduction bands.

The semiconductor as a whole is neutrally charged. This means that, as the negatively charged electron breaks away from its covalent bonding position, a positively
charged "empty state" is created in the original covalent bonding position in the
valence band. As the temperature further increases, more covalent bonds are broken,
more electrons jump to the conduction band, and more positive empty states are
created in the valence band.

2.3.3 Charge Carriers—Electrons and Holes

As mentioned previously, we are eventually interested in determining the current–voltage characteristics of semiconductor devices. Since current is a result of the flow of charge, we need to consider the charges in a semiconductor that can move when forces are applied. These charges are referred to as *carriers*.

Charge carriers

Electrons   From the previous discussion, one type of charge is the electron, a negatively charged particle. In a semiconductor, we will be interested in a relatively small number of electrons in the bottom of a conduction band. Since electrons are charged particles, a net drift of electrons in the conduction band will give rise to a drift current. If a force is applied to a particle and the particle moves, it must gain energy. This effect is expressed as

Electrons

$$dE = F\,dx = Fv\,dt \qquad (2.15)$$

where F is the applied force, dx is the differential distance the particle moves, v is the velocity, and dE is the increase in energy. If an external force is applied to the electrons in the bottom of the conduction band, there are empty energy states into which the electrons can move; therefore, due to the external force, electrons can gain energy and a net momentum.

We can write the drift current density due to the motion of electrons as

$$J_n = -e\sum_{i=1}^{N} v_i \qquad (2.16)$$

where e is the magnitude of the electronic charge and N is the number of electrons per unit volume in the conduction band. Again, the summation is taken over a unit volume so the current density is A/cm^2. We can note from Equation (2.16) that the current is directly related to the electron velocity; that is, the current is related to how well the electron can move in the crystal.

Hole   In considering the two-dimensional representation of the covalent bonding shown in Figure 2.10a, a positively charged empty state was created when a valence electron was elevated into the conduction band. For $T > 0\,\text{K}$, valence electrons may gain thermal energy; if a valence electron gains a small amount of energy, it may hop into the empty state. The movement of a valence electron into the empty state is equivalent to the movement of the positively charged empty state itself. Figure 2.11 schematically shows the movement of valence electrons in the crystal alternately filling one empty state and creating a new empty state, a motion equivalent to a positively charge moving in the valence band. The crystal now has a second equally important charge carrier that can give rise to a current. This charge carrier is called a *hole* and, as we will see, can also be thought of as a classical particle whose motion can be modeled using Newtonian mechanics.

Holes

The drift current density due to electrons in the valence band can be written as

$$J = -e\sum_{i(\text{filled})} v_i \qquad (2.17)$$

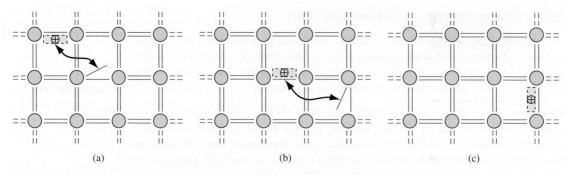

Figure 2.11 | Visualization of the movement of a hole in a semiconductor.

where the summation extends over all filled states. This summation is inconvenient since it extends over a nearly full valence band and takes into account a very large number of states. We can rewrite Equation (2.17) in the form

$$J = -e \sum_{i\,(\text{filled})} v_i = -\left[e \sum_{i\,(\text{total})} v_i - e \sum_{i\,(\text{empty})} v_i \right] = -e \sum_{i\,(\text{total})} v_i + e \sum_{i\,(\text{empty})} v_i$$

$$(2.18)$$

If we consider a band that is totally full, all available states are occupied by electrons. Since the band is full, there are no empty states into which electrons can move when an external force is applied. The net drift current density generated from a completely full band, then, is zero, or

$$J = -e \sum_{i\,(\text{total})} v_i = 0 \qquad (2.19)$$

We can now write the drift current density from Equation (2.18) for an almost full band as

$$J = +e \sum_{i\,(\text{empty})} v_i \qquad (2.20)$$

where v_i in the summation is associated with the empty state. Equation (2.20) is entirely equivalent to placing a positively charged particle in the empty state and assuming all other states in the band are empty, or neutrally charged. This concept is consistent with the discussion of the positively charged empty state in the valence band, as shown in Figure 2.11.

The net motion of electrons in a nearly full band can be described by considering just the empty states, provided that a positive charge is associated with each state. We can model this band as having particles with a positive electronic charge. The density of these particles in the valence band is the same as the density of empty electronic energy states. Again, this new particle is called the hole.

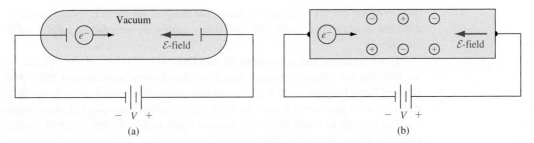

Figure 2.12 | Motion of an electron (a) in vacuum and (b) in a semiconductor.

2.3.4 Effective Mass

The movement of an electron in a lattice will, in general, be different from that of an electron in free space. In addition to an externally applied force, there are internal forces in the crystal due to positively charged ions or protons and other negatively charged electrons that will influence the motion of electrons in the lattice. There are also other forces such as phonon waves that will influence the electron movement. This effect is schematically shown in Figure 2.12. Figure 2.12a shows a vacuum tube in which an electron is moving due to an applied electric field. There are no other particles in the tube to generate additional forces besides the $\mathcal{E}$-field on the electron. Figure 2.12b shows a crystal in which electrons are moving due to an applied $\mathcal{E}$-field. In this case, the movement of electrons is influenced by the positively charged protons and by the other negatively charged electrons. So, the movement in the crystal is different from that in vacuum.

We can write

$$F_{\text{total}} = F_{\text{ext}} + F_{\text{int}} = ma \qquad (2.21)$$

where F_{total}, F_{ext}, and F_{int} are the total force, the externally applied force, and the internal forces, respectively, acting on a particle in a crystal. The parameter a is the acceleration and m is the rest mass of a particle.

Since it is difficult to take into account all of the internal forces, we will write the equation as

$$\boxed{F_{\text{ext}} = m^*a} \qquad (2.22)$$

where the acceleration a is now directly related to the external forces. The parameter m^*, called the *effective mass,* takes into account the particle mass and also takes into account the effect of the internal forces.   **Effective mass**

To use an analogy for the effective mass concept, consider the difference in motion between a glass marble in a container filled with water and in a container filled with oil. In general, the marble will drop through the water at a faster rate than through the oil. The external force in this example is the gravitational force and the internal forces are related to the viscosity of the liquids. Because of the difference in motion of the marble in these two cases, the mass of the particle would appear to be different in water than in oil. (As with many analogies, we must be careful not to be too literal.)

If we consider the movement of an electron in the top of the valence band, we find that the effective mass is negative. An electron moving near the top of an allowed band behaves as if it has a *negative mass*. We must keep in mind that the effective mass parameter is used to relate quantum mechanics and classical mechanics. The attempt to relate these two theories leads to this strange result of a negative effective mass. However, solutions to Schrödinger's wave equation also lead to results that contradict classical mechanics (see results from Appendix E). The negative effective mass is another such example.

In discussing the concept of effective mass in this section, we used an analogy of marbles moving through two liquids. Now consider placing an ice cube in the center of a container filled with water: the ice cube will move upward toward the surface in a direction opposite to the gravitational force. The ice cube appears to have a negative effective mass since its acceleration is opposite to the external force. The effective mass parameter takes into account all internal forces acting on the particle.

If we again consider an electron near the top of an allowed energy band and use Newton's force equation with an applied electric field, we will have

$$F = m^*a = -e\mathcal{E} \tag{2.23}$$

However, m^* is now a negative quantity, so we can write

$$a = \frac{-e\mathcal{E}}{-|m^*|} = \frac{+e\mathcal{E}}{|m^*|} \tag{2.24}$$

An electron moving near the top of an allowed energy band moves in the same direction as the applied electric field. The hole, then, has a positive effective mass denoted by m_p^* and a positive electronic charge so that it will move in the same direction as an applied electric field.

The effective mass just discussed is referred to as the density of states effective mass. These parameters for various semiconductors are given in Appendix B.

2.3.5 Metals, Insulators, and Semiconductors

Each crystal has its own energy-band structure. We noted that the splitting of the energy states in silicon, for example, to form the valence and conduction bands, was complex. Complex band splitting occurs in other crystals, leading to large variations in band structures between various solids and to a wide range of electrical characteristics observed in these various materials. We can qualitatively begin to understand some basic differences in electrical characteristics caused by variations in band structures by considering some simplified energy bands.

There are several possible energy-band conditions to consider. Figure 2.13a shows an allowed energy band that is completely empty of electrons. If an electric field is applied, there are no particles to move, so there will be no current. Figure 2.13b

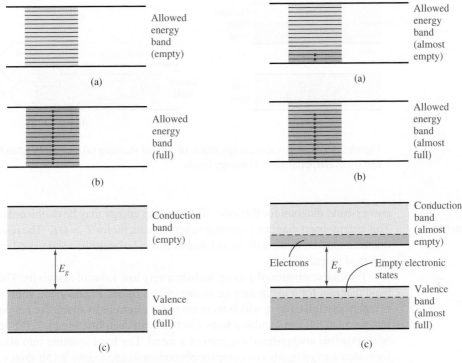

Figure 2.13 | Allowed energy bands showing (a) an empty band, (b) a completely full band, and (c) the bandgap energy between the two allowed bands.

Figure 2.14 | Allowed energy bands showing (a) an almost empty band, (b) an almost full band, and (c) the bandgap energy between the two allowed bands.

shows another allowed energy band whose states are completely full of electrons. We argued in Section 2.3.3 that a completely full energy band will also not give rise to a current. A material that has energy bands either completely empty or completely full is an insulator. The resistivity of an insulator is very large or, conversely, the conductivity of an insulator is very small. There are essentially no charged particles that can contribute to a drift current. Figure 2.13c shows a simplified energy-band diagram of an insulator. The bandgap energy E_g of an insulator is usually on the order of 3.5 to 6 eV or larger, so that at room temperature, there are essentially no electrons in the conduction band and the valence band remains completely full. There are very few thermally generated electrons and holes in an insulator.

Insulator

Figure 2.14a shows an energy band with relatively few electrons near the bottom of the band. Now, if an electric field is applied, the electrons can gain energy, move to higher energy states, and move through the crystal. The net flow of charge is a current. Figure 2.14b shows an allowed energy band that is almost full of electrons, which means that we can consider the holes in this band. If an electric field is applied, the holes can move and give rise to a current. Figure 2.14c shows the simplified

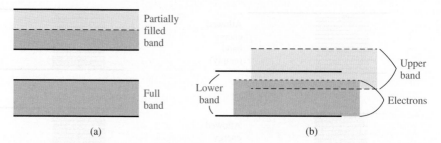

Figure 2.15 | Two possible energy bands of a metal showing (a) a partially filled band and (b) overlapping allowed energy bands.

Semiconductor

energy-band diagram for this case. The bandgap energy may be on the order of 1 eV. This energy-band diagram represents a semiconductor for $T > 0$ K. The resistivity of a semiconductor, as we will see in Chapter 3, can be controlled and varied over many orders of magnitude.

Metal

The characteristics of a metal include a very low value of resistivity. The energy-band diagram for a metal may be in one of two forms. Figure 2.15a shows the case of a partially full band in which there are many electrons available for conduction, so that the material can exhibit a large electrical conductivity. Figure 2.15b shows another possible energy-band diagram of a metal. The band splitting into allowed and forbidden energy bands is a complex phenomenon and Figure 2.15b shows a case in which the conduction and valence bands overlap at the equilibrium interatomic distance. As in the case shown in Figure 2.15a, there are large numbers of electrons as well as large numbers of empty energy states into which the electrons can move, so that this material can also exhibit a very high electrical conductivity.

2.3.6 The *k*-Space Diagram

The concept of energy bands, allowed bands and forbidden bands, in a single-crystal material has been developed in the previous sections. In considering the energy-band diagrams, the electron energy is being plotted on the vertical axis. The electron energy is also related to momentum. For a free particle, the energy and momentum are related by

$$ E = \frac{p^2}{2m} = \frac{\hbar^2 k^2}{2m} \tag{2.25} $$

Crystal momentum

where E is energy, p is momentum, and m is the electron mass. Considering the last term in the equation, we see that $p = \hbar k$. The parameter k is called the crystal momentum and is a parameter that results from applying Schrödinger's wave equation to a single-crystal lattice. Figure 2.16 is a plot of E versus p (or k) for a free particle.

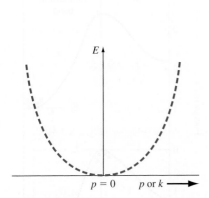

Figure 2.16 | The parabolic E versus k curve for a free electron.

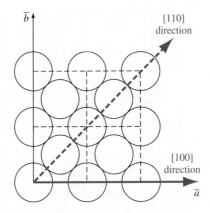

Figure 2.17 | The (100) plane of a face-centered cubic crystal showing the [100] and [110] directions.

E versus k diagram

We now want to consider the E versus k diagrams for a semiconductor material. The potential function varies through the crystal because of the protons and electrons within the crystal, so the E versus k diagrams for a semiconductor are more complex than for that of a free electron. In addition, the potential function changes as the direction through the single-crystal changes. Figure 2.17 shows one plane of a face-centered cubic structure with the [100] and [110] directions indicated. Electrons traveling in different directions encounter different potential patterns and therefore different k-space boundaries. The E versus k diagrams are in general a function of the k-space direction in a crystal.

Figure 2.18 shows the E versus k diagrams of gallium arsenide and of silicon. These relatively simplified diagrams show the basic properties considered in this text, but do not show many of the details more appropriate for advanced-level courses.

Note that the horizontal axes show two different crystal directions. It is normal practice to plot the [100] direction along the normal $+k$ axis and to plot the [111] portion of the diagram so that $+k$ points to the left. In the case of diamond or zincblende lattices, the maxima in the valence-band energy and minima in the conduction-band energy occur at $k = 0$ or along one of these two directions.

Figure 2.18a shows the E versus k diagram for GaAs. The valence-band maximum and the conduction-band minimum both occur at $k = 0$. The electrons in the conduction band tend to settle at the minimum conduction-band energy, which is $k = 0$. Similarly, holes in the valence band tend to congregate at the uppermost valence-band energy. In GaAs, the minimum conduction-band energy and maximum valence-band energy occur at the same k value. A semiconductor with this property is said to be a *direct* bandgap semiconductor; transitions between the two allowed bands can take place with no change in crystal momentum. This direct nature has a significant effect on the optical properties of the material. GaAs and other direct

Direct bandgap semiconductor

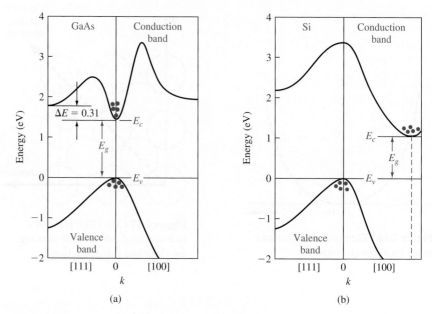

Figure 2.18 | E versus k diagrams for (a) GaAs and (b) Si.
(From Sze [14].)

bandgap materials are ideally suited for use in light-emitting diodes, semiconductor lasers, and other optical devices.

The E versus k diagram for silicon is shown in Figure 2.18b. The maximum in the valence-band energy occurs at $k = 0$, as before. The minimum in the conduction-band energy occurs not at $k = 0$, but along the [100] direction. The difference between the minimum conduction-band energy and the maximum valence-band energy is still defined as the bandgap energy E_g. A semiconductor whose maximum valence-band energy and minimum conduction-band energy do not occur at the same k value is called an *indirect* bandgap semiconductor. When electrons make a transition between the conduction and valence bands, we must invoke the law of conservation of momentum. A transition in an indirect bandgap material must necessarily include an interaction with the crystal so that crystal momentum is conserved.

Indirect bandgap semiconductor

Germanium is also an indirect bandgap material, whose valence-band maximum occurs at $k = 0$ and whose conduction-band minimum occurs along the [111] direction. GaAs is a direct bandgap semiconductor, but other compound semiconductors, such as GaP and AlAs, have indirect bandgaps.

We can relate the simple line representation of the energy-band diagram shown in Figure 2.10b to the energy bands given in Figure 2.18. In the line representation of the energy-band diagram, the energies E_v and E_c correspond to the maximum valence-band energy and minimum conduction-band energy, respectively. These same energies are shown in Figure 2.18. The line representation of the energy band does not show the direct or indirect bandgap nature of the semiconductor.

2.4 | DENSITY OF STATES FUNCTION

Objective: Discuss and develop the density of quantum states as a function of electron energy.

As we have stated, we eventually wish to describe the current–voltage characteristics of semiconductor devices. Since current is the result of the flow of charge, an important step in the process is to determine the number of electrons and holes in the semiconductor that will be available for conduction. The number of carriers that can contribute to the conduction process is a function of the number of available energy or quantum states since, by the Pauli exclusion principle, only one electron may occupy a given quantum state. When we discussed the splitting of energy levels into bands of allowed and forbidden energies, we indicated that the band of allowed energies was actually made up of discrete energy levels. We must determine the density of these allowed energy states as a function of energy to calculate the electron and hole concentrations.

To determine the density of allowed quantum states as a function of energy, we need to consider an appropriate mathematical model. Electrons are allowed to move relatively freely in the conduction band of a semiconductor, but are confined to the crystal. As a first step, we consider a free electron confined to a three-dimensional infinite potential well, where the potential well represents the crystal. Applying Schrödinger's wave equation to this model, we find, with no derivation, the density of quantum states per unit energy and per unit volume is given by

$$g(E) = \frac{4\pi(2m)^{3/2}}{h^3}\sqrt{E} \tag{2.26}$$

The density of quantum states is a function of energy E. As the energy of this free electron becomes small, the number of available quantum states decreases. This density function is really a double density, in that the units are given in terms of states per unit energy per unit volume.

The general form of the E versus k relation for an electron in the bottom of a conduction band is approximately the same parabolic form as that of the free electron, except the mass is replaced by the effective mass. We can then think of the electron in the bottom of the conduction band as being a "free" electron with its own particular mass. We can then generalize the density of states function given by Equation (2.26) for a free electron and write the density of allowed electronic energy states in the conduction band as

Density of quantum states in the conduction band

$$\boxed{g_c(E) = \frac{4\pi\left(2m_n^*\right)^{3/2}}{h^3}\sqrt{E - E_c}} \tag{2.27}$$

where Equation (2.27) is valid for $E \geq E_c$. As the energy of the electron in the conduction band decreases, the number of available quantum states also decreases.

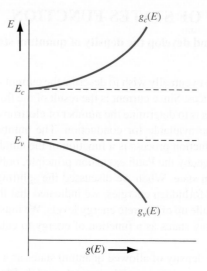

Figure 2.19 | The density of quantum states in the conduction band, $g_c(E)$, and the density of quantum states in the valence band, $g_v(E)$, as a function of energy.

The density of quantum states in the valence band can also be obtained using the same infinite potential well model, since the hole is also confined in the semiconductor crystal and can be treated as a "free" particle. We can then generalize the density of states function from Equation (2.26) to apply to the valence band, so that

$$g_v(E) = \frac{4\pi(2m_p^*)^{3/2}}{h^3}\sqrt{E_v - E} \qquad (2.28)$$

Density of quantum states in the valence band

where Equation (2.28) is valid for $E \leq E_v$. The parameter $g_v(E)$ is the density of states function in the valence band.

We have argued that allowed quantum states do not exist within the forbidden energy band, so $g(E) = 0$ for $E_v \leq E \leq E_c$. Figure 2.19 shows the plot of the density of quantum states as a function of electron energy. If the electron and hole effective masses were equal, then the functions $g_c(E)$ and $g_v(E)$ would be symmetrical about the energy midway between E_c and E_v, or the midgap energy, E_{midgap}.

EXAMPLE 2.5

OBJECTIVE

Find the density of states per unit volume over a particular energy range.

Consider the density of states for a free electron given by Equation (2.26). Calculate the density of states per unit volume with energies between zero and 1 eV.

■ **Solution**

The volume density of quantum states, using Equation (2.26), can be found from

$$N = \int_0^{1eV} g(E)\, dE = \frac{4\pi(2m)^{3/2}}{h^3} \int_0^{1eV} \sqrt{E}\, dE$$

or

$$N = \frac{4\pi(2m)^{3/2}}{h^3} \frac{2}{3} E^{3/2} \Big|_0^{1\,eV}$$

The density of states is now

$$N = \frac{4\pi[2(9.11 \times 10^{-31})]^{3/2}}{(6.625 \times 10^{-34})^3} \frac{2}{3}(1.6 \times 10^{-19})^{3/2} = 4.5 \times 10^{27}\,\text{m}^{-3}$$

or

$$N = 4.5 \times 10^{21}\,\text{states/cm}^3$$

■ **Comment**

The density of quantum states is typically a large number. An effective density of states in a semiconductor, as we will see in Chapter 3, is also a large number but is usually less than the density of atoms in the semiconductor crystal.

Exercise Problem

EX2.5 Calculate the density of states per unit volume for a free electron over the range of energies between 1 eV and 2 eV. [Ans. $N = 8.29 \times 10^{21}$ states/cm^3]

2.5 | STATISTICAL MECHANICS

Objective: Develop the Fermi–Dirac distribution function, which describes the probability of an electron occupying a quantum state as a function of electron energy.

In dealing with large numbers of particles, we are interested only in the statistical behavior of the group as a whole rather than in the behavior of each individual particle. For example, gas within a container will exert an average pressure on the walls of the vessel. The pressure is actually a result of the collisions of the individual gas molecules with the walls, but we do not follow each individual molecule as it collides with the wall. Likewise in a crystal, the electrical characteristics will be determined by the statistical behavior of a large number of electrons.

2.5.1 Statistical Laws

In determining the statistical behavior of particles, we must consider the laws that the particles obey. There are three distribution laws determining the distribution of particles among available energy states.

One distribution law is the Maxwell–Boltzmann probability function. In this case, the particles are considered to be distinguishable by being numbered, for example, from 1 to N, with no limit to the number of particles allowed in each energy state. The behavior of gas molecules in a container at fairly low pressure is an example of this distribution.

A second distribution law is the Bose–Einstein function. The particles in this case are indistinguishable and, again, there is no limit to the number of particles permitted in each quantum state. The behavior of photons, or blackbody radiation, is an example of this law.

The third distribution law is the Fermi–Dirac probability function. In this case, the particles are indistinguishable, but now only one particle is permitted in each quantum state. Electrons in a crystal obey this law. In each case, the particles are assumed to be noninteracting.

2.5.2 The Fermi–Dirac Distribution Function and the Fermi Energy

Fermi–Dirac distribution function

The Fermi–Dirac probability function is given by

$$\frac{N(E)}{g(E)} = f_F(E) = \frac{1}{1 + \exp\left(\dfrac{E - E_F}{kT}\right)} \tag{2.29}$$

where $N(E)$ is the number of particles per unit volume per unit energy and $g(E)$ is the number of quantum states per unit volume per unit energy. The function $f_F(E)$ is called the Fermi–Dirac distribution or probability function and gives the probability that an allowed quantum state at the energy E is occupied by an electron. Another interpretation of the distribution function is that $f_F(E)$ is the ratio of filled to total number of quantum states at the energy E. The parameter E_F in Equation (2.29) is called the *Fermi energy*.

Fermi energy

To begin to understand the meaning of the distribution function and the Fermi energy, we can plot the distribution function versus energy. Initially, let $T = 0\,\mathrm{K}$ and consider the case when $E < E_F$. The exponential term in Equation (2.29) becomes $\exp[(E - E_F)/kT] \rightarrow \exp(-\infty) = 0$. The resulting distribution function is $f_F(E < E_F) = 1$. Again let $T = 0\,\mathrm{K}$ and consider the case when $E > E_F$. The exponential term in the distribution function becomes $\exp[(E - E_F)/kT] \rightarrow \exp(+\infty) = +\infty$. The resulting Fermi–Dirac distribution function now becomes $f_F(E > E_F) = 0$.

The Fermi–Dirac distribution for $T = 0\,\mathrm{K}$ is plotted in Figure 2.20. This result shows that, for $T = 0\,\mathrm{K}$, the electrons are in their lowest possible energy states. The probability of a quantum state being occupied is unity for $E < E_F$ and the probability of a state being occupied is zero for $E > E_F$. All electrons have energies below the Fermi energy at $T = 0\,\mathrm{K}$.

Figure 2.21 shows discrete energy levels of a particular system as well as the number of available quantum states at each energy level. If we assume, for this case, that the system contains 13 electrons, then Figure 2.21 shows how these electrons are

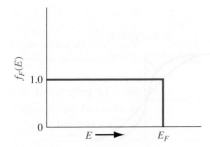

Figure 2.20 | The Fermi–Dirac probability function versus energy at $T = 0$ K.

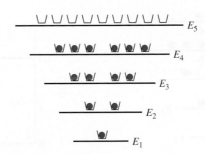

Figure 2.21 | Discrete energy states and quantum states for a particular system at $T = 0$ K.

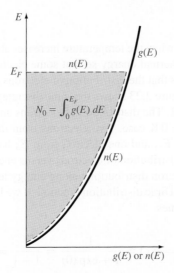

Figure 2.22 | Density of quantum states and electrons in a continuous energy system at $T = 0$ K.

distributed among the various quantum states at $T = 0$ K. The electrons will be in the lowest possible energy state, so the probability of a quantum state being occupied in energy levels E_1 through E_4 is unity, and the probability of a quantum state being occupied in energy level E_5 is zero. The Fermi energy, for this case, must be above E_4 but less than E_5. The Fermi energy determines the statistical distribution of electrons and does not have to correspond to an allowed energy level.

Now consider a case in which the density of quantum states $g(E)$ is a continuous function of energy as shown in Figure 2.22. If there are N_0 electrons in this system, then the distribution of these electrons among the quantum states at $T = 0$ K is shown by the dashed line. The electrons are in the lowest possible energy state so that all states below E_F are filled and all states above E_F are empty. If $g(E)$ and N_0 are known for this particular system, then the Fermi energy E_F can be determined.

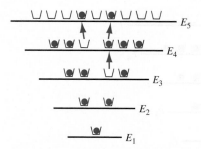

Figure 2.23 | Discrete energy states and quantum states for the same system shown in Figure 2.21 for $T > 0$ K.

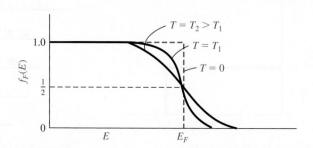

Figure 2.24 | The Fermi–Dirac probability function versus energy for different temperatures.

Consider the situation when the temperature increases above $T = 0$ K. Electrons gain a certain amount of thermal energy so that some electrons can jump to higher energy levels, which means that the distribution of electrons among the available energy states will change. Figure 2.23 shows the same discrete energy levels and quantum states as in Figure 2.21. The distribution of electrons among the quantum states has changed from the $T = 0$ K case. Two electrons from the E_4 level have gained enough energy to jump to E_5, and one electron from E_3 has jumped to E_4. As the temperature changes, the distribution of electrons versus energy changes.

The change in the electron distribution among energy levels for $T > 0$ K can be seen by plotting the Fermi–Dirac distribution function. If we let $E = E_F$ and $T > 0$ K, then Equation (2.29) becomes

$$f_F(E = E_F) = \frac{1}{1 + \exp{(0)}} = \frac{1}{1 + 1} = \frac{1}{2}$$

The probability of a state being occupied at $E = E_F$ is $\frac{1}{2}$. Figure 2.24 shows the Fermi–Dirac distribution function plotted for several temperatures, assuming that the Fermi energy is independent of temperature.

We can see that for temperatures above absolute zero, there is a nonzero probability that some energy states above E_F will be occupied by electrons and some energy states below E_F will be empty. This result again means that some electrons have jumped to higher energy levels with increasing thermal energy.

EXAMPLE 2.6

OBJECTIVE

Determine the probability that an energy state above E_F is occupied by an electron.

Let $T = 300$ K. Determine the probability that an energy level $3kT$ above the Fermi energy level is occupied by an electron. (Assume that such an energy level is allowed.)

■ **Solution**

From Equation (2.29), we can write

$$f_F(E) = \frac{1}{1 + \exp\left(\dfrac{E - E_F}{kT}\right)} = \frac{1}{1 + \exp\left(\dfrac{3kT}{kT}\right)}$$

which becomes

$$f_F(E) = \frac{1}{1 + \exp(3)} = 0.0474 \Rightarrow 4.74\%$$

■ **Comment**

At energies above E_F, the probability of a state being occupied by an electron can become significantly less than unity, or the ratio of electrons to available quantum states can be quite small.

Exercise Problem

EX2.6 Assume the Fermi energy level is 0.30 eV below the conduction band energy.
(a) Determine the probability of a state being occupied by an electron at $E = E_c + kT$. (b) Repeat part (a) for an energy state at $E = E_c + 2kT$.
Assume $T = 300$ K. [Ans. (a) 3.43×10^{-6}, (b) 1.26×10^{-6}]

We can see from Figure 2.24 that the probability of an energy above E_F being occupied increases as the temperature increases and the probability of a state below E_F being empty increases as the temperature increases.

EXAMPLE 2.7

OBJECTIVE

Find the temperature at which there is a 1 percent probability that an energy state is empty.

Assume that the Fermi energy level for a particular material is 6.25 eV and that the electrons in this material follow the Fermi–Dirac distribution function. Calculate the temperature at which there is a 1 percent probability that a state 0.30 eV below the Fermi energy level will not contain an electron.

■ **Solution**

The probability that a state is empty is

$$1 - f_F(E) = 1 - \frac{1}{1 + \exp\left(\dfrac{E - E_F}{kT}\right)}$$

Then,

$$0.01 = 1 - \frac{1}{1 + \exp\left(\dfrac{5.95 - 6.25}{kT}\right)}$$

We find that $kT = 0.06529$ eV, which corresponds to a temperature of $T = 756$ K.

■ **Comment**

The Fermi probability function is a strong function of temperature.

Exercise Problem

EX2.7 Assume that the electrons in a material follow the Fermi–Dirac distribution function and assume that the Fermi level is 5.50 eV. Determine the temperature at which there is a 0.5 percent probability that a state 0.20 eV above the Fermi level is occupied by an electron. (Ans. $T = 438$ K)

We can note that the probability of a state a distance dE above E_F being occupied is the same as the probability of a state a distance dE below E_F being empty. The function $f_F(E)$ is symmetrical with the function $1 - f_F(E)$ about the Fermi energy E_F. This symmetry effect is shown in Figure 2.25 and will be used in Chapter 3.

2.5.3 Maxwell–Boltzmann Approximation

Consider the case when $E - E_F \gg kT$, so that the exponential term in the denominator of Equation (2.29) is much greater than unity. We can then neglect the 1 in the denominator, so the Fermi–Dirac distribution function becomes

$$f_F(E) \approx \exp\left[\frac{-(E - E_F)}{kT}\right] \tag{2.30}$$

Maxwell–Boltzmann approximation

Equation (2.30) is known as the Maxwell–Boltzmann approximation, or simply the Boltzmann approximation, to the Fermi–Dirac distribution function. Figure 2.26 shows the Fermi–Dirac probability function and the Boltzmann approximation. This figure gives an indication of the range of energies over which the approximation is valid.

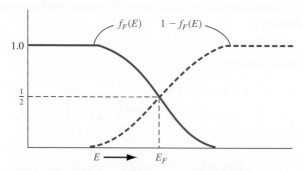

Figure 2.25 | The probability of a state being occupied, $f_F(E)$, and the probability of a state being empty, $1 - f_F(E)$ versus energy.

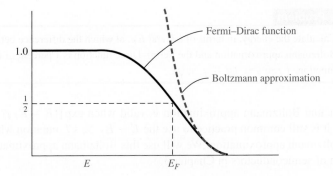

Figure 2.26 | The Fermi–Dirac probability function and the Maxwell–Boltzmann approximation versus energy.

EXAMPLE 2.8

OBJECTIVE

Determine the energy at which the Boltzmann approximation can be considered valid.

Calculate the energy, in terms of kT and E_F, at which the difference between the Boltzmann approximation and the Fermi–Dirac function is 5 percent of the Fermi function.

■ Solution

We can write

$$\frac{\exp\left[\dfrac{-(E - E_F)}{kT}\right] - \dfrac{1}{1 + \exp\left(\dfrac{E - E_F}{kT}\right)}}{\dfrac{1}{1 + \exp\left(\dfrac{E - E_F}{kT}\right)}} = 0.05$$

If we multiply both the numerator and denominator by the $1 + \exp(\ )$ function, we have

$$\exp\left[\frac{-(E - E_F)}{kT}\right]\left[1 + \exp\left(\frac{E - E_F}{kT}\right)\right] - 1 = 0.05$$

which becomes

$$\exp\left[\frac{-(E - E_F)}{kT}\right] = 0.05$$

or

$$E - E_F = kT \ln\left(\frac{1}{0.05}\right) \approx 3kT$$

■ Comment

As seen in this example and in Figure 2.26, the $E - E_F \gg kT$ notation is somewhat misleading. The Maxwell–Boltzmann and Fermi–Dirac functions are within 5 percent of each other when $E - E_F > 3kT$.

Exercise Problem

EX2.8 Calculate the energy, in terms of kT and E_F, at which the difference between the Boltzmann approximation and the Fermi–Dirac function is 1 percent of the Fermi function. (Ans. $E - E_F = 4.6kT$.)

The actual Boltzmann approximation is valid when $\exp[(E - E_F)/kT] \gg 1$. However, it is still common practice to use the $E - E_F \gg kT$ notation when applying the Boltzmann approximation. We will use this Boltzmann approximation in our discussion of semiconductors in Chapter 3.

TEST YOUR UNDERSTANDING

TYU2.1 Assume the Fermi energy level is 0.35 eV above the valence band energy. (*a*) Determine the probability of a state being empty of an electron at $E = E_v - kT$. (*b*) Repeat part (*a*) for an energy state at $E = E_v - 2kT$. Assume $T = 300$K. (Ans. (*a*) 4.98×10^{-7}, (*b*) 1.83×10^{-7}.)

TYU2.2 Repeat Example 2.6 for an energy $4kT$ above the Fermi level. (Ans. 1.8 percent)

2.6 | SUMMARY

1. We have considered a few of the basic principles of quantum mechanics that are used to describe the behavior of electrons under various potential functions.
   A. In some applications, such as the photoelectric effect, light waves behave as particles called photons.
   B. The wave–particle duality principle states that particles can have wave-like behavior and light waves can have particle-like behavior. The wave–particle duality principle is then the basis for using wave theory to predict and describe the behavior of electrons in crystals.

2. Schrödinger's wave equation forms the basis for describing and predicting the behavior of electrons.
   A. Schrödinger's wave function is used to determine the probability of finding an electron at a particular position or energy.
   B. One result of applying Schrödinger's wave equation to a bound particle (e.g., the one-electron atom) is that the energy of the bound particle is *quantized*. The electron, therefore, can take on only discrete values of energy.
   C. The basic structure of the periodic table is predicted by applying Schrödinger's wave equation to the one-electron atom.

3. The concept of allowed and forbidden energy bands in a single crystal was developed.
   A. The concept of the conduction band and the valence band was presented.
   B. The concept of effective mass was developed.
   C. Two types of charged particles exist in a semiconductor. An electron is a negatively charged particle with a positive effective mass existing at the bottom of an allowed energy band. A hole is a positively charged particle with a positive effective mass existing at the top of an allowed energy band.

4. Energies within an allowed energy band are actually at discrete levels and each allowed band contains a very large but finite number of quantum states. The density per unit energy of quantum states was presented.

5. In dealing with large numbers of electrons and holes, we must consider the statistical behavior of these particles. The Fermi–Dirac probability function was considered, which gives the probability of an allowed quantum state at an energy E of being occupied by an electron. The Fermi energy was defined.

CHECKPOINT

After studying this chapter, the reader should have the ability to

1. Discuss the principle of energy quanta (photon) and the wave–particle duality principle.
2. A. Discuss the concept of quantized energy levels for the one-electron atom.
   B. Discuss the reason that only a limited number of electrons may occupy a given energy level in a one-electron atom.
   C. Discuss the formation of the periodic table from the results of applying Schrödinger's wave equation to the one-electron atom.
3. A. Discuss the splitting of energy bands in silicon.
   B. Discuss the concept of effective mass of a particle in a crystal.
   C. Discuss the concept of a hole.
4. Discuss the concept of the density of states in an allowed energy band in a solid.
5. Understand the meaning of the Fermi–Dirac distribution function and the Fermi energy level.

REVIEW QUESTIONS

1. State the wave–particle duality principle and give the relationship between momentum and wavelength.
2. A. What is the physical meaning of Schrödinger's wave function?
   B. What is meant by a probability density function?
   C. What is meant by quantized energy levels?
   D. What are quantum numbers?
3. A. Why do energy levels split as atoms are brought close to each other?
   B. What is effective mass?
   C. What is a direct bandgap semiconductor? What is an indirect bandgap semiconductor?
   D. Describe the concept of a hole.
4. What is meant by the density of states function?
5. A. What is the meaning of the Fermi–Dirac probability function?
   B. What is the Fermi energy level?

PROBLEMS

Section 2.1   Principles of Quantum Mechanics

2.1 The work function of a material refers to the minimum energy required to remove an electron from the material. Assume that the work function of gold is 4.90 eV and that of cesium is 1.90 eV. Calculate the maximum wavelength of light for the photoelectric emission of electrons for gold and cesium.

2.2   Calculate the de Broglie wavelength, $\lambda = h/p$, for: (a) An electron with kinetic energy of (i) 1.0 eV, and (ii) 100 eV. (b) A proton with kinetic energy of 1.0 eV.

2.3   According to classical physics, the average energy of an electron in an electron gas at thermal equilibrium is $3kT/2$. Determine, for $T = 300$ K, the average electron energy (in eV), average electron momentum, and the de Broglie wavelength.

2.4   (a) An electron is moving with a velocity of 2×10^6 cm/s. Determine the electron energy (in eV), momentum, and de Broglie wavelength (in Å). (b) The de Broglie wavelength of an electron is 125 Å. Determine the electron energy (in eV), momentum, and velocity.

2.5   It is desired to produce x-ray radiation with a wavelength of 1 Å. (a) Through what potential voltage difference must the electron be accelerated in vacuum so that it can, upon colliding with a target, generate such a photon? (Assume that all of the electron's energy is transferred to the photon.) (b) What is the de Broglie wavelength of the electron in part (a) just before it hits the target?

Section 2.2   Energy Quantization and Probability Concepts

2.6   Calculate the energy of an electron in the hydrogen atom (in units of eV) for the first four allowed energy levels.

2.7   Show that the most probable value of the radius r for the $1s$ electron in a hydrogen atom is equal to the Bohr radius a_0.

2.8   Consider the periodic table. (a) Determine three elements that have the following properties: (i) one-valence electron and (ii) four-valence electrons. (b) What do the following elements (i) F, Cl, Br, and (ii) He, Ne, Ar have in common?

[Note: the following problems are for readers who have studied Schrödinger's wave equation in Appendix E.]

2.9   The solution to Schrödinger's wave equation for a particular situation is given by $\psi(x) = \sqrt{2/a_0} \cdot e^{-x/a_0}$. Determine the probability of finding the particle between the following limits: (a) $0 \leq x \leq a_0/4$, (b) $a_0/4 \leq x \leq a_0/2$, and (c) $0 \leq x \leq a_0$.

2.10   An electron is bound in a one-dimensional infinite potential well with a width of 100 Å. Determine the electron energy levels for $n = 1, 2, 3$.

2.11   A one-dimensional infinite potential well with a width of 12 Å contains an electron. (a) Calculate the first two energy levels that the electron may occupy. (b) If an electron drops from the second energy level to the first, what is the wavelength of a photon that might be emitted?

2.12   Consider a three-dimensional infinite potential well. The potential function is given by $V(x) = 0$ for $0 < x < a, 0 < y < a, 0 < z < a$, and $V(x) = \infty$ elsewhere. Start with Schrödinger's wave equation, use the separation of variables technique, and show that the energy is quantized and is given by

$$E_{n_x n_y n_z} = \frac{\hbar^2 \pi^2}{2ma^2} \left(n_x^2 + n_y^2 + n_z^2\right)$$

where $n_x = 1, 2, 3, \ldots, n_y = 1, 2, 3, \ldots, n_z = 1, 2, 3, \ldots$.

2.13   Evaluate the transmission coefficient for an electron of energy 2.2 eV impinging on a potential barrier of height 6.0 eV and thickness 10^{-10} m. Repeat the calculation for a barrier thickness of 10^{-9} m. Assume that Equation (E.27) in Appendix E is valid.

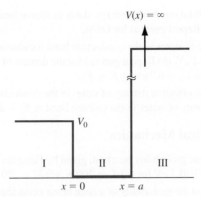

Figure P2.15 | Potential function for Problem 2.15.

2.14 (a) Estimate the tunneling probability of a particle with an effective mass of $0.067\,m_0$ (an electron in gallium arsenide), where m_0 is the mass of an electron, tunneling through a rectangular potential barrier of height $V_0 = 0.8$ eV and width 15 Å. The particle kinetic energy is 0.20 eV. (b) Repeat part (a) if the effective mass of the particle is $1.08\,m_0$ (an electron in silicon).

2.15 Consider the one-dimensional potential function shown in Figure P2.15. Assume the total energy of an electron is $E < V_0$. (a) Write the wave solutions that apply in each region. (b) Write the set of equations that result from applying the boundary conditions. (c) Show explicitly why, or why not, the energy levels of the electron are quantized.

Section 2.3   Energy-Band Theory

2.16 Consider Figure 2.8b, which shows the energy-band splitting of silicon. If the equilibrium lattice spacing were to change by a small amount, discuss how you would expect the electrical properties of silicon to change. Determine at what point the material would behave like an insulator or like a metal.

2.17 The bandgap energy in a semiconductor is usually a slight function of temperature. In some cases, the bandgap energy versus temperature can be modeled by

$$E_g = E_g(0) - \frac{\alpha T^2}{(\beta + T)}$$

where $E_g(0)$ is the value of the bandgap energy at $T = 0$ K. For silicon, the parameter values are $E_g(0) = 1.170$ eV, $\alpha = 4.73 \times 10^{-4}$ eV/K and $\beta = 636$ K. Plot E_g versus T over the range $0 \leq T \leq 600$ K. In particular, note the value at $T = 300$ K.

2.18 The forbidden energy band of GaAs is 1.42 eV. (a) Determine the minimum frequency of an incident photon that can interact with a valence electron and elevate the electron to the conduction band. (b) What is the corresponding wavelength?

Section 2.4   Density of States Function

2.19 (a) Determine the total number of energy states in silicon between E_c and $E_c + kT$ at $T = 300$ K. (b) Repeat part (a) for GaAs.

2.20 (a) Determine the total number of energy states in silicon between E_v and $E_v - kT$ at $T = 300$ K. (b) Repeat part (a) for GaAs.

2.21 (a) Plot the density of states in the conduction band for silicon over the range $E_c \le E \le E_c + 0.2$ eV. (b) Repeat part (a) for the density of states in the valence band over the range $E_v - 0.2\,\text{eV} \le E \le E_v$.

2.22 Find the ratio of the effective density of states in the conduction band at $E_c + kT$ to the effective density of states in the valence band at $E_v - kT$.

Section 2.5   Statistical Mechanics

2.23 Plot the Fermi–Dirac probability function, given by Equation (2.29), over the range $-0.2 \le (E - E_F) \le 0.2$ eV for (a) $T = 200$ K, (b) $T = 300$ K, and (c) $T = 400$ K.

2.24 (a) If $E_F = E_c$, find the probability of a state being occupied at $E = E_c + kT$. (b) If $E_F = E_v$, find the probability of a state being empty at $E = E_v - kT$.

2.25 Determine the probability that an allowed energy state is occupied by an electron if the state is above the Fermi level by (a) kT, (b) $3kT$, and (c) $6kT$.

2.26 Determine the probability than an allowed energy state is empty of an electron if the state is below the Fermi level by (a) kT, (b) $3kT$, and (c) $6kT$.

2.27 The Fermi energy in silicon is 0.25 eV below the conduction band energy E_c. (a) Plot the probability of a state being occupied by an electron over the range $E_c \le E \le E_c + 2kT$. Assume $T = 300$ K. (b) Repeat part (a) for $T = 400$ K.

2.28 Show that the probability of an energy state being occupied ΔE above the Fermi energy is the same as the probability of a state being empty ΔE below the Fermi level.

2.29 (a) Determine for what energy above E_F (in terms of kT) the Fermi–Dirac probability function is within 2 percent of the Boltzmann approximation. (b) Give the value of the probability function at this energy.

2.30 The Fermi energy level for a particular material at $T = 300$ K is 6.25 eV. The electrons in this material follow the Fermi–Dirac distribution function. (a) Find the probability of an energy level at 6.50 eV being occupied by an electron. (b) Repeat part (a) if the temperature is increased to $T = 950$ K. (Assume that E_F is a constant.) (c) Calculate the temperature at which there is a 1 percent probability that a state 0.30 eV below the Fermi level will be empty of an electron.

2.31 The Fermi energy for copper at $T = 300$ K is 7.0 eV. The electrons in copper follow the Fermi–Dirac distribution function. (a) Find the probability of an energy level at 7.15 eV being occupied by an electron. (b) Repeat part (a) for $T = 1000$ K. (Assume that E_F is a constant.) (c) Repeat part (a) for $E = 6.85$ eV and $T = 300$ K. (d) Determine the probability of the energy state at $E = E_F$ being occupied at $T = 300$ K and at $T = 1000$ K.

2.32 Consider the energy levels shown in Figure P 2.32. Let $T = 300$ K. (a) If $E_1 - E_F = 0.30$ eV, determine the probability that an energy state at $E = E_1$ is occupied by an electron and the probability that an energy state at $E = E_2$ is empty. (b) Repeat part (a) if $E_F - E_2 = 0.40$ eV.

2.33 Repeat problem 2.32 for the case when $E_1 - E_2 = 1.42$ eV.

2.34 Determine the derivative with respect to energy of the Fermi–Dirac distribution function. Plot the derivative with respect to energy for (a) $T = 0$ K, (b) $T = 300$ K, and (c) $T = 500$ K.

2.35 Assume the Fermi energy level is exactly in the center of the bandgap energy of a semiconductor at $T = 300$ K. (a) Calculate the probability that an energy state at

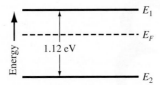

Figure P2.32 | Energy levels for Problem 2.32.

$E = E_c + kT/2$ is occupied by an electron for Si, Ge, and GaAs. (*b*) Calculate the probability that an energy state at $E = E_v - kT/2$ is empty for Si, Ge, and GaAs.

2.36 Calculate the temperature at which there is a 10^{-6} probability that an energy state 0.55 eV above the Fermi energy level is occupied by an electron.

2.37 Calculate the energy range (in eV) between $f_F(E) = 0.95$ and $f_F(E) = 0.05$ for $E_F = 7.0$ eV and for (*a*) $T = 300$ K and (*b*) $T = 500$ K.

READING LIST

*1. Datta. S. *Quantum Phenomena*, Vol. 8 of *Modular Series on Solid State Devices*. Reading, MA: Addison-Wesley, 1989.

*2. deCogan, D. *Solid State Devices: A Quantum Physics Approach*. New York: Springer-Verlag, 1987.

3. Eisberg, R. M. *Fundamentals of Modern Physics*. New York: Wiley, 1961.

4. Eisberg, R., and R. Resnick. *Quantum Physics of Atoms, Molecules, Solids, Nuclei, and Particles*. New York: Wiley, 1974.

5. Kittel, C. *Introduction to Solid State Physics,* 7th ed. Berlin: Springer-Verlag, 1993.

6. McKelvey, J. P. *Solid State Physics for Engineering and Materials Science*. Malabar, FL: Krieger Publishing, 1993.

7. Neamen, D. A. *Semiconductor Physics and Devices: Basic Principles,* 3rd ed. New York: McGraw-Hill, 2003.

8. Pauling, L., and E. B. Wilson. *Introduction to Quantum Mechanics*. New York: McGraw-Hill, 1935.

9. Pierret, R. F. *Semiconductor Device Fundamentals*. Reading, MA: Addison-Wesley, 1996.

*10. Shockley, W. *Electrons and Holes in Semiconductors*. New York: D. Van Nostrand, 1950.

11. Shur, M. *Introduction to Electronic Devices*. New York: John Wiley and Sons, 1996.

12. Singh, J. *Semiconductor Devices: Basic Principles*. New York: John Wiley and Sons, 2001.

13. Streetman, B. G., and S. Banerjee. *Solid State Electronic Devices,* 5th ed. Upper Saddle River, NJ: Prentice-Hall, 2000.

14. Sze, S. M. *Semiconductor Devices: Physics and Technology,* 2nd ed. New York: John Wiley and Sons, 2002.

*15. Wang, S. *Fundamentals of Semiconductor Theory and Device Physics*. Englewood Cliffs, NJ: Prentice-Hall, 1988.

*Indicates references are at an advanced level compared to this text.

CHAPTER

3

The Semiconductor in Equilibrium

So far, we have been considering a general crystal and determining a few of the characteristics of electrons in the single-crystal lattice. In this chapter, we will specifically apply the concepts considered to a semiconductor material. In particular, we will use the density of quantum states in the conduction band and the density of quantum states in the valence band along with the Fermi–Dirac probability function to determine the concentration of electrons and holes in the conduction and valence bands, respectively. We will also apply the concept of the Fermi energy to the semiconductor material.

This chapter deals with the semiconductor in equilibrium. Equilibrium, or thermal equilibrium, implies that no external forces such as voltages, electric fields, magnetic fields, or temperature gradients are acting on the semiconductor. All properties of the semiconductor are independent of time in this case. Equilibrium is our starting point for developing the physics of the semiconductor. We will then be able to determine the characteristics that result when deviations from equilibrium occur, such as when a voltage is applied to a semiconductor material.

3.0 | PREVIEW

In this chapter, we will

1. Determine the thermal equilibrium concentration of charge carriers (electrons and holes) in semiconductors.
2. Determine the effect of adding specific impurity atoms to a semiconductor material.
3. Define an extrinsic semiconductor and determine the thermal equilibrium concentration of electrons and holes as a function of energy.

4. Determine the statistics of electrons and holes as a function of energy and temperature.
5. Determine the thermal-equilibrium concentration of electrons and holes in semiconductors as a function of impurity atoms added to the material.
6. Determine the position of the Fermi energy level as a function of the concentration of impurity atoms added to the semiconductor material.
7. Describe the two primary doping processes in semiconductors—diffusion and ion implantation.

Historical Insight

Semiconductor device characteristics are determined to a great extent by the semiconductor conductivity. The conductivity of a semiconductor can be varied over approximately 10 orders of magnitude (from a good conductor to a good insulator) by controlling the concentration of specific impurities in the material. The process by which these impurities are introduced into the semiconductor is called doping. The doping process in silicon, by diffusion techniques, was disclosed in a patent in 1952 by W. G. Pfann. The doping process, by the ion implantation process, was proposed by W. Shockley in 1958.

Present-Day Insight

The doping process, especially ion implantation, continues to be a vital part of semiconductor device fabrication. Specific regions of the semiconductor near the surface of the wafer can be doped with one type of impurity atom, while the region directly adjacent can be doped with another type of impurity. This flexibility in changing the conductivity type over very short distances is one basic reason that millions of semiconductor devices can be fabricated as a single integrated circuit.

3.1 | CHARGE CARRIERS IN SEMICONDUCTORS

Objective: Determine the thermal equilibrium concentration of charge carriers (electrons and holes) in semiconductors.

Current is the rate at which charge flows. In a semiconductor, two types of charge carrier, the electron and the hole, can contribute to a current. Since the current in a semiconductor is determined largely by the number of electrons in the conduction band and the number of holes in the valence band, an important characteristic of the semiconductor is the density of these charge carriers. The density of electrons and holes is related to the density of states function and the Fermi–Dirac distribution function, both of which we have considered. A qualitative discussion of these relationships will be followed by a more rigorous mathematical derivation of the thermal-equilibrium concentration of electrons and holes.

3.1.1   Equilibrium Distribution of Electrons and Holes

The distribution (with respect to energy) of electrons in the conduction band is given by the density of allowed quantum states times the probability that a state is occupied by an electron. This statement is written in equation form as

$$n(E) = g_c(E)f_F(E) \tag{3.1}$$

where $f_F(E)$ is the Fermi–Dirac probability function and $g_c(E)$ is the density of quantum states in the conduction band. The units of $n(E)$ are # of electrons per cm^3 per unit of energy. The total electron concentration per unit volume in the conduction band is then found by integrating Equation (3.1) over the entire range of energies for the conduction-band energies.

Similarly, the distribution (with respect to energy) of holes in the valence band is the density of allowed quantum states in the valence band multiplied by the probability that a state is *not* occupied by an electron. We can express this as

$$p(E) = g_v(E)[1 - f_F(E)] \tag{3.2}$$

The units of $p(E)$ are # of holes per cm^3 per unit of energy. The total hole concentration per unit volume is found by integrating Equation (3.2) over the entire range of energies for the valence-band energy.

To find the thermal-equilibrium electron and hole concentrations, we need to determine the position of the Fermi energy E_F with respect to the bottom of the conduction-band energy E_c and the top of the valence-band energy E_v. To address this question, we will initially consider an intrinsic semiconductor. An ideal intrinsic semiconductor is a pure semiconductor with no impurity atoms and no lattice defects in the crystal (e.g., pure silicon). We have argued in Chapter 2 that, for an intrinsic semiconductor at $T = 0$ K, all energy states in the valence band are filled with electrons and all energy states in the conduction band are empty of electrons. The Fermi energy must, therefore, be somewhere between E_c and E_v. (The Fermi energy does not need to correspond to an allowed energy.)

As the temperature begins to increase above 0 K, the valence electrons will gain thermal energy. A few electrons in the valence band may gain sufficient energy to jump to the conduction band. As an electron jumps from the valence band to the conduction band, an empty state, or hole, is created in the valence band. In an intrinsic semiconductor, then, electrons and holes are created in pairs by the thermal energy so that the number of electrons in the conduction band is equal to the number of holes in the valence band.

Density of states

Fermi–Dirac probability function

Figure 3.1a shows a plot of the density of states function in the conduction band $g_c(E)$, the density of states function in the valence band $g_v(E)$, and the Fermi–Dirac probability function for $T > 0$ K when E_F is approximately halfway between E_c and E_v. If we assume, for the moment, that the electron and hole effective masses are equal, then $g_c(E)$ and $g_v(E)$ are symmetrical functions about the midgap energy (the energy midway between E_c and E_v). We noted previously that the function $f_F(E)$ for $E > E_F$ is symmetrical to the function $1 - f_F(E)$ for $E < E_F$ about the energy $E = E_F$. This also means that the function $f_F(E)$ for $E = E_F + dE$ is equal to the function $1 - f_F(E)$ for $E = E_F - dE$.

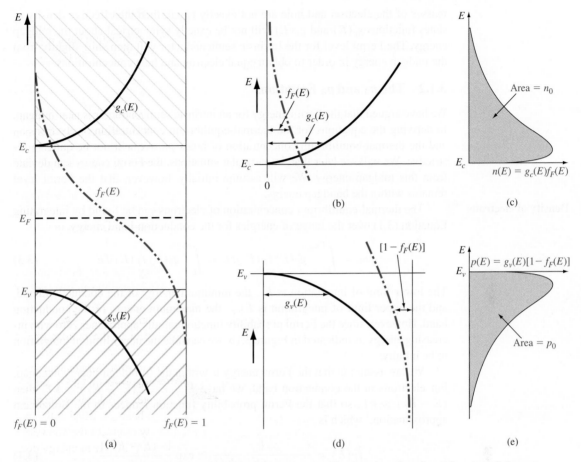

Figure 3.1 | (a) Density of states functions and Fermi–Dirac probability function plotted as a function of electron energy for the case when E_F is near the midgap energy; (b) expanded view of $g_c(E)$ and $f_F(E)$ near the conduction-band energy; (c) electron density in the conduction band; (d) expanded view of $g_v(E)$ and $[1 - f_F(E)]$ near the valence-band energy; and (e) hole density in the valence band.

Figure 3.1b is an expanded view of the plot in Figure 3.1a showing $f_F(E)$ and $g_c(E)$ above the conduction-band energy E_c. The product of $g_c(E)$ and $f_F(E)$ is the distribution of electrons $n(E)$ in the conduction band given by Equation (3.1). This product is plotted in Figure 3.1c. The area of the curve represents the total density (#/cm³) of electrons in the conduction band. Figure 3.1d is an expanded view of the plot in Figure 3.1a showing $[1 - f_F(E)]$ and $g_v(E)$ below the valence-band energy E_v. The product of $g_v(E)$ and $[1 - f_F(E)]$ is the distribution of holes $p(E)$ in the valence band given by Equation (3.2). This product is plotted in Figure 3.1e. The area under this curve is the total density (#/cm³) of holes in the valence band. From this we see that if $g_c(E)$ and $g_v(E)$ are symmetrical, the Fermi energy must be at the midgap energy to obtain equal electron and hole concentrations. If the effective masses of the electron and hole are not exactly equal, then the effective density of states functions $g_c(E)$ and $g_v(E)$ will not be exactly symmetrical about the midgap energy. The Fermi level for the intrinsic semiconductor will then shift slightly from the midgap energy in order to obtain equal electron and hole concentrations.

3.1.2 The n_0 and p_0 Equations

We have argued that the Fermi energy for an intrinsic semiconductor is near midgap. In deriving the equations for the thermal-equilibrium concentration of electrons n_0 and the thermal-equilibrium concentration of holes p_0, we will not be quite so restrictive. We will see later that, in particular situations, the Fermi energy can deviate from this midgap energy. We will assume initially, however, that the Fermi level remains within the bandgap energy.

Density of electrons   The thermal-equilibrium concentration of electrons can be found by integrating Equation (3.1) over the range of energies for the conduction-band energy, or

$$n_0 = \int_{E_c}^{E_{\text{Top}}} g_c(E) f_F(E) \, dE = \int_{E_c}^{\infty} g_c(E) f_F(E) \, dE \tag{3.3}$$

The lower limit of integration is E_c, the minimum energy of the conduction band, and the upper limit of integration is E_{Top}, the maximum energy of the conduction band. However, since the Fermi probability function rapidly approaches zero with increasing energy as indicated in Figure 3.1b, we can take the upper limit of integration to be infinity.

We are assuming that the Fermi energy is within the forbidden-energy bandgap. For electrons in the conduction band, we have $E > E_c$. If $(E_c - E_F) \gg kT$, then $(E - E_F) \gg kT$, so that the Fermi probability function reduces to the Boltzmann approximation,[1] which is

$$f_F(E) = \frac{1}{1 + \exp \dfrac{(E - E_F)}{kT}} \approx \exp \frac{[-(E - E_F)]}{kT} \tag{3.4}$$

Applying the Boltzmann approximation to Equation (3.3), the thermal-equilibrium density of electrons in the conduction band is found from

$$n_0 = \int_{E_c}^{\infty} \frac{4\pi (2m_n^*)^{3/2}}{h^3} \sqrt{E - E_c} \, \exp \left[\frac{-(E - E_F)}{kT} \right] dE \tag{3.5}$$

The integral of Equation (3.5) may be solved more easily by making a change of variable. If we let

$$\eta = \frac{E - E_c}{kT} \tag{3.6}$$

---

[1]The Maxwell–Boltzmann and Fermi–Dirac distribution functions are within 5 percent of each other when $E - E_F \approx 3kT$ (see Figure 2.26). The $\gg$ notation is then somewhat misleading to indicate when the Boltzmann approximation is valid, although it is commonly used.

then Equation (3.5) becomes

$$n_0 = \frac{4\pi (2m_n^* kT)^{3/2}}{h^3} \exp\left[\frac{-(E_c - E_F)}{kT}\right] \int_0^\infty \eta^{1/2} \exp(-\eta)\, d\eta \qquad (3.7)$$

The integral is the gamma function, with a value of

$$\int_0^\infty \eta^{1/2} \exp(-\eta)\, d\eta = \frac{1}{2}\sqrt{\pi} \qquad (3.8)$$

Then Equation (3.7) becomes

$$n_0 = 2\left(\frac{2\pi m_n^* kT}{h^2}\right)^{3/2} \exp\left[\frac{-(E_c - E_F)}{kT}\right] \qquad (3.9)$$

We may define a parameter N_c as

$$N_c = 2\left(\frac{2\pi m_n^* kT}{h^2}\right)^{3/2} \qquad (3.10)$$

so that the thermal-equilibrium electron concentration in the conduction band can be written as

$$\boxed{n_0 = N_c \exp\left[\frac{-(E_c - E_F)}{kT}\right]} \qquad (3.11)$$

The parameter N_c is called the *effective density of states function in the conduction band*. If we were to assume that $m_n^* = m_0$, then the value of the effective density of states function at $T = 300$ K is $N_c = 2.5 \times 10^{19}$ cm^{-3}, which is the order of magnitude of N_c for most semiconductors. If the effective mass of the electron is larger or smaller than m_0, then the value of the effective density of states function changes accordingly, but is still of the same order of magnitude.

Effective density of states function in the conduction band

EXAMPLE 3.1

OBJECTIVE

Calculate the probability that an energy state in the conduction band at $E = E_c + kT$ is occupied by an electron and calculate the thermal equilibrium electron concentration in silicon at $T = 300$ K.

Assume the Fermi energy is 0.20 eV below the conduction band energy E_c. The value of N_c for silicon at $T = 300$ K is $N_c = 2.8 \times 10^{19}$ cm^{-3}.

■ **Solution**

The probability that an energy state at $E = E_c + kT$ is occupied by an electron is given by

$$f_F(E_c + kT) = \frac{1}{1 + \exp\left(\dfrac{E_c + kT - E_F}{kT}\right)} \approx \exp\left[\frac{-(E_c + kT - E_F)}{kT}\right]$$

or

$$f_F(E_c + kT) = \exp\left[\frac{-(0.20 + 0.0259)}{0.0259}\right] = 1.63 \times 10^{-4}$$

The electron concentration is given by

$$n_0 = N_c \exp\left[\frac{-(E_c - E_F)}{kT}\right] = (2.8 \times 10^{19}) \exp\left[\frac{-0.20}{0.0259}\right]$$

or

$$n_0 = 1.24 \times 10^{16} \text{ cm}^{-3}$$

■ **Comment**

The probability of a state being occupied in the conduction band can be quite small, but the thermal equilibrium value of electron concentration can be a reasonable value since the density of states is large.

Exercise Problem

EX3.1 Calculate the thermal equilibrium electron concentration in silicon at $T = 300$ K for the case when the Fermi level is 0.25 eV below the conduction-band energy, E_c. (Ans. 1.8×10^{15} cm^{-3}.)

Density of holes

The thermal-equilibrium concentration of holes in the valence band is found by integrating Equation (3.2) over the range of energies in the valence-band energy, or

$$p_0 = \int_{E_{Bot}}^{E_v} g_v(E)[1 - f_F(E)]\, dE = \int_{-\infty}^{E_v} g_v(E)[1 - f_F(E)]\, dE. \quad (3.12)$$

where E_v is the maximum energy of the valence band and E_{Bot} is the minimum energy of the valence band. However, the function $1 - f_F(E)$ approaches zero very quickly as the energy decreases, as seen in Figure 3.1d, so we may let $E_{Bot} = -\infty$.

We can note that

$$1 - f_F(E) = \frac{1}{1 + \exp\left(\dfrac{E_F - E}{kT}\right)} \quad (3.13a)$$

For energy states in the valence band, $E < E_v$. If $(E_F - E_v) \gg kT$ (the Fermi function is still assumed to be within the bandgap), then we have a slightly different form of the Boltzmann approximation. Equation (3.13a) can be written as

$$1 - f_F(E) = \frac{1}{1 + \exp\left(\dfrac{E_F - E}{kT}\right)} \approx \exp\left[\frac{-(E_F - E)}{kT}\right] \quad (3.13b)$$

Applying the Boltzmann approximation of Equation (3.13b) to Equation (3.12), we find the thermal-equilibrium concentration of holes in the valence band is

$$p_0 = \int_{-\infty}^{E_v} \frac{4\pi (2m_p^*)^{3/2}}{h^3} \sqrt{E_v - E} \, \exp\left[\frac{-(E_F - E)}{kT}\right] dE \quad (3.14)$$

where the lower limit of integration is taken as minus infinity instead of the bottom of the valence band. The exponential term decays fast enough so that this approximation is valid.

Equation (3.14) can be solved more easily by again making a change of variable. If we let

$$\eta' = \frac{E_v - E}{kT} \quad (3.15)$$

then Equation (3.14) becomes

$$p_0 = \frac{-4\pi (2m_p^* kT)^{3/2}}{h^3} \exp\left[\frac{-(E_F - E_v)}{kT}\right] \int_{+\infty}^{0} (\eta')^{1/2} \exp(-\eta') \, d\eta' \quad (3.16)$$

where the negative sign comes from the differential $dE = -kT d\eta'$. Note that the lower limit of η' becomes $+\infty$ when $E = -\infty$. If we change the order of integration, we introduce another minus sign. From Equation (3.8), Equation (3.16) becomes

$$p_0 = 2\left(\frac{2\pi m_p^* kT}{h^2}\right)^{3/2} \exp\left[\frac{-(E_F - E_v)}{kT}\right] \quad (3.17)$$

We may define a parameter N_v as

$$N_v = 2\left(\frac{2\pi m_p^* kT}{h^2}\right)^{3/2} \quad (3.18)$$

which is called the *effective density of states function in the valence band*. The thermal-equilibrium concentration of holes in the valence band can now be written as

Effective density of states function in the valence band

$$\boxed{p_0 = N_v \exp\left[\frac{-(E_F - E_v)}{kT}\right]} \quad (3.19)$$

The magnitude of N_v is also on the order of 10^{19} cm^{-3} at $T = 300$ K for most semiconductors.

EXAMPLE 3.2

OBJECTIVE

Calculate the probability that an energy state in the valence band at $E = E_v - kT$ is empty of an electron and calculate the thermal-equilibrium hole concentration in silicon at $T = 350$ K.

Assume the Fermi energy is 0.25 eV above the valence-band energy. The value of N_v for silicon at $T = 300$ K is $N_v = 1.04 \times 10^{19}$ cm^{-3}.

■ **Solution**

The parameter values at $T = 350$ K are found as

$$N_v = (1.04 \times 10^{19}) \left(\frac{350}{300}\right)^{3/2} = 1.31 \times 10^{19} \text{ cm}^{-3}$$

and

$$kT = (0.0259) \left(\frac{350}{300}\right) = 0.0302 \text{ eV}$$

The probability that an energy state at $E = E_v - kT$ is empty is given by

$$1 - f_F(E_v - kT) = 1 - \frac{1}{1 + \exp\left(\dfrac{E_v - kT - E_F}{kT}\right)} \approx \exp\left[\frac{-(E_F - (E_v - kT))}{kT}\right]$$

or

$$1 - f_F(E_v - kT) = \exp\left[\frac{-(0.25 + 0.0302)}{0.0302}\right] = 9.34 \times 10^{-5}$$

The hole concentration is

$$p_0 = N_v \exp\left[\frac{-(E_F - E_v)}{kT}\right] = (1.31 \times 10^{19}) \exp\left[\frac{-0.25}{0.0302}\right]$$

or

$$p_0 = 3.33 \times 10^{15} \text{ cm}^{-3}$$

■ **Comment**

The parameter values at any temperature can easily be found using the 300 K values and the temperature dependence of the parameter.

Exercise Problem

EX3.2 Calculate the thermal-equilibrium hole concentration in silicon at $T = 300$ K for the case when the Fermi level is 0.20 eV above the valence-band energy E_v.

(Ans. 4.61×10^{15} cm^{-3})

The effective density of states functions, N_c and N_v, are constant for a given semiconductor material at a fixed temperature. Table 3.1 gives the values of the density of states function and of the effective masses for silicon, gallium arsenide, and germanium. Note that the value of N_c for gallium arsenide is smaller than the typical 10^{19} cm^{-3} value. This difference is due to the small electron effective mass in gallium arsenide.

The thermal-equilibrium concentrations of electrons in the conduction band and of holes in the valence band are directly related to the effective density of states constants and to the Fermi energy level.

Table 3.1 | Effective density of states function and effective mass values

	N_c (cm^{-3})	N_v (cm^{-3})	m_n^*/m_0	m_p^*/m_0
Silicon	2.8×10^{19}	1.04×10^{19}	1.08	0.56
Gallium arsenide	4.7×10^{17}	7.0×10^{18}	0.067	0.48
Germanium	1.04×10^{19}	6.0×10^{18}	0.55	0.37

3.1.3 The Intrinsic Carrier Concentration

For an intrinsic semiconductor, the concentration of electrons in the conduction band is equal to the concentration of holes in the valence band. We can denote n_i and p_i as the electron and hole concentrations, respectively, in the intrinsic semiconductor. These parameters are usually referred to as the intrinsic electron concentration and intrinsic hole concentration. However, $n_i = p_i$, so normally we simply use the parameter n_i as the intrinsic carrier concentration, which refers to either the intrinsic electron or hole concentration.

Intrinsic carrier concentration

The Fermi energy level for the intrinsic semiconductor is called the intrinsic Fermi energy, or $E_F = E_{Fi}$. If we apply Equations (3.11) and (3.19) to the intrinsic semiconductor, then we can write

$$n_0 = n_i = N_c \exp\left[\frac{-(E_c - E_{Fi})}{kT}\right] \tag{3.20}$$

and

$$p_0 = p_i = n_i = N_v \exp\left[\frac{-(E_{Fi} - E_v)}{kT}\right] \tag{3.21}$$

If we take the product of Equations (3.20) and (3.21), we obtain

$$n_i^2 = N_c N_v \exp\left[\frac{-(E_c - E_{Fi})}{kT}\right] \cdot \exp\left[\frac{-(E_{Fi} - E_v)}{kT}\right] \tag{3.22}$$

or

$$n_i^2 = N_c N_v \exp\left[\frac{-(E_c - E_v)}{kT}\right] = N_c N_v \exp\left[\frac{-E_g}{kT}\right] \tag{3.23}$$

where E_g is the bandgap energy. For a given semiconductor material at a constant temperature, the value of n_i is a constant, and independent of the Fermi energy.

The intrinsic carrier concentration for silicon at $T = 300$ K can be calculated by using the effective density of states function values from Table 3.1. The value of n_i calculated from Equation (3.23) for $E_g = 1.12$ eV is $n_i = 6.95 \times 10^9$ cm^{-3}. The commonly accepted value[2] of n_i for silicon at $T = 300$ K is approximately

---

[2]Various references may list slightly different values of the intrinsic silicon concentration at room temperature. In general, they are all between 1×10^{10} and 1.5×10^{10} cm^{-3}. This difference is, in most cases, not significant.

Table 3.2 | Commonly accepted values of n_i at $T = 300$ K

Silicon	$n_i = 1.5 \times 10^{10}$ cm^{-3}
Gallium arsenide	$n_i = 1.8 \times 10^6$ cm^{-3}
Germanium	$n_i = 2.4 \times 10^{13}$ cm^{-3}

1.5×10^{10} cm^{-3}. This discrepancy may arise from several sources. First, the values of the effective masses are determined at a low temperature where the cyclotron resonance experiments are performed. Since the effective mass is an experimentally determined parameter, and since the effective mass is a measure of how well a particle moves in a crystal, this parameter may be a slight function of temperature. Next, the density of states function for a semiconductor was obtained by generalizing the model of an electron in a three-dimensional infinite potential well. This theoretical function may also not agree exactly with experiment. However, the difference between the theoretical value and the experimental value of n_i is approximately a factor of 2, which, in many cases, is not significant. Table 3.2 lists the commonly accepted values of n_i for silicon, gallium arsenide, and germanium at $T = 300$ K.

The intrinsic carrier concentration is a very strong function of temperature.

Figure 3.2 is a plot of n_i from Equation (3.23) for silicon, gallium arsenide, and germanium as a function of temperature. As seen in the figure, the value of n_i for these semiconductors may easily vary over several orders of magnitude as the temperature changes over a reasonable range.

EXAMPLE 3.3

OBJECTIVE

Calculate the intrinsic carrier concentration in silicon at $T = 350$ K and at $T = 400$ K.

The values of N_c and N_v vary as $T^{3/2}$. As a first approximation, neglect any variation of bandgap energy with temperature. Assume that the bandgap energy of silicon is 1.12 eV. The value of kT at 350 K is

$$kT = (0.0259)\left(\frac{350}{300}\right) = 0.0302 \text{ eV}$$

and the value of kT at 400 K is

$$kT = (0.0259)\left(\frac{400}{300}\right) = 0.0345 \text{ eV}$$

■ Solution

Using Equation (3.23), we find for $T = 350$ K

$$n_i^2 = (2.8 \times 10^{19})(1.04 \times 10^{19})\left(\frac{350}{300}\right)^3 \exp\left(\frac{-1.12}{0.0302}\right) = 3.62 \times 10^{22}$$

so that

$$n_i(350 \text{ K}) = 1.90 \times 10^{11} \text{ cm}^{-3}$$

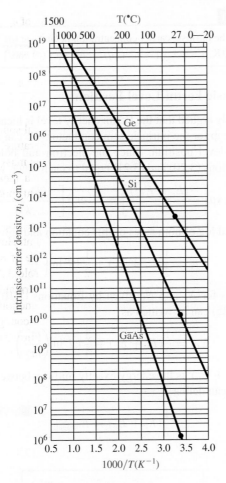

Figure 3.2 | The intrinsic carrier concentration in Ge, Si, and GaAs as a function of temperature.
(From Sze [17].)

For $T = 400$ K, we find

$$n_i^2 = (2.8 \times 10^{19})(1.04 \times 10^{19}) \left(\frac{400}{300} \right)^3 \exp \left(\frac{-1.12}{0.0345} \right) = 5.50 \times 10^{24}$$

so that

$$n_i (400 \text{ K}) = 2.34 \times 10^{12} \text{ cm}^{-3}$$

■ Comment

We can note from this example that the intrinsic carrier concentration increases by approximately one order of magnitude for each increase in temperature of $50°$C.

EX3.3 Determine the intrinsic carrier concentration in GaAs at (*a*) $T = 200$ K and at (*b*) $T = 400$ K. [Ans. (*a*) 1.48 cm^{-3}, (*b*) 3.22 × 10^9 cm^{-3}]

3.1.4 The Intrinsic Fermi-Level Position

We have qualitatively argued that the Fermi energy level is located near the center of the forbidden bandgap for the intrinsic semiconductor. We can specifically calculate the intrinsic Fermi-level position. Since the electron and hole concentrations are equal, setting Equations (3.20) and (3.21) equal to each other, we have

$$N_c \exp\left[\frac{-(E_c - E_{Fi})}{kT}\right] = N_v \exp\left[\frac{-(E_{Fi} - E_v)}{kT}\right] \tag{3.24}$$

If we take the natural log of both sides of this equation and solve for E_{Fi}, we obtain

$$E_{Fi} = \frac{1}{2}(E_c + E_v) + \frac{1}{2}kT \ln\left(\frac{N_v}{N_c}\right) \tag{3.25}$$

From the definitions for N_c and N_v given by Equations (3.10) and (3.18), respectively, Equation (3.25) can be written as

$$E_{Fi} = \frac{1}{2}(E_c + E_v) + \frac{3}{4}kT \ln\left(\frac{m_p^*}{m_n^*}\right) \tag{3.26a}$$

Midgap energy

The first term, $\frac{1}{2}(E_c + E_v)$, is the energy exactly midway between E_c and E_v, or the midgap energy. We can define

$$\frac{1}{2}(E_c + E_v) = E_{\text{midgap}}$$

so that

$$E_{Fi} - E_{\text{midgap}} = \frac{3}{4}kT \ln\left(\frac{m_p^*}{m_n^*}\right) \tag{3.26b}$$

Intrinsic Fermi level

If the electron and hole effective masses are equal so that $m_p^* = m_n^*$, then the intrinsic Fermi level is exactly in the center of the bandgap. If $m_p^* > m_n^*$, the intrinsic Fermi level is slightly above the center, and if $m_p^* < m_n^*$, it is slightly below the center of the bandgap. The density of states function is directly related to the carrier effective mass; thus, a larger effective mass means a larger density of states function. The intrinsic Fermi level must shift away from the band with the larger density of states in order to maintain equal numbers of electrons and holes.

EXAMPLE 3.4

OBJECTIVE

Determine the position of the intrinsic Fermi level with respect to the center of the bandgap in silicon at $T = 300$ K.

The density of states effective mass of the electron is $m_n^* = 1.08m_0$ and that of the hole is $m_p^* = 0.56m_0$.

■ **Solution**

The intrinsic Fermi level with respect to the center of the bandgap is

$$E_{Fi} - E_{\text{midgap}} = \frac{3}{4}kT \ln\left(\frac{m_p^*}{m_n^*}\right) = \frac{3}{4}(0.0259)\ln\left(\frac{0.56}{1.08}\right)$$

or

$$E_{Fi} - E_{\text{midgap}} = -12.8 \text{ meV}$$

■ **Comment**

For silicon, the intrinsic Fermi level is 12.8 meV below the midgap energy. If we compare 12.8 meV to 560 meV, which is one-half of the bandgap energy of silicon, we can, in many applications, simply approximate the intrinsic Fermi level to be in the center of the bandgap.

Exercise Problem

EX3.4 Determine the position of the intrinsic Fermi level with respect to the center of the bandgap in GaAs at $T = 300$ K. (Ans. +38.2 meV)

TEST YOUR UNDERSTANDING

TYU3.1 Determine the thermal equilibrium electron and hole concentrations in GaAs at $T = 300$ K for the case when the Fermi energy level is 0.25 eV above the valence-band energy E_v. Assume the bandgap energy is $E_g = 1.42$ eV. (Ans. $n_0 = 0.0113$ cm^{-3}, $p_0 = 4.50 \times 10^{14}$ cm^{-3})

TYU3.2 Find the intrinsic carrier concentration in silicon at (a) $T = 200$ K and at (b) $T = 400$ K. [Ans. (a) 8.13×10^4 cm^{-3}, (b) 2.34×10^{12} cm^{-3}]

TYU3.3 Determine the intrinsic carrier concentration in germanium at (a) $T = 200$ K and at (b) $T = 400$ K. [Ans. (a) 2.23×10^{10} cm^{-3}, (b) 8.53×10^{14} cm^{-3}]

3.2 | DOPANT ATOMS AND ENERGY LEVELS

Objective: Determine the effect of adding specific impurity atoms to a semiconductor material.

The intrinsic semiconductor may be an interesting material, but the real power of semiconductors is realized by adding small, controlled amounts of specific dopant, or impurity, atoms. This doping process, described in Section 3.7, can greatly alter the electrical characteristics of the semiconductor. The ability to produce a doped semiconductor, called an *extrinsic* material, is the primary reason we can fabricate the various semiconductor devices that we will consider in later chapters.

3.2.1 Qualitative Description

In Chapter 2, we discussed the covalent bonding of silicon and considered the simple two-dimensional representation of the single-crystal silicon lattice, as shown in

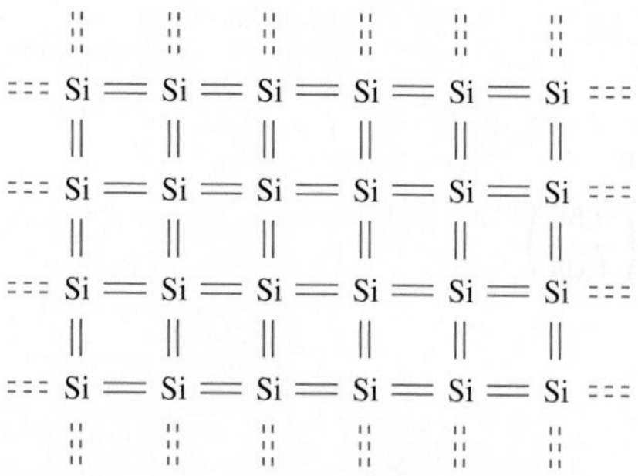

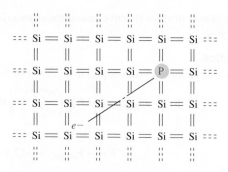

Figure 3.3 | Two-dimensional representation of the intrinsic silicon lattice at $T = 0$ K. All valence electrons bound in covalent bonding.

Figure 3.4 | Two-dimensional representation of the silicon lattice doped with a phosphorus atom at $T = 0$ K, showing the "fifth" valence electron of the phosphorus atom.

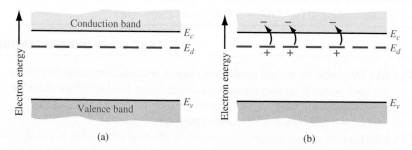

Figure 3.5 | The energy-band diagram showing (a) the discrete donor energy states ($T = 0$ K) and (b) the effect of some donor states being ionized creating free electrons ($T > 0$ K).

Figure 3.3. Now consider adding a group V element, such as phosphorus, as a substitutional impurity. The group V element has five valence electrons. Four of these will contribute to the covalent bonding with the silicon atoms, leaving the fifth more loosely bound to the phosphorus atom. This effect is schematically shown in Figure 3.4. We refer to the fifth valence electron as a donor electron.

The phosphorus atom without the donor electron is positively charged. At very low temperatures, the donor electron is bound to the phosphorus atom. However, by intuition, it should seem clear that the energy required to elevate the donor electron into the conduction band is considerably less than that for the electrons involved in the covalent bonding. Figure 3.5 shows the energy-band diagram that we would expect. The energy level, E_d, is the energy state of the donor electron. We normally draw the E_d energy states as a dashed line in the energy band diagram to demonstrate that the donor state is localized in space within the semiconductor, since the concentration of donor atoms is much smaller than the density of semiconductor material atoms.

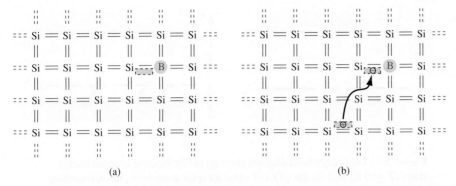

(a)   (b)

Figure 3.6 | Two-dimensional representation of a silicon lattice (a) doped with a boron atom at $T = 0$ K and (b) showing the ionization of the boron atom ($T > 0$ K) producing a hole.

If a small amount of energy, such as thermal energy, is added to the donor electron, it can be elevated into the conduction band, leaving behind a positively charged phosphorus ion. The electron in the conduction band can now move through the crystal generating a current, while the positively charged ion is fixed in the crystal. This type of impurity atom donates an electron to the conduction band and so is called a *donor impurity atom*. The donor impurity atoms add electrons to the conduction band without creating holes in the valence band. The resulting material is referred to as an *n-type* semiconductor (*n* for the negatively charged electron).

Now consider adding a group III element, such as boron, as a substitutional impurity to silicon. The group III element has three valence electrons, which are all taken up in the covalent bonding. As shown in Figure 3.6a, one covalent bonding position appears to be empty. If an electron were to occupy this "empty" position, its energy would have to be greater than that of the valence electrons, since the net charge state of the boron atom would now be negative. However, the electron occupying this "empty" position does not have sufficient energy to be in the conduction band, so its energy is far smaller than the conduction-band energy. Figure 3.6b shows how valence electrons may gain a small amount of thermal energy and move about in the crystal. The "empty" position associated with the boron atom becomes occupied, and other valence electron positions become vacated. These other vacated electron positions can be thought of as holes in the semiconductor material.

Figure 3.7 shows the expected energy state of the "empty" position and also the formation of a hole in the valence band. The hole can move through the crystal generating a current, while the negatively charged boron atom is fixed in the crystal. The group III atom accepts an electron from the valence band and so is referred to as an *acceptor impurity atom*. The acceptor atom can generate holes in the valence band without generating electrons in the conduction band. This type of semiconductor material is referred to as a *p-type* material (*p* for the positively charged hole).

The pure single-crystal semiconductor material is called an intrinsic material. Adding controlled amounts of dopant atoms, either donors or acceptors, creates a material called an *extrinsic semiconductor.* An extrinsic semiconductor will have either a preponderance of free electrons (n type) or a preponderance of free holes (p type).

Donor impurity atom

n type

Acceptor impurity atom

p type

Extrinsic semiconductor

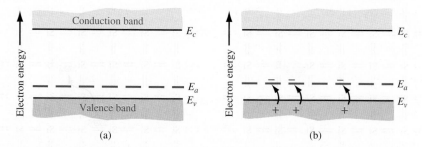

Figure 3.7 | The energy-band diagram showing (a) the discrete acceptor energy states $(T = 0 \text{ K})$ and (b) the effect of some acceptor states being ionized creating free holes $(T > 0 \text{ K})$.

3.2.2 Ionization Energy

We can calculate the approximate distance of the donor electron from the donor impurity ion, and also the approximate energy required to elevate the donor electron into the conduction band. This energy is referred to as the ionization energy. We will use the Bohr model of the atom for these calculations. The justification for using this model is that the most probable distance of an electron from the nucleus in a hydrogen atom, determined from quantum mechanics, is the same as the Bohr radius. The energy levels in the hydrogen atom determined from quantum mechanics are also the same as obtained from the Bohr theory.

In the case of the donor impurity atom, we can visualize the donor electron orbiting the donor ion, which is embedded in the semiconductor material. We will need to use the permittivity of the semiconductor material in the calculations rather than the permittivity of free space as is used in the case of the hydrogen atom. We will also use the effective mass of the electron in the calculations.

The analysis begins by setting the coulomb force of attraction between the electron and ion equal to the centripetal force of the orbiting electron. This condition will give a steady orbit. We have

$$\frac{e^2}{4\pi\epsilon r_n^2} = \frac{m^* v^2}{r_n} \tag{3.27}$$

where v is the magnitude of the velocity and r_n is the radius of the orbit. If we assume the angular momentum is also quantized, then we can write

$$m^* r_n v = n\hbar \tag{3.28}$$

where n is a positive integer. Solving for v from Equation (3.28), substituting into Equation (3.27), and solving for the radius, we obtain

$$r_n = \frac{n^2 \hbar^2 4\pi\epsilon}{m^* e^2} \tag{3.29}$$

The assumption of the angular momentum being quantized leads to the radius also being quantized.

The Bohr radius is defined as

$$a_0 = \frac{4\pi\epsilon_0\hbar^2}{m_0 e^2} = 0.53\,\text{Å} \tag{3.30}$$

We can normalize the radius of the donor orbital to that of the Bohr radius, which gives

$$\frac{r_n}{a_0} = n^2\epsilon_r\left(\frac{m_0}{m^*}\right) \tag{3.31}$$

where ϵ_r is the relative dielectric constant of the semiconductor material, m_0 is the rest mass of an electron, and m^* is the conductivity effective mass of the electron in the semiconductor.

If we consider the lowest energy state in which $n = 1$, and if we consider silicon in which $\epsilon_r = 11.7$ and the conductivity effective mass is $m^*/m_0 = 0.26$, then we have that

$$\frac{r_1}{a_0} = 45 \tag{3.32}$$

or $r_1 = 23.9\,\text{Å}$. This radius corresponds to approximately four lattice constants of silicon. Recall that one unit cell in silicon effectively contains eight atoms, so the radius of the orbiting donor electron encompasses many silicon atoms. The donor electron is not tightly bound to the donor atom.

The total energy of the orbiting electron is given by

$$E = T + V \tag{3.33}$$

where T is the kinetic energy and V is the potential energy of the electron. The kinetic energy is

$$T = \frac{1}{2}m^* v^2 \tag{3.34}$$

Using the velocity v from Equation (3.28) and the radius r_n from Equation (3.29), the kinetic energy becomes

$$T = \frac{m^* e^4}{2(n\hbar)^2(4\pi\epsilon)^2} \tag{3.35}$$

The potential energy is

$$V = \frac{-e^2}{4\pi\epsilon r_n} = \frac{-m^* e^4}{(n\hbar)^2(4\pi\epsilon)^2} \tag{3.36}$$

The total energy is the sum of the kinetic and potential energies, so that

$$E = T + V = \frac{-m^* e^4}{2(n\hbar)^2(4\pi\epsilon)^2} \tag{3.37}$$

For the hydrogen atom, $m^* = m_0$ and $\epsilon = \epsilon_0$. The ionization energy of the hydrogen atom in the lowest energy state is then $E = -13.6$ eV. If we consider silicon, the

Donor electron ionization energy

ionization energy is $E = -25.8$ meV, much less than the bandgap energy of silicon. This energy is the approximate ionization energy of the donor atom, or the energy required to elevate the donor electron into the conduction band.

For ordinary donor impurities such as phosphorus or arsenic in silicon or germanium, this hydrogenic model works quite well and gives some indication of the magnitudes of the ionization energies involved. Table 3.3 lists the actual experimentally measured ionization energies for a few impurities in silicon and germanium. Germanium and silicon have different relative dielectric constants and effective masses; thus, we expect the ionization energies to differ.

3.2.3   Group III–V Semiconductors

We have been discussing the donor and acceptor impurities in a group IV semiconductor, such as silicon. The situation in the group III–V compound semiconductors, such as gallium arsenide, is more complicated. Group II elements, such as beryllium, zinc, and cadmium, can enter the lattice as substitutional impurities, replacing the group III gallium element to become acceptor impurities. Similarly, group VI elements, such as selenium and tellurium, can enter the lattice substitutionally, replacing the group V arsenic element to become donor impurities. The corresponding ionization energies for these impurities are smaller than for the impurities in silicon. The ionization energies for the donors in gallium arsenide are also smaller than the ionization energies for the acceptors, because of the smaller effective mass of the electron compared to that of the hole.

Group IV elements, such as silicon and germanium, can also be impurity atoms in gallium arsenide. If a silicon atom replaces a gallium atom, the silicon impurity will act as a donor, but if the silicon atom replaces an arsenic atom, then the silicon impurity will act as an acceptor. The same is true for germanium as an impurity atom. Such impurities are called *amphoteric*. Experimentally in gallium arsenide, it is found that germanium is predominantly an acceptor and silicon is predominantly a donor. Table 3.4 lists the ionization energies for the various impurity atoms in gallium arsenide.

Table 3.3 | Impurity ionization energies in silicon and germanium

	Ionization Energy (eV)	
Impurity	**Si**	**Ge**
Donors		
Phosphorus	0.045	0.012
Arsenic	0.05	0.0127
Acceptors		
Boron	0.045	0.0104
Aluminum	0.06	0.0102

Table 3.4 | Impurity ionization energies in gallium arsenide

Impurity	**Ionization Energy (eV)**
Donors	
Selenium	0.0059
Tellurium	0.0058
Silicon	0.0058
Germanium	0.0061
Acceptors	
Beryllium	0.028
Zinc	0.0307
Cadmium	0.0347
Silicon	0.0345
Germanium	0.0404

TEST YOUR UNDERSTANDING

TYU3.4 Calculate the radius (normalized to a Bohr radius) of a donor electron in its lowest energy state in GaAs. (Ans. 195.5)

3.3 | CARRIER DISTRIBUTIONS IN THE EXTRINSIC SEMICONDUCTOR

Objective: Define an extrinsic semiconductor and determine the thermal equilibrium concentration of electrons and holes as a function of energy.

We defined an intrinsic semiconductor as a material with no impurity atoms present in the crystal. An *extrinsic semiconductor* is defined as a semiconductor in which controlled amounts of specific dopant or impurity atoms have been added so that the thermal-equilibrium electron and hole concentrations are different from the intrinsic carrier concentration. One type of carrier will predominate in an extrinsic semiconductor.

Intrinsic semiconductor

Extrinsic semiconductor

3.3.1 Equilibrium Distribution of Electrons and Holes

Adding donor or acceptor impurity atoms to a semiconductor will change the distribution of electrons and holes in the material. Since the Fermi energy is related to the distribution function, the Fermi energy will change as dopant atoms are added. If the Fermi energy changes from near the midgap value, the density of electrons in the conduction band and the density of holes in the valence band will change. These effects are shown in Figures 3.8 and 3.9. Figure 3.8 shows the case for $E_F > E_{Fi}$ and Figure 3.9 shows the case for $E_F < E_{Fi}$. When $E_F > E_{Fi}$, the electron concentration is larger than the hole concentration, and when $E_F < E_{Fi}$, the hole concentration is larger than the electron concentration. When the density of electrons is greater than the density of holes, the semiconductor is n type; donor impurity atoms have been added. When the density of holes is greater than the density of electrons, the semiconductor is p type; acceptor impurity atoms have been added. The Fermi energy changes as donor or acceptor impurities are added and, as the Fermi energy level in a semiconductor varies, the electron and hole concentrations change. The variation in Fermi level as a function of impurity concentrations will be considered in Section 3.6.

n type

p type

The expressions previously derived for the thermal-equilibrium concentration of electrons and holes, given by Equations (3.11) and (3.19) are general equations for n_0 and p_0 in terms of the Fermi energy. These equations are again given as

$$n_0 = N_c \exp\left[\frac{-(E_c - E_F)}{kT}\right]$$

and

$$p_0 = N_v \exp\left[\frac{-(E_F - E_v)}{kT}\right]$$

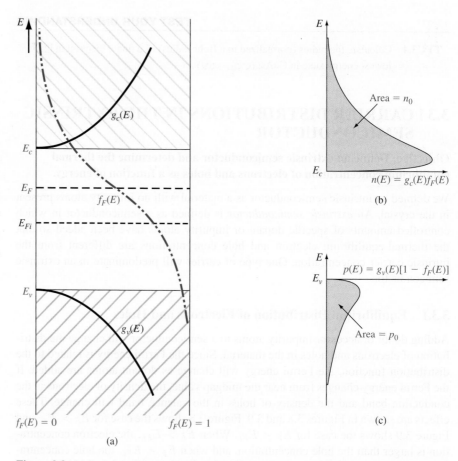

Figure 3.8 | (a) Density of states functions and Fermi–Dirac probability function plotted as a function of electron energy for the case when E_F is above the intrinsic Fermi energy (n-type semiconductor); (b) electron density in the conduction band; and (c) hole density in the valence band.

As just discussed, the Fermi energy may vary through the bandgap energy as a result of adding donor and acceptor impurities which, in turn, will change the values of n_0 and p_0.

EXAMPLE 3.5

OBJECTIVE

Calculate the thermal equilibrium concentrations of electrons and holes for a given Fermi energy.

Consider silicon at $T = 300$ K. Assume that the Fermi level is 0.25 eV above the valence-band energy. If we assume the bandgap energy of silicon is 1.12 eV, then the Fermi energy will be 0.87 below the conduction-band energy.

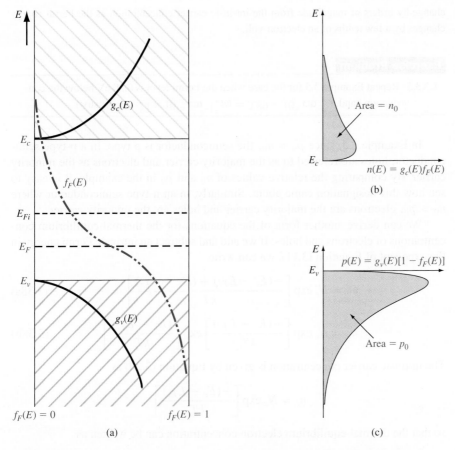

Figure 3.9 | (a) Density of states functions and Fermi–Dirac probability function plotted as a function of electron energy for the case when E_F is below the intrinsic Fermi energy (p-type semiconductor); (b) electron density in the conduction band; and (c) hole density in the valence band.

■ **Solution**

Using Equation (3.19), we can write

$$p_0 = (1.04 \times 10^{19}) \exp\left(\frac{-0.25}{0.0259}\right) = 6.68 \times 10^{14} \text{ cm}^{-3}$$

Using Equation (3.11), we can write

$$n_0 = (2.8 \times 10^{19}) \exp\left(\frac{-0.87}{0.0259}\right) = 7.23 \times 10^{4} \text{ cm}^{-3}$$

■ **Comment**

The change in the Fermi level is a function of the donor and acceptor impurity concentrations that are added to the semiconductor. This example shows that electron and hole concentrations change by orders of magnitude from the intrinsic carrier concentration as the Fermi energy changes by a few tenths of an electron-volt.

Exercise Problem

EX3.5 Repeat Example 3.5 for the case when the Fermi level is 0.20 eV below the conduction band. $(\text{Ans. } n_0 = 1.24 \times 10^{16} \text{ cm}^{-3}, \ p_0 = 3.89 \times 10^{3} \text{ cm}^{-3})$

Majority and minority carriers

In Example 3.5, since $p_0 > n_0$, the semiconductor is p type. In a p-type semiconductor, holes are referred to as the majority carrier and electrons as the minority carrier. By comparing the relative values of n_0 and p_0 in the example, it is easy to see how this designation came about. Similarly, in an n-type semiconductor where $n_0 > p_0$, electrons are the majority carrier and holes are the minority carrier.

We can derive another form of the equations for the thermal-equilibrium concentrations of electrons and holes. If we add and subtract an intrinsic Fermi energy in the exponent of Equation (3.11), we can write

$$n_0 = N_c \exp \left[\frac{-(E_c - E_{Fi}) + (E_F - E_{Fi})}{kT} \right] \tag{3.38a}$$

$$n_0 = N_c \exp \left[\frac{-(E_c - E_{Fi})}{kT} \right] \exp \left[\frac{(E_F - E_{Fi})}{kT} \right] \tag{3.38b}$$

The intrinsic carrier concentration is given by Equation (3.20) as

$$n_i = N_c \exp \left[\frac{-(E_c - E_{Fi})}{kT} \right]$$

Electron concentration

so that the thermal-equilibrium electron concentration can be written as

$$n_0 = n_i \exp \left[\frac{E_F - E_{Fi}}{kT} \right] \tag{3.39}$$

Similarly, if we add and subtract an intrinsic Fermi energy in the exponent of Equation (3.19), we will obtain

Hole concentration

$$p_0 = n_i \exp \left[\frac{-(E_F - E_{Fi})}{kT} \right] \tag{3.40}$$

As we will see, the Fermi level changes when donors and acceptors are added, but Equations (3.39) and (3.40) show that, as the Fermi level changes from the intrinsic Fermi level, n_0 and p_0 change from the n_i value. If $E_F > E_{Fi}$, then we will have $n_0 > n_i$ and $p_0 < n_i$. One characteristic of an n-type semiconductor is that $E_F > E_{Fi}$ so that $n_0 > p_0$. Similarly, in a p-type semiconductor, $E_F < E_{Fi}$ so that $p_0 > n_i$ and $n_0 < n_i$; thus, $p_0 > n_0$.

We can see the functional dependence of n_0 and p_0 with E_F in Figures 3.8 and 3.9. As E_F moves above or below E_{Fi}, the overlapping probability function with the density of states functions in the conduction band and valence band changes. As E_F moves above E_{Fi}, the probability function in the conduction band increases, while the probability, $1 - f_F(E)$, of an empty state (hole) in the valence band decreases. As E_F moves below E_{Fi}, the opposite occurs.

3.3.2 The $n_0 p_0$ Product

We can take the product of the general expressions for n_0 and p_0, as given in Equations (3.11) and (3.19), respectively. The result is

$$n_0 p_0 = N_c N_v \exp\left[\frac{-(E_c - E_F)}{kT}\right] \exp\left[\frac{-(E_F - E_v)}{kT}\right] \qquad (3.41)$$

which can be written as

$$n_0 p_0 = N_c N_v \exp\left[\frac{-E_g}{kT}\right] \qquad (3.42)$$

As Equation (3.42) was derived for a general value of Fermi energy, the values of n_0 and p_0 are not necessarily equal. However, Equation (3.42) is exactly the same as Equation (3.23), which we derived for the case of an intrinsic semiconductor. We then have that, for the semiconductor in thermal equilibrium,

$$\boxed{n_0 p_0 = n_i^2} \qquad (3.43)$$

Fundamental semiconductor equation

Equation (3.43) states that the product of n_0 and p_0 is always a constant for a given semiconductor material at a given temperature. Although this equation seems very simple, it is one of the fundamental principles of semiconductors in thermal equilibrium. The significance of this relation will become more apparent throughout the rest of the book. It is important to keep in mind that Equation (3.43) was derived using the Boltzmann approximation. If the Boltzmann approximation is not valid, then likewise, Equation (3.43) is not valid.

An extrinsic semiconductor in thermal equilibrium does not, strictly speaking, contain an intrinsic carrier concentration, although some thermally generated carriers are present. The intrinsic electron and hole carrier concentrations are modified by the donor or acceptor impurities. However, we may think of the intrinsic concentration n_i in Equation (3.43) simply as a parameter of the semiconductor material.

EXAMPLE 3.6

OBJECTIVE

Determine the hole concentration in silicon at $T = 300\,\text{K}$ given the electron concentration.

   Assume the electron concentration is $n_0 = 1 \times 10^{16}\,\text{cm}^{-3}$.

■ **Solution**

From Equation (3.43), we can write

$$p_0 = \frac{n_i^2}{n_0} = \frac{(1.5 \times 10^{10})^2}{1 \times 10^{16}}$$

or

$$p_0 = 2.25 \times 10^4 \text{ cm}^{-3}$$

■ **Comment**

As we have seen previously, the concentrations of electrons and holes can vary by orders of magnitude. The charge carrier that has the greater concentration is referred to as the majority carrier, and the charge carrier that has the lesser concentration is referred to as the minority carrier. In this example, the electron is the majority carrier and the hole is the minority carrier.

The fundamental semiconductor equation given by Equation (3.43) will prove to be extremely useful throughout the remainder of the text.

Exercise Problem

EX3.6   Find the hole concentration in silicon at $T = 300 \text{ K}$ if the electron concentration is $n_0 = 1 \times 10^5 \text{ cm}^{-3}$. Which carrier is the majority carrier and which carrier is the minority carrier?

(Ans. $p_0 = 2.25 \times 10^{15} \text{ cm}^{-3}$; hole, majority carrier; electron, minority carrier)

Σ^3 3.3.3   The Fermi–Dirac Integral

In the derivation of the Equations (3.11) and (3.19) for the thermal equilibrium electron and hole concentrations, we assumed that the Boltzmann approximation was valid. If the Boltzmann approximation does not hold, the thermal equilibrium electron concentration is written from Equation (3.3) as

$$n_0 = \frac{4\pi}{h^3}(2m_n^*)^{3/2} \int_{E_c}^{\infty} \frac{(E - E_c)^{1/2}\, dE}{1 + \exp\left(\dfrac{E - E_F}{kT}\right)} \tag{3.44}$$

If we again make a change of variable and let

$$\eta = \frac{E - E_c}{kT} \tag{3.45a}$$

and also define

$$\eta_F = \frac{E_F - E_c}{kT} \tag{3.45b}$$

---

[3]Σ indicates those sections that will aid in the total summation of understanding of semiconductor devices, but can be skipped the first time through the text.

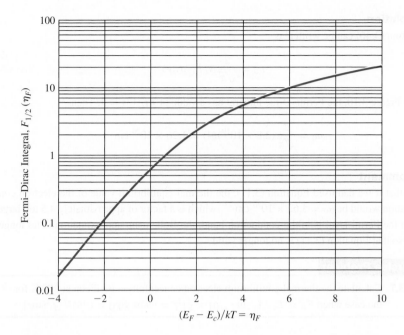

Figure 3.10 | The Fermi–Dirac integral $F_{1/2}$ as a function of normalized Fermi energy.

then we can rewrite Equation (3.44) as

$$n_0 = 4\pi \left(\frac{2m_n^* kT}{h^2} \right)^{3/2} \int_0^\infty \frac{\eta^{1/2} \, d\eta}{1 + \exp(\eta - \eta_F)} \qquad (3.46)$$

The integral is defined as

$$F_{1/2}(\eta_F) = \int_0^\infty \frac{\eta^{1/2} \, d\eta}{1 + \exp(\eta - \eta_F)} \qquad (3.47)$$

This function, called the Fermi–Dirac integral, is a tabulated function of the variable η_F. Figure 3.10 is a plot of the Fermi–Dirac integral. Note that if $\eta_F > 0$, then $E_F > E_c$; thus, the Fermi energy is actually in the conduction band.

Fermi–Dirac integral

EXAMPLE 3.7

OBJECTIVE

Determine the electron concentration using the Fermi–Dirac integral.

Assume that $\eta_F = 3$, which means that the Fermi energy is above the conduction-band energy by approximately 77.7 meV at 300 K.

■ **Solution**

Equation (3.46) can be written as

$$n_0 = \frac{2}{\sqrt{\pi}} N_c F_{1/2}(\eta_F)$$

From Figure 3.10, the Fermi–Dirac integral has a value of $F_{1/2}(3) \cong 4$. Then

$$n_0 = \frac{2}{\sqrt{\pi}}(2.8 \times 10^{19})(4) = 1.26 \times 10^{20} \text{ cm}^{-3}$$

■ **Comment**

Note that if we had used Equation (3.11), the thermal-equilibrium value of the electron concentration would be $n_0 = 5.62 \times 10^{20}$ cm^{-3}, which is a factor of approximately 4.5 too large. When the Fermi level is in the conduction band, the Boltzmann approximation is no longer valid so that Equation (3.11) is no longer valid.

Exercise Problem

EX3.7 Calculate the thermal-equilibrium electron concentration is silicon at 300 K for the case when $E_F = E_c$. [$_{\varepsilon}-$wɔ $_{6\iota}0\mathrm{I} \times \mathrm{SI'Z} = {}^0u$ os $89'0 = (\mathit{J}\mathit{u})\mathit{z}/\mathit{I}\mathit{J}$ ·su∀]

We can use the same general method to calculate the thermal-equilibrium concentration of holes. We obtain

$$p_0 = 4\pi \left(\frac{2m_p^* kT}{h^2}\right)^{3/2} \int_0^\infty \frac{(\eta')^{1/2}\, d\eta'}{1 + \exp{(\eta' - \eta'_F)}} \tag{3.48}$$

where

$$\eta' = \frac{E_v - E}{kT} \tag{3.49a}$$

and

$$\eta'_F = \frac{E_v - E_F}{kT} \tag{3.49b}$$

The integral in Equation (3.48) is the same Fermi–Dirac integral defined by Equation (3.47), although the variables have slightly different definitions. We can note that if $\eta'_F > 0$, then the Fermi level is in the valence band.

3.3.4   Degenerate and Nondegenerate Semiconductors

In our discussion of adding dopant atoms to a semiconductor, we have implicitly assumed that the concentration of dopant atoms added is small when compared to the density of host or semiconductor atoms. The small number of impurity atoms are spread far enough apart so that there is no interaction between donor electrons, for example, in an n-type material. We have assumed that the impurities introduce discrete, noninteracting donor energy states in the n-type semiconductor and discrete,

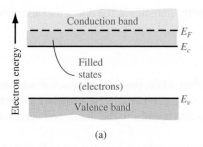 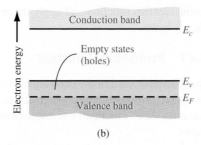

(a)   (b)

Figure 3.11 | Simplified energy-band diagrams for degenerately doped (a) n-type and (b) p-type semiconductors. The Fermi energy level is in the conduction band and valence band, respectively.

noninteracting acceptor states in the p-type semiconductor. These types of semiconductors are referred to as nondegenerate semiconductors.

Nondegenerate semiconductor

If the impurity concentration increases, the distance between the impurity atoms decreases and a point will be reached when donor electrons, for example, will begin to interact with each other. When this occurs, the single discrete donor energy will split into a band of energies. As the donor concentration further increases, the band of donor states widens and may overlap the bottom of the conduction band. This overlap occurs when the donor concentration becomes comparable with the effective density of states. When the concentration of electrons in the conduction band exceeds the density of states N_c, the Fermi energy lies within the conduction band. This type of semiconductor is called a degenerate n-type semiconductor.

Degenerate n-type semiconductor

In a similar way, as the acceptor doping concentration increases in a p-type semiconductor, the discrete acceptor energy states will split into a band of energies and may overlap the top of the valence band. The Fermi energy will lie in the valence band when the concentration of holes exceeds the density of states N_v. This type of semiconductor is called a degenerate p-type semiconductor.

Degenerate p-type semiconductor

Schematic models of the energy-band diagrams for a degenerate n-type and degenerate p-type semiconductor are shown in Figure 3.11. The energy states below E_F are mostly filled with electrons and the energy states above E_F are mostly empty. In the degenerate n-type semiconductor, the states between E_F and E_c are mostly filled with electrons; thus, the electron concentration in the conduction band is very large. Similarly, in the degenerate p-type semiconductor, the energy states between E_v and E_F are mostly empty; thus, the hole concentration in the valence band is very large.

3.4 | STATISTICS OF DONORS AND ACCEPTORS

Objective: Determine the statistics of electrons and holes as a function of energy and temperature.

In Chapter 2, we discussed the Fermi–Dirac distribution function, which gives the probability that a particular energy state will be occupied by an electron. We need to reconsider this function and apply the probability statistics to the donor and acceptor energy states.

3.4.1 Probability Function

One postulate used in the derivation of the Fermi–Dirac probability function was the Pauli exclusion principle, which states that only one particle is permitted in each quantum state. The Pauli exclusion principle also applies to the donor and acceptor states.

Suppose we have N_i electrons and g_i quantum states, where the subscript i indicates the ith energy level. There are g_i ways of choosing where to put the first particle. Each donor level has two possible spin orientations for the donor electron; thus, each donor level has two quantum states. The insertion of an electron into one quantum state, however, precludes putting an electron into the second quantum state. By adding one electron, the vacancy requirement of the atom is satisfied, and the addition of a second electron in the donor level is not possible. The distribution function of donor electrons in the donor energy states is then slightly different than the Fermi–Dirac function.

Donor state electron density

The probability function of electrons occupying the donor state is

$$n_d = \frac{N_d}{1 + \frac{1}{2} \exp\left(\dfrac{E_d - E_F}{kT}\right)} \tag{3.50}$$

where n_d is the density of electrons occupying the donor level and E_d is the energy of the donor level. The factor $\frac{1}{2}$ in this equation is a direct result of the spin factor just mentioned. The $\frac{1}{2}$ factor is sometimes written as $1/g$, where g is called a degeneracy factor.

Equation (3.50) can also be written in the form

$$n_d = N_d - N_d^+ \tag{3.51}$$

where N_d^+ is the concentration of ionized donors. In many applications, we will be interested more in the concentration of ionized donors than in the concentration of electrons remaining in the donor states.

Acceptor state hole density

If we do the same type of analysis for acceptor atoms, we obtain the expression

$$p_a = \frac{N_a}{1 + \frac{1}{g} \exp\left(\dfrac{E_F - E_a}{kT}\right)} = N_a - N_a^- \tag{3.52}$$

where N_a is the concentration of acceptor atoms, E_a is the acceptor energy level, p_a is the concentration of holes in the acceptor states, and N_a^- is the concentration of ionized acceptors. A hole in an acceptor state corresponds to an acceptor atom that is neutrally charged and still has an "empty" bonding position as we discussed in Section 3.2.1. The parameter g is, again, a degeneracy factor. The ground state degeneracy factor g is normally taken as four for the acceptor level in silicon and gallium arsenide because of the detailed band structure.

Σ 3.4.2 Complete Ionization and Freeze-Out

The probability function for electrons in the donor energy state was just given by Equation (3.50). If we assume that $(E_d - E_F) \gg kT$, then

$$n_d \approx \frac{N_d}{\frac{1}{2} \exp\left(\frac{E_d - E_F}{kT}\right)} = 2N_d \exp\left[\frac{-(E_d - E_F)}{kT}\right] \qquad (3.53)$$

If $(E_d - E_F) \gg kT$, then the Boltzmann approximation is also valid for the electrons in the conduction band so that, from Equation (3.11),

$$n_0 = N_c \exp\left[\frac{-(E_c - E_F)}{kT}\right]$$

We can determine the relative number of electrons in the donor state compared with the total number of electrons; therefore we can consider the ratio of electrons in the donor state to the total number of electrons in the conduction band plus donor state. Using the expressions of Equations (3.53) and (3.11), we write

$$\frac{n_d}{n_d + n_0} = \frac{2N_d \exp\left[\dfrac{-(E_d - E_F)}{kT}\right]}{2N_d \exp\left[\dfrac{-(E_d - E_F)}{kT}\right] + N_c \exp\left[\dfrac{-(E_c - E_F)}{kT}\right]} \qquad (3.54)$$

The Fermi energy cancels out of this expression. Dividing by the numerator term, we obtain

$$\frac{n_d}{n_d + n_0} = \frac{1}{1 + \dfrac{N_c}{2N_d} \exp\left[\dfrac{-(E_c - E_d)}{kT}\right]} \qquad (3.55)$$

The factor $(E_c - E_d)$ is just the ionization energy of the donor electrons.

EXAMPLE 3.8

OBJECTIVE

Determine the fraction of total electrons still in the donor states at $T = 300$ K.

Assume silicon is doped with phosphorus to a concentration of $N_d = 5 \times 10^{15}$ cm^{-3}.

■ **Solution**

Using Equation (3.55), we find

$$\frac{n_d}{n_d + n_0} = \frac{1}{1 + \dfrac{2.8 \times 10^{19}}{2(5 \times 10^{15})} \exp\left(\dfrac{-0.045}{0.0259}\right)} = 0.00203 = 0.203\%$$

■ **Comment**

This example shows that the vast majority of the donor electrons are in the conduction band and, in this case, only approximately 0.2 percent of the donor electrons are still in the donor states. For this reason, at room temperature, we can say that the donor states are completely ionized.

EX3.8   Determine the phosphorus doping concentration in silicon at 300 K such that 1 percent of the donor electrons are still in the donor states.

(Ans. $N_d = 2.49 \times 10^{16}$ cm^{-3})

At room temperature, then, the donor states are essentially completely ionized and, for a typical doping of 10^{16} cm^{-3}, almost all donor impurity atoms have donated an electron to the conduction band.

Complete ionization   At room temperature, there is also essentially *complete ionization* of the acceptor atoms. This means that each acceptor atom has accepted an electron from the valence band so that p_a is zero. At typical acceptor doping concentrations, a hole is created in the valence band for each acceptor atom. This ionization effect and the creation of electrons and holes in the conduction band and valence band, respectively, are shown in Figure 3.12.

The opposite of complete ionization occurs at $T = 0$ K. At absolute zero degrees, all electrons are in their lowest possible energy state; that is, for an n-type semiconductor, each donor state must contain an electron, therefore $n_d = N_d$ or $N_d^+ = 0$. We must have, then, from Equation (3.50) that $\exp[(E_d - E_F)/kT] = 0$. Since $T = 0$ K, this will occur for $\exp(-\infty) = 0$, which means that $E_F > E_d$. The Fermi energy level must be above the donor energy level at absolute zero. In the case of a p-type semiconductor at absolute zero temperature, the impurity atoms will not contain any electrons, so that the Fermi energy level must be below the acceptor energy state. The distribution of electrons among the various energy states, and hence the Fermi energy, is a function of temperature.

A detailed analysis, not given in this text, shows that at $T = 0$ K, the Fermi energy is halfway between E_c and E_d for the n-type material and halfway between E_a and E_v for the p-type material. Figure 3.13 shows these effects. No electrons from the donor state are thermally elevated into the conduction band; this effect is called

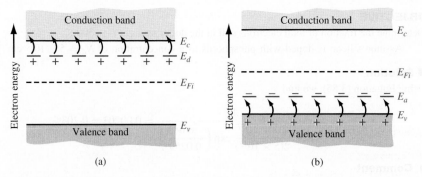

Figure 3.12 | Energy-band diagrams showing complete ionization of (a) donor states and (b) acceptor states.

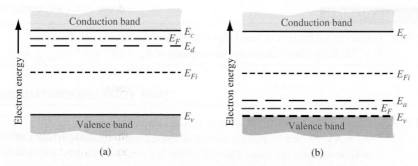

Figure 3.13 | Energy-band diagrams showing the position of the Fermi level at $T = 0$ K for (a) n-type and (b) p-type semiconductors.

freeze-out. Similarly, when no electrons from the valance band are elevated into the acceptor states, the effect is also called freeze-out.

Between $T = 0$ K, freeze-out, and $T = 300$ K, complete ionization, we have partial ionization of donor or acceptor atoms.

Freeze-out

EXAMPLE 3.9

OBJECTIVE
Determine the temperature at which 90 percent of acceptor atoms are ionized.

Consider p-type silicon doped with boron at a concentration of $N_a = 10^{16}$ cm^{-3}.

■ Solution
Find the ratio of holes in the acceptor state to the total number of holes in the valence band plus acceptor state. Taking into account the Boltzmann approximation and assuming the degeneracy factor is $g = 4$, we write

$$\frac{p_a}{p_0 + p_a} = \frac{1}{1 + \dfrac{N_v}{4N_a} \exp\left[\dfrac{-(E_a - E_v)}{kT}\right]}$$

For 90 percent ionization,

$$\frac{p_a}{p_0 + p_a} = 0.10 = \frac{1}{1 + \dfrac{(1.04 \times 10^{19})\left(\dfrac{T}{300}\right)^{3/2}}{4(10^{16})} \exp\left[\dfrac{-0.045}{0.0259\left(\dfrac{T}{300}\right)}\right]}$$

Using trial and error, we find that $T = 193$ K.

■ Comment
This example shows that at approximately $100°$C below room temperature, we still have 90 percent of the acceptor atoms ionized; in other words, 90 percent of the acceptor atoms have "donated" a hole to the valence band.

Exercise Problem

EX3.9 Determine the fraction of total holes still in the acceptor states in silicon at $T = 300$ K for a boron impurity concentration of $N_a = 10^{17}$ cm^{-3}. (Ans. 0.179)

TEST YOUR UNDERSTANDING

TYU3.5 Consider silicon with a phosphorus impurity concentration of $N_d = 5 \times 10^{15}$ cm^{-3}. Plot the percent of ionized impurity atoms versus temperature over the range $100 \le T \le 400$ K.

3.5 | CARRIER CONCENTRATIONS—EFFECTS OF DOPING

Objective: Determine the thermal-equilibrium concentration of electrons and holes in semiconductors as a function of impurity atoms added to the material.

In thermal equilibrium, the semiconductor crystal is electrically neutral. The electrons are distributed among the various energy states, creating negative and positive charges, but the net charge density is zero. This charge-neutrality condition is used to determine the thermal-equilibrium electron and hole concentrations as a function of the impurity doping concentration. We will define a compensated semiconductor and then determine the electron and hole concentrations as a function of the donor and acceptor concentrations.

3.5.1   Compensated Semiconductors

Compensated semiconductor

A *compensated semiconductor* is one that contains both donor and acceptor impurity atoms in the same region. A compensated semiconductor can be formed, for example, by diffusing acceptor impurities into an n-type material, or by diffusing donor impurities into a p-type material. An n-type compensated semiconductor occurs when $N_d > N_a$, and a p-type compensated semiconductor occurs when $N_a > N_d$. If $N_a = N_d$, we have a completely compensated semiconductor that has, as we will show, the characteristics of an intrinsic material. Compensated semiconductors are created quite naturally during device fabrication as we will see later.

3.5.2   Equilibrium Electron and Hole Concentrations

To determine the electron and hole concentrations as a function of the impurity donor and acceptor densities, we use the concept of *charge neutrality*. We equate the density of negative charge to the density of positive charge in the semiconductor. Figure 3.14a is the energy-band diagram showing the negative charges in a semiconductor. These charges include the density of free electrons and the density of ionized acceptors. Figure 3.14b is the energy-band diagram showing the positive charges in

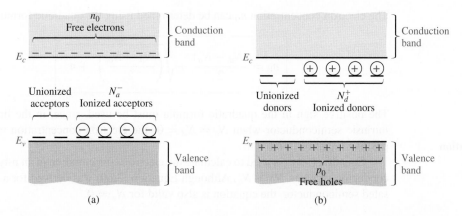

Figure 3.14 | (a) Energy-band diagram showing negative charges and (b) energy-band diagram showing positive charges for a semiconductor material. These charges are incorporated in the charge-neutrality equation.

a semiconductor. These charges include the density of free holes and the density of ionized donors.

The charge-neutrality condition is expressed by equating the density of negative charges to the density of positive charges. We then have   **Charge neutrality**

$$n_0 + N_a^- = p_0 + N_d^+ \tag{3.56}$$

or

$$n_0 + (N_a - p_a) = p_0 + (N_d - n_d) \tag{3.57}$$

where n_0 and p_0 are the thermal-equilibrium concentrations of electrons and holes in the conduction band and valence band, respectively. The parameter n_d is the concentration of electrons in the donor energy states, so $N_d^+ = N_d - n_d$ is the concentration of positively charged donor states. Similarly, p_a is the concentration of holes in the acceptor states, so $N_a^- = N_a - p_a$ is the concentration of negatively charged acceptor states. We have expressions for n_0, p_0, n_d, and p_a in terms of the Fermi energy and temperature.

If we assume complete ionization, n_d and p_a are both zero, and Equation (3.57) becomes

$$n_0 + N_a = p_0 + N_d \tag{3.58}$$

If we express p_0 as n_i^2/n_0, then Equation (3.58) can be written as

$$n_0 + N_a = \frac{n_i^2}{n_0} + N_d \tag{3.59a}$$

which in turn can be written as

$$n_0^2 - (N_d - N_a)n_0 - n_i^2 = 0 \tag{3.59b}$$

The electron concentration n_0 can be determined using the quadratic formula, or

$$n_0 = \frac{(N_d - N_a)}{2} + \sqrt{\left(\frac{N_d - N_a}{2}\right)^2 + n_i^2} \qquad (3.60)$$

Electron concentration

The positive sign in the quadratic formula must be used, since, in the limit of an intrinsic semiconductor when $N_a = N_d = 0$, the electron concentration must be a positive quantity, or $n_0 = n_i$.

Equation (3.60) is used to calculate the electron concentration in an n-type semiconductor, or when $N_d > N_a$. Although Equation (3.60) was derived for a compensated semiconductor, the equation is also valid for $N_a = 0$.

EXAMPLE 3.10

OBJECTIVE

Determine the thermal-equilibrium electron and hole concentrations for a given doping concentration.

Consider silicon at 300 K doped with phosphorus impurity atoms at a concentration of $N_d = 2 \times 10^{16}$ cm^{-3}. Assume $N_a = 0$.

■ Solution

From Equation (3.60), the majority-carrier electron concentration is

$$n_0 = \frac{2 \times 10^{16}}{2} + \sqrt{\left(\frac{2 \times 10^{16}}{2}\right)^2 + (1.5 \times 10^{10})^2} \cong 2 \times 10^{16} \text{ cm}^{-3}$$

The minority-carrier hole concentration is found as

$$p_0 = \frac{n_i^2}{n_0} = \frac{(1.5 \times 10^{10})^2}{2 \times 10^{16}} = 1.13 \times 10^4 \text{ cm}^{-3}$$

■ Comment

In this example, $N_d \gg n_i$ so that the thermal-equilibrium majority-carrier electron concentration is essentially equal to the donor impurity concentration. This example illustrates the fact that we can control the concentration of majority carriers and thus the conductivity of the semiconductor by controlling the concentration of impurity atoms added to the semiconductor material.

Exercise Problem

EX3.10   The concentration of majority-carrier electrons in n-type silicon at 300 K is to be $n_0 = 10^{15}$ cm^{-3}. Determine the concentration of phosphorus atoms that are to be added and determine the concentration of minority carrier holes.

(Ans. $N_d = 10^{15}$ cm^{-3}, $p_0 = 2.25 \times 10^5$ cm^{-3})

We have argued in our discussion and we can note from the results of Example 3.10 that the concentration of electrons in the conduction band increases above the intrinsic carrier concentration as we add donor impurity atoms. At the same time, the

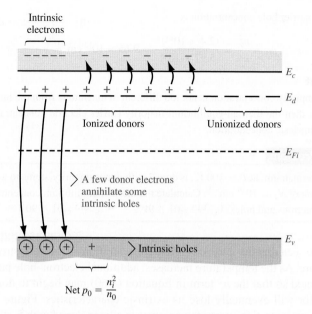

Figure 3.15 | Energy-band diagram showing the
redistribution of electrons when donors are added.

minority-carrier hole concentration decreases below the intrinsic carrier concentration as we add donor atoms. We must keep in mind that as we add donor impurity atoms and the corresponding donor electrons, there is a redistribution of electrons among available energy states. Figure 3.15 shows a schematic of this physical redistribution. A few of the donor electrons will fall into the empty states in the valence band and, in doing so, will annihilate some of the intrinsic holes. The minority-carrier hole concentration will therefore decrease, as we have seen in Example 3.10. At the same time, because of this redistribution, the net electron concentration in the conduction band is *not* simply equal to the donor concentration plus the intrinsic electron concentration.

EXAMPLE 3.11

OBJECTIVE
Calculate the thermal-equilibrium electron and hole concentrations in a germanium sample for a given doping density.

Consider a germanium sample at $T = 300$ K in which $N_d = 5 \times 10^{13}$ cm^{-3} and $N_a = 0$. Assume that $n_i = 2.4 \times 10^{13}$ cm^{-3}.

■ **Solution**
Again, from Equation (3.60), the majority-carrier electron concentration is

$$n_0 = \frac{5 \times 10^{13}}{2} + \sqrt{\left(\frac{5 \times 10^{13}}{2}\right)^2 + (2.4 \times 10^{13})^2} = 5.97 \times 10^{13} \text{ cm}^{-3}$$

The minority-carrier hole concentration is

$$p_0 = \frac{n_i^2}{n_0} = \frac{(2.4 \times 10^{13})^2}{5.97 \times 10^{13}} = 9.65 \times 10^{12} \, \text{cm}^{-3}$$

■ Comment

If the donor impurity concentration is not too different in magnitude from the intrinsic carrier concentration, then the thermal-equilibrium majority carrier electron concentration is influenced by the intrinsic concentration.

Exercise Problem

EX3.11   Germanium, at $T = 300$ K, is doped with donor impurity atoms to a concentration of $N_d = 10^{14}$ cm^{-3}. Calculate the thermal-equilibrium concentrations of electrons and holes. (Ans. $n_0 = 1.06 \times 10^{14}$ cm^{-3}, $p_0 = 5.46 \times 10^{12}$ cm^{-3})

We have seen that the intrinsic carrier concentration n_i is a very strong function of temperature. As the temperature increases, additional electron–hole pairs are thermally generated so that the n_i^2 term in Equation (3.60) may begin to dominate. The semiconductor will eventually lose its extrinsic characteristics. Figure 3.16 shows the electron concentration versus temperature in silicon doped with 5×10^{14} donors per cm^3. As the temperature increases, we can see where the intrinsic concentration begins to dominate. Also shown is the partial ionization, or the onset of freeze-out, at the low temperature.

If we reconsider Equation (3.58) and express n_0 as n_i^2/p_0, then we have

$$\frac{n_i^2}{p_0} + N_a = p_0 + N_d \qquad (3.61a)$$

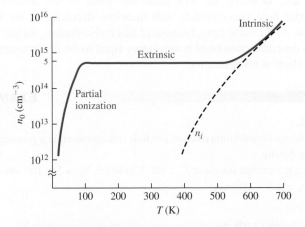

Figure 3.16 | Electron concentration versus temperature for an n-type semiconductor doped at $N_d = 5 \times 10^{14}$ cm^{-3} showing three regions: partial ionization, extrinsic, and intrinsic.

which we can write as

$$p_0^2 - (N_a - N_d)p_0 - n_i^2 = 0 \qquad (3.61b)$$

Using the quadratic formula, the hole concentration is given by

Hole concentration

$$\boxed{p_0 = \frac{N_a - N_d}{2} + \sqrt{\left(\frac{N_a - N_d}{2}\right)^2 + n_i^2}} \qquad (3.62)$$

where the positive sign, again, must be used. Equation (3.62) is used to calculate the thermal-equilibrium majority-carrier hole concentration in a p-type semiconductor, or when $N_a > N_d$. This equation also applies for $N_d = 0$.

EXAMPLE 3.12

OBJECTIVE

Calculate the thermal-equilibrium electron and hole concentrations in a compensated p-type semiconductor.

Consider a silicon semiconductor at $T = 300$ K in which the impurity doping concentrations are $N_a = 2 \times 10^{16}$ cm^{-3} and $N_d = 5 \times 10^{15}$ cm^{-3}.

■ **Solution**

Since $N_a > N_d$, the compensated semiconductor is p type and the thermal-equilibrium majority-carrier hole concentration is given by Equation (3.62), so that

$$p_0 = \frac{2 \times 10^{16} - 5 \times 10^{15}}{2} + \sqrt{\left(\frac{2 \times 10^{16} - 5 \times 10^{15}}{2}\right)^2 + (1.5 \times 10^{10})^2}$$

which yields

$$p_0 = 1.5 \times 10^{16} \text{ cm}^{-3}$$

The minority-carrier electron concentration is found to be

$$n_0 = \frac{n_i^2}{p_0} = \frac{(1.5 \times 10^{10})^2}{1.5 \times 10^{16}} = 1.5 \times 10^4 \text{ cm}^{-3}$$

■ **Comment**

If we assume complete ionization and if $(N_a - N_d) \gg n_i$, then the majority-carrier hole concentration is, to a very good approximation, just the difference between the acceptor and donor impurity concentrations.

Exercise Problem

EX3.12 Consider a compensated germanium semiconductor at $T = 300$ K doped at concentrations of $N_a = 5 \times 10^{13}$ cm^{-3} and $N_d = 1 \times 10^{13}$ cm^{-3}. Calculate the thermal-equilibrium electron and hole concentrations.

(Ans. $p_0 = 5.12 \times 10^{13}$ cm^{-3}, $n_0 = 1.12 \times 10^{13}$ cm^{-3})

We can note that, for a compensated p-type semiconductor, the minority-carrier electron concentration is determined from

$$n_0 = \frac{n_i^2}{p_0} = \frac{n_i^2}{(N_a - N_d)}$$

EXAMPLE 3.13

OBJECTIVE

Determine the required impurity doping concentration in a semiconductor material.

A silicon power device with n-type material is to be operated at $T = 475$ K. At this temperature, the intrinsic carrier concentration must contribute no more than 3 percent of the total electron concentration. Determine the minimum doping concentration required to meet this specification. (As a first approximation, neglect the variation of E_g with temperature.)

■ Solution

At $T = 475$ K, the intrinsic carrier concentration is found from

$$n_i^2 = N_c N_v \exp\left(\frac{-E_g}{kT}\right)$$

$$= (2.8 \times 10^{19})(1.04 \times 10^{19})\left(\frac{475}{300}\right)^3 \exp\left[\frac{-1.12}{0.0259}\left(\frac{300}{475}\right)\right]$$

or

$$n_i^2 = 1.59 \times 10^{27}$$

which yields

$$n_i = 3.99 \times 10^{13} \text{ cm}^{-3}$$

For the intrinsic carrier concentration to contribute no more than 3 percent of the total electron concentration, we set $n_0 = 1.03 N_d$.

From Equation (3.60), we have

$$n_0 = \frac{N_d}{2} + \sqrt{\left(\frac{N_d}{2}\right)^2 + n_i^2}$$

or

$$1.03 N_d = \frac{N_d}{2} + \sqrt{\left(\frac{N_d}{2}\right)^2 + (3.99 \times 10^{13})^2}$$

which yields

$$N_d = 2.27 \times 10^{14} \text{ cm}^{-3}$$

■ Comment

If the temperature remains less than or equal to 475 K, or if the impurity doping concentration is greater than 2.27×10^{14} cm^{-3}, then the intrinsic carrier concentration will contribute less than 3 percent of the total electron concentration.

Exercise Problem

EX3.13 A germanium power device with n-type material is to operate at a temperature of $T = 400$ K. At this temperature, the intrinsic carrier concentration must contribute no more than 10 percent of the total electron concentration. Determine the minimum donor concentration required to meet this specification. (As a first approximation, neglect the variation of E_g with temperature.)
(Ans. $N_d = 2.60 \times 10^{15}$ cm^{-3})

Equations (3.60) and (3.62) are used to calculate the majority-carrier electron concentration in an n-type semiconductor and majority-carrier hole concentration in a p-type semiconductor, respectively. The minority-carrier hole concentration in an n-type semiconductor could, theoretically, be calculated from Equation (3.62). However, we would be subtracting two numbers on the order of 10^{16} cm^{-3}, for example, to obtain a number on the order of 10^4 cm^{-3}, which from a practical point of view is not possible. The minority-carrier concentrations are calculated from $n_0 p_0 = n_i^2$ once the majority-carrier concentration has been determined.

TEST YOUR UNDERSTANDING

TYU3.6 Consider a compensated GaAs semiconductor at $T = 300$ K doped at $N_d = 5 \times 10^{15}$ cm^{-3} and $N_a = 2 \times 10^{16}$ cm^{-3}. Calculate the thermal-equilibrium electron and hole concentrations.
(Ans. $p_0 = 1.5 \times 10^{16}$ cm^{-3}, $n_0 = 2.16 \times 10^{-4}$ cm^{-3})

TYU3.7 Silicon is doped at $N_d = 10^{15}$ cm^{-3} and $N_a = 0$. (a) Plot the concentration of electrons versus temperature over the range $300 \leq T \leq 600$ K. (b) Calculate the temperature at which the electron concentration is equal to 1.1×10^{15} cm^{-3}. [Ans. (b) $T \approx 552$ K]

3.6 | POSITION OF FERMI ENERGY LEVEL—EFFECTS OF DOPING AND TEMPERATURE

Objective: Determine the position of the Fermi energy level as a function of the concentration of impurity atoms added to the semiconductor material.

We discussed qualitatively in Section 3.3.1 how the electron and hole concentrations change as the Fermi energy level moves through the bandgap energy. Then, in Section 3.5, we calculated the electron and hole concentrations as a function of donor and acceptor impurity concentrations. We can now determine the position of the Fermi energy level as a function of the doping concentrations and as a function of temperature. The relevance of the Fermi energy level will be further discussed after the mathematical derivations.

3.6.1 Mathematical Derivation

The position of the Fermi energy level within the bandgap can be determined by using the equations already developed for the thermal-equilibrium electron and hole concentrations. If we assume the Boltzmann approximation to be valid, then from Equation (3.11) we have $n_0 = N_c \exp\left[-(E_c - E_F)/kT\right]$. We can solve for $E_c - E_F$ from this equation and obtain

$$E_c - E_F = kT \ln\left(\frac{N_c}{n_0}\right) \qquad (3.63)$$

**Fermi energy,
n type**

where n_0 is given by Equation (3.60). If we consider an n-type semiconductor in which $N_d \gg n_i$, then $n_0 \approx N_d$, so that

$$E_c - E_F = kT \ln\left(\frac{N_c}{N_d}\right) \qquad (3.64)$$

The distance between the bottom of the conduction band and the Fermi energy is a logarithmic function of the donor concentration. As the donor concentration increases, the Fermi level moves closer to the conduction band. Conversely, if the Fermi level moves closer to the conduction band, then the electron concentration in the conduction band is increasing. We can note that if we have a compensated semiconductor, then the N_d term in Equation (3.64) is simply replaced by $N_d - N_a$, or the net effective donor concentration.

EXAMPLE 3.14

OBJECTIVE

Determine the required donor impurity concentration to obtain a specified Fermi energy.

Silicon at $T = 300$ K contains an acceptor impurity concentration of $N_a = 10^{16}$ cm^{-3}. Determine the concentration of donor impurity atoms that must be added so that the silicon is n type and the Fermi energy is 0.20 eV below the conduction-band edge.

■ **Solution**

From Equation (3.64), we have

$$E_c - E_F = kT \ln\left(\frac{N_c}{N_d - N_a}\right)$$

which can be rewritten as

$$N_d - N_a = N_c \exp\left[\frac{-(E_c - E_F)}{kT}\right]$$

Then

$$N_d - N_a = 2.8 \times 10^{19} \exp\left[\frac{-0.20}{0.0259}\right] = 1.24 \times 10^{16} \text{ cm}^{-3}$$

or

$$N_d = 1.24 \times 10^{16} + N_a = 2.24 \times 10^{16} \text{ cm}^{-3}$$

■ **Comment**

A compensated semiconductor can be fabricated to provide a specific Fermi energy level.

Exercise Problem

EX3.14 Determine the position of the Fermi level with respect to the valence-band energy in p-type GaAs at $T = 300$ K. The doping concentrations are $N_a = 5 \times 10^{16}$ cm^{-3} and $N_d = 4 \times 10^{15}$ cm^{-3}. (Ans. $E_F - E_a = 0.130$ eV.)

We can develop a slightly different expression for the position of the Fermi level. We had from Equation (3.39) that $n_0 = n_i \exp[(E_F - E_{Fi})/kT]$. We can solve for $E_F - E_{Fi}$ as

$$E_F - E_{Fi} = kT \ln\left(\frac{n_0}{n_i}\right) \qquad (3.65)$$

Equation (3.65) can be used specifically for an n-type semiconductor, where n_0 is given by Equation (3.60), to find the difference between the Fermi level and the intrinsic Fermi level as a function of the donor concentration. We can note that, if the net effective donor concentration is zero, that is, $N_d - N_a = 0$, then $n_0 = n_i$ and $E_F = E_{Fi}$. A completely compensated semiconductor has the characteristics of an intrinsic material in terms of carrier concentration and Fermi level position.

We can derive the same types of equations for a p-type semiconductor. From Equation (3.19), we have $p_0 = N_v \exp[-(E_F - E_v)/kT]$, so that

Fermi energy, p type

$$E_F - E_v = kT \ln\left(\frac{N_v}{p_0}\right) \qquad (3.66)$$

If we assume that $N_a \gg n_i$, then Equation (3.66) can be written as

$$E_F - E_v = kT \ln\left(\frac{N_v}{N_a}\right) \qquad (3.67)$$

The distance between the Fermi level and the top of the valence-band energy for a p-type semiconductor is a logarithmic function of the acceptor concentration: as the acceptor concentration increases, the Fermi level moves closer to the valence band. Equation (3.67) still assumes that the Boltzmann approximation is valid. Again, if we have a compensated p-type semiconductor, then the N_a term in Equation (3.67) is replaced by $N_a - N_d$, or the net effective acceptor concentration.

We can also derive an expression for the relationship between the Fermi level and the intrinsic Fermi level in terms of the hole concentration. We have from Equation (3.40) that $p_0 = n_i \exp[-(E_F - E_{Fi})/kT]$, which yields

$$E_{Fi} - E_F = kT \ln\left(\frac{p_0}{n_i}\right) \qquad (3.68)$$

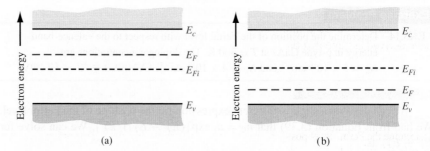

Figure 3.17 | Position of Fermi level relative to intrinsic Fermi level for (a) an n-type ($N_d > N_a$) and (b) a p-type ($N_a > N_d$) semiconductor.

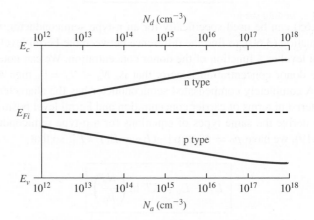

Figure 3.18 | Position of Fermi level as a function of donor concentration (n type) and acceptor concentration (p type).

Equation (3.68) can be used to find the difference between the intrinsic Fermi level and the Fermi energy in terms of the acceptor concentration. The hole concentration p_0 in Equation (3.68) is given by Equation (3.62).

We can again note from Equation (3.65) that, for an n-type semiconductor, $n_0 > n_i$ and $E_F > E_{Fi}$. The Fermi level for an n-type semiconductor is above E_{Fi}. For a p-type semiconductor, $p_0 > n_i$, and from Equation (3.68) we see that $E_{Fi} > E_F$. The Fermi level for a p-type semiconductor is below E_{Fi}. These results are shown in Figure 3.17.

3.6.2   Variation of E_F with Doping Concentration and Temperature

Fermi energy versus doping

We can plot the position of the Fermi energy level as a function of the doping concentration. Figure 3.18 shows the Fermi energy level as a function of donor concentration (n type) and as a function of acceptor concentration (p type) for silicon at $T = 300$ K. As the doping levels increase, the Fermi energy level moves closer to the conduction band for the n-type material and closer to the valence band for the p-type material. Keep in mind that the equations for the Fermi energy level that we have derived assume that the Boltzmann approximation is valid.

EXAMPLE 3.15

OBJECTIVE

Determine the Fermi-level position and the maximum doping at which the Boltzmann approximation is still valid.

Consider p-type silicon, at $T = 300$ K, doped with boron. We can assume that the limit of the Boltzmann approximation occurs when $E_F - E_a = 3kT$. (See Section 3.1.2.)

■ Solution

From Table 3.3, we find the ionization energy is $E_a - E_v = 0.045$ eV for boron in silicon. If we assume that $E_{Fi} \approx E_{\text{midgap}}$, then from Equation (3.68), the position of the Fermi level at the maximum doping is given by

$$E_{Fi} - E_F = \frac{E_g}{2} - (E_a - E_v) - (E_F - E_a) = kT \ln\left(\frac{N_a}{n_i}\right)$$

or

$$0.56 - 0.045 - 3(0.0259) = 0.437 = (0.0259) \ln\left(\frac{N_a}{n_i}\right)$$

We can then solve for the doping as

$$N_a = n_i \exp\left(\frac{0.437}{0.0259}\right) = 3.2 \times 10^{17} \text{ cm}^{-3}$$

■ Comment

If the acceptor (or donor) concentration in silicon is greater than approximately 3×10^{17} cm^{-3}, then the Boltzmann approximation of the distribution function becomes less valid and the equations for the Fermi-level position are no longer quite as accurate.

Exercise Problem

EX3.15 Consider n-type silicon at $T = 300$ K doped with phosphorus. Determine the doping concentration such that $E_d - E_F = 4.6kT$.

(Ans. $N_d = 6.52 \times 10^{16}$ cm^{-3})

The intrinsic carrier concentration n_i, in Equations (3.65) and (3.68), is a strong function of temperature, so that E_F is a function of temperature also. Figure 3.19 shows the variation of the Fermi energy level in silicon with temperature for several donor and acceptor concentrations. As the temperature increases, n_i increases, and E_F moves closer to the intrinsic Fermi level. At high temperature, the semiconductor material begins to lose its extrinsic characteristics and begins to behave more like an

Fermi energy versus temperature

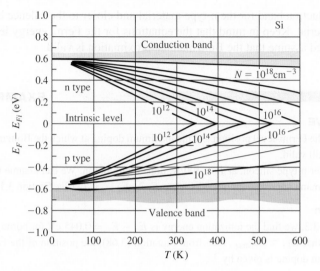

Figure 3.19 | Position of Fermi level as a function of temperature for various n-type and p-type doping concentrations.
(From Sze [17].)

intrinsic semiconductor. At the very low temperature, freeze-out occurs; the Boltzmann approximation is no longer valid and the equations we derived for the Fermi-level position no longer apply. At the low temperature where freeze-out occurs, the Fermi level goes above E_d for the n-type material and below E_a for the p-type material. At absolute zero degrees, all energy states below E_F are full and all energy states above E_F are empty.

3.6.3 Relevance of the Fermi Energy

We have been calculating the position of the Fermi energy level as a function of doping concentrations and temperature. This analysis may seem somewhat arbitrary and fictitious. However, these relations do become significant later in our discussion of pn junctions and the other semiconductor devices we consider. An important point is that, in thermal equilibrium, the Fermi energy level is a constant throughout a system. We will not prove this statement, but we can intuitively see its validity by considering the following example.

Suppose we have a particular material, A, whose electrons are distributed in the energy states of an allowed band as shown in Figure 3.20a. Most of the energy states below E_{FA} contain electrons and most of the energy states above E_{FA} are empty of electrons. Consider another material, B, whose electrons are distributed in the energy states of an allowed band as shown in Figure 3.20b. The energy states below E_{FB} are mostly full and the energy states above E_{FB} are mostly empty. If these two materials are brought into intimate contact, the electrons in the entire system will tend to seek the lowest possible energy. Electrons from material A will flow into the lower energy states of material B, as indicated in Figure 3.20c, until thermal equilibrium is

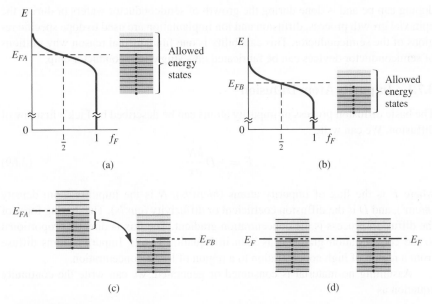

Figure 3.20 | The Fermi energy of (a) material A in thermal equilibrium, (b) material B in thermal equilibrium, (c) materials A and B at the instant they are placed in contact, and (d) materials A and B in contact at thermal equilibrium.

reached. Thermal equilibrium occurs when the distribution of electrons, as a function of energy, is the same in the two materials. This equilibrium state occurs when the Fermi energy is the same in the two materials as shown in Figure 3.20d. The Fermi energy, important in the physics of the semiconductor, also provides a good pictorial representation of the characteristics of the semiconductor materials and devices.

TEST YOUR UNDERSTANDING

TYU3.8 Calculate the position of the Fermi energy level in n-type silicon at $T = 300$ K with respect to the intrinsic Fermi energy level. The doping concentrations are $N_d = 2 \times 10^{17}$ cm^{-3} and $N_a = 3 \times 10^{16}$ cm^{-3}. (Ans. $E_F - E_{Fi} = 0.421$ eV)

TYU3.9 Repeat TYU3.8 for gallium arsenide. (Ans. $E_F - E_{Fi} = 0.655$ eV)

Σ 3.7 | DEVICE FABRICATION TECHNOLOGY: DIFFUSION AND ION IMPLANTATION

Objective: Describe the two primary doping processes in semiconductors— diffusion and ion implantation.

Impurity doping is the introduction of controlled amounts of impurity dopants into semiconductors. Doping changes and controls the conductivity of the semiconductor. *Diffusion* and *ion implantation* are the two primary methods of doping. Although doping can be and is done during the growth of semiconductor wafers or during the epitaxial growth process, diffusion and ion implantation are used to dope specific regions of the semiconductor. This capability is one fundamental reason why millions of semiconductor devices can be fabricated on a single semiconductor chip.

3.7.1 Impurity Atom Diffusion

The basic diffusion process of impurity atoms can be described by Fick's first law of diffusion. We can write

$$F = -D\frac{\partial N}{\partial x} \tag{3.69}$$

Impurity diffusion coefficient

where F is the flux of impurity atoms (#/cm^2/s), N is the impurity atom density (#/cm^3), and D is the diffusion coefficient or diffusivity (cm^2/s). The driving force of the diffusion process is the concentration gradient. The flux is directly proportional to the concentration gradient, as seen in Equation (3.69). Impurity atoms diffuse from a region of high concentration to a region of lower concentration.

Assuming no material is consumed or generated, we can write the continuity equation as

$$\frac{\partial N}{\partial t} = -\frac{\partial F}{\partial x} \tag{3.70}$$

Combining Equations (3.69) and (3.70), and assuming the diffusion coefficient is independent of the impurity doping concentration, we obtain

$$\frac{\partial N}{\partial t} = D\frac{\partial^2 N}{\partial x^2} \tag{3.71}$$

Equation (3.71) is referred to as Fick's diffusion equation.

In general, the diffusion coefficient, D, is an exponential function of temperature— the greater the temperature, the larger the diffusion coefficient.

The profile of the diffused dopant atoms is a function of the initial boundary conditions. Two basic diffusion processes are infinite source (constant surface concentration) and limited source (constant dopant atoms).

Infinite source diffusion

An infinite source process occurs when a semiconductor wafer is placed in a high-temperature furnace (on the order of 1100 to 1200°C) and the wafer is surrounded by a gas vapor that contains the impurity atoms. The concentration of impurity atoms is then a constant at the surface of the semiconductor. The solution to Equation (3.71), for this case, is

$$N(x, t) = N_S \left[1 - \text{erf}\left(\frac{x}{2\sqrt{Dt}}\right) \right] \tag{3.72}$$

where erf is the error function and N_S is the concentration of impurity atoms at the surface.

Figure 3.21 shows the impurity atom density profile as a function of distance into the semiconductor for three different diffusion times and for a given diffusion coefficient.

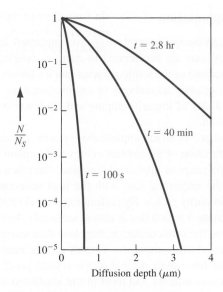

Figure 3.21 | Normalized diffusion profiles for the infinite source diffusion process for three diffusion times. A constant diffusion coefficient $D = 10^{-12} \text{cm}^2/\text{s}$ is assumed.

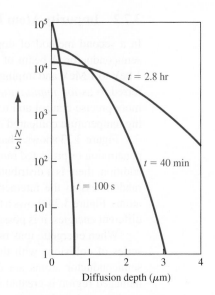

Figure 3.22 | Normalized diffusion profiles for the limited source diffusion process for three diffusion times. A constant diffusion coefficient $D = 10^{-12} \text{cm}^2/\text{s}$ is assumed.

A limited source diffusion process occurs when a finite number of impurity atoms is deposited on the surface of the semiconductor. The boundary condition for Equation (3.71) is that a fixed number S (#/cm^2) of impurities exist on the surface at $x = 0$ at $t = 0$. The solution to Equation (3.71), for this case, is then

Limited source diffusion

$$N(x, t) = \frac{S}{\sqrt{\pi Dt}} \exp\left(\frac{-x^2}{4Dt}\right) \qquad (3.73)$$

Figure 3.22 shows the impurity atom density profile as a function of distance into the semiconductor for three different diffusion times and for a given diffusion coefficient.

In integrated-circuit processing, a two-step diffusion process is normally used. The first step is called *predeposition,* in which a thin diffused layer is formed on the surface under an infinite source process. This step is followed by a *drive-in* diffusion, which is a limited source diffusion process. The diffusion time for the predeposition process is short compared to the diffusion time for the drive-in process. The predeposition profile can then generally be considered as a delta function.

Predeposition

Drive-in diffusion

The diffusion profiles shown in Figures 3.21 and 3.22 are for constant diffusion coefficients. This condition is valid for the case when the doping concentration is fairly small. The diffusion coefficient tends to become larger for higher impurity doping concentrations. This effect tends to produce steeper doping profiles than shown in Figures 3.21 and 3.22.

3.7.2 Impurity Atom Ion Implantation

In a second method of doping, high-energy impurity ions are implanted into the semiconductor. A beam of impurity ions are accelerated to energies ranging from 1 keV to 1 MeV and impinges the surface of the semiconductor. Such a process is referred to as *ion implantation*. Two primary advantages of ion implantation are the more precise control and reproducibility of impurity doping and the lower processing temperature compared to diffusion.

Figure 3.23 shows a basic schematic of an ion implantation system. The depth of penetration or projected range is a function of the implant energy and implant ion. In addition, there is a distribution in the range of implanted ions since there is a certain randomness in the interaction of the implanted ions with the host semiconductor atoms. Figure 3.24 shows a typical impurity profile. By performing several implants at different energies, it is possible to create a region that is almost uniformly doped.

When energetic ions impinge on the semiconductor, they lose their energy by a series of collisions with the semiconductor atoms. As a result of this interaction, semiconductor atoms are displaced from their normal single-crystal positions. A damaged region is created in the semiconductor and most of the implanted ions are not located in substitutional positions. To activate the implanted ion and repair the damaged area, the semiconductor must be annealed at an elevated temperature for a particular period of time. The conventional annealing temperature is on the order of 600°C and the annealing time is on the order of 30 min. Rapid thermal annealing processes are also used. The anneal temperatures and times are considerably lower than those used in the diffusion process.

The implant ions can be blocked from entering the semiconductor by metal, photoresist, or oxides. By defining specific patterns on the surface, only specific desired regions of the semiconductor will be doped. This technique is then used to create the many semiconductor devices in the integrated circuit.

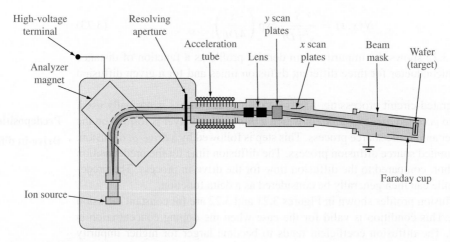

Figure 3.23 | Schematic of an ion implanter.
(Courtesy of Runyan and Bean [11])

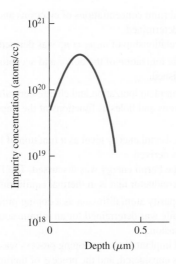

Figure 3.24 | Typical implanted impurity profile. The peak of the implanted concentration can occur below the surface of the semiconductor.

3.8 | SUMMARY

1. **A.** The concentration of electrons in the conduction band is found by integrating the product of the density of states function in the conduction band, $g_c(E)$, and the Ferm–Dirac probability function, $f_F(E)$, over the energy range of the conduction band.

  B. The concentration of holes in the valence band is found by integrating the product of the density of states function in the valence band, $g_v(E)$, and the probability of a state being empty, which is $[1 - f_F(E)]$, over the energy range of the valence band.

  C. Using the Boltzmann approximation, the thermal-equilibrium concentration of electrons in the conduction band is given by $n_0 = N_c \exp[\frac{-(E_c - E_F)}{kT}]$, where N_c is the effective density states in the conduction band.

  D. Using the Boltzmann approximation, the thermal-equilibrium concentration of holes in the valence band is given by $p_0 = N_v \exp[\frac{-(E_F - E_v)}{kT}]$, where N_v is the effective density states in the valence band.

  E. The intrinsic carrier concentration can be found from the relation $n_i^2 = N_c N_v \exp(\frac{-E_g}{kT})$.

  F. The position of the intrinsic Fermi level was found to be very close to the midgap energy.

2. **A.** The concept of doping the semiconductor with donor and acceptor impurities to form n-type and p-type extrinsic semiconductors was discussed.

  B. A group V element (phosphorus or arsenic) is a donor impurity in silicon and a group III element (boron) is an acceptor impurity in silicon.

3. A.   The thermal-equilibrium concentrations of electrons and holes as functions of the Fermi level were determined.

   B.   The fundamental relationship of $n_0 p_0 = n_i^2$ was derived.

4. The concept of complete ionization of the donor and acceptor impurities at room temperature was established.

5. Using the concept of complete ionization and charge neutrality, equations for the concentrations of electrons and holes as functions of the impurity concentrations were derived.

6. A.   The position of the Fermi energy level as a function of impurity doping concentrations was derived.

   B.   The relevance of the Fermi energy was discussed. The Fermi energy is a constant throughout a semiconductor that is in thermal equilibrium.

7. A.   The concept of impurity atom diffusion as a doping process was discussed. The impurity atom profile was determined for an infinite source diffusion and for a limited source diffusion.

   B.   The concept of ion implantation as a doping process was discussed. The range of implanted ions was considered, and the process of thermal annealing was discussed.

CHECKPOINT

After studying this chapter, the reader should have the ability to

1. A.   Derive the equations for the thermal-equilibrium concentrations for electrons and holes using the Boltzmann approximation.

   B.   Derive the equation for the intrinsic carrier concentration.

   C.   State the value of the intrinsic carrier concentration for silicon at $T = 300$ K.

2. A.   Describe the effect of adding a group V element to silicon.

   B.   Describe the effect of adding a group III element to silicon.

   C.   Define what is meant by a donor and an acceptor impurity atom.

3. Understand the derivation of the fundamental relationship $n_0 p_0 = n_i^2$.

4. Understand the concept of complete ionization.

5. A.   Write the charge neutrality equation assuming complete ionization.

   B.   Derive the equations for n_0 and p_0 in terms of the impurity doping concentrations using the concept of charge neutrality.

6. Understand the variation of the Fermi energy with doping concentration and temperature.

7. A.   Discuss the concept of an infinite source diffusion process and a finite source diffusion process.

   B.   Discuss the concept of ion implantation and the reason why a thermal anneal cycle is required

REVIEW QUESTIONS

1. A.   Write the equation for n_0 in integral form as a function of the density of states and the Fermi probability function. Repeat for the hole concentration p_0.

   B.   In deriving the equation for n_0 in terms of the Fermi energy, the upper limit of the integral should be the energy at the top of the conduction band. Justify using infinity instead.

    C.   Assuming the Boltzmann approximation applies, write the equations for n_0 and p_0 in terms of the Fermi energy, conduction-band energy, and valence-band energy.

    D.   What is the intrinsic carrier concentration in silicon at $T = 300$ K?

    E.   Under what condition would the intrinsic Fermi level be at the midgap energy?

2.   What is a donor impurity? What is an acceptor impurity?

3.   Derive the fundamental relationship $n_0 p_0 = n_i^2$.

4.   Discuss the concept of complete ionization.

5.   A.   Write the equation for charge neutrality for the condition of complete ionization.

    B.   Sketch a graph of n_0 versus temperature for an n-type semiconductor.

6.   A.   Sketch a graph of the Fermi energy versus donor impurity concentration for an n-type semiconductor.

    B.   Sketch a graph of the Fermi energy versus temperature for a p-type semiconductor.

7.   A.   Describe the infinite source diffusion process.

    B.   Describe the finite source diffusion process.

    C.   Describe the ion implantation process.

PROBLEMS

[Note: In the following problems, assume $T = 300$ K unless otherwise stated. Also, as a first approximation, neglect any variation of bandgap energy with temperature.]

Section 3.1   Charge Carriers in Semiconductors

3.1   Calculate the intrinsic carrier concentration, n_i, at $T = 200, 400,$ and 600 K for (*a*) silicon, (*b*) germanium, and (*c*) gallium arsenide.

3.2   Plot the intrinsic carrier concentration, n_i, for a temperature range of $200 \leq T \leq 600$ K for (*a*) silicon, (*b*) germanium, and (*c*) gallium arsenide. (Use a log scale for n_i.)

3.3   The intrinsic carrier concentration in silicon is to be no greater than $n_i = 1 \times 10^{12}$ cm^{-3}. Assume $E_g = 1.12$ eV. Determine the maximum temperature allowed for the silicon.

3.4   In a particular semiconductor material, the effective density of states functions are given by $N_c = N_{c0}T^{3/2}$ and $N_v = N_{v0}T^{3/2}$ where N_{c0} and N_{v0} are constants independent of temperature. The experimentally determined intrinsic carrier concentrations as a function of temperature are given in Table 3.5. Determine the product $N_{c0}N_{v0}$ and the bandgap energy E_g. (Assume E_g is independent of temperature.)

Table 3.5 | Intrinsic concentration as a function of temperature

T(K)	n_i(cm^{-3})
200	1.82×10^2
300	5.83×10^7
400	3.74×10^{10}
500	1.95×10^{12}

3.5   (*a*) The magnitude of the product $g_c(E)f_F(E)$ in the conduction band is a function of energy as shown in Figure 3.1. Assume the Boltzmann approximation is valid. Determine the energy with respect to E_c at which the maximum occurs. (*b*) Repeat part (*a*) for the magnitude of the product $g_v(E)\,[1 - f_F(E)]$ in the valence band.

3.6   Assume the Boltzmann approximation in a semiconductor is valid. Determine the ratio of $n(E) = g_c(E)f_F(E)$ at $E = E_c + 4kT$ to that at $E = E_c + kT/2$.

3.7   Two semiconductor materials have exactly the same properties except that material A has a bandgap energy of 1.2 eV and material B has a bandgap energy of 1.4 eV. Determine the ratio of n_i of material A to that of material B for $T = 300$ K.

3.8   Assume that $E_c - E_F = 0.20$ eV in silicon. (*a*) Assume $T = 200$ K. Determine $n(E) = g_c(E)f_F(E)$ at (*i*) $E = E_c$, (*ii*) $E = E_c + 0.015$ eV, (*iii*) $E = E_c + 0.030$ eV, and (*iv*) $E = E_c + 0.045$ eV. (*b*) Repeat part (*a*) for $T = 400$ K.

3.9   Consider silicon at $T = 300$ K. (*a*) Calculate n_0 for (*i*) $E_c - E_F = 0.2$ eV, (*ii*) $E_c - E_F = 0.3$ eV, and (*iii*) $E_c - E_F = 0.4$ eV. (*b*) Calculate p_0 for (*i*) $E_F - E_v = 0.2$ eV, (*ii*) $E_F - E_v = 0.3$ eV, and (*iii*) $E_F - E_v = 0.4$ eV.

3.10   Repeat Problem 3.9 for GaAs.

3.11   (*a*) The value of n_0 in silicon is 1.5×10^{16} cm^{-3}. Determine $E_c - E_F$. (*b*) The value of p_0 in silicon is 5×10^{15} cm^{-3}. Determine $E_F - E_v$. (*c*) Repeat part (*a*) for GaAs. (*d*) Repeat part (*b*) for GaAs.

3.12   Determine the position of the intrinsic Fermi energy level with respect to the center of the bandgap for (*a*) silicon, (*b*) germanium, and (*c*) gallium arsenide. [Use the density of states effective masses given in Appendix B.]

3.13   (*a*) The carrier effective masses in a particular semiconductor are $m_n^* = 1.15m_0$ and $m_p^* = 0.38m_0$. Determine the position of the intrinsic Fermi level with respect to the midgap energy. (*b*) Repeat part (*a*) if $m_n^* = 0.082m_0$ and $m_p^* = 1.15m_0$.

3.14   Calculate E_{Fi} with respect to the center of the bandgap in silicon for $T = 200, 400$, and 600 K.

3.15   Plot the intrinsic Fermi energy E_{Fi} with respect to the center of the bandgap in GaAs for $200 \le T \le 600$ K.

3.16   If the density of states function in the conduction band of a particular semiconductor is a constant equal to K, derive the expression for the thermal-equilibrium concentration of electrons in the conduction band, assuming Fermi–Dirac statistics and assuming the Boltzmann approximation is valid.

3.17   Repeat Problem 3.16 if the density of states function is given by $g_c(E) = C_1(E - E_c)$ for $E \ge E_c$ where C_1 is a constant.

Section 3.2   Dopant Atoms and Energy Levels

3.18   Calculate the ionization energy and radius of the donor electron in germanium using the Bohr theory. (Use the density of states effective mass as a first approximation.)

3.19   Repeat Problem 3.18 for gallium arsenide.

Section 3.3   The Extrinsic Semiconductor

3.20   The electron concentration in silicon is $n_0 = 3 \times 10^4$ cm^{-3}. (*a*) Determine p_0. (*b*) Is this material n or p type? (*c*) Determine $E_F - E_v$.

3.21 Determine the values of n_0 and p_0 for silicon at $T = 300$ K if the Fermi energy is 0.22 eV above the valence band energy.

3.22 The electron concentration in silicon at $T = 375$ K is $n_0 = 3 \times 10^{16}$ cm^{-3}. (a) Determine p_0. (b) Is this material n or p type? (c) Determine $E_c - E_F$.

3.23 Repeat Problem 3.22 for GaAs.

3.24 Repeat Problem 3.22 for Ge.

3.25 (a) If $E_c - E_F = 0.25$ eV in gallium arsenide at $T = 400$ K, calculate the values of n_0 and p_0. (b) Assuming the value of n_0 from part (a) remains constant, determine $E_c - E_F$ and p_0 at $T = 300$ K.

3.26 The value of p_0 in silicon at $T = 300$ K is 10^{15} cm^{-3}. Determine (a) $E_c - E_F$ and (b) n_0.

3.27 (a) Consider silicon at $T = 300$ K. Determine p_0 if $E_{Fi} - E_F = 0.35$ eV. (b) Assuming that p_0 from part (a) remains constant, determine the value of $E_{Fi} - E_F$ when $T = 400$ K. (c) Find the value of n_0 in both parts (a) and (b).

3.28 Repeat problem 3.27 for GaAs.

3.29 Assume that $E_F = E_v$ at $T = 300$ K in silicon. Determine p_0.

3.30 Consider silicon at $T = 300$ K, which has $n_0 = 5 \times 10^{19}$ cm^{-3}. Determine $E_c - E_F$.

Section 3.4   Statistics of Donors and Acceptors

3.31 The electron and hole concentrations as a function of energy in the conduction band and valence band peak at a particular energy as shown in Figure 3.8. Consider silicon and assume $E_c - E_F = 0.20$ eV. Determine the energy, relative to the band edges, at which the concentrations peak.

3.32 For the Boltzmann approximation to be valid for a semiconductor, the Fermi level must be at least $3kT$ below the donor level in an n-type material and at least $3kT$ above the acceptor level in a p-type material. If $T = 300$ K, determine the maximum electron concentration in an n-type semiconductor and the maximum hole concentration in a p-type semiconductor for the Boltzmann approximation to be valid in (a) silicon and (b) gallium arsenide.

3.33 Plot the ratio of unionized donor atoms to the total electron concentration versus temperature for silicon over the range $50 \leq T \leq 200$ K. Assume $N_d = 10^{15}$ cm^{-3}.

Section 3.5   Charge Neutrality

3.34 Consider a germanium semiconductor at $T = 300$ K. Calculate the thermal equilibrium concentrations of n_0 and p_0 for (a) $N_a = 10^{13}$ cm^{-3}, $N_d = 0$, and (b) $N_d = 5 \times 10^{15}$ cm^{-3}, $N_a = 0$.

3.35 The Fermi level in n-type silicon at $T = 300$ K is 245 meV below the conduction band and 200 meV below the donor level. Determine the probability of finding an electron (a) in the donor level and (b) in a state in the conduction band kT above the conduction band edge.

3.36 Determine the equilibrium electron and hole concentrations in silicon for the following conditions:

(a) $T = 300$ K, $N_d = 2 \times 10^{15}$ cm^{-3}, $N_a = 0$

(b) $T = 300$ K, $N_d = 0$, $N_a = 10^{16}$ cm^{-3}

(c) $T = 300$ K, $N_d = N_a = 10^{15}$ cm^{-3}

(d) $T = 400$ K, $N_d = 0$, $N_a = 10^{14}$ cm^{-3}

(e) $T = 500$ K, $N_d = 10^{14}$ cm^{-3}, $N_a = 0$

3.37 Repeat problem 3.36 for GaAs.

3.38 Assume that silicon, germanium, and gallium arsenide each have dopant concentrations of $N_d = 1 \times 10^{13}$ cm^{-3} and $N_a = 2.5 \times 10^{13}$ cm^{-3} at $T = 300$ K. For each of the three materials (a) Is this material n type or p type? (b) Calculate n_0 and p_0.

3.39 A sample of silicon at $T = 450$ K is doped with boron at a concentration of 1.5×10^{15} cm^{-3} and with arsenic at a concentration of 8×10^{14} cm^{-3}. (a) Is the material n or p type? (b) Determine the electron and hole concentrations. (c) Calculate the total ionized impurity concentration.

3.40 The thermal equilibrium hole concentration in silicon at $T = 300$ K is $p_0 = 2 \times 10^5$ cm^{-3}. Determine the thermal-equilibrium electron concentration. Is the material n type or p type?

3.41 In a sample of GaAs at $T = 200$ K, we have experimentally determined that $n_0 = 5p_0$ and that $N_a = 0$. Calculate n_0, p_0, and N_d.

3.42 Consider a sample of silicon doped at $N_d = 10^{14}$ cm^{-3} and $N_a = 0$. Calculate the majority-carrier concentration at (a) $T = 300$ K, (b) $T = 350$ K, (c) $T = 400$ K, (d) $T = 450$ K, and (e) $T = 500$ K.

3.43 Consider a sample of silicon doped at $N_d = 0$ and $N_a = 10^{14}$ cm^{-3}. Plot the majority-carrier concentration versus temperature over the range $200 \le T \le 500$ K.

3.44 The temperature of a sample of silicon is $T = 300$ K and the acceptor doping concentration is $N_a = 0$. Plot the minority-carrier concentration (on a log–log plot) versus N_d over the range $10^{15} \le N_d \le 10^{18}$ cm^{-3}.

3.45 Repeat problem 3.44 for GaAs.

3.46 A particular semiconductor material is doped at $N_d = 2 \times 10^{13}$ cm^{-3}, $N_a = 0$, and the intrinsic carrier concentration is $n_i = 2 \times 10^{13}$ cm^{-3}. Assume complete ionization. Determine the thermal-equilibrium majority- and minority-carrier concentrations.

3.47 (a) Silicon at $T = 300$ K is uniformly doped with arsenic atoms at a concentration of 2×10^{16} cm^{-3} and boron atoms at a concentration of 1×10^{16} cm^{-3}. Determine the thermal-equilibrium concentrations of majority and minority carriers. (b) Repeat part (a) if the impurity concentrations are 2×10^{15} cm^{-3} phosphorus atoms and 3×10^{16} cm^{-3} boron atoms.

3.48 In silicon at $T = 300$ K, we have experimentally found that $n_0 = 4.5 \times 10^4$ cm^{-3} and $N_d = 5 \times 10^{15}$ cm^{-3}. (a) Is the material n type or p type? (b) Determine the majority- and minority-carrier concentrations. (c) What types and concentrations of impurity atoms exist in the material?

Section 3.6   Position of Fermi Energy Level

3.49 Consider germanium with an acceptor concentration of $N_a = 10^{15}$ cm^{-3} and a donor concentration of $N_d = 0$. Consider temperatures of $T = 200, 400,$ and 600 K. Calculate the position of the Fermi energy with respect to the intrinsic Fermi level at these temperatures.

3.50 Consider germanium at $T = 300$ K with donor concentrations of $N_d = 10^{14}, 10^{16},$ and 10^{18} cm^{-3}. Let $N_a = 0$. Calculate the position of the Fermi energy level with respect to the intrinsic Fermi level for these doping concentrations.

3.51 A GaAs device is doped with a donor concentration of 3×10^{15} cm^{-3}. For the device to operate properly, the intrinsic carrier concentration must remain less than 5 percent of the total electron concentration. What is the maximum temperature that the device may operate?

3.52 Consider germanium with an acceptor concentration of $N_a = 10^{15}$ cm^{-3} and a donor concentration of $N_d = 0$. Plot the position of the Fermi energy with respect to the intrinsic Fermi level as a function of temperature over the range $200 \leq T \leq 600$ K.

3.53 Consider silicon at $T = 300$ K with $N_a = 0$. Plot the position of the Fermi energy level with respect to the intrinsic Fermi level as a function of the donor doping concentration over the range $10^{14} \leq N_d \leq 10^{18}$ cm^{-3}.

3.54 For a particular semiconductor, $E_g = 1.50$ eV, $m_p^* = 10m_n^*$, $T = 300$ K, and $n_i = 1 \times 10^5$ cm^{-3}. (*a*) Determine the position of the intrinsic Fermi energy level with respect to the center of the bandgap. (*b*) Impurity atoms are added so that the Fermi energy level is 0.45 eV below the center of the bandgap. (*i*) Are acceptor or donor atoms added? (*ii*) What is the concentration of impurity atoms added?

3.55 Silicon at $T = 300$ K contains acceptor atoms at a concentration of $N_a = 5 \times 10^{15}$ cm^{-3}. Donor atoms are added forming an n-type compensated semiconductor such that the Fermi level is 0.215 eV below the conduction band edge. What concentration of donor atoms are added?

3.56 Silicon at $T = 300$ K is doped with acceptor atoms at a concentration of $N_a = 7 \times 10^{15}$ cm^{-3}. (*a*) Determine $E_F - E_v$. (*b*) Calculate the concentration of additional acceptor atoms that must be added to move the Fermi level a distance kT closer to the valence-band edge.

3.57 (*a*) Determine the position of the Fermi level with respect to the intrinsic Fermi level in silicon at $T = 300$ K that is doped with phosphorus atoms at a concentration of 10^{15} cm^{-3}. (*b*) Repeat part (*a*) if the silicon is doped with boron atoms at a concentration of 10^{15} cm^{-3}. (*c*) Calculate the electron concentration in the silicon for parts (*a*) and (*b*).

3.58 Gallium arsenide at $T = 300$ K contains acceptor impurity atoms at a density of 10^{15} cm^{-3}. Additional impurity atoms are to be added so that the Fermi level is 0.45 eV below the intrinsic level. Determine the concentration and type (donor or acceptor) of impurity atoms to be added.

3.59 Determine the Fermi energy level with respect to the intrinsic Fermi level for each condition given in Problem 3.36.

3.60 Find the Fermi energy level with respect to the valence band energy for the conditions given in Problem 3.37.

3.61 Calculate the position of the Fermi energy level with respect to the intrinsic Fermi for the conditions given in Problem 3.48.

Summary and Review

3.62 A special semiconductor material is to be "designed." The semiconductor is to be n type and doped with 1×10^{15} cm^{-3} donor atoms. Assume complete ionization and assume $N_a = 0$. The effective density of states functions are given by $N_c = N_v = 1.5 \times 10^{19}$ cm^{-3} and are independent of temperature. A particular semiconductor device fabricated with this material requires the electron concentration to be no greater than 1.01×10^{15} cm^{-3} at $T = 400$ K. What is the minimum value of the bandgap energy?

3.63   Silicon atoms, at a concentration of 10^{10} cm^{-3}, are added to gallium arsenide. Assume that the silicon atoms act as fully ionized dopant atoms and that 5 percent of the concentration added replace gallium atoms and 95 percent replace arsenic atoms. Let $T = 300$ K. (a) Determine the donor and acceptor concentrations. (b) Calculate the electron and hole concentrations and the position of the Fermi level with respect to E_{Fi}.

3.64   Defects in a semiconductor material introduce allowed energy states within the forbidden bandgap. Assume that a particular defect in silicon introduces two discrete levels: a donor level 0.25 eV above the top of the valence band, and an acceptor level 0.65 eV above the top of the valence band. The charge state of each defect is a function of the position of the Fermi level. (a) Sketch the charge density of each defect as the Fermi level moves from E_v to E_c. Which defect level dominates in heavily doped n-type material? In heavily doped p-type material? (b) Determine the electron and hole concentrations and the location of the Fermi level in (i) an n-type sample doped at $N_d = 10^{17}$ cm^{-3} and (ii) in a p-type sample doped at $N_a = 10^{17}$ cm^{-3}. (c) Determine the Fermi level position if no dopant atoms are added. Is the material n type, p type, or intrinsic?

READING LIST

1. Anderson, B. L., and R. L. Anderson. *Fundamentals of Semiconductor Devices*. New York: McGraw-Hill, 2005.

*2. Brennan, K. F. *The Physics of Semiconductors with Applications to Optoelectronic Devices*. New York: Cambridge University Press, 1999.

*3. Hess, K. *Advanced Theory of Semiconductor Devices*. Englewood Cliffs, NJ: Prentice-Hall, 1988.

4. Kano, K. *Semiconductor Devices*. Upper Saddle River, NJ: Prentice-Hall, 1998.

*5. Li, S. S. *Semiconductor Physical Electronics*. New York: Plenum Press, 1993.

6. McKelvey, J. P. *Solid State Physics for Engineers and Materials Science*. Malabar, FL: Krieger Publishing, 1993.

7. Muller, R. S., T. I. Kamins, and W. Chan. *Device Electronics for Integrated Circuits*, 3rd ed. New York: John Wiley and Sons, 2003.

8. Navon, D. H. *Semiconductor Microdevices and Materials*. New York: Holt, Rinehart and Winston, 1986.

9. Neamen, D. A. *Semiconductor Physics and Devices: Basic Principles*, 3rd ed. New York: McGraw-Hill, 2003.

10. Pierret, R. F. *Semiconductor Device Fundamentals*. Reading, MA: Addison-Wesley, 1996.

11. Runyan, W. R., and K. E. Bean. *Semiconductor Integrated Circuit Processing Technology*. Reading, MA: Addison-Wesley, 1990.

12. Shur, M. *Introduction to Electronic Devices*. New York: John Wiley and Sons, 1996.

*13. Shur, M. *Physics of Semiconductor Devices*. Englewood Cliffs, NJ: Prentice-Hall, 1990.

14. Singh, J. *Semiconductor Devices: Basic Principles*. New York: John Wiley and Sons, 2001.

*15. Smith, R. A. *Semiconductors*, 2nd ed. New York: Cambridge University Press, 1978.

16. Streetman, B. G., and S. Banerjee. *Solid State Electronic Devices*, 5th ed. Upper Saddle River, NJ: Prentice-Hall, 2000.
17. Sze, S. M. *Physics of Semiconductor Devices*, 2nd ed. New York: Wiley, 1981.
18. Sze, S. M. *Semiconductor Devices: Physics and Technology*, 2nd ed. New York: John Wiley and Sons, 2002.
*19. Wang, S. *Fundamentals of Semiconductor Theory and Device Physics*. Englewood Cliffs, NJ: Prentice-Hall, 1989.
*20. Wolfe, C. M., N. Holonyak, Jr., and G. E. Stillman. *Physical Properties of Semiconductors*. Englewood Cliffs, NJ: Prentice-Hall, 1989.
21. Yang, E. S. *Microelectronic Devices*. New York: McGraw-Hill, 1988.

*Indicates references are at an advanced level compared to this text.

4

Carrier Transport and Excess Carrier Phenomena

In Chapter 3, we considered the semiconductor in thermal equilibrium and determined electron and hole concentrations in the conduction and valence bands, respectively. Knowledge of the densities of these charged particles is important toward an understanding of the electrical properties of a semiconductor material. The net flow of electrons and holes in a semiconductor will generate currents. The process by which these charged particles move is called transport. The two transport mechanisms, drift and diffusion, will be analyzed. We will implicitly assume, initially, that, although there will be a net flow of electrons and holes due to the transport processes, thermal equilibrium will not be substantially disturbed. However, any deviation from thermal equilibrium will tend to change the electron and hole concentrations in a semiconductor. We will discuss generation and recombination processes in a semiconductor material. ∎

4.0 | PREVIEW

In this chapter, we will

1. Describe the mechanism of carrier drift and drift current due to an applied electric field.

2. Describe the mechanism of carrier diffusion and diffusion current due to a gradient in the carrier concentration.

3. Describe the effects in a semiconductor when a nonuniform impurity concentration exists.

4. Describe the generation and recombination processes of excess carriers in a semiconductor.

5. Describe and analyze the Hall effect in a semiconductor material.

Historical Insight

Ohm's law was formulated by Georg Simon Ohm in 1826 and gives the relationship among the three important electrical quantities of resistance, voltage, and current. However, the electron was not discovered until the 1890s. The French physicist Jean Baptiste Perrin demonstrated that the current in a vacuum tube consisted of negatively charged particles. In the early 1900s, the idea that electrons in metals are "free" to move with an applied voltage was being investigated as the mechanism of current in metals. In 1928, Felix Bloch applied quantum mechanics to the periodic potential function and demonstrated the concept of a free electron in a periodic crystal. The transport of electrons and holes in semiconductors is an important property that determines semiconductor device performance.

Present-Day Insight

The transport of electrons and holes in semiconductors due to electric fields and density gradients continues to be a fundamental property that determines semiconductor device performance. Quantum transport approaches are now required for structures that are only a few hundred angstroms wide.

4.1 | CARRIER DRIFT

Objective: Describe the mechanism of carrier drift and drift current due to an applied electric field.

An electric field applied to a semiconductor will produce a force on electrons and holes so that they will experience a net acceleration and net movement, provided there are available energy states in the conduction and valence bands. This net movement of charge due to an electric field is called *drift*. The net drift of charge gives rise to a *drift current*.

Drift current

4.1.1 Drift Current Density

If we have a positive volume charge density ρ moving at an average drift velocity v_d, the drift current density is given by

$$J_{drf} = \rho v_d \tag{4.1}$$

where J is in units of C/cm^2-s or amps/cm^2. If the volume charge density is due to positively charged holes, then

$$J_{p|drf} = (ep)v_{dp} \tag{4.2}$$

where $J_{p|drf}$ is the drift current density due to holes, v_{dp} is the average drift velocity of holes, and p is the hole concentration.[1]

---

[1] In Chapter 3, we included a subscript zero on the electron and hole concentration parameters (n_0 and p_0) to indicate thermal equilibrium. In this chapter, we drop the subscript zero so that n and p indicate the total electron and hole concentrations and may include nonequilibrium effects.

The equation of motion of a positively charged hole in the presence of an electric field is

$$F = m_p^* a = e\mathcal{E} \tag{4.3}$$

where e is the magnitude of the electronic charge, a is the acceleration, $\mathcal{E}$ is the electric field, and m_p^* is the effective mass of the hole. If the electric field is constant, then we expect the velocity to increase linearly with time. However, charged particles in a semiconductor are involved in collisions with ionized impurity atoms and with waves of thermally vibrating lattice atoms. These collisions, or scattering events, alter the velocity characteristics of the particle.

As the hole accelerates in a crystal due to the electric field, the velocity increases. When the charged particle collides with an atom in the crystal, for example, the particle loses most, or all, of its energy. The particle will again begin to accelerate and gain energy until it is again involved in a scattering process. This continues over and over again. Throughout this process, the particle will gain an average drift velocity which, for low electric fields, is directly proportional to the electric field. We can then write

$$v_{dp} = \mu_p \mathcal{E} \tag{4.4}$$

Hole mobility

where μ_p is the proportionality factor and is called the *hole mobility*. The mobility is an important parameter of the semiconductor since it describes how well a particle will move due to an electric field. The unit of mobility is usually expressed in terms of cm^2/ V-s.

Hole drift current density

By combining Equations (4.2) and (4.4), we can write the drift current density due to holes as

$$J_{p|drf} = (ep)v_{dp} = e\mu_p p\mathcal{E} \tag{4.5}$$

The drift current due to holes is in the same direction as the applied electric field.

The same discussion of drift applies to electrons. We can write

$$J_{n|drf} = \rho v_{dn} = (-en)v_{dn} \tag{4.6}$$

where $J_{n|drf}$ is the drift current density due to electrons and v_{dn} is the average drift velocity of electrons. The net charge density of electrons is negative $(-e)$.

The average drift velocity of an electron is also proportional to the electric field for small fields. However, since the electron is negatively charged, the net motion of the electron is opposite to the electric field direction. We can then write

$$v_{dn} = -\mu_n \mathcal{E} \tag{4.7}$$

Electron mobility

where μ_n is the *electron mobility* and is a positive quantity. Equation (4.6) can now be written as

$$J_{n|drf} = (-en)(-\mu_n \mathcal{E}) = e\mu_n n\mathcal{E} \tag{4.8}$$

Electron drift current density

The conventional drift current due to electrons is also in the same direction as the applied electric field even though the electron movement is in the opposite direction.

Table 4.1 | Typical mobility values at $T = 300$ K and low doping concentrations

	μ_n (cm^2/V-s)	μ_p (cm^2/V-s)
Silicon	1350	480
Gallium arsenide	8500	400
Germanium	3900	1900

Electron and hole mobilities are functions of temperature and doping concentrations, as we will see in the next section. Table 4.1 shows some typical mobility values at $T = 300$ K for low doping concentrations.

Since both electrons and holes contribute to the drift current, the total *drift current density* is the sum of the individual electron and hole drift current densities, so we may write

$$J_{drf} = e(\mu_n n + \mu_p p)\mathcal{E} \qquad (4.9)$$

EXAMPLE 4.1

OBJECTIVE

Calculate the drift current density induced in a semiconductor for a given applied electric field.

Consider a silicon semiconductor at $T = 300$ K with an impurity doping concentration of $N_d = 10^{16}$ cm^{-3} and $N_a = 0$. Assume electron and hole mobilities given in Table 4.1. Calculate the drift current density for an applied electric field of $\mathcal{E} = 35$ V/cm.

■ **Solution**

Since $N_d > N_a$, the semiconductor is n type and, at room temperature, we can assume complete ionization so that

$$n \approx N_d = 10^{16} \text{ cm}^{-3}$$

Then, the hole concentration is

$$p = \frac{n_i^2}{n} = \frac{(1.5 \times 10^{10})^2}{10^{16}} = 2.25 \times 10^4 \text{ cm}^{-3}$$

Since $n \gg p$, the drift current density is

$$J_{drf} = e(\mu_n n + \mu_p p)\mathcal{E} \approx e\mu_n n\mathcal{E}$$

so

$$J_{drf} = (1.6 \times 10^{-19})(1350)(10^{16})(35) = 75.6 \text{ A/cm}^2$$

■ **Comment**

Significant drift current densities can be obtained in a semiconductor with relatively small applied electric fields. This result then implies that currents in the mA range can be generated in very small semiconductor devices.

Exercise Problem

EX4.1   Consider a gallium arsenide sample at $T = 300$ K with doping concentrations of $N_a = 0$ and $N_d = 10^{16}$ cm^{-3}. Assume electron and hole mobilities given in Table 4.1. Calculate the drift current density if the applied electric field is $\mathcal{E} = 10$ V/cm. (Ans. $J_{drf} = 136$ A/cm^2.)

4.1.2   Mobility Effects

In Section 4.1.1, we defined mobility, which relates the average drift velocity of a carrier to the electric field. Electron and hole mobilities are important semiconductor parameters in the characterization of carrier drift, as seen in Equation (4.9).

Equation (4.3) related the acceleration of a hole to a force such as an electric field. We can write this equation as

$$F = m_p^* \frac{dv}{dt} = e\mathcal{E} \tag{4.10}$$

where v is the velocity of the particle due to the electric field and does not include the random thermal velocity. If we assume that the effective mass and electric field are constants, then we may integrate Equation (4.10) and obtain

$$v = \frac{e\mathcal{E}t}{m_p^*} \tag{4.11}$$

where we have assumed the initial drift velocity to be zero.

Scattering effects

Figure 4.1a shows a schematic model of the random thermal velocity and motion of a hole in a semiconductor with zero applied electric field. The direction of motion is altered by a scattering (collision) event. There is a mean time between collisions which may be denoted by τ_{cp}. If a small electric field ($\mathcal{E}$-field) is applied as indicated in Figure 4.1b, there will be a net drift of the hole in the direction of the $\mathcal{E}$-field, and the net drift velocity will be a small perturbation on the random thermal velocity, so the time between collisions will not be altered appreciably.

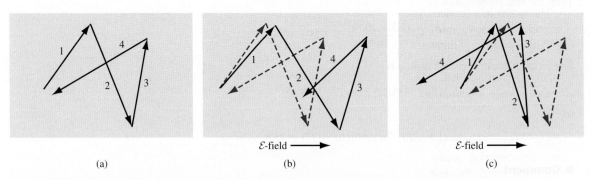

(a)   (b)   (c)

Figure 4.1 | (a) Typical random behavior of a hole or electron in a semiconductor with no applied electric field. (b) Behavior of a hole in a semiconductor—dotted lines for $\mathcal{E} = 0$ and solid lines for $\mathcal{E} > 0$. (c) Behavior of an electron in a semiconductor—dotted lines for $\mathcal{E} = 0$ and solid lines for $\mathcal{E} > 0$.

Figure 4.1a can also represent a schematic model of the random thermal velocity and motion of an electron in a semiconductor with zero applied electric field. The mean time between collisions can be denoted by τ_{cn}. If a small electric field is applied as indicated in Figure 4.1c, there will be a net drift of the electron *in the opposite direction* of the $\mathcal{E}$-field. The net drift velocity of the electron will also be a small perturbation on the random thermal velocity, so the time between collisions will not be altered appreciably.

If we use the mean time between collisions τ_{cp} for a hole in place of the time t in Equation (4.11), then the mean peak velocity just prior to a collision or scattering event is

$$v_{d|\text{peak}} = \left(\frac{e\tau_{cp}}{m_p^*} \right) \mathcal{E} \tag{4.12a}$$

The average drift velocity is one half the peak value so that we can write

$$\langle v_d \rangle = \frac{1}{2} \left(\frac{e\tau_{cp}}{m_p^*} \right) \mathcal{E} \tag{4.12b}$$

However, the collision process is not as simple as this model, but is statistical in nature. In a more accurate model including the effect of a statistical distribution, the factor $\frac{1}{2}$ in Equation (4.12b) does not appear. The hole mobility is then given by

$$\mu_p = \frac{v_{dp}}{\mathcal{E}} = \frac{e\tau_{cp}}{m_p^*} \tag{4.13}$$

The same analysis applies to electrons; thus we can write the electron mobility as

$$\mu_n = \frac{e\tau_{cn}}{m_n^*} \tag{4.14}$$

Mobility versus scattering

where τ_{cn} is the mean time between collisions for an electron.

There are two collision or scattering mechanisms that dominate in a semiconductor and affect the carrier mobility: phonon or lattice scattering, and ionized impurity scattering.

The atoms in a semiconductor crystal have a certain amount of thermal energy at temperatures above absolute zero that causes the atoms to randomly vibrate about their lattice position within the crystal. The lattice vibrations cause a disruption in the perfect periodic potential function. A perfect periodic potential in a solid allows electrons to move unimpeded, or with no scattering, through the crystal. But the thermal vibrations cause a disruption of the potential function, resulting in an interaction between the electrons or holes and the vibrating lattice atoms. This *lattice scattering* is also referred to as *phonon scattering*.

Lattice scattering

Since lattice scattering is related to the thermal motion of atoms, the rate at which the scattering occurs is a function of temperature. If we denote μ_L as the mobility that would be observed if only lattice scattering existed, then the scattering theory states that to first order

$$\mu_L \propto T^{-3/2} \tag{4.15}$$

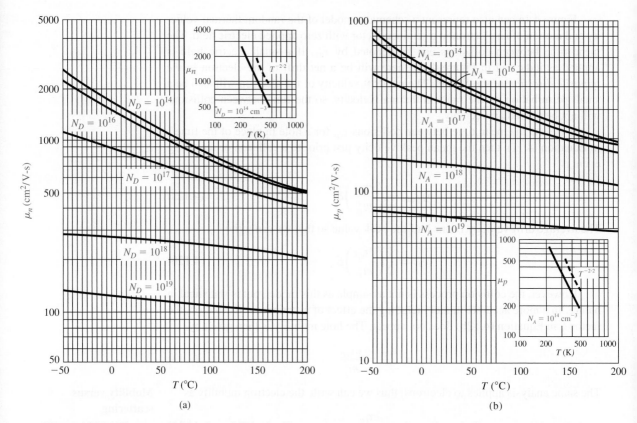

Figure 4.2 | (a) Electron and (b) hole mobilities in silicon versus temperature for various doping concentrations. Inserts show temperature dependence for "almost" intrinsic silicon.
(From Pierret [8].)

Mobility versus temperature

Mobility that is due to lattice scattering increases as the temperature decreases. Intuitively, we expect the lattice vibrations to decrease as the temperature decreases, which implies that the probability of a scattering event also decreases, thus increasing mobility.

Figure 4.2 shows the temperature dependence of electron and hole mobilities in silicon. In lightly doped semiconductors, lattice scattering dominates and the carrier mobility decreases with temperature as we have discussed. The temperature dependence of mobility is proportional to T^{-n}. The inserts in the figure show that the parameter n is not equal to $\frac{3}{2}$ as the first-order scattering theory predicted. However, mobility does increase as the temperature decreases.

Ionized impurity scattering

The second interaction mechanism affecting carrier mobility is called *ionized impurity scattering*. We have seen that impurity atoms are added to the semiconductor to control or alter its characteristics. These impurities are ionized at room temperature so that a coulomb interaction exists between the electrons or holes and the ionized impurities. This coulomb interaction produces scattering or collisions and also alters the velocity characteristics of the charge carrier. If we denote μ_I as the mobility that would be observed if only ionized impurity scattering existed, then to first order we have

$$\mu_I \propto \frac{T^{+3/2}}{N_I} \tag{4.16}$$

where $N_I = N_d^+ + N_a^-$ is the total ionized impurity concentration in the semiconductor. If temperature increases, the random thermal velocity of a carrier increases, reducing the time the carrier spends in the vicinity of the ionized impurity center. The less time spent in the vicinity of a coulomb force, the smaller the scattering effect and the larger the expected value of μ_I. If the number of ionized impurity centers increases, then the probability of a carrier encountering an ionized impurity center increases, implying a smaller value of μ_I.

Figure 4.3 is a plot of electron and hole mobilities in germanium, silicon, and gallium arsenide at $T = 300$ K as a function of impurity concentration.[2] More accurately, these curves are of mobility versus ionized impurity concentration N_I. As the impurity concentration increases, the number of impurity scattering centers increases, thus reducing mobility.

EXAMPLE 4.2

OBJECTIVE

Find the electron and hole mobilities in silicon at various temperatures.

(a) Find the electron mobility for (i) $N_d = 10^{17}$ cm^{-3}, $T = 150°$C and for (ii) $N_d = 10^{16}$ cm^{-3}, $T = 0°$C. (b) Find the hole mobility for (i) $N_a = 10^{16}$ cm^{-3}, $T = 50°$C and for (ii) $N_a = 10^{17}$ cm^{-3}, $T = 150°$C.

■ **Solution**

Using Figure 4.2, we find

(a) (i) For $N_d = 10^{17}$ cm^{-3}, $T = 150°$C $\rightarrow \mu_n \approx 500$ cm^2/V-s
(a) (ii) For $N_d = 10^{16}$ cm^{-3}, $T = 0°$C $\rightarrow \mu_n \approx 1500$ cm^2/V-s
(b) (i) For $N_a = 10^{16}$ cm^{-3}, $T = 50°$C $\rightarrow \mu_p \approx 380$ cm^2/V-s
(b) (ii) For $N_a = 10^{17}$ cm^{-3}, $T = 150°$C $\rightarrow \mu_p \approx 200$ cm^2/V-s

■ **Comment**

We can see that the mobility decreases as the temperature increases.

Exercise Problem

EX4.2 Using Figure 4.3, determine the electron and hole mobilities in (a) silicon for $N_d = 10^{17}$ cm^{-3}, $N_a = 5 \times 10^{16}$ cm^{-3} and (b) GaAs for $N_d = N_a = 10^{17}$ cm^{-3}.

[Ans. (a) $\mu_n \approx 800$ cm^2/V-s, $\mu_p \approx 300$ cm^2/V-s; (b) $\mu_n \approx 3800$ cm^2/V-s, $\mu_p \approx 200$ cm^2/V-s]

---

[2]There may be differences between majority-carrier and minority-carrier mobilities (e.g., electron mobility in n-type and p-type material). For simplicity, however, we will neglect such differences in this text.

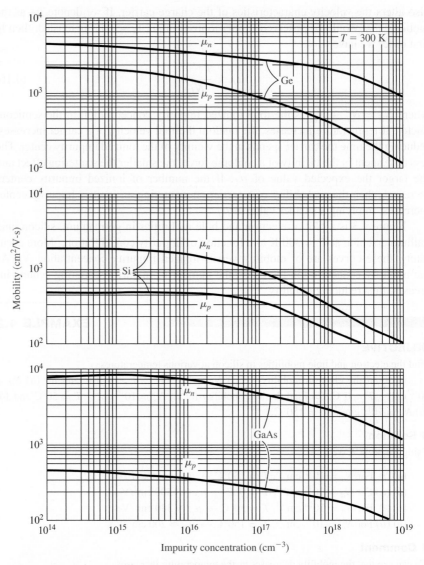

Figure 4.3 | Electron and hole mobilities versus impurity concentrations for germanium, silicon, and gallium arsenide at $T = 300\,\text{K}$.
(From Sze [14].)

If τ_L is the mean time between collisions due to lattice scattering, then dt/τ_L is the probability of a lattice scattering event occurring in a differential time dt. Likewise, if τ_I is the mean time between collisions due to ionized impurity scattering, then dt/τ_I is the probability of an ionized impurity scattering event occurring in the differential time dt. If these two scattering processes are independent, then the total probability of a scattering event occurring in the differential time dt is the sum of the individual events, or

$$\frac{dt}{\tau} = \frac{dt}{\tau_I} + \frac{dt}{\tau_L} \tag{4.17}$$

where τ is the mean time between any scattering event.

Comparing Equation (4.17) with the definitions of mobility given by Equation (4.13) or (4.14), we can write

Mobility versus two scattering events

$$\boxed{\frac{1}{\mu} = \frac{1}{\mu_I} + \frac{1}{\mu_L}} \tag{4.18}$$

where μ_I is the mobility due to the ionized impurity scattering process and μ_L is the mobility due to the lattice scattering process. The parameter μ is the net mobility. With two or more independent scattering mechanisms, the inverse mobilities add, which means that the net mobility decreases.

4.1.3 Semiconductor Conductivity and Resistivity

The drift current density, given by Equation (4.9), can be written as

$$J_{drf} = e(\mu_n n + \mu_p p)\mathcal{E} = \sigma\mathcal{E} \tag{4.19}$$

where σ is the *conductivity* of the semiconductor material. The conductivity is given in units of $(\Omega\text{-cm})^{-1}$ and is a function of the electron and hole concentrations and mobilities. We have just seen that the mobilities are functions of impurity concentrations; conductivity, then is a somewhat complicated function of impurity concentration.

Conductivity

The reciprocal of conductivity is *resistivity,* which is denoted by ρ and is given in units of ohm-cm.[3] We can write resistivity as

Resistivity

$$\boxed{\rho = \frac{1}{\sigma} = \frac{1}{e(\mu_n n + \mu_p p)}} \tag{4.20}$$

Figure 4.4 is a plot of resistivity as a function of impurity concentration in silicon, germanium, gallium arsenide, and gallium phosphide at $T = 300$ K. Obviously, the curves are not linear functions of N_d or N_a because of mobility effects.

If we have a bar of semiconductor material as shown in Figure 4.5 with a voltage applied that produces a current I, then we can write

$$J = \frac{I}{A} \tag{4.21a}$$

---

[3]The symbol ρ is also used for charge density. However, the context in which the symbol is used should make it clear as to whether resistivity or charge density is implied.

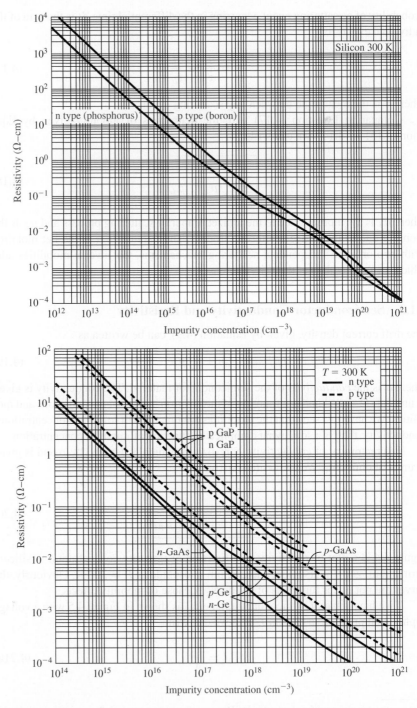

Figure 4.4 | Resistivity versus impurity concentration at $T = 300\,\text{K}$ in (a) silicon and (b) germanium, gallium arsenide, and gallium phosphide.

(From Sze [14].)

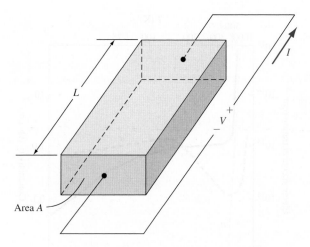

Figure 4.5 | Bar of semiconductor material as a resistor.

and

$$\mathcal{E} = \frac{V}{L} \tag{4.21b}$$

We can now rewrite Equation (4.19) as

$$\frac{I}{A} = \sigma \left(\frac{V}{L} \right) \tag{4.22a}$$

or

$$V = \left(\frac{L}{\sigma A} \right) I = \left(\frac{\rho L}{A} \right) I = IR \tag{4.22b}$$

Equation (4.22b) is Ohm's law for a semiconductor. The resistance is a function of   **Ohm's law**
resistivity, or conductivity, as well as the geometry of the semiconductor.

If we consider, for example, a p-type semiconductor with an acceptor doping $N_a(N_d = 0)$ in which $N_a \gg n_i$, and if we assume that the electron and hole mobilities are of the same order of magnitude, then the conductivity becomes

$$\sigma = e(\mu_n n + \mu_p p) \approx e\mu_p p \tag{4.23}$$

If we also assume complete ionization, then Equation (4.23) becomes

$$\sigma \approx e\mu_p N_a \approx \frac{1}{\rho} \tag{4.24}$$

The conductivity and resistivity of an extrinsic semiconductor are a function primarily of the concentration and mobility of the majority carrier.

We can plot the carrier concentration and conductivity of a semiconductor as a function of temperature for a particular doping concentration. Figure 4.6 shows the

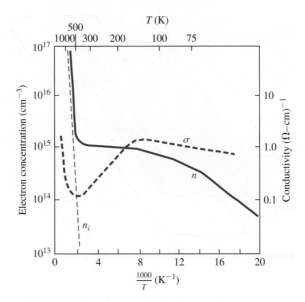

Figure 4.6 | Electron concentration and conductivity versus inverse temperature for silicon.
(After Sze [14].)

electron concentration and conductivity of silicon as a function of inverse temperature for the case when $N_d = 10^{15}$ cm^{-3}. In the midtemperature, or extrinsic range (approximately 200 to 450 K), we have complete ionization—the electron concentration remains essentially constant. However, the mobility decreases with increasing temperature so the conductivity decreases with increasing temperature in this range. At higher temperatures, the intrinsic carrier concentration increases and begins to dominate the electron concentration as well as the conductivity. In the lower temperature range, freeze-out begins to occur: the electron concentration and conductivity decrease with decreasing temperature.

For an intrinsic material, the conductivity can be written as

$$\sigma_i = e(\mu_n + \mu_p)n_i \tag{4.25}$$

The concentrations of electrons and holes are equal in an intrinsic semiconductor, so the intrinsic conductivity includes both the electron and hole mobility. Since, in general, the electron and hole mobilities are not equal, the intrinsic conductivity is not the minimum value possible at a given temperature.

DESIGN EXAMPLE 4.3

OBJECTIVE

Determine the required impurity doping concentration in silicon at $T = 300$ K to produce a semiconductor resistor with specified current–voltage characteristics.

Consider a bar of silicon uniformly doped with acceptor impurities and having the geometry shown in Figure 4.5. For an applied voltage of 5 V, a current of 2 mA is required. The current density is to be no larger than $J_{drf} = 100$ A/cm^2. Find the required cross-sectional area, length, and doping concentration.

■ **Solution**

The cross-sectional area can be found as

$$I = J_{drf} A \rightarrow A = \frac{I}{J_{drf}} = \frac{2 \times 10^{-3}}{100} = 2 \times 10^{-5} \text{ cm}^2$$

The resistance of the device is

$$R = \frac{V}{I} = \frac{5}{2 \times 10^{-3}} = 2.5 \times 10^3 \ \Omega \rightarrow 2.5 \text{ k}\Omega$$

From Equation (4.22b), the resistance, for the bar of semiconductor, is given by

$$R = \frac{L}{\sigma A} \approx \frac{L}{e\mu_p pA} = \frac{L}{e\mu_p N_a A}$$

From this relation, we see that there is no unique solution for N_a and L. If we choose a very small value of L, then N_a might be unreasonably small. On the other hand, if we choose a very large value of L, then N_a might be unreasonably large. Hence, we will choose a value of the doping concentration and then determine the required length.

Let $N_a = 10^{16}$ cm^{-3}. From Figure 4.3, we find $\mu_p \approx 400$ cm^2/V-s. The device length is then found to be

$$L = \sigma AR = e\mu_p N_a AR$$
$$= (1.6 \times 10^{-19})(400)(10^{16})(2 \times 10^{-5})(2.5 \times 10^3)$$

or

$$L = 3.2 \times 10^{-2} \text{ cm}$$

■ **Comment**

We must make sure that we use the mobility that corresponds to the doping concentration in our analysis and design.

Exercise Problem

EX4.3 For a particular silicon semiconductor device at $T = 300$ K, the required material is to be n type with a resistivity of $\rho = 0.10$ Ω-cm. (a) Determine the required impurity doping concentration and (b) the resulting electron mobility.
[Ans. (a) From Figure 4.5, $N_d \approx 6 \times 10^{16}$ cm^{-3}, then (b) $\mu_n \approx 695$ cm^2/V-s.]

DESIGN EXAMPLE 4.4

OBJECTIVE

Design a p-type semiconductor resistor with a specified resistance to handle a given current density.

A silicon semiconductor at $T = 300$ K and with the geometry shown in Figure 4.5 is initially doped with donors at a concentration of $N_d = 5 \times 10^{15}$ cm^{-3}. Acceptors are to added to form a compensated p-type material. The resistor is to have a resistance of $R = 10$ kΩ, handle a current density of $J_{drf} = 50$ A/cm^2 when 5 V is applied, and have an applied electric field no larger than $\mathcal{E} = 100$ V/cm.

■ **Solution**

For 5 V applied to a 10-kΩ resistor, the total current is

$$I = \frac{V}{R} = \frac{5}{10} = 0.5 \text{ mA}$$

For a current density limited to 50A/cm^2, the cross-sectional area must be

$$A = \frac{I}{J} = \frac{0.5 \times 10^{-3}}{50} = 10^{-5} \text{ cm}^2$$

From the specified voltage and electric field, the device length is found to be

$$L = \frac{V}{\mathcal{E}} = \frac{5}{100} = 5 \times 10^{-2} \text{ cm}$$

The semiconductor conductivity, from Equation (4.22b) is

$$\sigma = \frac{L}{RA} = \frac{5 \times 10^{-2}}{(10^4)(10^{-5})} = 0.50 \text{ (Ω-cm)}^{-1}$$

The conductivity of a compensated p-type semiconductor is

$$\sigma \approx e\mu_p p = e\mu_p(N_a - N_d)$$

where the mobility μ_p is a function of the total ionized impurity concentration $N_a + N_d$.

Using trial and error, if $N_a = 1.25 \times 10^{16}$ cm^{-3}, then $N_a + N_d = 1.75 \times 10^{16}$ cm^{-3}, and the hole mobility, from Figure 4.3 is $\mu_p \approx 410$ cm^2/V-s. The conductivity is then

$$\sigma = e\mu_p(N_a - N_d)$$
$$= (1.6 \times 10^{-19})(410)(1.25 \times 10^{16} - 5 \times 10^{15}) = 0.492 \text{ (Ω-cm)}^{-1}$$

which is very close to the value we need.

■ **Comment**

Since the mobility is related to the total ionized impurity concentration, the determination of the impurity concentration to achieve a particular conductivity is not straightforward.

Exercise Problem

EX4.4 Consider compensated n-type silicon at $T = 300$ K with a conductivity of $\sigma = 16$ (Ω-cm)$^{-1}$ and an acceptor doping concentration of $N_a = 10^{17}$ cm^{-3}. Determine the donor concentration and the resulting electron mobility.

(Ans. By trial and error, and using Figure 4.4, we find $N_d \approx 3.4 \times 10^{17}$ cm^{-3} and $\mu_n \approx 420$ cm^2/V-s.)

4.1.4 Velocity Saturation

So far in our discussion of drift velocity, we have assumed that mobility is not a function of electric field, meaning that the drift velocity will increase linearly with applied electric field. The total velocity of a particle is the sum of the random thermal velocity and drift velocity. At $T = 300$ K, the average random thermal energy is given by

$$\frac{1}{2}mv_{th}^2 = \frac{3}{2}kT = \frac{3}{2}(0.0259) = 0.03885 \text{ eV} \qquad (4.26)$$

This energy translates into a mean thermal velocity of approximately 10^7 cm/s for an electron in silicon. If we assume an electron mobility of $\mu_n = 1350$ cm^2/V-s in low-doped silicon, a drift velocity of 10^5 cm/s, or 1 percent of the thermal velocity, is achieved if the applied electric field is approximately 75 V/cm. This applied electric field is relatively small and does not appreciably alter the energy of the electron.

Figure 4.7 is a plot of average drift velocity as a function of applied electric field for electrons and holes in silicon, gallium arsenide, and germanium. At low electric fields, where there is a linear variation of velocity with electric field, the slope of the drift velocity versus electric field curve is the mobility. The behavior of the drift velocity of carriers at high electric fields deviates substantially from the linear relationship observed at low fields. The drift velocity of electrons in silicon, for example, saturates at approximately 10^7 cm/s at an electric field of approximately 30 kV/cm. If the drift velocity of a charge carrier saturates, then the drift current density also saturates and becomes independent of the applied electric field.

Drift velocity saturation

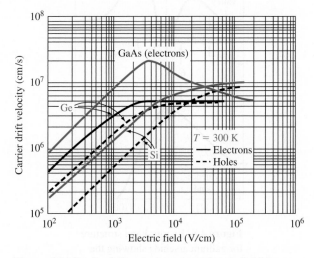

Figure 4.7 | Carrier drift velocity versus electric field for high-purity silicon, germanium, and gallium arsenide. *(From Sze [14].)*

The drift velocity versus electric field characteristic of gallium arsenide is more complicated than for silicon or germanium. At low fields, the slope of the drift velocity versus $\mathcal{E}$-field is constant and is the low-field electron mobility, which is approximately 8500 cm^2/V-s for gallium arsenide. The low-field electron mobility in gallium arsenide is much larger than in silicon. As the field increases, the electron drift velocity in gallium arsenide reaches a peak and then decreases. A differential mobility is the slope of the v_d versus $\mathcal{E}$-field at a particular point on the curve and the negative slope of the drift velocity versus electric field represents a negative differential mobility. The negative differential mobility produces a negative differential resistance; this characteristic is used in the design of oscillators.

Negative differential mobility

The negative differential mobility can be understood by considering the E versus k diagram for gallium arsenide, which is shown again in Figure 4.8. The density of states effective mass of the electron in the lower valley is $m_n^* = 0.067m_0$. The small effective mass leads to a large mobility. As the $\mathcal{E}$-field increases, the energy of the electron increases and the electron can be scattered into the upper valley, where the density of states effective mass is $0.55m_0$. The larger effective mass in the upper valley yields a smaller mobility. This intervalley transfer mechanism results in a decreasing average drift velocity of electrons with electric field, or the negative differential mobility characteristic.

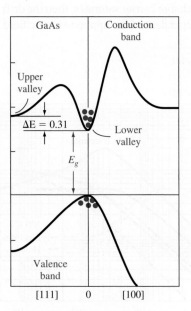

Figure 4.8 | Energy-band structure for gallium arsenide showing the upper valley and lower valley in the conduction band.
(From Sze [15].)

TEST YOUR UNDERSTANDING

TYU4.1 A drift current density of $J_{drf} = 150$ A/cm^2 is required in a semiconductor device using n-type silicon with an applied electric field of $\mathcal{E} = 25$V/cm. Determine the impurity doping concentration that will achieve this specification. (Ans. If $N_d \approx 3.13 \times 10^{16}$ cm^{-3}, then $\mu_n \approx 1200$ cm^2/V-s.)

TYU4.2 Silicon at $T = 300$ K is doped with impurity doping concentrations of $N_a = 5 \times 10^{16}$ cm^{-3} and $N_d = 2 \times 10^{16}$ cm^{-3}. (a) What are the electron and hole mobilities? (b) Determine the resistivity and conductivity of the material. [Ans. (a) $\mu_n \approx 1000$ cm^2/V-s, $\mu_p \approx 350$ cm^2/V-s; (b) $\sigma = 1.68$ (Ω-cm)$^{-1}$, $\rho = 0.595$ Ω-cm]

TYU4.3 Repeat TYU4.1 for GaAs. (Ans. If $N_d \approx 4.41 \times 10^{15}$ cm^{-3}, then $\mu_n \approx 8500$ cm^2/V-s)

TYU4.4 Repeat TYU4.2 for GaAs. [Ans. (a) $\mu_n \approx 4500$ cm^2/V-s, $\mu_p \approx 250$ cm^2/V-s; (b) $\sigma = 1.2$ (Ω-cm)$^{-1}$, $\rho = 0.833$ Ω-cm]

4.2 | CARRIER DIFFUSION

Objective: Describe the mechanism of carrier diffusion and diffusion current due to a gradient in the carrier concentration.

There is a second mechanism, in addition to drift, that can induce a current in a semiconductor. We can consider a classic physics example in which a container, as shown in Figure 4.9, is divided into two parts by a membrane. The left side contains gas molecules at a particular temperature and the right side is initially empty. The gas molecules are in continual random thermal motion so that, when the membrane is broken, there will be a net flow of gas molecules into the right side of the container. *Diffusion* is the process whereby particles flow from a region of high concentration toward a region of low concentration. If the gas molecules were electrically charged, the net flow of charge would result in a *diffusion current*.

Diffusion process

4.2.1 Diffusion Current Density

To begin to understand the diffusion process in a semiconductor, we will consider a simplified analysis. Assume that an electron concentration varies in one dimension as shown in Figure 4.10. The temperature is assumed to be uniform so that the average thermal velocity of electrons is independent of x. To calculate the current, we will determine the net flow of electrons per unit time per unit area crossing the plane at $x = 0$. If the distance l shown in Figure 4.10 is the mean-free path of an electron, that is, the average distance an electron travels between collisions ($l = v_{th}\tau_{cn}$), then on the average, electrons moving to the right at $x = -l$ and electrons moving to the left at $x = +l$ will cross the $x = 0$ plane. One half of the electrons at $x = -l$ will be traveling to the right at any instant of time and one half of the electrons at $x = +l$

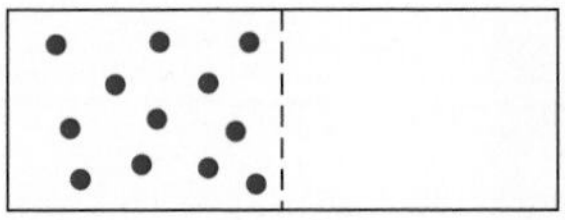

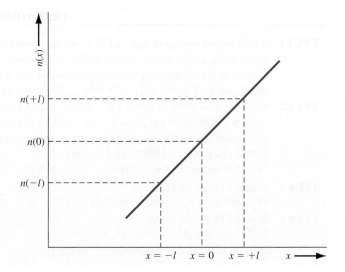

Figure 4.10 | Electron concentration versus distance.

Figure 4.9 | Container divided by a membrane with gas molecules on one side.

will be traveling to the left at any given time. The net rate of electron flow, F_n, in the $+x$ direction at $x = 0$ is given by

$$F_n = \tfrac{1}{2}n(-l)v_{th} - \tfrac{1}{2}n(+l)v_{th} = \tfrac{1}{2}v_{th}[n(-l) - n(+l)] \quad (4.27)$$

If we expand the electron concentration in a Taylor series about $x = 0$ keeping only the first two terms, then we can write Equation (4.27) as

$$F_n = \frac{1}{2}v_{th}\left\{\left[n(0) - l\frac{dn}{dx}\right] - \left[n(0) + l\frac{dn}{dx}\right]\right\} \quad (4.28)$$

which becomes

$$F_n = -v_{th}l\frac{dn}{dx} \quad (4.29)$$

Each electron has a charge $(-e)$, so the current is

$$J = -eF_n = +ev_{th}l\frac{dn}{dx} \quad (4.30)$$

The current described by Equation (4.30) is the electron diffusion current and is proportional to the spatial derivative, or density gradient, of the electron concentration.

The diffusion of electrons from a region of high concentration to a region of low concentration produces a flux of electrons flowing in the negative x direction for this example. Since electrons have a negative charge, the conventional current direction is in the positive x direction. Figure 4.11a shows these one-dimensional flux and current directions. We can write the electron diffusion current density for this one-dimensional case in the form

Electron diffusion current density

$$\boxed{J_{nx|dif} = eD_n\frac{dn}{dx}} \quad (4.31)$$

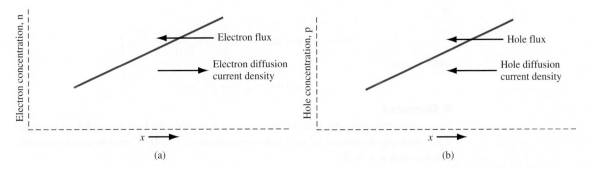

Figure 4.11 | (a) Diffusion of electrons due to a density gradient. (b) Diffusion of holes due to a density gradient.

where D_n is called the *electron diffusion coefficient,* has units of cm²/s, and is a positive quantity. If the electron density gradient becomes negative, the electron diffusion current density will be in the negative x direction.

Electron diffusion coefficient

Figure 4.11b shows an example of a hole concentration as a function of distance in a semiconductor. The diffusion of holes, from a region of high concentration to a region of low concentration, produces a flux of holes in the negative x direction. Since holes are positively charged particles, the conventional diffusion current density is also in the negative x direction. The hole diffusion current density is proportional to the hole density gradient and to the electronic charge, so we can write

Hole diffusion current density

$$J_{px|dif} = -eD_p \frac{dp}{dx} \qquad (4.32)$$

for the one-dimensional case. The parameter D_p is called the *hole diffusion coefficient,* has units of cm²/s, and is a positive quantity. If the hole density gradient becomes negative, the hole diffusion current density will be in the positive x direction.

Hole diffusion coefficient

EXAMPLE 4.5

OBJECTIVE
Determine the carrier density gradient to produce a given diffusion current density.

The hole concentration in silicon at $T = 300$ K varies linearly from $x = 0$ to $x = 0.01$ cm. The hole diffusion coefficient is $D_p = 10$ cm²/s, the hole diffusion current density is $J_{dif} = 20$ A/cm², and the hole concentration at $x = 0$ is $p = 4 \times 10^{17}$ cm⁻³. Determine the hole concentration at $x = 0.01$ cm.

■ **Solution**
The diffusion current density is given by

$$J_{dif} = -eD_p \frac{dp}{dx} \approx -eD_p \frac{\Delta p}{\Delta x} = -eD_p \left[\frac{p(0.01) - p(0)}{0.01 - 0} \right]$$

or

$$20 = -(1.6 \times 10^{-19})(10) \left(\frac{p(0.01) - 4 \times 10^{17}}{0.01 - 0} \right)$$

which yields

$$p(0.01) = 2.75 \times 10^{17} \text{ cm}^{-3}$$

■ **Comment**

We can note that, since the hole diffusion current is positive, the hole gradient must be negative, which implies that the value of hole concentration at $x = 0.01$ must be smaller than the concentration at $x = 0$.

Exercise Problem

EX4.5 Assume that, in an n-type GaAs semiconductor at $T = 300$ K, the electron concentration varies linearly from 1×10^{18} to 7×10^{17} cm^{-3} over a distance of 0.10 cm. Calculate the magnitude of the diffusion current density if the diffusion coefficient is $D_n = 225$ cm^2/s. (Ans. $J_{dif} = 108$ A/cm^2.)

4.2.2 Total Current Density

Total current density

We now have four possible independent current mechanisms in a semiconductor. These components are electron drift and diffusion currents and hole drift and diffusion currents. The total current density is the sum of these four components, or, for the one-dimensional case,

$$J = en\mu_n \mathcal{E}_x + ep\mu_p \mathcal{E}_x + eD_n \frac{dn}{dx} - eD_p \frac{dp}{dx} \tag{4.33}$$

This equation can be generalized to three dimensions as

$$J = en\mu_n \mathcal{E} + ep\mu_p \mathcal{E} + eD_n \nabla n - eD_p \nabla p \tag{4.34}$$

The electron mobility gives an indication of how well an electron moves in a semiconductor as a result of the force experienced by an electron in an electric field. The electron diffusion coefficient gives an indication of how well an electron moves in a semiconductor as a result of a density gradient. The electron mobility and diffusion coefficient are not independent parameters. Similarly, the hole mobility and diffusion coefficient are not independent parameters. The relationship between mobility and the diffusion coefficient will be developed in Section 4.3.

The expression for the total current in a semiconductor contains four terms. Fortunately in most situations, we will need to consider only one term at any one time at a particular point in a semiconductor.

TEST YOUR UNDERSTANDING

TYU4.5 The electron concentration in silicon is given by $n(x) = 10^{15} e^{-(x/L_n)}$ cm^{-3} ($x \geq 0$) where $L_n = 10^{-4}$ cm. The electron diffusion coefficient is $D_n = 25$ cm^2/s. Determine the electron diffusion current density at (a) $x = 0$, (b) $x = 10^{-4}$ cm, and (c) $x \to \infty$.

[Ans. (a) -40 A/cm^2, (b) -14.7 A/cm^2, (c) 0]

TYU4.6   The hole concentration in silicon is given by $p(x) = 2 \times 10^{15} e^{-(x/L_p)}$ cm^{-3} $(x \geq 0)$. The hole diffusion coefficient is $D_p = 10$ cm^2/s. The value of the diffusion current density at $x = 0$ is $J_{\text{dif}} = +6.4$ A/cm^2. What is the value of L_p? (Ans. $L_p = 5 \times 10^{-4}$ cm)

4.3 | GRADED IMPURITY DISTRIBUTION

Objective: Describe the effects in a semiconductor when a nonuniform impurity concentration exists.

In most cases so far, we have assumed that the semiconductor is uniformly doped. In many semiconductor devices, however, there may be regions that are nonuniformly doped. We will investigate how a nonuniformly doped semiconductor reaches thermal equilibrium and, from this analysis, we will derive the Einstein relation, which relates mobility and the diffusion coefficient.

4.3.1   Induced Electric Field

Consider a semiconductor that is nonuniformly doped with donor impurity atoms. If the semiconductor is in thermal equilibrium, the Fermi energy level is constant through the crystal so the energy-band diagram may qualitatively look like that shown in Figure 4.12. The doping concentration increases as x increases in this case. There will be a diffusion of majority carrier electrons from the region of high concentration to the region of low concentration, which is in the $-x$ direction. The flow of negative electrons leaves behind positively charged donor ions. The separation of positive and negative charge induces an electric field that is in a direction to oppose the diffusion process. When equilibrium is reached, the mobile carrier concentration is not exactly equal to the fixed impurity concentration and the induced electric field prevents any further separation of charge. In most cases of interest, the space charge induced by this diffusion process is a small fraction of the impurity

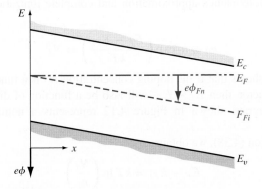

Figure 4.12 | Energy-band diagram for a semiconductor in thermal equilibrium with a nonuniform donor impurity concentration.

concentration, thus the mobile carrier concentration is not too different from the impurity dopant density.

The potential and electron energy are related by

$$E = -e\phi \qquad (4.35a)$$

or

$$\phi = \frac{-E}{e} \qquad (4.35b)$$

In considering the energy-band diagram, the electron energy is plotted on the positive vertical axis, which means a positive potential is plotted "downward," as shown in Figure 4.12.

Figure 4.12 is an example of an energy-band diagram for a nonuniformly doped n-type semiconductor. We are assuming the semiconductor is in thermal equilibrium so that the Fermi energy is a constant throughout the material.

We can define a potential difference between the Fermi level and intrinsic Fermi level as

$$\phi_{Fn} = \frac{E_F - E_{Fi}}{e} \qquad (4.36)$$

Since $E_F > E_{Fi}$, $\phi_{Fn} > 0$ and is positive "downward," as shown in Figure 4.12.

From Poisson's equation, the electric field can be written as

$$\mathcal{E}_x = -\frac{d\phi}{dx} \qquad (4.37a)$$

or, for the condition shown in Figure 4.12, we have

$$\mathcal{E}_x = -\frac{d\phi_{Fn}}{dx} = +\frac{1}{e}\frac{dE_{Fi}}{dx} \qquad (4.37b)$$

If E_{Fi} is a linear function of distance, as shown in Figure 4.12, then the induced electric field is a constant.

Assuming Boltzmann's approximation and complete ionization are valid, we have

$$n_0 = n_i \exp\left(\frac{E_F - E_{Fi}}{kT}\right) = N_d \qquad (4.38)$$

Equation (4.38) shows that if the doping concentration N_d is a function of distance in the semiconductor, then $E_F - E_{Fi}$ will also be a function of distance. Thus the energy band diagram shown in Figure 4.12 represents a nonuniformly doped semiconductor.

From Equation (4.38), we obtain

$$E_F - E_{Fi} = kT \ln\left(\frac{N_d}{n_i}\right) \qquad (4.39)$$

For the case shown in Figure 4.12, we can write

$$E_F - E_{Fi} = Cx \qquad (4.40)$$

where C is a constant. Combining Equations (4.39) and (4.40), we find

$$N_d = N_d(x) = n_i \exp\left(\frac{Cx}{kT}\right) \tag{4.41}$$

An exponential function of doping versus distance produces an energy-band diagram as shown in Figure 4.12 in which $(E_F - E_{Fi})$ is a linear function of distance.

Combining Equations (4.37b) and (4.39), we can also find the induced electric field to be given by

$$\mathcal{E}_x = +\frac{1}{e}\frac{dE_{Fi}}{dx} = -\left(\frac{kT}{e}\right)\frac{1}{N_d(x)}\frac{dN_d(x)}{dx} \tag{4.42}$$

Using Equations (4.42) and (4.41), we can show that an exponential doping profile induces a constant electric field. This same result was demonstrated in Equation (4.37b).

Since we have an electric field, there will be a potential difference through the semiconductor due to the nonuniform doping.

EXAMPLE 4.6

OBJECTIVE

Determine the induced electric field in a semiconductor in thermal equilibrium given a linear variation in doping concentration.

Assume that the donor concentration in an n-type semiconductor at $T = 300$ K is given by

$$N_d(x) = 10^{16} - 10^{19}x \quad (\text{cm}^{-3})$$

where x is given in cm and ranges between $0 \leq x \leq 1\ \mu$m.

■ Solution

Taking the derivative of the donor concentration, we have

$$\frac{dN_d(x)}{dx} = -10^{19} \quad (\text{cm}^{-4})$$

The induced electric field is given by Equation (4.42), so we have

$$\mathcal{E} = -\left(\frac{kT}{e}\right)\left[\frac{1}{N_d(x)}\right]\frac{dN_d(x)}{dx} = \frac{-(0.0259)(-10^{19})}{(10^{16} - 10^{19}x)}$$

At $x = 0$, for example, we find

$$\mathcal{E} = 25.9 \text{V/cm}$$

■ Comment

We can recall from our previous discussion of drift current that fairly small electric fields can produce significant drift current densities, so that an induced electric field from nonuniform doping can significantly influence semiconductor device characteristics.

Exercise Problem

EX4.6 Assume that the donor impurity concentration in a semiconductor is given by

$$N_d(x) = 10^{15} \exp\left(\frac{-x}{L_n}\right)$$

for $x \geq 0$ and where $L_n = 10^{-4}$ cm. Determine the electric field induced in the material due to this impurity concentration. (Ans. $\mathcal{E} = 259$ V/cm.)

4.3.2 The Einstein Relation

If we consider the nonuniformly doped semiconductor represented by the energy-band diagram shown in Figure 4.12 and assume there are no electrical connections so that the semiconductor is in thermal equilibrium, then the individual electron and hole currents must be zero. We can write

$$J_n = 0 = en\mu_n\mathcal{E}_x + eD_n \frac{dn}{dx} \qquad (4.43)$$

If we assume quasi-neutrality so that $n \approx N_d(x)$, then we can rewrite Equation (4.43) as

$$J_n = 0 = e\mu_n N_d(x)\mathcal{E}_x + eD_n \frac{dN_d(x)}{dx} \qquad (4.44)$$

Substituting the expression for the electric field from Equation (4.42) into Equation (4.44), we obtain

$$0 = -e\mu_n N_d(x)\left(\frac{kT}{e}\right)\frac{1}{N_d(x)}\frac{dN_d(x)}{dx} + eD_n \frac{dN_d(x)}{dx} \qquad (4.45)$$

Equation (4.45) is valid for the condition

$$\frac{D_n}{\mu_n} = \frac{kT}{e} \qquad (4.46a)$$

The hole current must also be zero in the semiconductor. From this condition, we can show that

$$\frac{D_p}{\mu_p} = \frac{kT}{e} \qquad (4.46b)$$

Combining Equations (4.46a) and (4.46b) gives

$$\boxed{\frac{D_n}{\mu_n} = \frac{D_p}{\mu_p} = \frac{kT}{e}} \qquad (4.47)$$

The diffusion coefficient and mobility are not independent parameters. This relation between the mobility and diffusion coefficient, given by Equation (4.47), is known as **Einstein relation**   the *Einstein relation*.

Table 4.2 | Typical mobility and diffusion coefficient values at $T = 300$ K ($\mu = $ cm^2/V-s and $D = $ cm^2/s)

	μ_n	D_n	μ_p	D_p
Silicon	1350	35	480	12.4
Gallium arsenide	8500	220	400	10.4
Germanium	3900	101	1900	49.2

EXAMPLE 4.7

OBJECTIVE

Determine the diffusion coefficient given the carrier mobility.

Assume that the mobility of a particular carrier is $\mu = 1200$ cm^2/V-s at $T = 300$ K.

■ Solution

Using the Einstein relation, we have that

$$D = \left(\frac{kT}{e} \right) \mu = (0.0259)(1200) = 31.1 \, \text{cm}^2/\text{s}$$

■ Comment

Although this example is simple and straightforward, it is important to keep in mind the relative orders of magnitude of the mobility and diffusion coefficient. The diffusion coefficient is approximately 40 times smaller in magnitude than the mobility at room temperature.

Exercise Problem

EX4.7   The diffusion coefficient of a particular semiconductor is $D = 210$ cm^2/s. Determine the carrier mobility at $T = 300$ K. (Ans. $\mu = 8108$ cm^2/V-s)

Table 4.2 shows the diffusion coefficient values at $T = 300$ K corresponding to the mobilities listed in Table 4.1 for silicon, gallium arsenide, and germanium.

The relation between the mobility and diffusion coefficient given by Equation (4.47) contains temperature. It is important to keep in mind that the major temperature effects are a result of lattice scattering and ionized impurity scattering processes, as discussed in Section 4.1.2. As the mobilities are strong functions of temperature because of the scattering processes, the diffusion coefficients are also strong functions of temperature. The specific temperature dependence given in Equation (4.47) is a small fraction of the real temperature characteristic.

4.4 | CARRIER GENERATION AND RECOMBINATION

Objective: Describe the generation and recombination processes of excess carriers in a semiconductor.

In this section, we discuss carrier generation and recombination, which can be defined as follows:

Generation—the process whereby electrons and holes (carriers) are created.

Carrier generation

**Carrier
recombination**

Recombination—the process whereby electrons and holes (carriers) are annihilated.

Any deviation from thermal equilibrium will tend to change the electron and hole concentrations in a semiconductor. A sudden increase in temperature, for example, will increase the rate at which electrons and holes are thermally generated so that their concentrations will change with time until new equilibrium values are reached. An external excitation, such as light (a flux of photons), can also generate electrons and holes, creating a nonequilibrium condition. To understand the generation and recombination processes, we will first consider direct band-to-band generation and recombination, and then, later, the effect of allowed electronic energy states within the bandgap, referred to as traps or recombination centers.

4.4.1 The Semiconductor in Equilibrium

We have determined the thermal-equilibrium concentration of electrons and holes in the conduction and valence bands, respectively. In thermal equilibrium, these concentrations are independent of time. However, electrons are continually being thermally excited from the valence band into the conduction band by the random nature of the thermal process. At the same time, electrons moving randomly through the crystal in the conduction band may come in close proximity to holes and "fall" into the empty states in the valence band. This recombination process annihilates both the electron and hole. Since the net carrier concentrations are independent of time in thermal equilibrium, the rate at which electrons and holes are generated and the rate at which they recombine must be equal. The generation and recombination processes are schematically shown in Figure 4.13.

**Thermal generation
rate**

Let G_{n0} and G_{p0} be the thermal-generation rates of electrons and holes, respectively, given in units of #/cm³-s. For the direct band-to-band generation, the electrons and holes are created in pairs, so we must have that

$$G_{n0} = G_{p0} \tag{4.48}$$

**Thermal
recombination rate**

Let R_{n0} and R_{p0} be the recombination rates of electrons and holes, respectively, for a semiconductor in thermal equilibrium, again given in units of #/cm³-s. In direct band-to-band recombination, electrons and holes recombine in pairs, so that

$$R_{n0} = R_{p0} \tag{4.49}$$

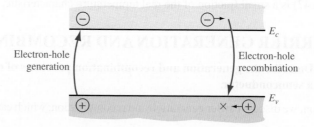

Figure 4.13 | Electron–hole generation and recombination.

In thermal equilibrium, the concentrations of electrons and holes are independent of time; therefore, the generation and recombination rates are equal, so we have

$$G_{n0} = G_{p0} = R_{n0} = R_{p0} \qquad (4.50)$$

4.4.2 Excess Carrier Generation and Recombination

Additional notation is introduced in this section. Table 4.3 lists some of the more pertinent symbols used throughout the section.

Electrons in the valence band may be excited into the conduction band when, for example, high-energy photons are incident on a semiconductor. When this happens, not only is an electron created in the conduction band, but a hole is created in the valence band; thus an electron–hole pair is generated. The additional electrons and holes created are called *excess electrons* and *excess holes.*

The excess electrons and holes are generated by an external force at a particular rate. Let g_n' be the generation rate of excess electrons and g_p' be that of excess holes. These generation rates also have units of #/cm^3-s. For the direct band-to-band generation, the excess electrons and holes are also created in pairs, so we must have

Excess carrier generation rate

$$g_n' = g_p' \qquad (4.51)$$

When excess electrons and holes are created, the concentration of electrons in the conduction band and of holes in the valence band increase above their thermal-equilibrium value. We can write

$$n = n_0 + \delta n \qquad (4.52a)$$

and

Excess electrons and holes

$$p = p_0 + \delta p \qquad (4.52b)$$

where n_0 and p_0 are the thermal-equilibrium concentrations, and δn and δp are the excess electron and hole concentrations, respectively. Figure 4.14 shows the excess electron–hole generation process and the resulting carrier concentrations. The external force has perturbed the equilibrium condition so that the semiconductor is no longer in thermal equilibrium. We can note from Equations (4.52a) and (4.52b) that, in a nonequilibrium condition, $np \neq n_0 p_0 = n_i^2$.

Table 4.3 | Relevant notation used in Section 4.4

Symbol	Definition
n_0, p_0	Thermal-equilibrium electron and hole concentrations (independent of time and also usually position).
n, p	Total electron and hole concentrations (may be functions of time and/or position).
$\delta n = n - n_0$ $\delta p = p - p_0$	Excess electron and hole concentrations (may be functions of time and/or position).
g_n', g_p'	Excess electron and hole generation rates.
R_n', R_p'	Excess electron and hole recombination rates.
τ_{n0}, τ_{p0}	Excess minority-carrier electron and hole lifetimes.

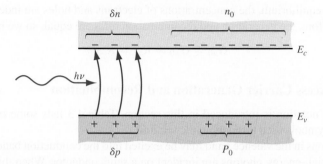

Figure 4.14 | Creation of excess electron and hole densities by photons.

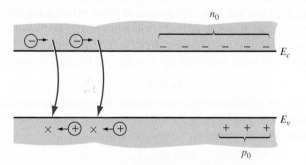

Figure 4.15 | Recombination of excess carriers reestablishing thermal equilibrium.

A steady-state generation of excess electrons and holes will not cause a continual buildup of the carrier concentrations. As in the case of thermal equilibrium, an electron in the conduction band may "fall down" into the valence band, leading to the process of excess electron–hole recombination. Figure 4.15 shows this process. The recombination rate for excess electrons is denoted by R_n' and for excess holes by R_p'. Both parameters have units of #/cm³-s. The excess electrons and holes recombine in pairs, so the recombination rates must be equal. We can then write

$$R_n' = R_p' \tag{4.53}$$

In the direct band-to-band recombination that we are considering, the recombination occurs spontaneously; thus, the probability of an electron and hole recombining is constant with time. The rate at which electrons recombine must be proportional to the electron concentration and must also be proportional to the hole concentration. If there are no electrons or holes, there can be no recombination.

The net rate of change in the electron concentration can be written as

$$\frac{dn(t)}{dt} = \alpha_r \left[n_i^2 - n(t)p(t) \right] \tag{4.54}$$

where

$$n(t) = n_0 + \delta n(t) \tag{4.55a}$$

and

$$p(t) = p_0 + \delta p(t) \tag{4.55b}$$

The first term, $\alpha_r n_i^2$, in Equation (4.54) is the thermal-equilibrium generation rate. Since excess electrons and holes are created and recombine in pairs, we have that $\delta n(t) = \delta p(t)$. (Excess electron and hole concentrations are equal so we can simply use the phrase excess carriers to mean either.) The thermal-equilibrium parameters, n_0 and p_0, being independent of time, Equation (4.54) becomes

$$\frac{d(\delta n(t))}{dt} = \alpha_r \left[n_i^2 - (n_0 + \delta n(t))(p_0 + \delta p(t)) \right]$$
$$= -\alpha_r \delta n(t)[(n_0 + p_0) + \delta n(t)] \tag{4.56}$$

Equation (4.56) can easily be solved if we impose the condition of *low-level injection*. Low-level injection puts limits on the magnitude of the excess carrier concentration compared with the thermal-equilibrium carrier concentrations. In an extrinsic n-type material, we generally have $n_0 \gg p_0$ and, in an extrinsic p-type material, we generally have $p_0 \gg n_0$. Low-level injection means that the excess carrier concentration is much less than the thermal-equilibrium majority-carrier concentration. Conversely, high-level injection occurs when the excess carrier concentration becomes comparable to or greater than the thermal-equilibrium majority-carrier concentrations.

If we consider a p-type material ($p_0 \gg n_0$) under low-level injection ($\delta n(t) \ll p_0$), then Equation (4.56) becomes

$$\frac{d(\delta n(t))}{dt} = -\alpha_r p_0 \delta n(t) \tag{4.57}$$

The solution to the equation is an exponential decay from the initial excess concentration, or

$$\delta n(t) = \delta n(0) e^{-\alpha_r p_0 t} = \delta n(0) e^{-t/\tau_{n0}} \tag{4.58}$$

where $\tau_{n0} = (\alpha_r p_0)^{-1}$ and is a constant for the low-level injection. Equation (4.58) describes the decay of excess minority carrier electrons so that τ_{n0} is often referred to as the *excess minority-carrier lifetime*.[4]

The recombination rate—which is defined as a positive quantity—of excess minority-carrier electrons can be written, using Equation (4.57), as

Excess minority-carrier lifetime

$$R_n' = \frac{-d(\delta n(t))}{dt} = +\alpha_r p_0 \delta n(t) = \frac{\delta n(t)}{\tau_{n0}} \tag{4.59}$$

---

[4]In Section 4.1.2, we defined τ as a mean time between collisions. We define τ here as the mean time before a recombination event occurs. The two parameters are not related.

For the direct band-to-band recombination, the excess majority-carrier holes recombine at the same rate, so that for the p-type material

$$R'_n = R'_p = \frac{\delta n(t)}{\tau_{n0}} \qquad (4.60)$$

In the case of an n-type material ($n_0 \gg p_0$) under low-level injection ($\delta n(t) \ll n_0$), the decay of minority-carrier holes occurs with a time constant $\tau_{p0} = (\alpha_r n_0)^{-1}$, where τ_{p0} is also referred to as the excess minority-carrier lifetime. The recombination rate of the majority-carrier electrons will be the same as that of the minority-carrier holes, so we have

$$R'_n = R'_p = \frac{\delta n(t)}{\tau_{p0}} \qquad (4.61)$$

The generation rates of excess carriers are not functions of electron or hole concentrations. In general, the generation and recombination rates may be functions of the space coordinates and time. A more in-depth study of the behavior of excess carriers is given in Chapter 8 of this text.

4.4.3 Generation–Recombination Processes

There are several mechanisms by which carriers are generated and by which the carriers can recombine.

Band-to-Band Generation and Recombination We have implicitly assumed in the previous discussion that the generation and recombination mechanism was a direct band-to-band process. These processes were shown in Figures 4.14 and 4.15. For recombination, an electron and hole moving in the semiconductor lattice may wonder into the same spatial region where the electron can drop into the empty state (the hole). The electron and hole are then annihilated.

Recombination–generation centers

Recombination–Generation Centers Lattice defects or impurity atoms in a lattice disrupt the ideal single-crystal lattice structure and result in allowed electronic energy states within the bandgap. These allowed energy states occur near the midgap energy in many cases. These energy states may now serve as "stepping stones" in the recombination–generation processes.

Figure 4.16 shows the recombination process. We can visualize the electron wandering into the vicinity of the energy trap state and dropping into this state. A short time later, a hole may wander into this same region and "drop" into the state occupied by the electron. The electron and hole are then annihilated. The hole may "drop" into the electronic energy state first and then the electron may drop into the state and annihilate the hole. This is also shown in Figure 4.16. A third way of visualizing the process is also shown in the figure. An electron can drop into the allowed electronic

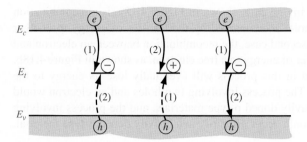

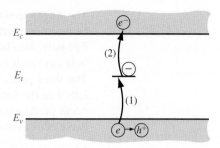

Figure 4.16 | Recombination via a trapping center: an electron is trapped and then a hole is trapped; or a hole is trapped and then an electron is trapped; or an electron is trapped and then the electron falls into an empty state (hole).

Figure 4.17 | Generation via a trapping center: an electron is elevated from the valence band into the trap creating a free hole and then the electron is elevated into the conduction band creating a free electron.

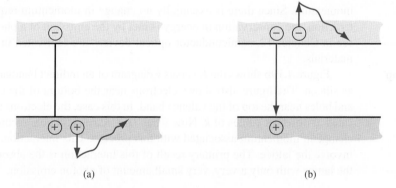

Figure 4.18 | (a) Auger recombination involving two holes and (b) Auger recombination involving two electrons.

energy state and then, when a hole wanders into the region, the electron may drop into the empty state (the hole). Again, the electron and hole are annihilated.

Figure 4.17 shows the generation process. An electron from the valence band can be elevated into the allowed electronic energy state due to, for example, thermal energy. A hole is created in the valence band. The electron in the allowed electronic energy state can then be elevated into the conduction band. Thus an electron–hole pair has been created.

Electron–hole pair generation and recombination via the energy traps within the bandgap is the predominate process in silicon. The statistics of the recombination–generation process with the trapping center is analyzed in detail in Chapter 8.

Auger Recombination   Figure 4.18 shows the Auger (oh-jay) process, which can become important in direct bandgap materials with high doping concentrations.

The Auger recombination, in one case, shown in Figure 4.18a, is a recombination between an electron and hole, accompanied by the transfer of energy to another free hole. Similarly, in the second case, the recombination between an electron and hole can result in the transfer of energy to a free electron, as shown in Figure 4.18b. The third particle involved in this process will eventually lose its energy to the lattice in the form of heat. The process involving two holes and an electron would occur predominantly in heavily doped p-type materials, and the process involving two electrons and a hole would occur primarily in a heavily doped n-type material.

Momentum Considerations   When electrons and holes recombine, energy is released. The form of the energy that is released depends on whether the semiconductor is a direct or indirect bandgap material. During any electron–hole interaction, both energy and momentum must be conserved.

Direct bandgap   Figure 4.19a shows the E versus k diagram of a direct bandgap material, such as GaAs. The figure shows electrons near the bottom of the conduction band and holes near the top of the valence band. All of the electrons and holes are located near $k = 0$, so that when an electron and hole recombine, there is very little change in momentum. Since there is essentially no change in momentum required in this interaction, the conservation in energy is met by the emission of a photon. As we will see in Chapter 12, semiconductor optical devices are fabricated in direct bandgap materials.

Indirect bandgap   Figure 4.19b shows the E versus k diagram of an indirect bandgap material, such as silicon. The figure also shows electrons near the bottom of the conduction band and holes near the top of the valence band. In this case, the electrons and holes are located at different values of k. Now when an electron and hole recombine, there is a change in momentum associated with this process. This interaction, therefore, must involve the lattice. The primary result of this interaction is the absorption of heat in the lattice with only a very, very small amount of photon emission.

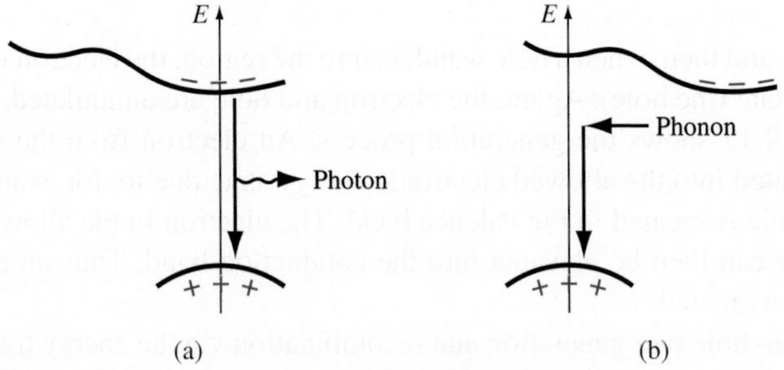

Figure 4.19 | (a) Recombination in a direct bandgap semiconductor (such as GaAs) with no change in momentum required. (b) Recombination in an indirect bandgap semiconductor (such as Si) with a change in momentum required.

TEST YOUR UNDERSTANDING

TYU4.7 Excess electrons have been generated in a semiconductor to a concentration of $\delta n(0) = 10^{15}$ cm^{-3}. The excess carrier lifetime is $\tau_{n0} = 10^{-6}$ s. The forcing function generating the excess carriers turns off at $t = 0$ so the semiconductor is allowed to return to an equilibrium condition for $t > 0$. Calculate the excess electron concentration for $(a)\ t = 0$, $(b)\ t = 1\ \mu$s, and $(c)\ t = 4\ \mu$s.

[Ans. $(a)\ 10^{15}$ cm^{-3}, $(b)\ 3.68 \times 10^{14}$ cm^{-3}, $(c)\ 1.83 \times 10^{13}$ cm^{-3}]

TYU4.8 Using the parameters given in TYU4.7, calculate the recombination rate of the excess electrons for $(a)\ t = 0$, $(b)\ t = 1\ \mu$s, and $(c)\ t = 4\ \mu$s.

[Ans. $(a)\ 10^{21}$ cm^{-3} s^{-1}, $(b)\ 3.68 \times 10^{20}$ cm^{-3} s^{-1}, $(c)\ 1.83 \times 10^{19}$ cm^{-3} s^{-1}]

Σ 4.5 | THE HALL EFFECT

Objective: Describe and analyze the Hall effect in a semiconductor material.

The Hall effect is a consequence of the forces that are exerted on moving charges by electric and magnetic fields. The Hall effect is used to distinguish whether a semiconductor is n type or p type[5] and to measure the majority-carrier concentration and majority-carrier mobility. The Hall effect device, as discussed in this section, is used to experimentally measure semiconductor parameters. However, it is also used extensively in engineering applications as a magnetic probe and in other circuit applications.

The force on a particle having a charge q and moving in a magnetic field is given by

$$F = qv \times B \tag{4.62}$$

where the cross product is taken between velocity and magnetic field so that the force vector is perpendicular to both the velocity and magnetic field.

Figure 4.20 illustrates the Hall effect. A semiconductor with a current I_x is placed in a magnetic field perpendicular to the current. In this case, the magnetic field is in the z direction. Electrons and holes flowing in the semiconductor will experience a force as indicated in the figure. The force on both electrons and holes is in the $(-y)$ direction. In a p-type semiconductor $(p_0 > n_0)$, there will be a buildup of positive charge on the $y = 0$ surface of the semiconductor and, in an n-type semiconductor $(n_0 > p_0)$, there will be a buildup of negative charge on the $y = 0$ surface. This net charge induces an electric field in the y direction as shown in the figure. In steady state, the magnetic field force will be exactly balanced by the induced electric field force. This balance can be written as

$$F = q[\mathcal{E} + v \times B] = 0 \tag{4.63a}$$

---

[5]We will assume an extrinsic semiconductor material in which the majority-carrier concentration is much larger than the minority-carrier concentration.

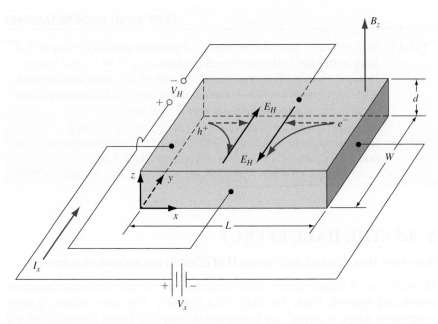

Figure 4.20 | Geometry for measuring the Hall effect.

which becomes

$$q\mathcal{E}_y = qv_x B_z \tag{4.63b}$$

Hall voltage

The induced electric field in the y direction is called the *Hall field*. The Hall field produces a voltage across the semiconductor, which is called the *Hall voltage*. We can write

$$V_H = +\mathcal{E}_H W \tag{4.64}$$

where $\mathcal{E}_H$ is assumed positive in the $+y$ direction and V_H is positive with the polarity shown.

In a p-type semiconductor, in which holes are the majority carrier, the Hall voltage will be positive as defined in Figure 4.20. In an n-type semiconductor, in which electrons are the majority carrier, the Hall voltage will have the opposite polarity. The polarity of the Hall voltage is used to determine whether an extrinsic semiconductor is n type or p type.

Substituting Equation (4.64) into Equation (4.63) gives

$$V_H = v_x W B_z \tag{4.65}$$

For a p-type semiconductor, the drift velocity of holes can be written as

$$v_{dx} = \frac{J_x}{ep} = \frac{I_x}{(ep)(Wd)} \tag{4.66}$$

where e is the magnitude of the electronic charge. Combining Equations (4.66) and (4.65), we have

$$V_H = \frac{I_x B_z}{epd} \tag{4.67}$$

or, solving for the hole concentration, we obtain

$$p = \frac{I_x B_z}{ed V_H} \tag{4.68}$$

The majority-carrier hole concentration is determined from the current, magnetic field, and Hall voltage.

For an n-type semiconductor, the Hall voltage is given by

$$V_H = -\frac{I_x B_z}{ned} \tag{4.69}$$

so that the electron concentration is

$$n = -\frac{I_x B_z}{ed V_H} \tag{4.70}$$

Note that the Hall voltage is negative for the n-type semiconductor; therefore, the electron concentration determined from Equation (4.70) is actually a positive quantity.

Once the majority-carrier concentration has been determined, we can calculate the low-field majority-carrier mobility. For a p-type semiconductor, we can write

$$J_x = ep\mu_p \mathcal{E}_x \tag{4.71}$$

The current density and electric field can be converted to current and voltage so that Equation (4.71) becomes

$$\frac{I_x}{Wd} = \frac{ep\mu_p V_x}{L} \tag{4.72}$$

The hole mobility is then given by

$$\mu_p = \frac{I_x L}{ep V_x Wd} \tag{4.73}$$

Similarly for an n-type semiconductor, the low-field electron mobility is determined from

$$\mu_n = \frac{I_x L}{en V_x Wd} \tag{4.74}$$

EXAMPLE 4.8

OBJECTIVE

Determine the majority-carrier concentration and mobility, given Hall effect parameters.

Consider the geometry shown in Figure 4.20. Let $L = 10^{-1}$ cm, $W = 10^{-2}$ cm, and $d = 10^{-3}$ cm. Also assume that $I_x = 1.0$ mA, $V_x = 12.5$ V, $B = 500$ gauss $= 5 \times 10^{-2}$ tesla, and $V_H = -6.25$ mV.

■ **Solution**

A negative Hall voltage for this geometry implies that we have an n-type semiconductor. Using Equation (4.70), we can calculate the electron concentration as

$$n = \frac{-(10^{-3})(5 \times 10^{-2})}{(1.6 \times 10^{-19})(10^{-5})(-6.25 \times 10^{-3})} = 5 \times 10^{21} \text{ m}^{-3}$$

or

$$n = 5 \times 10^{15} \text{ cm}^{-3}$$

The electron mobility is then determined from Equation (4.74) as

$$\mu_n = \frac{(10^{-3})(10^{-3})}{(1.6 \times 10^{-19})(5 \times 10^{21})(12.5)(10^{-4})(10^{-5})} = 0.10 \text{ m}^2/\text{V-s}$$

or

$$\mu_n = 1000 \text{ cm}^2/\text{V-s}$$

■ **Comment**

It is important to note that the MKS units must be used consistently in the Hall effect equations to yield correct results.

Exercise Problem

EX4.8 Consider an n-type GaAs Hall effect device with the geometry shown in Figure 4.20. Let $L = 10^{-2}$ cm, $W = 10^{-3}$ cm, and $d = 10^{-4}$ cm. Also assume $I_x = 2$ mA, $V_x = 4.9$ V, $B = 500$ gauss $= 5 \times 10^{-2}$ tesla, and $V_H = -10$ mV. Find the majority-carrier concentration and the carrier mobility.
(Ans. $n = 6.25 \times 10^{16}$ cm^{-3}, $\mu_n = 4082$ cm^2/V-s)

4.6 | SUMMARY

1. A. One charge transport mechanism in a semiconductor is carrier drift, which is the flow of carriers due to an applied electric field.
   B. Carriers reach an average drift velocity due to scattering events in a semiconductor with an applied electric field. Two scattering events within a semiconductor are lattice scattering and ionized impurity scattering.
   C. The average drift velocity is a linear function of the applied electric field for small values of electric field, but the drift velocity reaches a saturation limit that is on the order of 10^7 cm/s for electric fields on the order of 10^4 V/cm.
   D. Carrier mobility is the ratio of the average drift velocity to the applied electric field. The electron and hole mobilities are functions of temperature and of the ionized impurity concentration.
   E. The drift current density is the product of conductivity and electric field (a form of Ohm's law). Conductivity is a function of the carrier concentrations and mobilities. Resistivity is the inverse of conductivity.

2. A. The second charge transport mechanism in a semiconductor is carrier diffusion, which is the flow of charge due to a gradient in carrier concentration.

B. The diffusion current density is proportional to the diffusion coefficient and the gradient in carrier concentration.

3. A. An electric field is induced in a semiconductor in thermal equilibrium that has a nonuniform impurity doping concentration.
    B. The diffusion coefficient and mobility are related through the Einstein relation.

4. A. Generation is the process whereby electrons and holes are created; recombination is the process whereby electrons and holes are annihilated.
    B. Generation and recombination rates were defined for thermal equilibrium and for nonequilibrium excess carriers.
    C. Excess minority-carrier lifetimes were discussed and defined.

5. The Hall effect is a consequence of a charged carrier moving in the presence of perpendicular electric and magnetic fields. The charged carrier is deflected, inducing a Hall voltage. The polarity of the Hall voltage is a function of the semiconductor conductivity type. The majority-carrier concentration and mobility can be determined from the Hall voltage.

CHECKPOINT

After studying this chapter, the reader should have the ability to

1. A. Describe the mechanism of carrier drift.
    B. Explain why carriers reach an average drift velocity in the presence of an applied electric field.
    C. Discuss the mechanisms of lattice scattering and ionized impurity scattering.
    D. Define mobility and discuss the temperature and ionized impurity concentration dependence on mobility.
    E. Define conductivity and resistivity.
    F. Write the drift current density equation.

2. A. Describe the mechanism of carrier diffusion.
    B. Determine the direction of carrier diffusion and diffusion current given a specified carrier gradient.
    C. Write the diffusion current density equation.

3. A. Explain why an electric field is induced in a semiconductor with a nonuniform doping concentration.
    B. Explain the Einstein relation.

4. A. Discuss the difference between the thermal-equilibrium and nonequilibrium excess carrier generation rates.
    B. Explain the difference between direct band-to-band recombination and recombination with a midgap recombination center.

5. Describe the Hall effect.

REVIEW QUESTION

1. A. What is the direction of flow of electrons and holes for an applied electric field in the $+x$ direction?
    B. What is the direction of current due to the flow of electrons for an applied electric field in the $+x$ direction? Repeat for holes.

      C. Define carrier mobility. What is the unit of mobility?

      D. Explain the temperature dependence of mobility. Why is the carrier mobility a function of ionized impurity concentration?

      E. Define the conductivity and resistivity of a semiconductor material. What are the units of conductivity and resistivity?

      F. Sketch the drift velocity of electrons in silicon and GaAs versus electric field.

2. A. What is the direction of flow of electrons and holes for a positive gradient in the carrier concentration?

      B. What is the direction of current due to the flow of electrons for a positive gradient in the electron concentration? Repeat for holes.

      C. What is the unit of the diffusion coefficient?

3. A. The donor impurity concentration in a semiconductor increases in the $+x$ direction. What is the direction of the induced electric field?

      B. Write the equation for the Einstein relation.

4. A. Why must the thermal equilibrium generation and recombination rates for electrons and holes all be equal?

      B. If excess carriers in a semiconductor are being generated, why doesn't the total electron and hole concentrations approach infinity?

5. A. Describe the Hall effect in a semiconductor. What is the Hall voltage?

      B. Explain why the polarity of the Hall voltage changes depending on the conductivity type (n type or p type) of the semiconductor.

PROBLEMS

(*Note:* Use the semiconductor parameters given in Appendix B if the parameters are not specifically given in a problem.)

Section 4.1 Carrier Drift

4.1 A silicon semiconductor at $T = 300$ K is homogeneously doped with $N_d = 5 \times 10^{15}$ cm^{-3} and $N_a = 0$. (*a*) Determine the thermal equilibrium concentrations of free electrons and free holes. (*b*) Calculate the drift current density for an applied $\mathcal{E}$-field of 30 V/cm. (*c*) Repeat parts (*a*) and (*b*) for $N_d = 0$ and $N_a = 5 \times 10^{16}$ cm^{-3}.

4.2 A silicon crystal having a cross-sectional area of 0.001 cm^2 and a length of 10^{-3} cm is connected at its ends to a 10-V battery. At $T = 300$ K, we want a current of 100 mA in the silicon. Calculate: (*a*) the required resistance R, (*b*) the required conductivity, (*c*) the density of donor atoms to be added to achieve this conductivity, and (*d*) the concentration of acceptor atoms to be added to form a compensated p-type material with the conductivity given from part (*b*) if the initial concentration of donor atoms is $N_d = 10^{15}$ cm^{-3}.

4.3 (*a*) A silicon semiconductor is in the shape of a rectangular bar with a cross-sectional area of 10 μm $\times 10\,\mu$m, a length of 0.1 cm, and is doped with 5×10^{16} cm^{-3} arsenic atoms. The temperature is $T = 300$ K. Determine the current if 5 V is applied across the length. (*b*) Repeat part (*a*) if the length is reduced to 0.01 cm. (*c*) Calculate the average drift velocity of electrons in parts (*a*) and (*b*).

4.4 (*a*) A GaAs semiconductor resistor is doped with donor impurities at a concentration of $N_d = 10^{15}$ cm^{-3}. The cross-sectional area is 50×10^{-6} cm^2. The current in the resistor is to be $I = 10$ mA with 5 V applied. Determine the required length of the device. (*b*) Repeat part (*a*) for silicon.

4.5   (*a*) Two volts are applied across a 0.75-cm-long n-type semiconductor. The average electron drift velocity is 7×10^3 cm/s. Determine the electron mobility. (*b*) If the electron mobility in part (*a*) were 950 cm²/V-s, what is the average electron drift velocity?

4.6   Use the velocity–field relations for silicon and gallium arsenide shown in Figure 4.7 to determine the transit time of electrons through a 1-μm distance in these materials for an electric field of (*a*) 1 kV/cm and (*b*) 50 kV/cm.

4.7   A perfectly compensated semiconductor is one in which the donor and acceptor impurity concentrations are exactly equal. Assuming complete ionization, determine the conductivity of silicon at $T = 300$ K in which the impurity concentrations are (*a*) $N_a = N_d = 10^{14}$ cm^{-3} and (*b*) $N_a = N_d = 10^{18}$ cm^{-3}.

4.8   (*a*) The conductivity in a p-type silicon semiconductor at $T = 300$ K is $\sigma = 0.25$ (Ω-cm)$^{-1}$. Determine the thermal-equilibrium values of electron and hole concentrations. (*b*) Repeat part (*a*) for an n-type GaAs semiconductor if the resistivity is $\rho = 2$ Ω-cm.

4.9   In a particular semiconductor material, $\mu_n = 1000$ cm²/V-s, $\mu_p = 600$ cm²/V-s, and $N_c = N_v = 10^{19}$ cm^{-3}. These parameters are independent of temperature. The measured conductivity of the intrinsic material is $\sigma = 10^{-6}$ (Ω-cm)$^{-1}$ at $T = 300$ K. Find the conductivity at $T = 500$ K.

4.10   (*a*) Calculate the resistivity at $T = 300$ K of intrinsic (*i*) silicon, (*ii*) germanium, and (*iii*) gallium arsenide. (*b*) If rectangular semiconductor bars are fabricated using the materials in part (*a*), determine the resistance of each bar if its cross-sectional area is 85 μm² and length is 200 μm.

4.11   An n-type silicon sample has a resistivity of 5 Ω-cm at $T = 300$ K. (*a*) What is the donor impurity concentration? (*b*) What is the expected resistivity at (*i*) $T = 200$ K and (*ii*) $T = 400$ K.

4.12   Consider silicon doped at impurity concentrations of $N_d = 2 \times 10^{16}$ cm^{-3} and $N_a = 0$. An empirical expression relating electron drift velocity to electric field is given by

$$v_d = \frac{\mu_{n0}\mathcal{E}}{\sqrt{1 + \left(\dfrac{\mu_{n0}\mathcal{E}}{v_{\text{sat}}}\right)^2}}$$

where $\mu_{n0} = 1350$ cm²/V-s, $v_{\text{sat}} = 1.8 \times 10^7$ cm/s, and $\mathcal{E}$ is given in V/cm. Plot electron drift current density (magnitude) versus electric field (log–log scale) over the range $0 \le \mathcal{E} \le 10^6$ V/cm.

4.13   Consider silicon at $T = 300$ K. Assume the electron mobility is $\mu_n = 1200$ cm²/V-s. The kinetic energy component due to the drift velocity of an electron in the conduction band is given by $\frac{1}{2}m_n^* v_d^2$, where m_n^* is the effective mass and v_d is the drift velocity. Determine the kinetic energy of an electron in the conduction band if the applied electric field is (*a*) 20 V/cm and (*b*) 2 kV/cm.

4.14   Consider a semiconductor that is uniformly doped with $N_d = 10^{14}$ cm^{-3} and $N_a = 0$, with an applied electric field of $\mathcal{E} = 100$ V/cm. Assume that $\mu_n = 1000$ cm²/V-s and $\mu_p = 0$. Also assume the following parameters:

$$N_c = 2 \times 10^{19}(T/300)^{3/2} \text{ cm}^{-3}$$
$$N_v = 1 \times 10^{19}(T/300)^{3/2} \text{ cm}^{-3}$$
$$E_g = 1.10 \text{ eV}$$

(a) Calculate the electric-current density at $T = 300$ K. (b) At what temperature will this current density increase by 5 percent? (Assume the mobilities are independent of temperature.)

4.15 A semiconductor material has electron and hole mobilities μ_n and μ_p, respectively. When the conductivity is considered as a function of the hole concentration p_0, (a) show that the minimum value of conductivity, $\sigma_{\min}$, can be written as

$$\sigma_{\min} = \frac{2\sigma_i (\mu_n \mu_p)^{1/2}}{(\mu_n + \mu_p)}$$

where σ_i is the intrinsic conductivity, and (b) show that the corresponding hole concentration is $p_0 = n_i (\mu_n/\mu_p)^{1/2}$.

4.16 A particular intrinsic semiconductor has a resistivity of 50 Ω-cm at $T = 300$ K and 5 Ω-cm at $T = 330$ K. Neglecting the change in mobility with temperature, determine the bandgap energy of the semiconductor.

4.17 Three scattering mechanisms are present in a particular semiconductor material. If only the first scattering mechanism were present, the mobility would be $\mu_1 = 2000$ cm^2/V-s, if only the second mechanism were present, the mobility would be $\mu_2 = 1500$ cm^2/V-s, and if only the third mechanism were present, the mobility would be $\mu_3 = 500$ cm^2/V-s. What is the net mobility?

4.18 Assume that the mobility of electrons in silicon at $T = 300$ K is $\mu_n = 1300$ cm^2/V-s. Also assume that the mobility is limited by lattice scattering and varies as $T^{-3/2}$. Determine the electron mobility at (a) $T = 200$ K and (b) $T = 400$ K.

4.19 Two scattering mechanisms exist in a semiconductor. If only the first mechanism were present, the mobility would be 250 cm^2/V-s. If only the second mechanism were present, the mobility would be 500 cm^2/V-s. Determine the mobility when both scattering mechanisms exist at the same time.

4.20 The effective density of states functions in silicon can be written in the form

$$N_c = 2.8 \times 10^{19} \left(\frac{T}{300} \right)^{3/2} \qquad N_v = 1.04 \times 10^{19} \left(\frac{T}{300} \right)^{3/2}$$

Assume the mobilities are given by

$$\mu_n = 1350 \left(\frac{T}{300} \right)^{-3/2} \qquad \mu_p = 480 \left(\frac{T}{300} \right)^{-3/2}$$

Assume the bandgap energy is $E_g = 1.12$ eV and independent of temperature. Plot the intrinsic conductivity as a function of T over the range $200 \leq T \leq 500$ K.

4.21 (a) Assume that the electron mobility in an n-type semiconductor is given by

$$\mu_n = \frac{1350}{\left(1 + \dfrac{N_d}{5 \times 10^{16}} \right)^{1/2}} \text{ cm}^2/\text{V-s}$$

where 1350 is the value for a low-doped material and where N_d is the donor concentration in cm^{-3}. Assuming complete ionization, plot the conductivity as a function of N_d over the range $10^{15} \leq N_d \leq 10^{18}$ cm^{-3}. (b) Compare the results of part (a) to that if the mobility were assumed to be a constant equal to 1350 cm^2/V-s. (c) If an electric field of $\mathcal{E} = 10$ V/cm is applied to the semiconductor, plot the electron drift current density of parts (a) and (b).

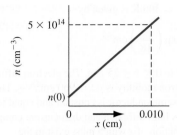

Figure P4.22 | Figure for Problem 4.22

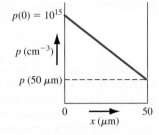

Figure P4.23 | Figure for Problem 4.23

Section 4.2   Carrier Diffusion

4.22   Consider a sample of silicon at $T = 300$ K. Assume that the electron concentration varies linearly with distance, as shown in Figure P4.22. The diffusion current density is found to be $J_n = 0.19$ A/cm^2. If the electron diffusion coefficient is $D_n = 25$ cm^2/s, determine the electron concentration at $x = 0$.

4.23   Consider a sample of p-type silicon at $T = 300$ K. Assume the hole concentration varies linearly with distance as shown in Figure P4.23. The diffusion current density is determined to be $J_p = 0.270$ A/cm^2. If the hole diffusion coefficient is $D_p = 12$ cm^2/s, find the hole concentration at $x = 50$ μm.

4.24   The electron concentration in silicon decreases linearly from 10^{16} cm^{-3} to 10^{15} cm^{-3} over a distance of 0.10 cm. The cross-sectional area of the sample is 0.05 cm^2. The electron diffusion coefficient is 25 cm^2/s. Calculate the electron diffusion current.

4.25   The hole concentration in silicon decreases linearly from 10^{15} cm^{-3} to 2×10^{14} cm^{-3} over a distance of 0.10 cm. The cross-sectional area is 0.075 cm^2. The hole diffusion coefficient is $D_p = 10$ cm^2/s. Determine the hole diffusion current.

4.26   The electron concentration in a sample of n-type silicon varies linearly from 10^{17} cm^{-3} at $x = 0$ to 6×10^{16} cm^{-3} at $x = 4$ μm. There is no applied electric field. The electron current density is experimentally measured to be -400 A/cm^2. What is the electron diffusion coefficient?

4.27   The hole concentration in p type GaAs is given by $p = 10^{16}(1 - x/L)$ cm^{-3} for $0 \leq x \leq L$, where $L = 10$ μm. The hole diffusion coefficient is 10 cm^2/s. Calculate the hole diffusion current density at (a) $x = 0$, (b) $x = 5$ μm, and (c) $x = 10$ μm.

4.28   The hole concentration is given by $p = 10^{15} \exp(-x/L_p)$ cm^{-3} for $x \geq 0$ and the electron concentration is given by $5 \times 10^{14} \exp(+x/L_n)$ cm^{-3} for $x \leq 0$. The values of L_p and L_n are 5×10^{-4} cm and 10^{-3} cm, respectively. The hole and electron diffusion coefficients are 10 cm^2/s and 25 cm^2/s, respectively. The total current density is defined as the sum of the hole diffusion current density at $x = 0$ and the electron diffusion current density at $x = 0$. Calculate the total current density.

4.29   The hole concentration in germanium at $T = 300$ K varies as

$$p(x) = 10^{15} \exp\left(\frac{-x}{22.5}\right) \text{cm}^{-3}$$

where x is measured in μm. If the hole diffusion coefficient is $D_p = 48$ cm^2/s, determine the hole diffusion current density as a function of x.

4.30   The electron concentration in silicon at $T = 300$ K is given by

$$n(x) = 10^{16} \exp\left(\frac{-x}{18}\right) cm^{-3}$$

where x is measured in μm and is limited to $0 \le x \le 25$ μm. The electron diffusion coefficient is $D_n = 25$ cm^2/s and the electron mobility is $\mu_n = 960$ cm^2/V-s. The total electron current density through the semiconductor is constant and equal to $J_n = -40$ A/cm^2. The electron current has both diffusion and drift current components. Determine the electric field as a function of x which must exist in the semiconductor.

4.31   The total current in a semiconductor is constant and is composed of electron drift current and hole diffusion current. The electron concentration is constant and is equal to 10^{16} cm^{-3}. The hole concentration is given by

$$p(x) = 10^{15} \exp\left(\frac{-x}{L}\right) cm^{-3} \qquad (x \ge 0)$$

where $L = 12$ μm. The hole diffusion coefficient is $D_p = 12$ cm^2/s and the electron mobility is $\mu_n = 1000$ cm^2/V-s. The total current density is $J = 4.8$ A/cm^2. Calculate (a) the hole diffusion current density versus x, (b) the electron current density versus x, and (c) the electric field versus x.

4.32   A constant electric field, $\mathcal{E} = 12$ V/cm, exists in the $+x$ direction of an n-type gallium arsenide semiconductor for $0 \le x \le 50$ μm. The total current density is a constant and is $J = 100$ A/cm^2. At $x = 0$, the drift and diffusion currents are equal. Let $T = 300$ K and $\mu_n = 8000$ cm^2/V-s. (a) Determine the expression for the electron concentration $n(x)$. (b) Calculate the electron concentration at $x = 0$ and at $x = 50$ μm. (c) Calculate the drift and diffusion current densities at $x = 50$ μm.

4.33   In n-type silicon, the Fermi energy level varies linearly with distance over a short range. At $x = 0$, $E_F - E_{Fi} = 0.4$ eV and, at $x = 10^{-3}$ cm, $E_F - E_{Fi} = 0.15$ eV. (a) Write the expression for the electron concentration over the distance. (b) If the electron diffusion coefficient is $D_n = 25$ cm^2/s, calculate the electron diffusion current density at (i) $x = 0$ and (ii) $x = 5 \times 10^{-4}$ cm.

4.34   (a) The electron concentration in a semiconductor is given by $n = 10^{16}(1 - x/L)$ cm^{-3} for $0 \le x \le L$, where $L = 10$ μm. The electron mobility and diffusion coefficient are $\mu_n = 1000$ cm^2/V-s and $D_n = 25.9$ cm^2/s. An electric field is applied such that the total electron current density is a constant over the given range of x and is $J_n = -80$ A/cm^2. Determine the required electric field versus distance function. (b) Repeat part (a) if $J_n = -20$ A/cm^2.

Section 4.3   Graded Impurity Distribution

4.35   Consider a semiconductor in thermal equilibrium (no current). Assume that the donor concentration varies exponentially as

$$N_d(x) = N_{d0} \exp(-ax)$$

over the range $0 \le x \le 1/\alpha$ where N_{d0} is a constant. (a) Calculate the electric field as a function of x for $0 \le x \le 1/\alpha$. (b) Calculate the potential difference between $x = 0$ and $x = 1/\alpha$.

4.36   Using the data in Example 4.5, calculate the potential difference between $x = 0$ and $x = 1$ μm.

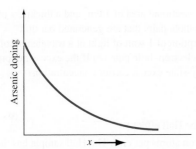
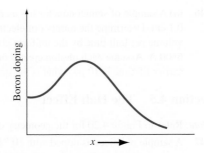

Figure P4.41 | Figure for Problem 4.41.   **Figure P4.42** | Figure for Problem 4.42.

4.37 Determine a doping profile in a semiconductor at $T = 300$ K that will induce an electric field of 1 kV/cm over a length of 0.2 μm.

4.38 In GaAs, the donor impurity concentration varies as $N_{d0} \exp(-x/L)$ for $0 \leq x \leq L$, where $L = 0.1$ μm and $N_{d0} = 5 \times 10^{16}$ cm^{-3}. Assume $\mu_n = 6000$ cm^2/V-s and $T = 300$ K. (*a*) Derive the expression for the electron diffusion current density versus distance over the given range of x. (*b*) Determine the induced electric field that generates a drift current density that compensates the diffusion current density.

4.39 (*a*) Consider the electron mobility in silicon for $N_d = 10^{17}$ cm^{-3} from Figure 4.2a. Calculate and plot the electron diffusion coefficient versus temperature over the range $-50 \leq T \leq 200°$C. (*b*) Repeat part (*a*) if the electron diffusion coefficient is given by $D_n = (0.0259)\mu_n$ for all temperatures. What conclusion can be made about the temperature dependence of the diffusion coefficient?

4.40 (*a*) Assume that the mobility of a carrier at $T = 300$ K is $\mu = 925$ cm^2/V-s. Calculate the carrier diffusion coefficient. (*b*) Assume that the diffusion coefficient of a carrier at $T = 300$ K is $D = 28.3$ cm^2/s. Calculate the carrier mobility.

4.41 Arsenic is diffused into an intrinsic silicon sample and has the general profile shown in Figure P4.41. Sketch the equilibrium energy-band diagram. Show the direction of the electric field.

4.42 Boron is ion implanted into an intrinsic silicon sample. The general boron profile is shown in Figure P4.42. Sketch the equilibrium energy-band diagram.

Section 4.4 Carrier Generation and Recombination

4.43 Consider a semiconductor in which $n_0 = 10^{15}$ cm^{-3} and $n_i = 10^{10}$ cm^{-3}. Assume that the excess carrier lifetime is 10^{-6} s. Determine the electron–hole recombination rate if the excess hole concentration is $\delta p = 5 \times 10^{13}$ cm^{-3}.

4.44 A semiconductor, in thermal equilibrium, has a hole concentration of $p_0 = 10^{16}$ cm^{-3} and an intrinsic concentration of $n_i = 10^{10}$ cm^{-3}. The minority-carrier lifetime is 2×10^{-7} s. (*a*) Determine the thermal-equilibrium recombination rate of electrons. (*b*) Determine the change in the recombination rate of electrons if an excess electron concentration of $\delta n = 10^{12}$ cm^{-3} exists.

4.45 An n-type silicon sample contains a donor concentration of $N_d = 10^{16}$ cm^{-3}. The minority carrier hole lifetime is found to be $\tau_{p0} = 20$ μs. (*a*) What is the lifetime of the majority carrier electrons? (*b*) Determine the thermal-equilibrium generation rate for electrons and holes in this material. (*c*) Determine the thermal-equilibrium recombination rate for electrons and holes in this material.

4.46 (*a*) A sample of semiconductor has a cross-sectional area of 1 cm^2 and a thickness of 0.1 cm. Determine the number of electron–hole pairs that are generated per unit volume per unit time by the uniform absorption of 1 watt of light at a wavelength of 6300 Å. Assume each photon creates one electron–hole pair. (*b*) If the excess minority carrier lifetime is 10 μs, what is the steady-state excess carrier concentration?

Section 4.5   The Hall Effect

(*Note:* Refer to Figure 4.20 for the geometry of the Hall effect.)

4.47 A sample of silicon is doped with 10^{16} boron atoms per cm^3. The Hall sample has the same geometrical dimensions given in Example 4.8. The current is $I_x = 1$ mA with $B_z = 350$ gauss $= 3.5 \times 10^{-2}$ tesla. Determine (*a*) the Hall voltage and (*b*) the Hall field.

4.48 Germanium is doped with 5×10^{15} donor atoms per cm^3 at $T = 300$ K. The dimensions of the Hall device are $d = 5 \times 10^{-3}$ cm, $W = 2 \times 10^{-2}$ cm, and $L = 10^{-1}$ cm. The current is $I_x = 250$ μA, the applied voltage is $V_x = 100$ mV, and the magnetic flux density is $B_z = 500$ gauss $= 5 \times 10^{-2}$ tesla. Calculate: (*a*) the Hall voltage, (*b*) the Hall field, and (*c*) the carrier mobility.

4.49 A silicon Hall device at $T = 300$ K has the following geometry: $d = 10^{-3}$ cm, $W = 10^{-2}$ cm, and $L = 10^{-1}$ cm. The following parameters are measured: $I_x = 0.75$ mA, $V_x = 15$ V, $V_H = +5.8$ mV, and $B_z = 1000$ gauss $= 10^{-1}$ tesla. Determine (*a*) the conductivity type, (*b*) the majority-carrier concentration, and (*c*) the majority-carrier mobility.

4.50 Consider silicon at $T = 300$ K. A Hall effect device is fabricated with the following geometry: $d = 5 \times 10^{-3}$ cm, $W = 5 \times 10^{-2}$ cm, and $L = 0.50$ cm. The electrical parameters measured are: $I_x = 0.50$ mA, $V_x = 1.25$ V, and $B_z = 650$ gauss $= 6.5 \times 10^{-2}$ tesla. The Hall field is $E_H = -16.5$ mV/cm. Determine (*a*) the Hall voltage, (*b*) the conductivity type, (*c*) the majority-carrier concentration, and (*d*) the majority-carrier mobility.

4.51 Consider a gallium arsenide sample at $T = 300$ K. A Hall effect device has been fabricated with the following geometry: $d = 0.01$ cm, $W = 0.05$ cm, and $L = 0.5$ cm. The electrical parameters are: $I_x = 2.5$ mA, $V_x = 2.2$ V, and $B_z = 2.5 \times 10^{-2}$ tesla. The Hall voltage is $V_H = -4.5$ mV. Find: (*a*) the conductivity type, (*b*) the majority-carrier concentration, (*c*) the mobility, and (*d*) the resistivity.

Summary and Review

4.52 An n-type silicon semiconductor resistor is to be designed so that it carries a current of 5 mA with an applied voltage of 5 V. (*a*) If $N_d = 3 \times 10^{14}$ cm^{-3} and $N_a = 0$, design a resistor to meet the required specifications. (*b*) If $N_d = 3 \times 10^{16}$ cm^{-3} and $N_a = 2.5 \times 10^{16}$ cm^{-3}, redesign the resistor. (*c*) Discuss the relative lengths of the two designs compared to the doping concentration. Is there a linear relationship?

4.53 In fabricating a Hall effect device, the two points at which the Hall voltage is measured may not be lined up exactly perpendicular to the current I_x (see Figure 4.20). Discuss the effect this misalignment will have on the Hall voltage. Show that a valid Hall voltage can be obtained from two measurements: first with the magnetic field in the $+z$ direction, and then in the $-z$ direction.

4.54 Another technique for determining the conductivity type of a semiconductor is called the hot probe method. It consists of two probes and an ammeter that indicates the direction of current. One probe is heated and the other is at room temperature. No voltage is applied, but a current will exist when the probes touch the semiconductor. Explain the operation of this hot probe technique and sketch a diagram indicating the direction of current for p- and n-type semiconductor samples.

READING LIST

1. Anderson, B. L., and R. L. Anderson. *Fundamentals of Semiconductor Devices.* New York: McGraw-Hill, 2005.

*2. Bube, R. H. *Electrons in Solids: An Introductory Survey.* 3rd ed. San Diego, CA: Academic Press, 1992.

3. Kano, K. *Semiconductor Devices.* Upper Saddle River, NJ: Prentice-Hall, 1998.

*4. Lundstrom, M. *Fundamentals of Carrier Transport.* Vol. X of *Modular Series on Solid State Devices.* Reading, MA: Addison-Wesley, 1990.

5. Muller, R. S., T. I. Kamins, and W. Chan. *Device Electronics for Integrated Circuits,* 3rd ed. New York: John Wiley and Sons, 2003.

6. Navon, D. H. *Semiconductor Microdevices and Materials.* New York: Holt, Rinehart & Winston, 1986.

7. Neamen, D. A. *Semiconductor Physics and Devices: Basic Principles,* 3rd ed. New York: McGraw-Hill, 2003.

8. Pierret, R. F. *Semiconductor Device Fundamentals.* Reading, MA: Addison-Wesley Publishing Co., 1996.

9. Shur, M. *Introduction to Electronic Devices.* New York: John Wiley and Sons, 1996.

*10. Shur, M. *Physics of Semiconductor Devices.* Englewood Cliffs, NJ: Prentice-Hall, 1990.

*11. Singh, J. *Semiconductor Devices: An Introduction.* New York: McGraw-Hill, 1994.

12. Singh, J. *Semiconductor Devices: Basic Principles.* New York: John Wiley and Sons, 2001.

13. Streetman, B. G., and S. Banerjee. *Solid State Electronic Devices,* 5th ed. Upper Saddle River, NJ: Prentice-Hall, 2000.

14. Sze, S. M. *Physics of Semiconductor Devices.* 2nd ed. New York: John Wiley and Sons, 1981.

15. Sze, S. M. *Semiconductor Devices: Physics and Technology,* 2nd ed. New York: John Wiley and Sons, 2002.

*16. van der Ziel, A. *Solid State Physical Electronics.* 2nd ed. Englewood Cliffs, NJ: Prentice-Hall, 1968.

*17. Wang, S. *Fundamentals of Semiconductor Theory and Device Physics.* Englewood Cliffs, NJ: Prentice-Hall, 1989.

18. Yang, E. S. *Microelectronic Devices.* New York: McGraw-Hill, 1988.

---

*Indicates references are at an advanced level compared to this text.

5

The pn Junction and Metal–Semiconductor Contact

U p to this point in the text, we have been considering the properties of the semi-conductor material. We calculated electron and hole concentrations in thermal equilibrium and determined the position of the Fermi level. We will now consider the situation in which one region of a semiconductor is doped p type and the region directly adjacent is doped n type to form a *pn junction*. Most semiconductor devices contain at least one pn junction.

The electrostatics of the pn junction is considered in this chapter. This material is necessary for the study of the metal–oxide semiconductor (MOS) transistor that is discussed in Chapters 6 and 7. The current-voltage characteristics of the pn junction diode are developed in Chapter 9.

We also introduce the metal–semiconductor contact, including both the ideal rectifying junction and ideal ohmic contact.

5.0 | PREVIEW

In this chapter, we will

1. Describe the physical structure and space charge region of the pn junction.
2. Determine characteristics of the zero-biased pn junction, such as built-in potential barrier, electric field, and space charge widths.
3. Determine the space charge widths, electric fields, and capacitances of a reverse-biased pn junction.
4. Analyze the metal–semiconductor rectifying junction.
5. Qualitatively describe the current–voltage characteristics of a forward-biased pn junction and Schottky barrier junction.

6. Describe the characteristics of a metal–semiconductor ohmic contact.
7. Describe the characteristics of nonuniformly doped pn junctions.
8. Describe the general fabrication techniques of a pn junction.

Historical Insight

Around 1874, it was observed that a rectifier could be fabricated by pressing a metal wire on the surface of a metal sulfide (e.g., pyrite). These rectifiers (cat's-whisker detectors) were used in the early days of radio. By 1935, selenium rectifiers and silicon point contact diodes were being used. However, these devices were unreliable. Work at Purdue University and Bell Labs produced germanium diodes that were used in radar systems during World War II. In 1949, W. Shockley published his paper describing the characteristics of the pn junction.

Present-Day Insight

The pn junction continues to be a basic building block in semiconductor devices, and the theory of the pn junction is still fundamental in the physics of semiconductor devices. The pn junction by itself performs nonlinear rectification. Other semiconductor devices are formed by combining two or more pn junctions in various configurations.

5.1 | BASIC STRUCTURE OF THE pn JUNCTION

Objective: Describe the physical structure and the space charge region of the pn junction.

Figure 5.1a schematically shows the pn junction. It is important to realize that the entire semiconductor is a single-crystal material in which one region is doped with acceptor impurity atoms to form the p region and the adjacent region is doped with donor atoms to form the n region. The interface separating the n and p regions is referred to as the *metallurgical junction*.

The impurity doping concentrations in the p and n regions are shown in Figure 5.1b. For simplicity, we will consider a *step junction* in which the doping concentration is uniform in each region and there is an abrupt change in doping at the metallurgical junction. Initially, at the metallurgical junction, there is a very large density gradient in both the electron and hole concentrations. Majority-carrier electrons in the n region will begin diffusing into the p region and majority-carrier holes in the p region will begin diffusing into the n region. If we assume there are no external connections to the semiconductor, then this diffusion process cannot continue indefinitely. As electrons diffuse from the n region, positively charged donor atoms are left behind. Similarly, as holes diffuse from the p region, they uncover negatively charged acceptor atoms. The net positive and negative charges in the n and p regions induce an electric field in the region near the metallurgical junction, in the direction from the positive to the negative charge, or from the n to the p region.

Metallurgical junction
Step junction

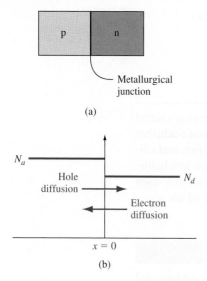

Metallurgical junction

(a)

N_a

Hole diffusion →

← Electron diffusion

N_d

$x = 0$

(b)

Figure 5.1 | (a) Simplified geometry of a pn junction; (b) doping profile of an ideal uniformly doped pn junction.

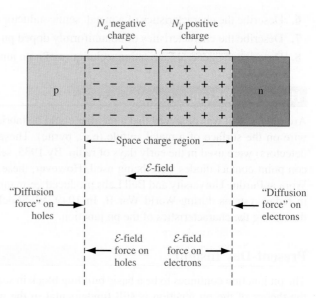

N_a negative charge N_d positive charge

p   n

← Space charge region →

$\mathcal{E}$-field

"Diffusion force" on holes →

← "Diffusion force" on electrons

← $\mathcal{E}$-field force on holes

$\mathcal{E}$-field force on electrons →

Figure 5.2 | The space charge region, the electric field, and the forces acting on the charged carriers.

Space charge region

Depletion region

The net positively and negatively charged regions are shown in Figure 5.2. These two regions are referred to as the *space charge region*. Essentially all electrons and holes are swept out of the space charge region by the electric field. Since the space charge region is depleted of any mobile charge, this region is also referred to as the *depletion region;* these two terms will be used interchangeably. Density gradients still exist in the majority-carrier concentrations at each edge of the space charge region. We can think of a density gradient as producing a "diffusion force" that acts on the majority carriers. These diffusion forces, acting on the electrons and holes at the edges of the space charge region, are shown in the figure. The electric field in the space charge region produces another force on the electrons and holes which is in the opposite direction to the diffusion force for each type of particle. In thermal equilibrium, the diffusion force and the $\mathcal{E}$-field force exactly balance each other.

5.2 | THE pn JUNCTION—ZERO APPLIED BIAS

Objective: Determine characteristics of the zero-biased pn junction, such as the built-in potential barrier, electric field, and space charge widths.

We have considered the basic pn junction structure and discussed briefly how the space charge region is formed. In this section, we will examine the properties of the step junction in thermal equilibrium, where no currents exist and no external excitation is applied. We will determine the space charge region width, electric field, and potential through the depletion region.

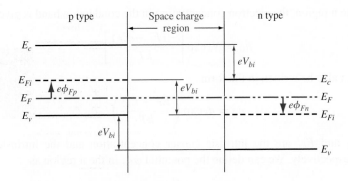

Figure 5.3 | Energy-band diagram of a pn junction in thermal equilibrium (constant Fermi level) showing the energy bands in the neutral p and n regions. Three definitions of the built-in potential barrier are shown—all being equivalent.

5.2.1 Built-In Potential Barrier

If we assume that no voltage is applied across the pn junction, then the junction is in thermal equilibrium—the Fermi energy level is constant throughout the entire system. Figure 5.3 shows the energy bands in the neutral p and n regions on either side of the space charge region, and the constant Fermi energy through the thermal-equilibrium system. The conduction and valence bands as well as the intrinsic Fermi energy must bend in the space charge region since their position relative to the Fermi level changes between the p and n regions. We will determine the shape of these energy levels within the space charge region.

Electrons in the conduction band of the n region see a potential barrier in trying to move into the conduction band of the p region. This potential barrier is referred to as the *built-in potential barrier* and is denoted by V_{bi}. The built-in potential barrier maintains equilibrium between majority-carrier electrons in the n region and minority-carrier electrons in the p region, Likewise, holes in the valence band in the p region see a potential barrier in trying to move into the valence band of the n region. This potential barrier also maintains equilibrium between majority-carrier holes in the p region and minority-carrier holes in the n region. This potential difference across the junction cannot be measured with a voltmeter because new potential barriers will be formed between the probes and the semiconductor that will cancel V_{bi}. The potential V_{bi} maintains equilibrium, so no current is produced by this voltage.

Built-in potential barrier

The intrinsic Fermi level is equidistant from the conduction band edge through the junction, thus the built-in potential barrier can be determined as the difference between the intrinsic Fermi levels in the p and n regions. We can define the potentials ϕ_{Fn} and ϕ_{Fp} as shown in Figure 5.3, so we have[1]

$$V_{bi} = |\phi_{Fn}| + |\phi_{Fp}| \tag{5.1}$$

[1]In general, the term V, with an appropriate subscript, is used for a terminal voltage or device voltage parameter, and the term ϕ, with an appropriate subscript, is used for a potential or potential difference within the device structure.

In the n region, the electron concentration in the conduction band is given by

$$n_0 = N_c \exp \left[\frac{-(E_c - E_F)}{kT} \right] \qquad (5.2)$$

which can also be written in the form

$$n_0 = n_i \exp \left(\frac{E_F - E_{Fi}}{kT} \right) \qquad (5.3)$$

where n_i and E_{Fi} are the intrinsic carrier concentration and the intrinsic Fermi energy, respectively. We can define the potential ϕ_{Fn} in the n region as

$$e\phi_{Fn} = E_F - E_{Fi} \qquad (5.4)$$

Equation (5.3) can then be written as

$$n_0 = n_i \exp \left[\frac{+(e\phi_{Fn})}{kT} \right] \qquad (5.5)$$

Taking the natural log of both sides of Equation (5.5), setting $n_0 = N_d$, and solving for the potential, we obtain

$$\phi_{Fn} = \frac{+kT}{e} \ln \left(\frac{N_d}{n_i} \right) \qquad (5.6)$$

Similarly, in the p region, the hole concentration is given by

$$p_0 = N_a = n_i \exp \left(\frac{E_{Fi} - E_F}{kT} \right) \qquad (5.7)$$

where N_a is the acceptor concentration. We can define the potential ϕ_{Fp} in the p region as

$$e\phi_{Fp} = E_F - E_{Fi} \qquad (5.8)$$

Note that ϕ_{Fp} is a negative quantity. Combining Equations (5.7) and (5.8), we find that

$$\phi_{Fp} = \frac{-kT}{e} \ln \left(\frac{N_a}{n_i} \right) \qquad (5.9)$$

Finally, the built-in potential barrier for the step junction is found by substituting Equations (5.6) and (5.9) into Equation (5.1), which yields

$$\boxed{V_{bi} = \frac{kT}{e} \ln \left(\frac{N_a N_d}{n_i^2} \right) = V_t \ln \left(\frac{N_a N_d}{n_i^2} \right)} \qquad (5.10)$$

Thermal voltage where $V_t = kT/e$ and is defined as the thermal voltage.

At this time, we should note a subtle but important point concerning notation. Previously in the discussion of a semiconductor material, N_d and N_a denoted donor and acceptor impurity concentrations in the same region, thereby forming a compensated semiconductor. From this point on in the text, N_d and N_a will denote the net donor and acceptor concentrations in the individual n and p regions, respectively. If the p region, for example, is a compensated material, then N_a will represent the difference between the actual acceptor and donor impurity concentrations. The parameter N_d is defined in a similar manner for the n region.

EXAMPLE 5.1

OBJECTIVE
Calculate the built-in potential barrier of a pn junction.

Consider a silicon pn junction at $T = 300$ K with doping concentrations of $N_a = 2 \times 10^{16}$ cm^{-3} and $N_d = 5 \times 10^{15}$cm^{-3}.

■ Solution
The built-in potential barrier is determined from

$$V_{bi} = V_t \ln \left(\frac{N_a N_d}{n_i^2} \right) = (0.0259) \ln \left[\frac{(2 \times 10^{16})(5 \times 10^{15})}{(1.5 \times 10^{10})^2} \right]$$

or

$$V_{bi} = 0.695 \text{ V}$$

■ Comment
The built-in potential barrier changes only slightly as the doping concentrations change by orders of magnitude because of the logarithmic dependence.

Exercise Problem
EX5.1 Calculate the built-in potential barrier in a silicon pn junction at $T = 300$ K for (a) $N_a = 5 \times 10^{17}$ cm^{-3}, $N_d = 10^{16}$ cm^{-3} and (b) $N_a = 10^{15}$ cm^{-3}, $N_d = 2 \times 10^{16}$ cm^{-3}. [Ans. (a) 0.796 V, (b) 0.653 V]

5.2.2 Electric Field

An electric field is created in the depletion region by the separation of positive and negative space charge densities. Figure 5.4 shows the volume charge density distribution in the pn junction assuming uniform doping and assuming an abrupt junction approximation. We will assume that the space charge region abruptly ends in the n region at $x = +x_n$ and abruptly ends in the p region at $x = -x_p$ (x_p is a positive quantity).

Abrupt junction approximation

The electric field is determined from Poisson's equation which, for a one-dimensional analysis, is

$$\frac{d^2 \phi(x)}{dx^2} = \frac{-\rho(x)}{\epsilon_s} = -\frac{d\mathcal{E}(x)}{dx} \tag{5.11}$$

where $\phi(x)$ is the electric potential, $\mathcal{E}(x)$ is the electric field, $\rho(x)$ is the volume charge density, and ϵ_s is the permittivity of the semiconductor. From Figure 5.4, the

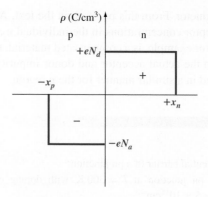

Figure 5.4 | The space charge density in a uniformly doped pn junction assuming the abrupt junction approximation.

charge densities are

$$\rho(x) = -eN_a \qquad -x_p < x < 0 \tag{5.12a}$$

and

$$\rho(x) = eN_d \qquad 0 < x < x_n \tag{5.12b}$$

The electric field in the p region is found by integrating Equation (5.11). We have that

$$\mathcal{E} = \int \frac{\rho(x)}{\epsilon_s} \, dx = -\int \frac{eN_a}{\epsilon_s} \, dx = \frac{-eN_a}{\epsilon_s} x + C_1 \tag{5.13}$$

where C_1 is a constant of integration. The electric field is assumed to be zero in the neutral p region for $x \le -x_p$ since the currents are zero in thermal equilibrium. As there are no surface charge densities within the pn junction structure, the electric field is a continuous function. The constant of integration is determined by setting $\mathcal{E} = 0$ at $x = -x_p$. The electric field in the p region is then given by

$$\mathcal{E} = \frac{-eN_a}{\epsilon_s} (x + x_p) \qquad -x_p \le x \le 0 \tag{5.14}$$

Since the space charge density in the p region is assumed to be a constant (uniform doping), the electric field is a linear function of distance.

In the n region, the electric field is determined from

$$\mathcal{E} = \int \frac{eN_d}{\epsilon_s} \, dx = \frac{eN_d}{\epsilon_s} x + C_2 \tag{5.15}$$

where C_2 is again a constant of integration. The constant C_2 is determined by setting $\mathcal{E} = 0$ at $x = x_n$, since the $\mathcal{E}$-field is assumed to be zero in the n region and is a continuous function. Then

$$\mathcal{E} = \frac{-eN_d}{\epsilon_s} (x_n - x) \qquad 0 \le x \le x_n \tag{5.16}$$

Since the space charge density in the n region is assumed to be a constant (uniform doping), the electric field is also a linear function of distance in this region.

The electric field is also continuous at the metallurgical junction, or at $x = 0$. Setting Equations (5.14) and (5.16) equal to each other at $x = 0$ gives

$$N_a x_p = N_d x_n \qquad (5.17)$$

Equation (5.17) states that the number of negative charges per unit area in the p region is equal to the number of positive charges per unit area in the n region.

Figure 5.5 is a plot of the electric field in the depletion region. The electric field direction is from the n to the p region, or in the negative x direction for this geometry. For the uniformly doped pn junction, the $\mathcal{E}$-field is again a linear function of distance through the junction, and the maximum (magnitude) electric field occurs at the metallurgical junction. An electric field exists in the depletion region even when no voltage is applied between the p and n regions.

The potential in the junction is found by integrating the electric field. In the p region then, we have

$$\phi(x) = -\int \mathcal{E}(x)\, dx = \int \frac{eN_a}{\epsilon_s}(x + x_p)\, dx \qquad (5.18)$$

or

$$\phi(x) = \frac{eN_a}{\epsilon_s}\left(\frac{x^2}{2} + x_p x\right) + C_1' \qquad (5.19)$$

where C_1' is again a constant of integration. The potential difference through the pn junction is the important parameter, rather than the absolute potential, so we may arbitrarily set the potential equal to zero at $x = -x_p$. The constant of integration is then found as

$$C_1' = \frac{eN_a}{2\epsilon_s} x_p^2 \qquad (5.20)$$

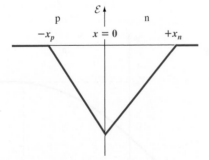

Electric field profile

Figure 5.5 | Electric field in the space charge region of a uniformly doped pn junction. The linear $\mathcal{E}$-field versus distance is a result of a uniformly doped junction.

so that the potential in the p region can now be written as

$$\phi(x) = \frac{eN_a}{2\epsilon_s}(x + x_p)^2 \qquad (-x_p \leq x \leq 0) \tag{5.21}$$

The potential in the n region is determined by integrating the electric field in the n region, or

$$\phi(x) = \int \frac{eN_d}{\epsilon_s}(x_n - x)\, dx \tag{5.22}$$

Then

$$\phi(x) = \frac{eN_d}{\epsilon_s}\left(x_n x - \frac{x^2}{2}\right) + C_2' \tag{5.23}$$

where C_2' is another constant of integration. The potential is a continuous function, so setting Equation (5.21) equal to Equation (5.23) at the metallurgical junction, or at $x = 0$, gives

$$C_2' = \frac{eN_a}{2\epsilon_s}x_p^2 \tag{5.24}$$

The potential in the n region can thus be written as

$$\phi(x) = \frac{eN_d}{\epsilon_s}\left(x_n x - \frac{x^2}{2}\right) + \frac{eN_a}{2\epsilon_s}x_p^2 \qquad (0 \leq x \leq x_n) \tag{5.25}$$

Figure 5.6 is a plot of the potential through the junction and shows the quadratic dependence on distance. The magnitude of the potential at $x = x_n$ is equal to the built-in potential barrier. Then from Equation (5.25), we have

$$V_{bi} = |\phi(x = x_n)| = \frac{e}{2\epsilon_s}\left(N_d x_n^2 + N_a x_p^2\right) \tag{5.26}$$

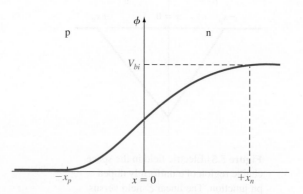

Figure 5.6 | Electric potential through the space charge region of a uniformly doped pn junction. The built-in potential is shown.

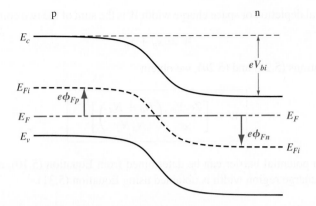

Figure 5.7 | Energy-band diagram of a pn junction in thermal equilibrium.

The potential energy of an electron is given by $E = -e\phi$, which means that the electron energy also varies as a quadratic function of distance through the space charge region. The quadratic dependence is shown in the energy-band diagram of Figure 5.7. We saw the same effect in Chapter 4. If an electric field exists in a semiconductor, the conduction, valence, and intrinsic Fermi energy levels vary with distance in the semiconductor.

5.2.3 Space Charge Width

We can determine the distance that the space charge region extends into the p and n regions from the metallurgical junction. This distance is known as the space charge width. From Equation (5.17), we can write, for example,

$$x_p = \frac{N_d x_n}{N_a} \qquad (5.27)$$

Then, substituting Equation (5.27) into Equation (5.26) and solving for x_n, we obtain

$$\boxed{x_n = \left[\frac{2\epsilon_s V_{bi}}{e} \left(\frac{N_a}{N_d} \right) \left(\frac{1}{N_a + N_d} \right) \right]^{1/2}} \qquad (5.28)$$

n-region space charge width

Equation (5.28) gives the space charge width, or the width of the depletion region, x_n extending into the n-type region for the case of zero applied voltage.

Similarly, if we solve for x_n from Equation (5.17) and substitute into Equation (5.26), we find

$$\boxed{x_p = \left[\frac{2\epsilon_s V_{bi}}{e} \left(\frac{N_d}{N_a} \right) \left(\frac{1}{N_a + N_d} \right) \right]^{1/2}} \qquad (5.29)$$

p-region space charge width

where x_p is the width of the depletion region extending into the p region for the case of zero applied voltage.

The total depletion or space charge width W is the sum of the two components, or

$$W = x_n + x_p \tag{5.30}$$

Using Equations (5.28) and (5.29), we obtain

$$\boxed{W = \left[\frac{2\epsilon_s V_{bi}}{e} \left(\frac{N_a + N_d}{N_a N_d} \right) \right]^{1/2}} \tag{5.31}$$

Total space charge width   The built-in potential barrier can be determined from Equation (5.10), and then the total space charge region width is obtained using Equation (5.31).

EXAMPLE 5.2

OBJECTIVE

Calculate the space charge widths and peak electric field in a pn junction.

Consider a silicon pn junction at $T = 300$ K with uniform doping concentrations of $N_a = 2 \times 10^{16}$ cm^{-3} and $N_d = 5 \times 10^{15}$ cm^{-3}. Determine x_n, x_p, W, and $\mathcal{E}_{\max}$.

■ **Solution**

In Example 5.1, we determined the built-in potential barrier, for these same doping concentrations, to be $V_{bi} = 0.695$ V.

We find the space charge width extending into the n region to be

$$x_n = \left[\frac{2\epsilon_s V_{bi}}{e} \left(\frac{N_a}{N_d} \right) \left(\frac{1}{N_a + N_d} \right) \right]^{1/2}$$

$$= \left[\frac{2(11.7)(8.85 \times 10^{-14})(0.695)}{1.6 \times 10^{-19}} \left(\frac{2 \times 10^{16}}{5 \times 10^{15}} \right) \left(\frac{1}{2 \times 10^{16} + 5 \times 10^{15}} \right) \right]^{1/2}$$

or

$$x_n = 0.379 \times 10^{-4} \text{ cm} = 0.379 \ \mu\text{m}$$

The space charge width extending into the p region is found to be

$$x_p = \left[\frac{2\epsilon_s V_{bi}}{e} \left(\frac{N_d}{N_a} \right) \left(\frac{1}{N_a + N_d} \right) \right]^{1/2}$$

$$= \left[\frac{2(11.7)(8.85 \times 10^{-14})(0.695)}{1.6 \times 10^{-19}} \left(\frac{5 \times 10^{15}}{2 \times 10^{16}} \right) \left(\frac{1}{2 \times 10^{16} + 5 \times 10^{15}} \right) \right]^{1/2}$$

or

$$x_p = 0.0948 \times 10^{-4} \text{ cm} = 0.0948 \ \mu\text{m}$$

The total space charge width, using Equation (5.31), is

$$W = \left[\frac{2\epsilon_s V_{bi}}{e} \left(\frac{N_a + N_d}{N_a N_d} \right) \right]^{1/2}$$

$$= \left\{ \frac{2(11.7)(8.85 \times 10^{-14})(0.695)}{1.6 \times 10^{-19}} \left[\frac{2 \times 10^{16} + 5 \times 10^{15}}{(2 \times 10^{16})(5 \times 10^{15})} \right] \right\}^{1/2}$$

or

$$W = 0.474 \times 10^{-4} \text{ cm} = 0.474 \ \mu\text{m}$$

We can note that the total space charge width can also be found from

$$W = x_n + x_p = 0.379 + 0.0948 = 0.474 \ \mu\text{m}$$

The maximum or peak electric field can be determined from, for example,

$$|\mathcal{E}_{\max}| = \frac{eN_d x_n}{\epsilon_s} = \frac{(1.6 \times 10^{-19})(5 \times 10^{15})(0.379 \times 10^{-4})}{(11.7)(8.85 \times 10^{-14})}$$

or

$$|\mathcal{E}_{\max}| = 2.93 \times 10^4 \text{ V/cm}$$

■ **Comment**

We can note from the space charge width calculations that the depletion region extends farther into the lower-doped region. Also, a space charge width on the order of a micrometer is very typical of depletion region widths. The peak electric field in the space charge region is fairly large. However, to a good first approximation, there are no mobile carriers in this region so there is no drift current. (We will modify this statement slightly in Chapter 9.)

Exercise Problem

EX5.2 A silicon pn junction at $T = 300$ K with zero applied bias has doping concentrations of $N_d = 5 \times 10^{16}$ cm^{-3} and $N_a = 5 \times 10^{15}$ cm^{-3}. Determine x_n, x_p, W, and $|\mathcal{E}_{\max}|$.

(Ans. $x_n = 4.11 \times 10^{-6}$ cm, $x_p = 4.11 \times 10^{-5}$ cm, $W = 4.52 \times 10^{-5}$ cm, $|\mathcal{E}_{\max}| = 3.18 \times 10^4$ V/cm)

TEST YOUR UNDERSTANDING

TYU5.1 Repeat Exercise Problem EX5.1 for a GaAs junction with the same doping concentrations. [Ans. (a) 1.26 V, (b) 1.12 V]

TYU5.2 Repeat Exercise Problem EX5.2 for a GaAs pn junction with the same doping concentrations.

(Ans. $x_n = 5.60 \times 10^{-6}$ cm, $x_p = 5.60 \times 10^{-5}$ cm, $W = 6.16 \times 10^{-5}$ cm, $|\mathcal{E}_{\max}| = 3.86 \times 10^4$ V/cm)

5.3 | THE pn JUNCTION—REVERSE APPLIED BIAS

Objective: Determine the space charge widths, electric fields, and capacitances of a reverse-biased pn junction.

If we apply a potential between the p and n regions, we will no longer be in an equilibrium condition—the Fermi energy level will no longer be constant through the system. Figure 5.8 shows the energy-band diagram of the pn junction for the case when a positive voltage is applied to the n region with respect to the p region. As the positive

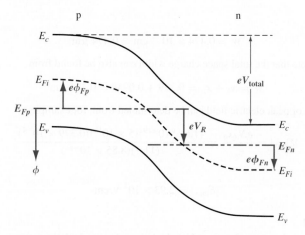

Figure 5.8 | Energy-band diagram of a pn junction under reverse bias (n region positive with respect to p region).

potential is downward, the Fermi level on the n side is now below the Fermi level on the p side. The difference between the two is equal to the applied voltage in units of energy.

The total potential barrier, indicated by V_{total}, has increased. The applied potential is the reverse-bias condition. The total potential barrier is now given by

$$V_{\text{total}} = |\phi_{Fn}| + |\phi_{Fp}| + V_R \qquad (5.32)$$

Reverse-bias voltage where V_R is the magnitude of the applied reverse-bias voltage. Equation (5.32) can be rewritten as

$$V_{\text{total}} = V_{bi} + V_R \qquad (5.33)$$

where V_{bi} is the same built-in potential barrier we had defined in thermal equilibrium.

5.3.1 Space Charge Width and Electric Field

Figure 5.9 shows a pn junction with an applied reverse-bias voltage V_R. Also indicated in the figure are the original electric field in the space charge region and the electric field $\mathcal{E}_{\text{app}}$, induced by the applied voltage. The electric fields in the neutral p and n regions are essentially zero, or at least very small, which means that the magnitude of the electric field in the space charge region must increase above the thermal-equilibrium value due to the applied voltage. The electric field originates on positive charge and terminates on negative charge; this means that the number of positive and negative charges must increase if the electric field increases. For given impurity doping concentrations, the number of positive and negative charges in the depletion region can be increased only if the space charge width W increases. The space charge width W increases, therefore, with an increasing reverse-bias voltage V_R. We are assuming that the electric field in the bulk n and p regions is zero. This assumption will become clearer in Chapter 9 when we discuss the current–voltage characteristics.

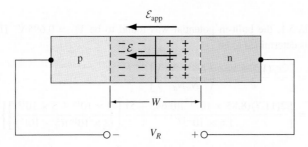

Figure 5.9 | A pn junction with an applied reverse-bias voltage, showing the direction of the electric field induced by V_R and the direction of the zero-biased space charge electric field.

In all of the previous equations, the built-in potential barrier can be replaced by the total potential barrier. The total space charge width can be written from Equation (5.31) as

$$W = \left[\frac{2\epsilon_s (V_{bi} + V_R)}{e} \left(\frac{N_a + N_d}{N_a N_d} \right) \right]^{1/2} \tag{5.34a}$$

showing that the total space charge width increases as we apply a reverse-bias voltage. By substituting the total potential barrier V_{total} into Equations (5.28) and (5.29), the space charge widths in the n and p regions, respectively, can be found as a function of applied reverse-bias voltage. We find

$$x_p = \left[\frac{2\epsilon_s (V_{bi} + V_R)}{e} \left(\frac{N_d}{N_a} \right) \frac{1}{N_a + N_d} \right]^{1/2} \tag{5.34b}$$

and

$$x_n = \left[\frac{2\epsilon_s (V_{bi} + V_R)}{e} \left(\frac{N_a}{N_d} \right) \frac{1}{N_a + N_d} \right]^{1/2} \tag{5.34c}$$

EXAMPLE 5.3

OBJECTIVE

Calculate the width of the space charge region in a pn junction when a reverse-bias voltage is applied.

Again, consider the silicon pn junction at $T = 300$ K with uniform doping concentrations of $N_a = 2 \times 10^{16}$ cm^{-3} and $N_d = 5 \times 10^{15}$ cm^{-3}. Assume a reverse-bias voltage of $V_R = 5$ V is applied.

■ Solution

From Example 5.1, the built-in potential was found to be $V_{bi} = 0.695$ V. The total space charge width is determined to be

$$W = \left[\frac{2\epsilon_s(V_{bi} + V_R)}{e} \left(\frac{N_a + N_d}{N_a N_d} \right) \right]^{1/2}$$

$$= \left\{ \frac{2(11.7)(8.85 \times 10^{-14})(0.695 + 5)}{1.6 \times 10^{-19}} \left[\frac{2 \times 10^{16} + 5 \times 10^{15}}{(2 \times 10^{16})(5 \times 10^{15})} \right] \right\}^{1/2}$$

or

$$W = 1.36 \times 10^{-4} \text{ cm} = 1.36 \ \mu\text{m}$$

■ Comment

The space charge width has increased from 0.474 μm to 1.36 μm at a reverse bias voltage of 5 V.

Exercise Problem

EX5.3 (*a*) A silicon pn junction at $T = 300$ K is reverse-biased at $V_R = 8$ V. The doping concentrations are $N_a = 5 \times 10^{15}$ cm^{-3} and $N_d = 5 \times 10^{16}$ cm^{-3}. Determine x_n, x_p, and W. (*b*) Repeat part (*a*) for $V_R = 12$ V.

[Ans. (*a*) $x_n = 0.143 \ \mu$m, $x_p = 1.43 \ \mu$m, $W = 1.57 \ \mu$m; (*b*) $x_n = 0.173 \ \mu$m, $x_p = 1.73 \ \mu$m, $W = 1.90 \ \mu$m]

The magnitude of the electric field in the depletion region increases with an applied reverse-bias voltage. The electric field is still given by Equations (5.14) and (5.16) and is still a linear function of distance through the space charge region. Since x_n and x_p increase with reverse-bias voltage, the magnitude of the electric field also increases. The maximum electric field still occurs at the metallurgical junction.

The maximum electric field at the metallurgical junction, from Equations (5.14) and (5.16), is

$$\mathcal{E}_{\max} = \frac{-eN_d x_n}{\epsilon_s} = \frac{-eN_a x_p}{\epsilon_s} \tag{5.35}$$

If we use either Equation (5.28) or (5.29) in conjunction with the total potential barrier, $V_{bi} + V_R$, then

$$\boxed{\mathcal{E}_{\max} = -\left[\frac{2e(V_{bi} + V_R)}{\epsilon_s} \left(\frac{N_a N_d}{N_a + N_d} \right) \right]^{1/2}} \tag{5.36}$$

Peak electric field   We can show that the maximum electric field in the pn junction can also be written as

$$\boxed{\mathcal{E}_{\max} = \frac{-2(V_{bi} + V_R)}{W}} \tag{5.37}$$

where W is the total space charge width.

DESIGN EXAMPLE 5.4

OBJECTIVE

Design a pn junction to meet a maximum electric field specification at a particular reverse-bias voltage.

Consider a silicon pn junction at $T = 300$ K with a p-type doping concentration of $N_a = 10^{18}$ cm^{-3}. Determine the n-type doping concentration such that the maximum electric field in the space charge region is $|\mathcal{E}_{max}| = 10^5$ V/cm at a reverse bias voltage of $V_R = 10$ V.

The maximum electric field is given by

$$|\mathcal{E}_{max}| = \left[\frac{2e(V_{bi} + V_R)}{\epsilon_s} \left(\frac{N_a N_d}{N_a + N_d} \right) \right]^{1/2}$$

Since V_{bi} is also a function of N_d through the log term, this equation is transcendental in nature and cannot be solved analytically. However, as an approximation, we will assume that $V_{bi} \approx 0.75$ V.

We can then write

$$10^5 \approx \left\{ \frac{2(1.6 \times 10^{-19})(0.75 + 10)}{(11.7)(8.85 \times 10^{-14})} \left[\frac{(10^{18})(N_d)}{10^{18} + N_d} \right] \right\}^{1/2}$$

which yields

$$N_d = 3.02 \times 10^{15} \text{ cm}^{-3}$$

We can note that the built-in potential for this value of N_d is

$$V_{bi} = (0.0259) \ln \left[\frac{(10^{18})(3.02 \times 10^{15})}{(1.5 \times 10^{10})^2} \right] = 0.783 \text{ V}$$

which is very close to the assumed value used in the calculation. So the calculated value of N_d is a very good approximation.

■ **Comment**

A smaller value of N_d than calculated results in a smaller value of $|\mathcal{E}_{max}|$ for a given reverse-bias voltage. The value of N_d determined in this example, then, is the maximum value that will meet the specifications.

Exercise Problem

EX5.4 A silicon pn junction at $T = 300$ K has doping concentrations of $N_a = 5 \times 10^{15}$ cm^{-3} and $N_d = 5 \times 10^{16}$ cm^{-3}. Determine the maximum electric field in the junction if the junction is reverse biased at (a) $V_R = 8$ V and at (b) $V_R = 12$ V. [Ans. (a) 1.11×10^5 V/cm, (b) 1.34×10^5 V/cm.]

5.3.2 Junction Capacitance

Since we have a separation of positive and negative charges in the depletion region, a capacitance is associated with the pn junction. Figure 5.10 shows the charge densities in the depletion region for applied reverse-bias voltages of V_R and $V_R + dV_R$. An

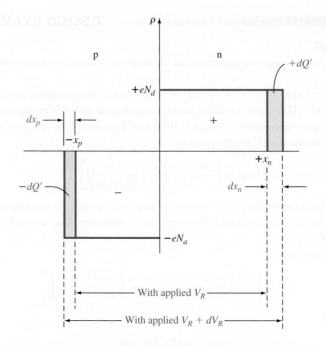

Figure 5.10 | Differential change in the space charge width with a differential change in reverse-bias voltage for a uniformly doped pn junction. Also shown are the additional charges uncovered by an increase in reverse-bias voltage.

increase in the reverse-bias voltage dV_R will uncover additional positive charges in the n region and additional negative charges in the p region. The junction capacitance is defined as

$$C' = \frac{dQ'}{dV_R} \tag{5.38}$$

where

$$dQ' = eN_d \, dx_n = eN_a \, dx_p \tag{5.39}$$

The differential charge dQ' is in units of C/cm^2 so that the capacitance C' is in units of farads per square centimeter (F/cm^2), or capacitance per unit area.

For the total potential barrier, Equation (5.28) may be written as

$$x_n = \left\{ \frac{2\epsilon_s(V_{bi} + V_R)}{e} \left(\frac{N_a}{N_d} \right) \left(\frac{1}{N_a + N_d} \right) \right\}^{1/2} \tag{5.40}$$

Junction capacitance

The junction capacitance can be written as

$$C' = \frac{dQ'}{dV_R} = eN_d \frac{dx_n}{dV_R} \tag{5.41}$$

so that

$$C' = \left[\frac{e\epsilon_s N_a N_d}{2(V_{bi} + V_R)(N_a + N_d)} \right]^{1/2} \tag{5.42}$$

Exactly the same capacitance expression is obtained by considering the space charge region extending into the p region x_p. The junction capacitance is also referred to as the *depletion layer capacitance*.

EXAMPLE 5.5

OBJECTIVE
Calculate the junction capacitance of a pn junction.

  Consider the same pn junction as described in Example 5.3. Calculate the junction capacitance at $V_R = 5$ V assuming the cross-sectional area of the pn junction is $A = 10^{-4}$ cm^2.

■ **Solution**
The built-in potential was found to be $V_{bi} = 0.695$ V. The junction capacitance per unit area is found to be

$$C' = \left[\frac{e\epsilon_s N_a N_d}{2(V_{bi} + V_R)(N_a + N_d)} \right]^{1/2}$$

$$= \left[\frac{(1.6 \times 10^{-19})(11.7)(8.85 \times 10^{-14})(2 \times 10^{16})(5 \times 10^{15})}{2(0.695 + 5)(2 \times 10^{16} + 5 \times 10^{15})} \right]^{1/2}$$

or

$$C' = 7.63 \times 10^{-9} \text{ F/cm}^2$$

  The total junction is found as

$$C = AC' = (10^{-4})(7.63 \times 10^{-9})$$

or

$$C = 0.763 \times 10^{-12} \text{ F} = 0.763 \text{ pF}$$

■ **Comment**
The value of the junction capacitance for a pn junction is usually in the pF range, or even smaller.

Exercise Problem

EX5.5 Consider a GaAs pn junction at $T = 300$ K doped at concentrations of $N_a = 1 \times 10^{15}$ cm^{-3} and $N_d = 2 \times 10^{16}$ cm^{-3}. The junction area is $A = 10^{-4}$ cm^2. Determine the junction capacitance for (a) $V_R = 0$ and (b) $V_R = 5$ V. [Ans. (a) 0.888 pF, (b) 0.380 pF]

  If we compare Equation (5.34) for the total depletion width W of the space charge region under reverse bias and Equation (5.42) for the junction capacitance C', we find that we can write

$$C' = \frac{\epsilon_s}{W} \tag{5.43}$$

Equation (5.43) is the same as the capacitance per unit area of a parallel plate capacitor. Considering Figure 5.10, we may have come to this same conclusion earlier. Keep in mind that the space charge width is a function of the reverse-bias voltage so that the junction capacitance is also a function of the reverse-bias voltage applied to the pn junction.

5.3.3   One-Sided Junctions

One-sided junction   Consider a special pn junction called the one-sided junction. If, for example, $N_a \gg N_d$, this junction is referred to as a p^+n junction. The total space charge width, from Equation (5.34), reduces to

$$W \approx \left[\frac{2\epsilon_s (V_{bi} + V_R)}{e N_d} \right]^{1/2} \tag{5.44}$$

Considering the expressions for x_n and x_p, we have for the p^+n junction

$$x_p \ll x_n \tag{5.45}$$

and

$$W \approx x_n \tag{5.46}$$

Almost the entire space charge layer extends into the low-doped region of the junction. This effect can be seen in Figure 5.11.

The junction capacitance of the p^+n junction reduces to

$$C' \approx \left[\frac{e \epsilon_s N_d}{2(V_{bi} + V_R)} \right]^{1/2} \tag{5.47}$$

The depletion layer capacitance of a one-sided junction is a function of the doping concentration in the low-doped region. Equation (5.47) may be manipulated to give

$$\left(\frac{1}{C'} \right)^2 = \frac{2(V_{bi} + V_R)}{e \epsilon_s N_d} \tag{5.48}$$

which shows that the inverse capacitance squared is a linear function of applied reverse-bias voltage.

Figure 5.12 shows a plot of Equation (5.48). The built-in potential of the junction can be determined by extrapolating the curve to the point where $(1/C')^2 = 0$. The slope of the curve is inversely proportional to the doping concentration of the low-doped region in the junction; thus, this doping concentration can be experimentally determined. The assumptions used in the derivation of this capacitance include uniform doping in both semiconductor regions, the abrupt junction approximation, and a planar junction.

A one-sided pn junction is useful for experimentally determining the doping concentrations and built-in potential.

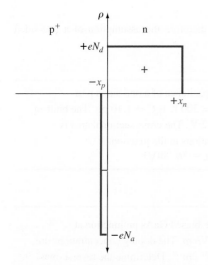

Figure 5.11 | Space charge density of a one-sided p$^+$n junction.

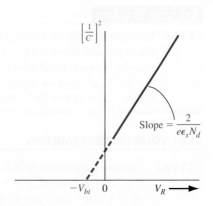

Figure 5.12 | $(1/C')^2$ versus V_R of a uniformly doped pn junction.

EXAMPLE 5.6

OBJECTIVE

Determine the impurity concentrations in a p$^+$n junction given the parameters from Figure 5.12.

Consider a silicon p$^+$n junction at $T = 300$ K. Assume the intercept of the curve on the voltage axis in Figure 5.12 gives $V_{bi} = 0.742$ V and that the slope is 3.92×10^{15} (F/cm^2)$^{-2}$/V.

■ Solution

The slope of the curve in Figure 5.12 is given by $2/e\epsilon_s N_d$, so we can write

$$N_d = \frac{2}{e\epsilon_s(\text{slope})} = \frac{2}{(1.6 \times 10^{-19})(11.7)(8.85 \times 10^{-14})(3.92 \times 10^{15})}$$

or

$$N_d = 3.08 \times 10^{15} \text{ cm}^{-3}$$

The built-in potential is given by

$$V_{bi} = V_t \ln\left(\frac{N_a N_d}{n_i^2}\right)$$

Solving for N_a, we find

$$N_a = \frac{n_i^2}{N_d} \exp\left(\frac{V_{bi}}{V_t}\right) = \frac{(1.5 \times 10^{10})^2}{3.08 \times 10^{15}} \exp\left(\frac{0.742}{0.0259}\right)$$

or

$$N_a = 2.02 \times 10^{17} \text{ cm}^{-3}$$

■ Comment

The results of this example show that $N_a \gg N_d$; therefore the assumption of a one-sided junction was valid.

Exercise Problem

EX5.6   The experimentally measured junction capacitance of a one-sided p^+n silicon junction biased at $V_R = 4$ V at $T = 300$ K is $C = 1.10$ pF. The built-in potential barrier is found to be $V_{bi} = 0.782$ V. The cross-sectional area is $A = 10^{-4}$ cm^2. Find the doping concentrations in the junction. (Ans. $N_a = 7 \times 10^{15}$ cm^{-3}, $N_d = 4.17 \times 10^{17}$ cm^{-3})

TEST YOUR UNDERSTANDING

TYU5.3   The maximum electric field in a reverse-biased GaAs pn junction at $T = 300$ K is to be $|\mathcal{E}_{max}| = 2.5 \times 10^5$ V/cm. The doping concentrations are $N_d = 5 \times 10^{15}$ cm^{-3} and $N_a = 8 \times 10^{15}$ cm^{-3}. Determine the reverse-bias voltage that will produce this maximum electric field. (Ans. 72.5 V)

TYU5.4   The experimentally measured junction capacitance at $T = 300$ K of a one-sided silicon p^+n junction biased at $V_R = 3$ V is $C = 1.25$ pF. The built-in potential barrier is found to be $V_{bi} = 0.775$ V. The cross-sectional area of the junction is $A = 10^{-4}$ cm^2. Find the doping concentrations. (Ans. $N_d = 7.12 \times 10^{15}$ cm^{-3}, $N_a = 3.13 \ 10^{17}$ cm^{-3})

5.4 | METAL–SEMICONDUCTOR CONTACT— RECTIFYING JUNCTION

Objective: Analyze the metal–semiconductor rectifying junction.

It has long been known that a rectifying contact can be achieved by pressing a sharp wire against selenium. A more reliable contact can be formed by depositing a metal, such as aluminum, onto the surface of a semiconductor. This type of junction is commonly known as a Schottky barrier junction, or just a Schottky junction.

5.4.1   The Schottky Barrier

In this section, we will consider the metal–semiconductor rectifying contact, or Schottky barrier junction, under zero bias. In most cases, the rectifying contacts are made on n-type semiconductors; for this reason, we will concentrate on this type of contact.

The ideal energy-band diagram for a particular metal and n-type semiconductor before making contact is shown in Figure 5.13a. The vacuum level is used as a reference level. The parameter ϕ_m is the metal work function (measured in volts), ϕ_s is the semiconductor work function, and χ is known as the *electron affinity*. The work functions of various metals are given in Table 5.1 and the electron affinities of several

Electron affinity

Table 5.1 | Work functions of some elements

Element	Work Function, ϕ_m
Ag, silver	4.26
Al, aluminum	4.28
Au, gold	5.1
Cr, chromium	4.5
Mo, molybdenum	4.6
Ni, nickel	5.15
Pd, palladium	5.12
Pt, platinum	5.65
Ti, titanium	4.33
W, tungsten	4.55

Table 5.2 | Electron affinity of some semiconductors

Element	Electron Affinity, χ
Ge, germanium	4.13
Si, silicon	4.01
GaAs, gallium arsenide	4.07
AlAs, aluminum arsenide	3.5

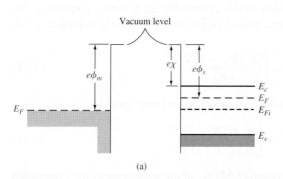 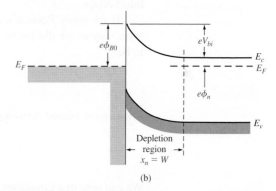

(a) (b)

Figure 5.13 | (a) Energy-band diagram of a metal and semiconductor before contact; (b) ideal energy-band diagram of a metal–n-semiconductor junction for $\phi_m > \phi_s$.

semiconductors are given in Table 5.2. In Figure 5.13a, we have assumed that $\phi_m > \phi_s$. The ideal thermal-equilibrium metal–semiconductor energy-band diagram, for this situation, is shown in Figure 5.13b. Before contact, the Fermi level in the semiconductor was above that in the metal. In order for the Fermi level to become a constant through the system in thermal equilibrium, electrons from the semiconductor flow into the lower energy states in the metal through a wire connected between the semiconductor and the metal. Positively charged donor atoms remain in the semiconductor, creating a space charge region.

The parameter ϕ_{B0} is the ideal barrier height of the semiconductor contact, the potential barrier seen by electrons in the metal trying to move into the semiconductor. This barrier is known as the *Schottky barrier* and is given, ideally, by

Schottky barrier height

$$\phi_{B0} = (\phi_m - \chi)$$ (5.49)

On the semiconductor side, V_{bi} is the built-in potential barrier. This barrier, similar to the case of the pn junction, is the barrier seen by electrons in the conduction band

Built-in potential barrier

trying to move into the metal. The built-in potential barrier is given by

$$V_{bi} = \phi_{B0} - \phi_n \qquad (5.50)$$

which makes V_{bi} a slight function of the semiconductor doping, as was the case in a pn junction. From Chapter 3, we note that $\phi_n = V_t \ln(N_c/N_d)$.

5.4.2   The Schottky Junction—Reverse Bias

If we apply a positive voltage to the semiconductor with respect to the metal, the semiconductor-to-metal barrier height increases, while ϕ_{B0} remains constant in this idealized case. This bias condition is the reverse bias. The energy-band diagram for the reverse bias is shown in Figure 5.14, where V_R is the magnitude of the reverse-bias voltage.

If we apply Poisson's equation to this reverse-biased Schottky junction in the same way as we did for the reverse-biased pn junction, we find the depletion width to be

$$x_n = \left[\frac{2\epsilon_s(V_{bi} + V_R)}{eN_d} \right]^{1/2} \qquad (5.51)$$

The reverse-biased Schottky junction also has a capacitance given by

$$C' = \left[\frac{e\epsilon_s N_d}{2(V_{bi} + V_R)} \right]^{1/2} \qquad (5.52)$$

We can note that Equations (5.51) and (5.52) are of the same form as for a one-sided p^+n junction.

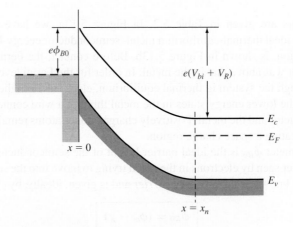

Figure 5.14 | Ideal energy-band diagram of a metal–semiconductor rectifying junction under reverse bias.

5.5 | FORWARD APPLIED BIAS—AN INTRODUCTION

Objective: Qualitatively describe the current-voltage characteristics of a forward-biased pn junction and Schottky junction.

Zero- and reverse-biased pn junctions are used in the MOS transistor that is to be discussed and studied in Chapters 6 and 7. However, a qualitative understanding of the forward-biased pn junction and Schottky junction should be considered at this point. A thorough analysis of the forward-biased junction is given in Chapter 9.

Figure 5.7 showed the energy-band diagram of a pn junction in thermal equilibrium (zero applied voltage). We argued that the potential barrier seen by the electrons, for example, holds back the large concentration of electrons in the n region and keeps them from flowing into the p region. Similarly, the potential barrier seen by the holes holds back the large concentration of holes in the p region and keeps them from flowing into the n region. The potential barrier, then, maintains thermal equilibrium.

Figure 5.8 showed the pn junction with an applied reverse-bias voltage, showing the directions of the electric fields. The induced electric field resulting from the applied voltage is in the same direction as the original zero-biased space charge electric field. These electric fields add to increase the potential barrier between the p and n regions, as shown in Figure 5.9. The increased potential barrier continues to hold back the holes in the p region and hold back the electrons in the n region. Hence, there is essentially no current through the junction when a reverse-bias voltage is applied. The same effects apply to the zero-biased and reverse-biased Schottky junctions shown in Figures 5.13b and 5.14.

5.5.1 The pn Junction

Figure 5.15 shows the pn junction with a forward-bias voltage applied. The p region is positive with respect to the n region. The induced electric field resulting from the applied voltage is now in the opposite direction to the original zero-biased space charge electric field. The net electric field in the space charge region is reduced from the zero-bias value and the potential barrier between the p and n regions is now reduced, as shown in Figure 5.16. A reduction in the potential barrier means that the thermal equilibrium situation created at zero bias is upset. In this case, holes may now diffuse from the p region across the depletion region into the n region, where they become minority-carrier holes. Similarly, electrons may now diffuse from the n region across the depletion region into the p region, where they become minority-carrier electrons. The steady-state minority-carrier distributions in the p and n regions are shown in Figure 5.17. There are gradients in the minority-carrier concentrations so that diffusion currents are induced in the pn junction.

An analysis of the diffusion currents produces the ideal current–voltage relationship given by

$$I_D = I_S \left[\exp\left(\frac{V_D}{V_t}\right) - 1 \right]$$

(5.53)   **Ideal diode equation**

Forward-bias voltage

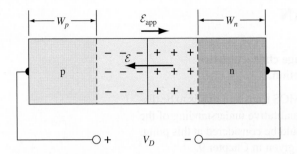

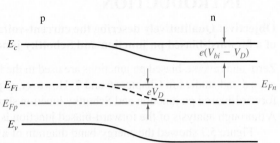

Figure 5.15 | The pn junction with an applied forward-bias voltage showing the direction of the electric field induced by V_D and the direction of the electric field of the zero-biased pn junction.

Figure 5.16 | Energy-band diagram of the forward biased pn junction showing the reduction of the barrier.

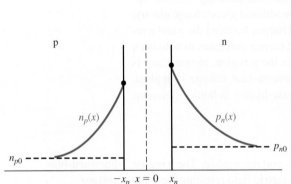

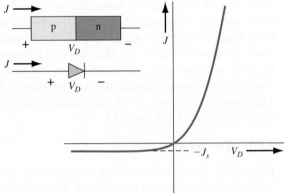

Figure 5.17 | Steady-state minority-carrier concentrations in a pn junction under forward bias.

Figure 5.18 | Plot of ideal *I–V* characteristics of a pn junction diode.

where I_S is called the reverse-saturation current and is a function of the doping concentrations, diffusion coefficients, and the cross-sectional area of the pn junction. Typical values of the reverse-saturation current for silicon pn junctions are in the range $10^{-14} < I_S < 10^{-12}$ A.

Figure 5.18 is a plot of Equation (5.53). When the pn junction is forward biased ($V_D > 0$), the current is an exponential function of voltage. When the pn junction is reverse-biased ($V_D < 0$), the exponential function very quickly becomes insignificant compared to the (1) term, so the junction current is $I_D = -I_S$. The reverse-bias current is not zero, but it is very small. Because of the nonlinear *I–V* characteristics of the pn junction, this device is called a *pn junction diode*.

In considering Equation (5.53), we can show that if $V_D > 0.1$ V, the exponential term becomes dominant so that we can write

$$I_D \approx I_S \exp \left(\frac{V_D}{V_t} \right) \tag{5.54}$$

EXAMPLE 5.7

OBJECTIVE

Determine the diode current in a silicon pn junction diode.

Consider a silicon pn junction diode at $T = 300$ K. The reverse-saturation current is $I_S = 10^{-14}$ A. Determine the forward-bias diode current at $V_D = 0.5$ V, 0.6 V, and 0.7 V.

■ **Solution**

The diode current is found from

$$I_D \approx I_S \exp \left(\frac{V_D}{V_t} \right) = (10^{-14}) \exp \left(\frac{V_D}{0.0259} \right) \quad \text{(A)}$$

so for $V_D = 0.5$ V,

$$I_D = 2.42 \ \mu A$$

and for $V_D = 0.6$ V,

$$I_D = 0.115 \ \text{mA}$$

and for $V_D = 0.7$ V

$$I_D = 5.47 \ \text{mA}$$

■ **Comment**

Because of the exponential function, reasonable diode currents can be achieved even though the reverse-saturation current is a small value.

Exercise Problem

EX5.7 A silicon pn junction diode at $T = 300$ K is forward biased. The reverse-saturation current is $I_S = 5 \times 10^{-14}$ A. Determine the required diode voltage to induce a diode current of $I_D = 4.25$ mA. (Ans. $V_D = 0.652$ V)

5.5.2 The Schottky Barrier Junction

The current transport in a metal–semiconductor junction is due mainly to majority carriers as opposed to minority carriers in a pn junction. The basic process in the rectifying contact with an n-type semiconductor is by transport of electrons over the potential barrier, which can be described by the thermionic emission theory.

Thermionic emission

The thermionic emission characteristics are derived by using the assumptions that the barrier height is much larger than kT, so that the Maxwell–Boltzmann

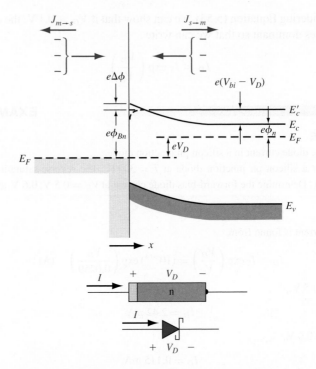

Figure 5.19 | Energy-band diagram of a forward-biased metal–semiconductor rectifying contact showing current directions. Also shown is the circuit symbol of a Schottky barrier diode.

approximation applies and that thermal equilibrium is not affected by this process. Figure 5.19 shows the one-dimensional barrier with an applied forward-bias voltage V_D and shows two electron current density components. The current $J_{s\rightarrow m}$ is the electron current density due to the flow of electrons from the semiconductor into the metal, and the current $J_{m\rightarrow s}$ is the electron current density due to the flow of electrons from the metal into the semiconductor. The subscripts of the currents indicate the direction of electron flow. The conventional current direction is opposite to electron flow.

The net current density in the metal-to-semiconductor junction can be written as

$$J = J_{s\rightarrow m} - J_{m\rightarrow s} \tag{5.55}$$

which is defined to be positive in the direction from the metal to the semiconductor. We find, in the ideal case, that

$$J = \left[A^* T^2 \exp\left(\frac{-e\phi_{B0}}{kT} \right) \right] \left[\exp\left(\frac{eV_D}{kT} \right) - 1 \right] \tag{5.56}$$

where

$$A^* \equiv \frac{4\pi e m_n^* k^2}{h^3}$$

(5.57)   **Richardson constant**

The parameter A^* is called the effective Richardson constant for thermionic emission.
    Equation (5.56) can be written in the usual diode form as

$$J = J_{sT}\left[\exp\left(\frac{eV_D}{kT}\right) - 1\right]$$

(5.58)   **Ideal current–voltage relation**

where J_{sT} is the reverse-saturation current density.

5.5.3   Comparison of the Schottky Diode and the pn Junction Diode

Although the ideal current–voltage relationship of the Schottky barrier diode given
by Equation (5.58) is of the same form as that of the pn junction diode, there are two
important differences between a Schottky diode and a pn junction diode. The first
difference is in the magnitudes of the reverse-saturation current densities, and the
second difference is in the switching characteristics.
    The magnitude of J_{sT} for the Schottky diode is typically several orders of mag-
nitude larger than J_S for the pn junction. Since $J_{sT} \gg J_S$, the forward-bias characteristics of the two types of diodes will also be different. Figure 5.20 shows the typical
I–V characteristics of a Schottky barrier diode and a pn junction diode. The forward
applied bias required to achieve a given current is less in a Schottky diode than in a

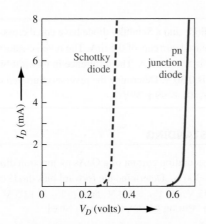

Figure 5.20 | Comparison of forward-
bias I–V characteristics between a
Schottky diode and a pn diode.

pn junction diode. In other words, the effective turn-on voltage of the Schottky diode is less than that of the pn junction diode.

We will discuss the difference in switching characteristics in Chapter 9.

EXAMPLE 5.8

OBJECTIVE

Calculate the forward-bias voltage required to generate a forward-bias current density of 10 A/cm^2 in a Schottky diode and a pn junction diode.

Consider diodes with parameters $J_{sT} = 6 \times 10^{-5}$ A/cm^2 and $J_S = 3.5 \times 10^{-11}$ A/cm^2.

■ **Solution**

For the Schottky diode, we have

$$J = J_{sT} \left[\exp\left(\frac{V_D}{V_t} \right) - 1 \right]$$

Neglecting the (-1) term, we can solve for the forward-bias voltage. We find

$$V_D = V_t \ln\left(\frac{J}{J_{sT}} \right) = (0.0259) \ln\left(\frac{10}{6 \times 10^{-5}} \right) = 0.311 \text{ V}$$

For the pn junction diode, we have

$$V_D = V_t \ln\left(\frac{J}{J_S} \right) = (0.0259) \ln\left(\frac{10}{3.5 \times 10^{-11}} \right) = 0.683 \text{ V}$$

■ **Comment**

A comparison of the two forward-bias voltages shows that the Schottky diode has an effective turn-on voltage that, in this case, is approximately 0.37 V smaller than the turn-on voltage of the pn junction diode.

Exercise Problem

EX5.8   A pn junction diode and a Schottky diode have equal cross-sectional areas and have forward-biased currents of 0.5 mA. The reverse-saturation current of the Schottky diode is 5×10^{-7} A. The difference in forward-bias voltage between the two diodes is 0.30 V. Determine the reverse-saturation current of the pn junction diode. (Ans. 4.66×10^{-12} A)

TEST YOUR UNDERSTANDING

TYU5.5   The reverse-saturation current of a GaAs pn junction diode is $I_S = 10^{-19}$ A. Assume $T = 300$ K. Determine the forward bias diode current for (a) $V_D = 0.95$ V, (b) $V_D = 1.0$ V, and (c) $V_D = 1.05$ V. [Ans. (a) 0.85 mA, (b) 5.86 mA, (c) 40.4 mA]

TYU5.6   The forward-bias current in a GaAs pn junction diode at $T = 300$ K is $I_D = 12$ mA. The reverse-saturation current is $I_S = 5 \times 10^{-19}$ A. Determine the required forward-bias diode voltage. (Ans. $V_D = 0.977$ V)

Σ 5.6 | METAL–SEMICONDUCTOR OHMIC CONTACTS

Objective: Describe the characteristics of a metal–semiconductor ohmic contact.

Contacts must be made between any semiconductor device, or integrated circuit, and the outside world. These contacts are made via *ohmic contacts*. Ohmic contacts are metal-to-semiconductor contacts, but in this case they are not rectifying contacts. An ohmic contact is a low-resistance junction providing conduction in both directions between the metal and the semiconductor. Ideally, the current through the ohmic contact is a linear function of applied voltage, and the applied voltage should be very small. Two general types of ohmic contacts are possible: The first type is the ideal nonrectifying barrier, and the second is the tunneling barrier.[2]

We considered an ideal metal-to-n-type-semiconductor contact in Figure 5.13 for the case when $\phi_m > \phi_s$. Figure 5.21 shows the same ideal contact for the opposite case of $\phi_m < \phi_s$. In Figure 5.21a we see the energy levels before contact and, in Figure 5.21b, the barrier after contact for thermal equilibrium. To achieve thermal equilibrium in this junction, electrons will flow from the metal into the lower energy states in the semiconductor, which makes the surface of the semiconductor more n type. The excess electron charge in the n-type semiconductor exists essentially as a surface charge density. If a positive voltage is applied to the metal, there is no barrier to electrons flowing from the semiconductor into the metal. If a positive voltage is applied to the semiconductor, the effective barrier height for electrons flowing from the metal into the semiconductor will be approximately $\phi_{Bn} = \phi_n$, which is fairly small for a moderately to heavily doped semiconductor. For this bias condition, electrons can easily flow from the metal into the semiconductor.

Figure 5.22a shows the energy-band diagram when a positive voltage is applied to the metal with respect to the semiconductor. Electrons can easily flow "downhill" from the semiconductor into the metal. Figure 5.22b shows the case when a positive voltage is applied to the semiconductor with respect to the metal. Electrons can easily flow over the barrier from the metal into the semiconductor. This junction, then, is an ohmic contact.

Figure 5.23 shows an ideal nonrectifying contact between a metal and a p-type semiconductor. Figure 5.23a shows the energy levels before contact for the case when $\phi_m > \phi_s$. When contact is made, electrons from the semiconductor will flow into the metal to achieve thermal equilibrium, leaving behind more empty states, or holes. The excess concentration of holes at the surface makes the surface of the semiconductor more p type. Electrons from the metal can readily move into the empty states in the semiconductor. This charge movement corresponds to holes flowing from the semiconductor into the metal. We can also visualize holes in the metal flowing into the semiconductor. This junction is also an ohmic contact.

Tunneling Barrier The space charge width in a rectifying metal–semiconductor contact is inversely proportional to the square root of the semiconductor doping. The

---

[2]The tunneling concept from quantum mechanics is discussed in Appendix E.

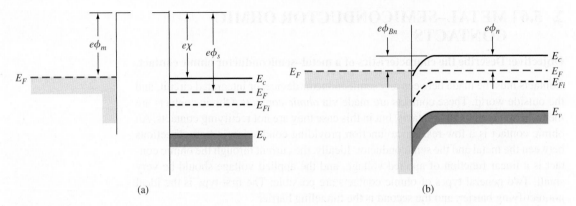

Figure 5.21 | Ideal energy-band diagram (a) before contact and (b) after contact for a metal–n-semiconductor junction for $\phi_m < \phi_s$.

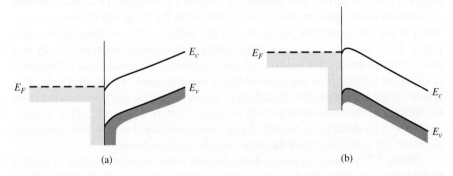

Figure 5.22 | Ideal energy-band diagram of a metal–n-semiconductor ohmic contact (a) with a positive voltage applied to the metal and (b) with a positive voltage applied to the semiconductor.

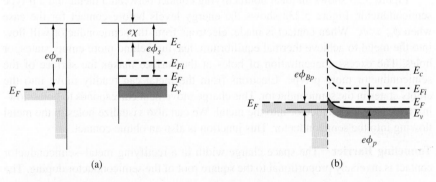

Figure 5.23 | Ideal energy-band diagram (a) before contact and (b) after contact for a metal–p-semiconductor junction for $\phi_m > \phi_s$.

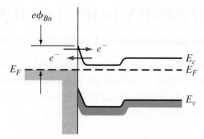

Figure 5.24 | Energy-band diagram of a heavily doped n-semiconductor-to-metal junction.

width of the depletion region decreases as the doping concentration in the semiconductor increases; thus, as the doping concentration increases, the probability of tunneling through the barrier increases. Figure 5.24 shows a junction in which the metal is in contact with a heavily doped n-type epitaxial layer.

EXAMPLE 5.9

OBJECTIVE

Calculate the space charge width for a Schottky barrier on a heavily doped semiconductor.

Consider silicon at $T = 300$ K doped at $N_d = 7 \times 10^{18}$ cm^{-3}. Assume a Schottky barrier with $\phi_{B0} = 0.67$ V. For this case, we can assume that $V_{bi} \approx \phi_{B0}$.

■ **Solution**

For a one-sided junction, we have for zero applied bias

$$x_n = \left(\frac{2\epsilon_s V_{bi}}{e N_d} \right)^{1/2} = \left[\frac{2(11.7)(8.85 \times 10^{-14})(0.67)}{(1.6 \times 10^{-19})(7 \times 10^{18})} \right]^{1/2}$$

or

$$x_n = 1.1 \times 10^{-6} \text{ cm} = 110 \text{ Å}$$

■ **Comment**

In a heavily doped semiconductor, the depletion width is on the order of angstroms, so that tunneling is now a distinct possibility. For these types of barrier widths, tunneling may become the dominant current mechanism.

Exercise Problem

EX5.9 Repeat Example 5.9 for a Schottky barrier on heavily doped gallium arsenide. Assume the n-type doping is $N_d = 7 \times 10^{18}$ cm^{-3} and assume the barrier height is $\phi_{Bn} = 0.80$ V. (Ans. $x_n = 129$ Å)

Σ 5.7 | NONUNIFORMLY DOPED pn JUNCTIONS

Objective: Describe the characteristics of nonuniformly doped pn junctions.

In the pn junctions considered so far, we have assumed that each semiconductor region has been uniformly doped. In actual pn junction structures, this is not always true. In some electronic applications, specific nonuniform doping profiles are used to obtain special pn junction capacitance characteristics.

5.7.1 Linearly Graded Junctions

If we start with a uniformly doped n-type semiconductor, for example, and diffuse acceptor atoms through the surface, the impurity concentrations will tend to be like those shown in Figure 5.25. The point $x = x'$ on the figure corresponds to the metallurgical junction. The depletion region extends into the p and n regions from the metallurgical junction as we have discussed previously. The net p-type doping concentration near the metallurgical junction can be approximated as a linear function of distance from the metallurgical junction. Likewise, as a first approximation, the net n-type doping concentration is also a linear function of distance extending into the n region from the metallurgical junction. This effective doping profile is referred to as a linearly graded junction.

Figure 5.26 shows the space charge density in the depletion region of the
Linearly graded junction linearly graded junction. For convenience, the metallurgical junction is placed at $x = 0$. The space charge density can be written as

$$\rho(x) = eax \tag{5.59}$$

where a is the gradient of the net impurity concentration.

The electric field and potential in the space charge region can be determined from Poisson's equation. We can write

$$\frac{d\mathcal{E}}{dx} = \frac{\rho(x)}{\epsilon_s} = \frac{eax}{\epsilon_s} \tag{5.60}$$

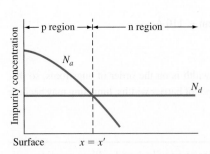

Figure 5.25 | Impurity concentrations of a pn junction with a nonuniformly doped p region.

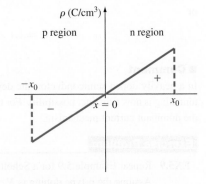

Figure 5.26 | Space charge density in a linearly graded pn junction.

so that the electric field can be found by integration as

$$\mathcal{E} = \int \frac{eax}{\epsilon_s} \, dx = \frac{ea}{2\epsilon_s} \left(x^2 - x_0^2 \right) \qquad (5.61)$$

The electric field in the linearly graded junction is a quadratic function of distance rather than the linear function found in the uniformly doped junction. The maximum electric field again occurs at the metallurgical junction. We can note that the electric field is zero at both $x = +x_0$ and at $x = -x_0$. The electric field in a nonuniformly doped semiconductor is not exactly zero, but the magnitude of this field is small, so setting $\mathcal{E} = 0$ in the bulk regions is still a good approximation.

The potential is again found by integrating the electric field as

$$\phi(x) = -\int \mathcal{E} \, dx \qquad (5.62)$$

If we arbitrarily set $\phi = 0$ at $x = -x_0$, then the potential through the junction is

$$\phi(x) = \frac{-ea}{2\epsilon_s} \left(\frac{x^3}{3} - x_0^2 x \right) + \frac{ea}{3\epsilon_s} x_0^3 \qquad (5.63)$$

The magnitude of the potential at $x = +x_0$ will equal the built-in potential barrier for this function. We then have that

$$\phi(x_0) = \frac{2}{3} \cdot \frac{eax_0^3}{\epsilon_s} = V_{bi} \qquad (5.64)$$

Another expression for the built-in potential barrier for a linearly graded junction can be approximated from the expression used for a uniformly doped junction. We can write

$$V_{bi} = V_t \ln \left[\frac{N_d(x_0) N_a(-x_0)}{n_i^2} \right] \qquad (5.65)$$

where $N_d(x_0)$ and $N_a(-x_0)$ are the doping concentrations at the edges of the space charge region. We can relate these doping concentrations to the gradient, so that

$$N_d(x_0) = ax_0 \qquad (5.66a)$$

and

$$N_a(-x_0) = ax_0 \qquad (5.66b)$$

Then the built-in potential barrier for the linearly graded junction becomes

$$V_{bi} = V_t \ln \left(\frac{ax_0}{n_i} \right)^2 \qquad (5.67)$$

There may be situations in which the doping gradient is not the same on either side of the junction, but we will not consider that condition here.

If a reverse-bias voltage is applied to the junction, the potential barrier increases. The built-in potential barrier V_{bi} in the preceding equations is then replaced by the

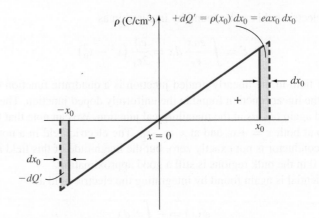

Figure 5.27 | Differential change in space charge width with a differential change in reverse-bias voltage for a linearly graded pn junction.

total potential barrier $V_{bi} + V_R$. Solving for x_0 from Equation (5.64) and using the total potential barrier, we obtain

$$x_0 = \left[\frac{3}{2} \frac{\epsilon_s}{ea} (V_{bi} + V_R) \right]^{1/3} \qquad (5.68)$$

The junction capacitance per unit area can be determined by the same method as we used for the uniformly doped junction. Figure 5.27 shows the differential charge dQ', which is uncovered as a differential voltage dV_R is applied. The junction capacitance is then

$$C' = \frac{dQ'}{dV_R} = (eax_0) \frac{dx_0}{dV_R} \qquad (5.69)$$

Using Equation (5.68), we obtain[3]

Junction capacitance

$$C' = \left[\frac{ea\epsilon_s^2}{12(V_{bi} + V_R)} \right]^{1/3} \qquad (5.70)$$

We can note that C' is proportional to $(V_{bi} + V_R)^{-1/3}$ for the linearly graded junction as compared to $C' \alpha (V_{bi} + V_R)^{-1/2}$ for the uniformly doped junction. In the linearly graded junction, the capacitance is less dependent on reverse-bias voltage than in the uniformly doped junction.

5.7.2 Hyperabrupt Junctions

The uniformly doped junction and linearly graded junction are not the only possible doping profiles. Figure 5.28 shows a generalized one-sided p^+n junction where the

---

[3]In a more exact analysis, V_{bi} in Equation (5.70) is replaced by a gradient voltage. However, this analysis is beyond the scope of this text.

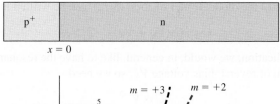

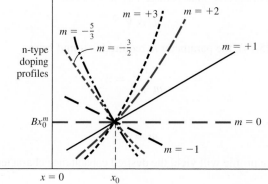

Figure 5.28 | Generalized doping profiles of a one-sided
p^+n junction.
(From Sze [15].)

generalized n-type doping concentration for $x > 0$ is given by

$$N = Bx^m \tag{5.71}$$

The case of $m = 0$ corresponds to the uniformly doped junction and $m = +1$ corresponds to the linearly graded junction just discussed. The cases of $m = +2$ and $m = +3$ shown would approximate a fairly low-doped epitaxial n-type layer grown on a much more heavily doped n^+ substrate layer. When the value of m is negative, we have what is referred to as a *hyperabrupt junction*. In this case, the n-type doping is larger near the metallurgical junction than in the bulk semiconductor. Equation (5.71) is used to approximate the n-type doping over a small region near $x = x_0$ and does not hold at $x = 0$ when m is negative.

Hyperabrupt junction

The junction capacitance can be derived using the same analysis method as before and is given by

$$C' = \left[\frac{eB\epsilon_s^{(m+1)}}{(m+2)(V_{bi} + V_R)} \right]^{1/(m+2)} \tag{5.72}$$

When m is negative, the capacitance becomes a very strong function of reverse-bias voltage, a desired characteristic in *varactor diodes*. The term *varactor* comes from the words *var*iable re*actor* and means a device whose reactance can be varied in a controlled manner with bias voltage.

Varactor diode

If a varactor diode and an inductance are in parallel, the resonant frequency of the LC circuit is

$$f_r = \frac{1}{2\pi\sqrt{LC}} \tag{5.73}$$

The capacitance of the diode, from Equation (5.72), can be written in the form

$$C = C_0(V_{bi} + V_R)^{-1/(m+2)} \tag{5.74}$$

In a circuit application, we would, in general, like to have the resonant frequency be a linear function of reverse-bias voltage V_R, so we need

$$C \propto V^{-2} \tag{5.75}$$

From Equation (5.74), the parameter m required is found from

$$\frac{1}{m+2} = 2 \tag{5.76a}$$

or

$$m = -\frac{3}{2} \tag{5.76b}$$

A specific doping profile will yield the desired capacitance characteristic.

Σ 5.8 | DEVICE FABRICATION TECHNIQUES: PHOTOLITHOGRAPHY, ETCHING, AND BONDING

Objective: Describe the general fabrication techniques of a pn junction.

In previous sections on device fabrication techniques, we have discussed thermal oxidation, diffusion, and ion implantation. In this section, we expand our discussion of device fabrication techniques, but will use oxidation, diffusion, and ion implantation in the fabrication of a pn junction.

We discussed the thermal oxidation process in which silicon dioxide is formed on the surface of silicon. One of the characteristics of silicon dioxide is that the diffusion coefficients of impurity atoms, such as phosphorus, arsenic, or boron, in this oxide is very, very low. For this reason, silicon dioxide can be used as a mask to prevent impurity diffusion into particular areas of the silicon. Silicon dioxide also acts as a mask to ion implantation.

5.8.1 Photomasks and Photolithography

Photomask

Photoresist

The actual circuitry and device layout on each chip is created through the use of photomasks and photolithography. The photomask is a physical representation of a device or a portion of a device. Opaque regions on the mask are made of an ultraviolet-light-absorbing material. A photosensitive layer, called photoresist, is first spread over the surface of a semiconductor. The photoresist is an organic polymer that undergoes chemical change when exposed to ultraviolet light. The photoresist is exposed to ultraviolet light through the photomask, as indicated in Figure 5.29. The photoresist is then developed in a chemical solution. The developer is used to remove the unwanted portions of the photoresist and generate the appropriate patterns on the silicon. The photomasks and photolithography process are critical in

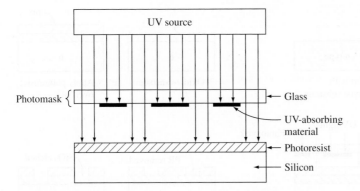

Figure 5.29 | Schematic showing the use of a photomask.

that they determine how small the devices can be made. Instead of using ultraviolet light, electrons and x-rays can also be used to expose the photoresist.

5.8.2 Etching

After the photoresist pattern is formed, the remaining photoresist can be used as a mask, so that the material not covered by the photoresist can be etched. Plasma etching is now the standard process used in IC fabrication. Typically, an etch gas such as chlorofluorocarbons are injected into a low-pressure chamber. A plasma is created by applying a radio-frequency voltage between cathode and anode terminals. The silicon wafer is placed on the cathode. Positively charged ions in the plasma are accelerated toward the cathode and bombard the wafer normal to the surface. The actual chemical and physical reaction at the surface is complex, but the net result is that silicon can be etched anisotropically in very selected regions of the wafer. If photoresist is applied on the surface of silicon dioxide, then the silicon dioxide can also be etched in a similar way.

5.8.3 Impurity Diffusion or Ion Implantation

Impurity diffusion or ion implantation can now be used to create the pn junction. Figure 5.30 shows the basic steps in the fabrication of two adjacent pn junctions. We assume that we start with an n-type wafer or substrate. Once the silicon dioxide and photoresist are etched, diffusion or ion implantation of acceptor impurities (boron) occurs. The pn junction can then be formed in specified areas or regions in the silicon, as shown in Figure 5.30(6).

5.8.4 Metallization, Bonding, and Packaging

After the semiconductor devices have been fabricated by the processing steps discussed, they need to be connected to each other to form the circuit. Metal films are generally deposited by a vapor deposition technique and the actual interconnect lines are formed using photolithography and etching. In general, a protective layer of silicon nitride is finally deposited over the entire chip.

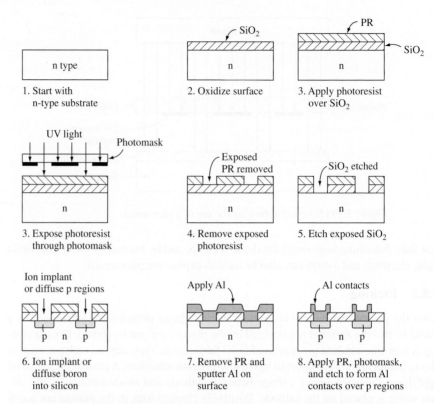

Figure 5.30 | The basic fabrication steps in forming two pn junction diodes. The n-region contact is at the bottom of the n substrate.

The individual integrated circuit chips are separated by scribing and breaking of the wafer. The integrated circuit chip is then mounted in a package. Lead bonders are finally used to attach gold or aluminum wires between the chip and package terminals.

5.9 | SUMMARY

1. A. A uniformly doped pn junction was initially considered, in which one region of a semiconductor is uniformly doped with acceptor impurities and the adjacent region is uniformly doped with donor impurities. This type of junction is called a homojunction.

   B. A space charge region, or depletion region, is formed on either side of the metallurgical junction separating the n and p regions. This region is essentially depleted of any mobile electrons or holes. A net positive charge density, due to the positively charged donor impurity ions, exists in the n region and a net negative charge density, due to the negatively charged acceptor impurity ions, exists in the p region.

2. A. An electric field exists in the depletion region due to the net space charge density. The direction of the electric field is from the n region to the p region.

   B. A potential difference exists across the space charge region. Under zero applied bias, this potential difference, known as the built-in potential barrier, maintains thermal equilibrium and holds back majority-carrier electrons in the n region and majority-carrier holes in the p region. The relationship for built-in potential barrier was derived in terms of doping concentrations.

   C.   Expressions were derived for the space charge width x_n that extends into the n region, the space charge width x_p that extends into the p region, the total space charge width W, and the electric field.

3. A.   An applied reverse bias voltage (n region positive with respect to the p region) increases the potential barrier, increases the space charge width, and increases the magnitude of the electric field in the depletion region.

   B.   As the reverse bias voltage changes, the amount of charge in the depletion region changes. This change in charge with voltage defines the junction capacitance.

4. A.   A metal-to-lightly doped n-type semiconductor contact can form a rectifying junction. A Schottky barrier is formed between the metal and semiconductor.

   B.   A space charge region is induced in the semiconductor under zero bias and reverse bias (semiconductor positive). Expressions for the built-in potential barrier, space charge width, and junction capacitance were developed.

5. A.   An applied forward-bias voltage to a pn junction (p region positive with respect to the n region) reduces the potential barrier allowing electrons and holes to flow across the junction.

   B.   A forward-bias voltage applied to a Schottky barrier junction (metal positive) reduces the potential barrier, allowing electrons from the semiconductor to flow across the junction.

   C.   In forward bias, the diode current in both junctions is an exponential function of diode voltage.

6. A.   An ohmic metal–semiconductor contact allows electrical conduction in both directions between the metal and semiconductor. Ideally, the current through the ohmic contact is a linear function of applied voltage, and the applied voltage is very small.

   B.   Two general types of ohmic contacts are possible. One is the ideal nonrectifying contact and the second is the tunneling diode.

7. A.   The linearly graded junction represents a nonuniformly doped pn junction. Expressions for the electric field, built-in potential barrier, and junction capacitance were derived. The functional relationships differ from those of the uniformly doped junction.

   B.   Specific doping profiles can be used to obtain specific capacitance characteristics. A hyperabrupt junction is one in which the doping decreases away from the metallurgical junction. This type of junction is advantageous in varactor diodes that are used in resonant circuits.

8. The pn junction is fabricated using the photolithography technique. Etching of the photoresist and oxide opens up regions so that impurity atoms can be diffused or ion implanted into selected regions to create the pn junction.

CHECKPOINT

After studying this chapter, the reader should have the ability to

1. A.   Sketch the energy-band diagram of a zero-biased pn junction and define the built-in potential barrier.

   B.   Describe why and how the space charge region is formed.

2. A.   Describe the formation of the electric field in the space charge region.

   B.   Describe how the built-in potential barrier maintains thermal equilibrium.
3. A.   Sketch the energy-band diagram of the pn junction when a reverse-bias voltage is applied.
   B.   Describe what happens to the space charge widths and electric field when a reverse-bias voltage is applied to the pn junction.
   C.   Explain the source of junction capacitance.
   D.   Describe the characteristics and properties of a one-sided pn junction.
4. A.   Describe the formation of a Schottky barrier junction in which $\phi_m > \phi_s$, and define the Schottky barrier junction and built-in potential barrier.
   B.   Sketch the energy-band diagram of a reverse-biased Schottky barrier junction.
5. A.   Sketch the energy-band diagram of a forward-biased pn junction and a forward-biased Schottky barrier junction.
   B.   Sketch the current–voltage characteristics of a pn junction diode and a Schottky barrier junction diode on the same plot. Describe similarities and differences.
6. A.   Sketch the energy-band diagram of an ideal nonrectifying contact with both n-type and p-type semiconductors.
   B.   Sketch the energy-band diagram of a tunneling ohmic contact.
7. A.   Describe how a linearly graded junction is formed.
   B.   Define a hyperabrupt junction.
8. Describe the general procedure of fabricating a pn junction.

REVIEW QUESTIONS

1. Sketch the energy-band diagram of a zero-biased pn junction.
2. A.   Why is the electric field a linear function of distance in a uniformly doped pn junction? What is the direction of the electric field?
   B.   If $N_a > N_d$ in a pn junction, is $x_p > x_n$, $x_n > x_p$, or $x_n = x_p$?
   C.   How does the built-in potential barrier depend on the doping concentrations in the pn junction?
3. A.   In a reverse-biased pn junction, which side has the higher potential?
   B.   Sketch the energy-band diagram of a reverse-biased pn junction.
   C.   Why does the space charge width increase with reverse-bias voltage?
   D.   Why does a capacitance exist in a reverse-biased pn junction? Why does the capacitance decrease with increasing reverse-bias voltage?
   E.   What is a one-sided pn junction? What parameters can be determined in a one-sided junction?
4. Sketch the energy-band diagram of a zero-biased rectifying metal-to-n-type semiconductor contact. Define the Schottky barrier and built-in potential barrier.
5. A.   Sketch the energy-band diagram of a forward-biased pn junction.
   B.   Why can charge flow across a forward-biased pn junction?
6. A.   Sketch the energy-band diagram of an ideal nonrectifying metal–semiconductor contact with a p-type semiconductor.
   B.   Discuss the electron flow in a tunneling ohmic contact under both bias conditions.
7. A.   What is a linearly graded junction?
   B.   What is a hyperabrupt junction and what is one advantage or characteristic of such a junction?
8. What are the various steps in the fabrication of a pn junction?

PROBLEMS

Section 5.2   The pn Junction—Zero Applied Bias

5.1   (a) Calculate V_{bi} in a silicon pn junction at $T = 300$ K for (a) $N_d = 10^{15}$ cm^{-3} and $N_a = $ (i) 10^{15}, (ii) 10^{16}, (iii) 10^{17}, (iv) 10^{18} cm^{-3}. (b) Repeat part (a) for $N_d = 10^{18}$ cm^{-3}.

5.2   Calculate the built-in potential barrier, V_{bi}, for Si, Ge, and GaAs pn junctions if they each have the following dopant concentrations at $T = 300$ K:

(a) $N_d = 10^{14}$ cm^{-3} $N_a = 10^{17}$ cm^{-3}

(b) $N_d = 5 \times 10^{16}$ $N_a = 5 \times 10^{16}$

(c) $N_d = 10^{17}$ $N_a = 10^{17}$

5.3   (a) Plot the built-in potential barrier for a symmetrical ($N_a = N_d$) silicon pn junction at $T = 300$ K over the range $10^{14} \le N_a = N_d \le 10^{19}$ cm^{-3}. (b) Repeat part (a) for a GaAs pn junction.

5.4   Consider a uniformly doped GaAs pn junction with doping concentrations of $N_a = 5 \times 10^{18}$ cm^{-3} and $N_d = 5 \times 10^{16}$ cm^{-3}. Plot the built-in potential barrier voltage, V_{bi}, versus temperature for $200 \le T \le 500$ K.

5.5   An abrupt silicon pn junction at zero bias has dopant concentrations of $N_a = 10^{17}$ cm^{-3} and $N_d = 5 \times 10^{15}$ cm^{-3}. $T = 300$ K. (a) Calculate the Fermi level on each side of the junction with respect to the intrinsic Fermi level. (b) Sketch the equilibrium energy-band diagram for the junction and determine V_{bi} from the diagram and the results of part (a). (c) Calculate V_{bi} using Equation (5.10), and compare the results to part (b). (d) Determine x_n, x_p, and the peak electric field for this junction.

5.6   Repeat problem 5.5 for the case when the doping concentrations are $N_a = N_d = 2 \times 10^{16}$ cm^{-3}.

5.7   A silicon abrupt junction in thermal equilibrium at $T = 300$ K is doped such that $E_c - E_F = 0.21$ eV in the n region and $E_F - E_v = 0.18$ eV in the p region. (a) Draw the energy band diagram of the pn junction. (b) Determine the impurity doping concentrations in each region. (c) Determine V_{bi}.

5.8   Consider the uniformly doped GaAs junction at $T = 300$ K. At zero bias, only 20 percent of the total space charge region is to be in the p region. The built-in potential barrier is $V_{bi} = 1.20$ V. For zero bias, determine (a) N_a, (b) N_d, (c) x_n, (d) x_p, and (e) $\mathcal{E}_{max}$.

5.9   Consider the impurity doping profile shown in Figure P5.9 in a silicon pn junction. For zero applied voltage, (a) determine V_{bi}, (b) calculate x_n and x_p, (c) sketch the thermal equilibrium energy band diagram, and (d) plot the electric field versus distance through the junction.

*5.10   A uniformly doped silicon pn junction is doped to levels of $N_d = 5 \times 10^{15}$ cm^{-3} and $N_a = 10^{16}$ cm^{-3}. The measured built-in potential barrier is $V_{bi} = 0.40$ V. Determine the temperature at which this result occurs. (You may have to use trial and error to solve this problem.)

5.11   Consider a uniformly doped silicon pn junction with doping concentrations $N_a = 5 \times 10^{17}$ cm^{-3} and $N_d = 10^{17}$ cm^{-3}. (a) Calculate V_{bi} at $T = 300$ K. (b) Determine the temperature at which V_{bi} decreases by 1 percent.

5.12   An "isotype" step junction is one in which the same impurity type doping changes from one concentration value to another value. An n-n isotype doping profile is shown

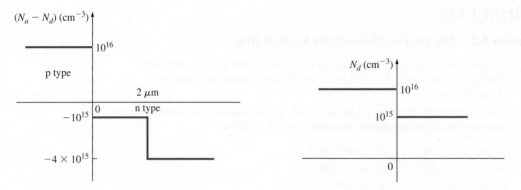

Figure P5.9 | Figure for Problem 5.9.   **Figure P5.12 |** Figure for Problem 5.12.

in Figure P5.12. (*a*) Sketch the thermal equilibrium energy-band diagram of the iso-type junction. (*b*) Using the energy-band diagram, determine the built-in potential barrier. (*c*) Discuss the charge distribution through the junction.

5.13 A particular type of junction is an n region adjacent to an intrinsic region. This junction can be modeled as an n-type region to a lightly doped p-type region. Assume the doping concentrations in silicon at $T = 300$ K are $N_d = 10^{16}$ cm^{-3} and $N_a = 10^{12}$ cm^{-3}. For zero applied bias, determine (*a*) V_{bi}, (*b*) x_n, (*c*) x_p, and (*d*) $|\mathcal{E}_{max}|$. Sketch the electric field versus distance through the junction.

5.14 We are assuming an abrupt depletion approximation for the space charge region. That is, no free carriers exist within the depletion region and the semiconductor abruptly changes to a neutral region outside the space charge region. This approximation is adequate for most applications, but the abrupt transition does not exist. The space charge region changes over a distance of a few Debye lengths, where the Debye length in the n region is given by

$$L_D = \left(\frac{\epsilon_s kT}{e^2 N_d} \right)^{1/2}$$

Calculate L_D and find the ratio of L_D/x_n for the following conditions. The p-type doping concentration is $N_a = 8 \times 10^{17}$ cm^{-3} and the n-type doping concentration is (*a*) $N_d = 8 \times 10^{14}$ cm^{-3}, (*b*) $N_d = 2.2 \times 10^{16}$ cm^{-3}, and (*c*) $N_d = 8 \times 10^{17}$ cm^{-3}.

5.15 Examine how the electric field versus distance through a uniformly doped pn junction varies as the doping concentrations vary. For example, consider $N_d = 10^{18}$ cm^{-3} and let $10^{14} \le N_a \le 10^{18}$ cm^{-3}, then consider $N_d = 10^{14}$ cm^{-3} and let $10^{14} \le N_a \le 10^{18}$ cm^{-3}, and finally consider $N_d = 10^{16}$ cm^{-3} and let $10^{14} \le N_a \le 10^{18}$ cm^{-3}. What can be said about the results for $N_a \ge 100 N_d$ or $N_d \ge 100 N_a$? Assume zero applied bias.

Section 5.3   The pn Junction—Reverse Applied Bias

5.16 An abrupt silicon pn junction has dopant concentrations of $N_a = 2 \times 10^{16}$ cm^{-3} and $N_d = 2 \times 10^{15}$ cm^{-3} at $T = 300$ K. Calculate (*a*) V_{bi}, (*b*) W at $V_R = 0$ and $V_R = 8$ V, and (*c*) the maximum electric field in the space charge region at $V_R = 0$ and $V_R = 8$ V.

5.17 Consider the junction described in Problem 5.11. The junction has a cross-sectional area of 10^{-4} cm^2 and has an applied reverse-bias voltage of $V_R = 5$ V. Calculate (a) V_{bi}, (b) x_n, x_p, W, (c) $\mathcal{E}_{max}$, and (d) the total junction capacitance.

5.18 An ideal one-sided silicon n$^+$p junction has uniform doping on both sides of the abrupt junction. The doping relation is $N_d = 50N_a$. The built-in potential barrier is $V_{bi} = 0.752$ V. The maximum electric field in the junction is $\mathcal{E}_{max} = 1.14 \times 10^5$ V/cm for a reverse-bias voltage of 10 V. $T = 300$ K. Determine (a) N_a, N_d (b) x_p for $V_R = 10$, and (c) C_j' for $V_R = 10$.

5.19 A silicon n$^+$p junction is biased at $V_R = 10$ V. Determine the percent change in (a) junction capacitance and (b) built-in potential if the doping in the p region increases by a factor of 2.

5.20 Consider two p$^+$n silicon junctions at $T = 300$ K reverse biased at $V_R = 5$ V. The impurity doping concentrations in junction A are $N_a = 10^{18}$ cm^{-3} and $N_d = 10^{15}$ cm^{-3}, and those in junction B are $N_a = 10^{18}$ cm^{-3} and $N_d = 10^{16}$ cm^{-3}. Calculate the ratio of the following parameters for junction A to junction B: (a) W, (b) $|\mathcal{E}_{max}|$, and (c) C_j'.

5.21 (a) The peak electric field in a reverse-biased silicon pn junction is $|\mathcal{E}_{max}| = 3 \times 10^5$ V/cm. The doping concentrations are $N_d = 4 \times 10^{15}$ cm^{-3} and $N_a = 4 \times 10^{17}$ cm^{-3}. Find the magnitude of the reverse-bias voltage. (b) Repeat part (a) for $N_d = 4 \times 10^{16}$ cm^{-3} and $N_a = 4 \times 10^{17}$ cm^{-3}. (c) Repeat part (a) for $N_d = N_a = 4 \times 10^{17}$ cm^{-3}.

5.22 Consider a uniformly doped GaAs pn junction at $T = 300$ K. The junction capacitance at zero bias is $C_j(0)$ and the junction capacitance with a 10-V reverse-bias voltage is $C_j(10)$. The ratio of the capacitances is

$$\frac{C_j(0)}{C_j(10)} = 3.13$$

Also under reverse bias, the space charge width into the p region is 0.2 of the total space charge width. Determine (a) V_{bi} and (b) N_a, N_d.

5.23 A GaAs pn junction at $T = 300$ K has impurity doping concentrations of $N_a = 10^{16}$ cm^{-3} and $N_d = 5 \times 10^{16}$ cm^{-3}. For a particular device application, the ratio of junction capacitances at two values of reverse bias voltage must be $C_j'(V_{R1})/C_j'(V_{R2}) = 3$, where the reverse bias voltage $V_{R1} = 1$ V. Determine V_{R2}.

5.24 An abrupt silicon pn junction at $T = 300$ K is uniformly doped with $N_a = 10^{18}$ cm^{-3} and $N_d = 10^{15}$ cm^{-3}. The pn junction area is 6×10^{-4} cm^2. An inductance of 2.2 millihenry is placed in parallel with the pn junction. Calculate the resonant frequency of the circuit for reverse-bias voltages of (a) $V_R = 1$ V and (b) $V_R = 10$ V.

5.25 A uniformly doped silicon p$^+$n junction at $T = 300$ K is to be designed such that at a reverse-bias voltage of $V_R = 10$ V, the maximum electric field is limited to $\mathcal{E}_{max} = 10^6$ V/cm. Determine the maximum doping concentration in the n region.

5.26 A silicon pn junction is to be designed that meets the following specifications at $T = 300$ K. At a reverse-bias voltage of 1.2 V, 10 percent of the total space charge region is to be in the n region and the total junction capacitance is to be 3.5×10^{-12} F with a cross-sectional area of 5.5×10^{-4} cm^2. Determine (a) N_a, (b) N_d, and (c) V_{bi}.

5.27 A silicon pn junction at $T = 300$ K has the doping profile shown in Figure P5.27. Calculate (a) V_{bi}, (b) x_n and x_p at zero bias, and (c) the applied bias required so that $x_n = 30$ μm.

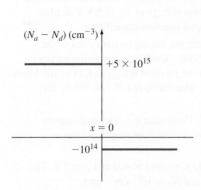

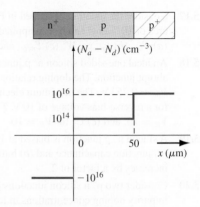

Figure P5.27 | Figure for Problem 5.27.   **Figure P5.28 |** Figure for Problem 5.28.

5.28   Consider a silicon pn junction with the doping profile shown in Figure P5.28. $T = 300$ K. (*a*) Calculate the applied reverse-bias voltage required so that the space charge region extends entirely through the p region. (*b*) Determine the space charge width into the n^+ region with the reverse-bias voltage calculated in part (*a*). (*c*) Calculate the peak electric field for this applied voltage.

5.29   (*a*) A silicon p^+n junction has doping concentrations of $N_a = 10^{18}$ cm^{-3} and $N_d = 5 \times 10^{15}$ cm^{-3}. The cross-sectional area of the junction is $A = 5 \times 10^{-5}$ cm^2. Calculate the junction capacitance for (*i*) $V_R = 0$, (*ii*) $V_R = 3$ V, and (*iii*) $V_R = 6$ V. Plot $1/C^2$ versus V_R. Show that the slope of the curve can be used to find N_d and that the intersection with the voltage axis yields V_{bi}. (*b*) Repeat part (*a*) if the n-type doping concentration changes to $N_d = 6 \times 10^{16}$ cm^{-3}.

5.30   The total junction capacitance of a one-sided silicon pn junction at $T = 300$ K is measured at $V_R = 50$ mV and found to be 1.3 pF. The junction area is 10^{-5} cm^2 and $V_{bi} = 0.95$ V. (*a*) Find the impurity doping concentration of the low-doped side of the junction. (*b*) Find the impurity doping concentration of the higher-doped region.

5.31   Examine how the capacitance C' and the function $(1/C')^2$ vary with reverse-bias voltage V_R as the doping concentrations change. In particular, consider these plots versus N_a for $N_a \geq 100N_d$ and versus N_d for $N_d \geq 100N_a$.

*5.32   A pn junction has the doping profile shown in Figure P5.32. Assume that $x_n > x_0$ for all reverse-bias voltages. (*a*) What is the built-in potential across the junction? (*b*) For the abrupt junction approximation, sketch the charge density through the junction. (*c*) Derive the expression for the electric field through the space charge region.

*5.33   A silicon PIN junction has the doping profile shown in Figure P5.33. The "I" corresponds to an ideal intrinsic region in which there is no impurity doping concentration. A reverse-bias voltage is applied to the PIN junction so that the total depletion width extends from -2 μm to $+2$ μm. (*a*) Using Poisson's equation, calculate the magnitude of the electric field at $x = 0$. (*b*) Sketch the electric field through the PIN junction. (*c*) Calculate the reverse-bias voltage that must be applied.

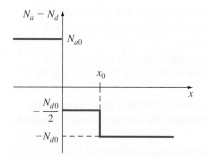

Figure P5.32 | Figure for Problem 5.32.

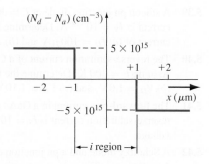

Figure P5.33 | Figure for Problem 5.33.

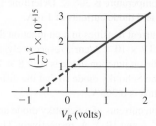

Figure P5.37 | Figure for Problem 5.37.

Section 5.4   Metal–Semiconductor Contact—Rectifying Junction

(In the following problems, assume $A^* = 120$ A/K^2-cm^2 for silicon and
$A^* = 1.12$ A/K^2-cm^2 for gallium arsenide Schottky diodes unless otherwise stated.)

5.34 Consider a contact between Al and n Si doped at $N_d = 10^{16}$ cm^{-3}. $T = 300$ K.
(a) Draw the energy-band diagrams of the two materials before the junction is formed.
(b) Draw the ideal energy band at zero bias after the junction is formed. (c) Calculate
ϕ_{B0}, x_d, and $\mathcal{E}_{max}$ for part (b).

5.35 An ideal rectifying contact is formed by depositing gold on n-type silicon doped at
10^{15} cm^{-3}. At $T = 300$ K, determine (a) ϕ_{B0}, (b) V_{bi}, (c) W, and (d) $\mathcal{E}_{max}$, all under
equilibrium conditions.

5.36 Consider a gold Schottky diode at $T = 300$ K formed on n-type GaAs doped at $N_d =
5 \times 10^{16}$ cm^{-3}. Determine (a) the theoretical barrier height, ϕ_{B0}, (b) ϕ_n, (c) V_{bi},
(d) the space charge width, x_n, for $V_R = 5$ V, and (e) the electric field at the metal
junction for $V_R = 5$ V.

5.37 A Schottky diode with n-type GaAs at $T = 300$ K yields the $1/C'^2$ versus V_R plot
shown in Figure P5.37, where C' is the capacitance per cm^2. Determine (a) V_{bi},
(b) N_d, (c) ϕ_n, and (d) ϕ_{B0}.

Section 5.5   Forward Applied Bias—An Introduction

5.38 Consider a silicon pn junction diode at $T = 300$ K. The reverse-saturation current is
$I_S = 4 \times 10^{-13}$A. Determine the forward-bias diode current at $V_D = 0.5$ V, 0.6 V,
and 0.7 V.

5.39 A silicon pn junction diode at $T = 300$ K is forward biased. The reverse-saturation current is $I_S = 10^{-14}$ A. Determine the required diode voltage to induce a diode current of (a) $I_D = 100\,\mu$A and (b) $I_D = 1.50$ mA.

5.40 The reverse-saturation current of a GaAs pn junction diode is $I_S = 5 \times 10^{-21}$ A. Assume $T = 300$ K. Determine the forward-bias diode current for (a) $V_D = 0.90$ V, (b) $V_D = 1.0$ V, and (c) $V_D = 1.10$ V.

5.41 The forward-bias current in a GaAs pn junction at $T = 300$ K is $I_D = 15$ mA. The reverse-saturation current is $I_S = 10^{-19}$ A. Determine the required forward-bias diode voltage.

5.42 A Schottky diode and a pn junction diode have cross-sectional areas of $A = 5 \times 10^{-4}$ cm^2. The reverse saturation current density of the Schottky diode is 3×10^{-8} A/cm^2 and the reverse saturation current density of the pn junction diode is 3×10^{-12} A/cm^2. The temperature is 300 K. Determine the forward-bias voltage in each diode required to yield diode currents of 1 mA.

5.43 The reverse saturation current densities in a pn junction diode and a Schottky diode are 5×10^{-12} A/cm^2 and 7×10^{-8} A/cm^2, respectively, at $T = 300$ K. The cross-sectional area of the pn junction diode is $A = 8 \times 10^{-4}$ cm^2. Determine the cross-sectional area of the Schottky diode so that the difference in forward-bias voltages to achieve 1.2 mA is 0.265 V.

5.44 (a) The reverse-saturation currents of a Schottky diode and a pn junction diode at $T = 300$ K are 5×10^{-8} A and 10^{-12} A, respectively. The diodes are connected in parallel and are driven by a constant current of 0.5 mA. (i) Determine the current in each diode. (ii) Determine the voltage across each diode. (b) Repeat part (a) if the diodes are connected in series.

Section 5.6   Metal–Semiconductor Ohmic Contacts

5.45 A metal, with a work function $\phi_m = 4.2$ V, is deposited on an n-type silicon semiconductor with $\chi_s = 4.0$ V and $E_g = 1.12$ eV. Assume no interface states exist at the junction. Let $T = 300$ K. (a) Sketch the energy-band diagram for zero bias for the case when no space charge region exists at the junction. (b) Determine N_d so that the condition in part (a) is satisfied. (c) What is the potential barrier height seen by electrons in the metal moving into the semiconductor?

5.46 Consider the energy-band diagram of a silicon Schottky junction under zero bias shown in Figure P5.46. Let $\phi_{B0} = 0.7$ V and $T = 300$ K. Determine the doping required so that $x_d = 50$ Å at the point where the potential is $\phi_{B0}/2$ below the peak value.

5.47 A metal–semiconductor junction is formed between a metal with a work function of 4.3 eV and p-type silicon with an electron affinity of 4.0 eV. The acceptor doping concentration in the silicon is $N_a = 5 \times 10^{16}$ cm^{-3}. Assume $T = 300$ K. (a) Sketch the thermal-equilibrium energy-band diagram. (b) Determine the height of the Schottky barrier. (c) Sketch the energy-band diagram with an applied reverse-bias voltage of $V_R = 3$ V. (d) Sketch the energy-band diagram with an applied forward-bias voltage of $V_a = 0.25$ V.

Section 5.7   Nonuniformly Doped pn Junctions

5.48 The built-in potential barrier of a linearly graded silicon pn junction at $T = 300$ K is $V_{bi} = 0.70$ V. The junction capacitance measured at $V_R = 3.5$ V is $C' = 7.2 \times 10^{-9}$ F/cm^2. Find the gradient, a, of the net impurity concentration.

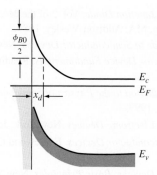

Figure P5.46 | Figure for
Problem 5.46.

Summary and Review

5.49 A one-sided $p^{+}n$ silicon diode at $T = 300$ K is doped at $N_a = 10^{18}$ cm^{-3}. Design the junction so that $C_j = 0.95$ pF at $V_R = 3.5$ V. Calculate the junction capacitance when $V_R = 1.5$ V.

5.50 A one-sided $p^{+}n$ junction with a cross-sectional area of 10^{-5} cm^2 has a measured built-in potential of $V_{bi} = 0.8$ V at $T = 300$ K. A plot of $(1/C_j)^2$ versus V_R is linear for $V_R < 1$ V and is essentially constant for $V_R > 1$ V. The capacitance is $C_j = 0.082$ pF at $V_R = 1$ V. Determine the doping concentrations on either side of the metallurgical junction that will produce this capacitance characteristic.

5.51 Silicon, at $T = 300$ K, is doped at $N_{d1} = 10^{15}$ cm^{-3} for $x < 0$ and $N_{d2} = 5 \times 10^{16}$ cm^{-3} for $x > 0$ to form an n–n step junction. (a) Sketch the energy-band diagram. (b) Derive an expression for V_{bi}. (c) Sketch the charge density, electric field, and potential through the junction. (d) Explain where the charge density came from and is located.

5.52 A diffused silicon pn junction has a linearly graded junction on the p side with $a = 2 \times 10^{19}$ cm^{-4}, and a uniform doping of 10^{15} cm^{-3} on the n side. (a) If the depletion width on the p side is 0.7 μm at zero bias, find the total depletion width, built-in potential, and maximum electric field at zero bias. (b) Plot the potential function through the junction.

READING LIST

1. `Dimitrijev, S. *Understanding Semiconductor Devices.* New York: Oxford University Press, 2000.

2. Kano, K. *Semiconductor Devices.* Upper Saddle River, NJ: Prentice-Hall, 1998.

*3. Li, S. S. *Semiconductor Physical Electronics.* New York: Plenum Press, 1993.

4. Muller, R. S., T. I. Kamins, and W. Chan. *Device Electronics for Integrated Circuits,* 3rd ed. New York: John Wiley and Sons, 2003.

5. Navon, D. H. *Semiconductor Microdevices and Materials.* New York: Holt, Rinehart & Winston, 1986.

6. Neamen, D. A. *Semiconductor Physics and Devices: Basic Principles,* 3rd ed. New York: McGraw-Hill, 2003.

7. Neudeck, G. W. *The PN Junction Diode.* Vol. 2 of the *Modular Series on Solid State Devices.* 2nd ed. Reading, MA: Addison-Wesley, 1989.

*8. Ng, K. K. *Complete Guide to Semiconductor Devices.* New York: McGraw-Hill, 1995.

9. Pierret, R. F. *Semiconductor Device Fundamentals.* Reading, MA: Addison-Wesley, 1996.

*10. Roulston, D. J. *An Introduction to the Physics of Semiconductor Devices.* New York: Oxford University Press, 1999.

11. Shur, M. *Introduction to Electronic Devices.* New York: John Wiley and Sons, 1996.

*12. Shur, M. *Physics of Semiconductor Devices.* Englewood Cliffs, NJ: Prentice-Hall, 1990.

13. Singh, J. *Semiconductor Devices: Basic Principles.* New York: John Wiley and Sons, 2001.

14. Streetman, B. G., and S. Banerjee. *Solid State Electronic Devices,* 5th ed. Upper Saddle River, NJ: Prentice-Hall, 2000.

15. Sze, S. M. *Physics of Semiconductor Devices.* 2nd ed. New York: Wiley, 1981.

16. Sze, S. M. *Semiconductor Devices: Physics and Technology,* 2nd ed. New York: John Wiley and Sons, Inc., 2002.

*17. Wang, S. *Fundamentals of Semiconductor Theory and Device Physics.* Englewood Cliffs, NJ: Prentice-Hall, 1989.

18. Wolf, S. *Silicon Processing for the VLSI Era: Volume 3—The Submicron MOSFET.* Sunset Beach, CA: Lattice Press, 1995.

19. Yang, E. S. *Microelectronic Devices.* New York: McGraw-Hill, 1988.

Fundamentals of the Metal–Oxide–Semiconductor Field-Effect Transistor

The fundamental physics of the **m**etal–**o**xide–**s**emiconductor **f**ield-**e**ffect **t**ransistor (MOSFET) is developed in this chapter. The MOSFET, in conjunction with other circuit elements, is capable of voltage gain and signal power gain and is therefore called an active device. The MOSFET is used extensively in digital circuit applications where, because of its relatively small size, millions of devices can be fabricated in a single integrated circuit. The MOSFET is the core of integrated circuit design.

The MOS designation is implicitly used only for the metal–silicon dioxide (SiO_2)–silicon system. The more general terminology is metal–insulator–semiconductor (MIS), where the insulator is not necessarily silicon dioxide and the semiconductor is not necessarily silicon. We will use the MOS system throughout this chapter although the same basic physics applies to the MIS system.

We will consider the basic MOSFET operation and characteristics in this chapter. In the next chapter, we will consider more advanced MOSFET topics.

6.0 | PREVIEW

In this chapter, we will

1. Briefly describe the structure and qualitatively discuss the operation of the MOSFET.

2. Describe the characteristics of the two-terminal MOS capacitor, including energy-band diagrams and charge distributions.

3. Analyze the potentials in an MOS capacitor, including work function difference, flat-band voltage, and threshold voltage.

4. Describe and analyze the capacitance–voltage characteristics of a MOS capacitor.

5. Describe the structure and analyze the characteristics of a MOSFET, including the current–voltage relationship.

6. Derive the small-signal equivalent circuit of the MOSFET and analyze the frequency limitations of the device.

7. Describe a few of the MOSFET fabrication techniques including the gate oxide, gate "metallization," and the CMOS technology.

Historical Insight

The idea of controlling a current in a device by a gate voltage (field effect) was patented by Julius Lilienfeld in 1926. However, the technology did not exist at that time to fabricate such a device. The MOSFET was reported by D. Kahng and M. Atalla in 1960, and by 1962, an MOS IC consisting of 16 MOS transistors was fabricated. The CMOS, that employs both NMOS and PMOS, concept was proposed by F. Wanlass and C. Sah in 1963. The first microprocessor was made by M. Hoff et al. in 1971 (Intel 4004). The entire central processing unit (CPU) of a simple computer was fabricated on a single chip. This IC contained 2300 MOSFETs and was a major breakthrough in integrated circuit technology.

Present-Day Insight

The MOSFET technology (in particular CMOS) continues to be the core of digital integrated circuits. One aim is to make smaller devices so that more devices can be fabricated on a single chip. In general, smaller devices also lead to increased speed and lower power dissipation.

6.1 | THE MOS FIELD-EFFECT TRANSISTOR ACTION

Objective: Briefly describe the structure and qualitatively discuss the operation of the MOSFET.

A simplified cross section of an n-channel MOSFET is shown in Figure 6.1. The device is actually a four-terminal structure. The metal–oxide–semiconductor portion of the device, or the MOS capacitor, is the heart of the transistor. The MOS capacitor will be analyzed in detail starting in Section 6.2. On either side of the gate oxide are n-type regions called the source and drain terminals. The region under the oxide between the source and drain terminals is referred to as the channel region. Two parameters of interest are the channel length L and channel width W, as shown in the figure. Another geometrical parameter that will be considered is the oxide thickness t_{ox}.

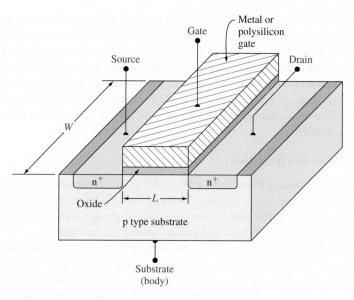

Figure 6.1 | Basic structure of an n-channel MOSFET.

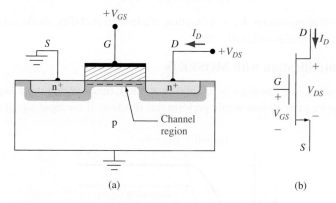

Figure 6.2 | (a) Typical biases applied to the n-channel MOSFET ($V_{GS} > V_T$). (b) Simplified circuit symbol with the same biases.

6.1.1 Basic Principle of Operation

Figure 6.2a shows typical biases applied to the device and Figure 6.2b shows a simplified circuit symbol with the same biases. By applying a positive gate voltage, a vertical electric field is induced in the oxide. This electric field also penetrates the semiconductor, and, if the electric field is large enough, a layer of electrons is created directly under the oxide. This layer of electrons is called an inversion layer and is also referred to as the channel region.

Channel region

Field-effect

Transistor action

When a drain-to-source voltage, V_{DS}, is applied, electrons flow from the source through the channel to the drain. The current is a function of the amount of charge in the inversion layer that, in turn, is a function of the vertical electric field. The term *field-effect* refers to the concept that the current is controlled by an electric field perpendicular to the flow of charge. The basic *transistor action* is that the voltage across two terminals (gate-to-source) controls the current in the third terminal (drain). This device is called an n-channel MOSFET since the current is due to the flow of electrons in the channel.

6.1.2 Modes of Operation

Threshold voltage

One primary electrical parameter of a MOSFET is the threshold voltage, V_T. If the gate-to-source voltage is less than the threshold voltage, the transistor is cut off and all currents are zero. If the gate-to-source voltage is greater than the threshold voltage, an inversion layer is formed and a drain current can be induced.

Figure 6.3 shows the transistor current–voltage characteristics. The drain current is plotted as a function of drain-to-source voltage for various gate voltages. In this case, a threshold voltage of $V_T = 0.5$ V is assumed. If the transistor is biased in the saturation region, $V_{DS} > V_{GS} - V_T$, then ideally the drain current is independent of the drain-to-source bias and is given by

$$I_D = K_n(V_{GS} - V_T)^2 \tag{6.1}$$

The conduction parameter K_n is a function of electron mobility, oxide capacitance, and the channel width-to-length ratio.

6.1.3 Amplification with MOSFETs

One application of a transistor is to amplify a small, time-varying input signal. Figure 6.4a shows a circuit that would perform this function. If the input signal is $v_i = 0$,

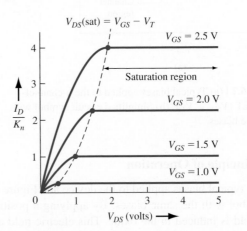

Figure 6.3 | Ideal current–voltage characteristics of n-channel MOSFET assuming $V_T = 0.5$ V.

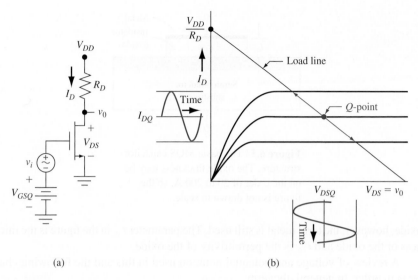

Figure 6.4 | (a) A circuit that can amplify a time-varying input signal v_i. (b) Load line and time-varying signals superimposed on transistor characteristics.

then the transistor is to be biased in the saturation region at the Q-point shown in Figure 6.4b. Writing the voltage law equation around the drain–source loop, we find

$$V_{DS} = V_{DD} - I_D R_D \qquad (6.2)$$

Equation (6.2) is called the load line equation and is superimposed on the transistor characteristics in Figure 6.4b.

When a time-varying input signal v_i is applied, the gate-to-source voltage changes with time. A time-varying drain current is induced that in turn causes a time-varying drain-to-source voltage. A time-varying output signal is generated whose magnitude can be greater than the magnitude of the input signal. Thus, the circuit is an amplifier.

We now begin to analyze the MOS capacitor to gain an understanding of the formation of the inversion layer.

6.2 | THE TWO-TERMINAL MOS CAPACITOR

Objective: Describe the characteristics of the two-terminal MOS capacitor, including energy-band diagrams and charge distributions.

The heart of the MOSFET is the metal–oxide–semiconductor capacitor. An understanding of the MOS capacitor is fundamental in understanding the characteristics and operation of the MOSFET. For this reason, we will spend time initially in studying the characteristics of the MOS capacitor. The MOS capacitor is shown in Figure 6.5. The metal may be aluminum or some other type of metal, although in most cases now, it is actually a high-conductivity polycrystalline silicon that has been deposited on the

The MOS capacitor

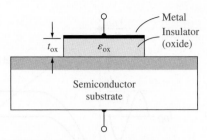

Figure 6.5 | The basic MOS capacitor structure. The oxide thickness may be on the order of 20 to 200 Å, so the figure is not drawn to scale.

oxide; however, the term metal is still used. The parameter t_{ox} in the figure is the thickness of the oxide and ϵ_{ox} is the permittivity of the oxide.

A review of voltage and potential notation used in this and the following chapter is in order. In general, the term

Potential notation

1. V, with an appropriate subscript, is used for a terminal voltage or device voltage parameter, such as threshold voltage or flat-band voltage (defined later); and

2. ϕ, with an appropriate subscript, is used for a potential or potential difference within the device structure.

As with most engineering notation, there may be a few exceptions noted within the chapter.

6.2.1 Energy-Band Diagrams and Charge Distributions

The physics of the MOS structure can be more easily explained with the aid of the simple parallel-plate capacitor. Figure 6.6a shows a parallel-plate capacitor with the top plate at a negative voltage with respect to the bottom plate. An insulator material separates the two plates. With this bias, a negative charge exists on the top plate, a positive charge exists on the bottom plate, and an electric field is induced between the two plates as shown. The capacitance per unit area for this geometry is

$$C' = \frac{\epsilon}{d} \tag{6.3}$$

where ϵ is the permittivity of the insulator and d is the distance between the two plates. The magnitude of the charge per unit area on either plate is

$$Q' = C'V \tag{6.4}$$

where the prime indicates charge or capacitance per unit area. The magnitude of the electric field is

$$\mathcal{E} = \frac{V}{d} \tag{6.5}$$

Figure 6.6b shows an MOS capacitor with a p-type semiconductor substrate. The top metal gate is at a negative voltage with respect to the semiconductor substrate.

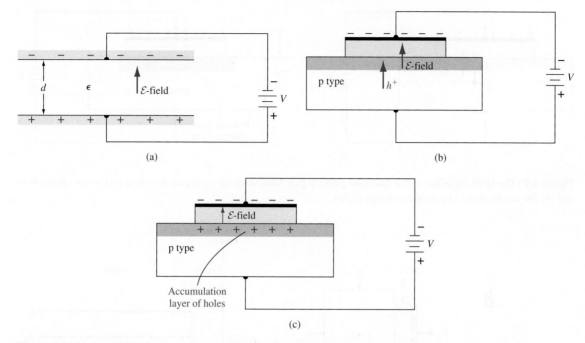

Figure 6.6 | (a) A parallel-plate capacitor showing the electric field and conductor charges. (b) A corresponding MOS capacitor with a negative gate bias showing the electric field and initial charge flow. (c) The MOS capacitor with a steady-state accumulation layer of holes adjacent to the semiconductor–oxide interface.

From the example of the parallel-plate capacitor, we can see that a negative charge will exist on the top metal plate and an electric field will be induced with the direction shown in the figure. If the electric field were to penetrate into the semiconductor, the majority carrier holes would experience a force toward the oxide–semiconductor interface. Figure 6.6c shows the equilibrium distribution of charge in the MOS capacitor with this particular applied voltage. An *accumulation layer* of holes in the oxide–semiconductor junction corresponds to the positive charge on the bottom "plate" of the MOS capacitor.

Figure 6.7a shows the same MOS capacitor in which the polarity of the applied voltage is reversed. A positive charge now exists on the top metal plate and the induced electric field is in the opposite direction as shown. If the electric field penetrates the semiconductor in this case, majority carrier holes will experience a force away from the oxide–semiconductor interface. As the holes are pushed away from the interface, a negative space charge region is created because of the fixed ionized acceptor atoms. The negative charge in the induced depletion region corresponds to the negative charge on the bottom "plate" of the MOS capacitor. Figure 6.7b shows the equilibrium distribution of charge in the MOS capacitor with this applied voltage.

The energy-band diagrams and charge distributions in the MOS capacitor help us to visualize the operation and characteristics of this device, and to eventually improve our understanding of the operation of the MOSFET. Figure 6.8a shows the

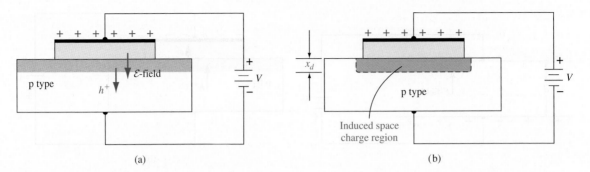

Figure 6.7 | The MOS capacitor with a moderate positive gate bias, showing (a) the electric field and initial charge flow and (b) the steady-state induced space charge region.

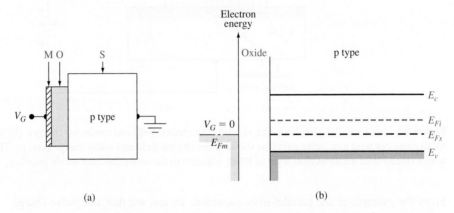

Figure 6.8 | (a) The MOS capacitor with a p-type substrate turned on its side. (b) *Idealized* energy-band diagram with the p-type substrate and zero gate voltage applied.

MOS capacitor turned on its side. The p-type substrate is at ground potential and a voltage V_G is applied to the gate terminal. Figure 6.8b is an idealized energy band diagram of this structure. The gate voltage is $V_G = 0$ and there is no net charge in the semiconductor. All energy bands are flat.

If there is a net charge density in a region of the semiconductor, then, from Poisson's equation, we have

$$\frac{d^2\phi(x)}{dx^2} = -\frac{\rho(x)}{\epsilon_s} = -\frac{d\mathcal{E}(x)}{dx} \tag{6.6}$$

An electric field and potential will exist in a region with a net charge density. The electron energy and potential are related by

$$E = -e\phi \tag{6.7}$$

A combination of Equations (6.6) and (6.7) shows that the conduction, valence, and intrinsic Fermi energies bend in a region in which an electric field exists. This effect was also shown in Chapter 5. Keep in mind that positive electron energy is plotted "upward" on the vertical axis and positive potential is plotted "downward."

Figure 6.9a(i) shows the energy bands when a negative gate voltage is applied. There is no current through the oxide, which implies that there is no current in the semiconductor. For this reason, the semiconductor is in thermal equilibrium and the Fermi level is a constant.

For a negative gate bias, we argued that an accumulation layer of holes forms adjacent to the oxide surface. Additional holes means that the semiconductor is now more p type near the oxide. The valence-band energy must then move closer to the Fermi level, as shown in Figure 6.9a(i). The charge distribution through the capacitor is shown in Figure 6.9a(ii). A negative gate voltage means that a negative charge exists on the metal gate and the corresponding positive charge is the accumulation charge in the semiconductor.

Accumulation layer of holes

Figure 6.9b(i) shows the energy bands when a positive gate voltage is applied. A negatively charged depletion region is induced in the p-type semiconductor so the bands bend downward, as shown. This band bending is very similar to that in a pn junction. The charge distribution is shown in Figure 6.9b(ii). A positive charge now exists on the metal gate and the corresponding negative charge in the MOS capacitor is due to the depletion region in the semiconductor.

Induced depletion region

Now consider the case when a still larger positive voltage is applied to the gate of the MOS capacitor. We expect the induced electric field to increase in magnitude and the corresponding positive and negative charges on the MOS capacitor to increase. A larger negative charge in the semiconductor implies a larger induced space charge region and more band bending. Figure 6.9c(i) shows such a condition. The intrinsic Fermi level at the surface is now below the Fermi level; thus, the conduction band is closer to the Fermi level than the valence band. This result implies that the surface of the semiconductor adjacent to the oxide is now n type. By applying a sufficiently large positive gate voltage, we have inverted the surface of the semiconductor from a p-type to an n-type semiconductor. We have created an *inversion layer* of electrons at the oxide–semiconductor interface.

Inversion layer of electrons

Figure 6.9c(ii) shows the charge distribution. For this case, we have assumed a particular situation in which the intrinsic Fermi level at the surface is as far below the Fermi level as the intrinsic Fermi level is above the Fermi level in the neutral p region. This condition means that the density (#/cm^3) of electrons in the inversion layer at the surface is the same as the density (#/cm^3) of holes in the neutral p region. This condition is referred to as threshold and will be further defined and discussed later in the chapter.

For a still larger applied gate voltage, there is more band bending as shown in Figure 6.9d(i). The conduction band at the surface moves closer to the Fermi level so that the surface is more n type. A larger inversion layer charge density Q_n' is shown in Figure 6.9d(ii).

Inversion charge density

In the MOS capacitor structure that we have just considered, we assumed a p-type semiconductor substrate. The same type of energy-band diagrams can be constructed for an MOS capacitor with an n-type semiconductor substrate. Figure 6.10a shows the MOS capacitor structure with a positive voltage applied to the top gate terminal. A positive charge exists on the top gate and an electric field is

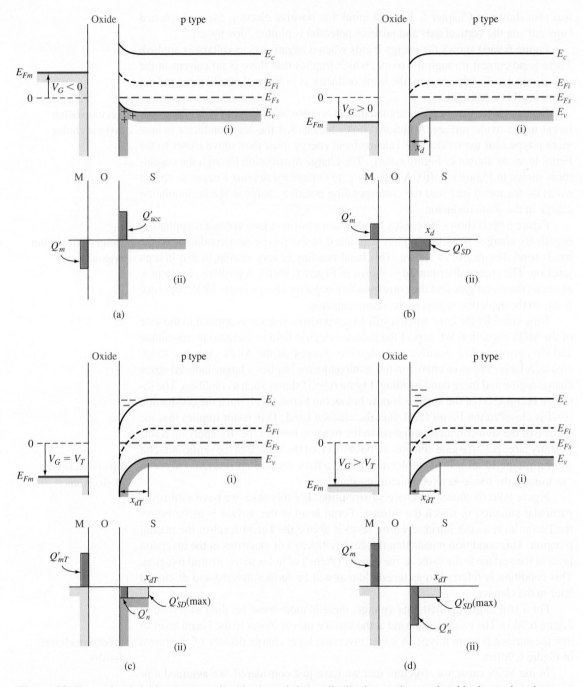

Figure 6.9 | Energy bands in the p-type semiconductor and charge distribution on the metal and in the semiconductor for (a) $V_G < 0$ (accumulation), (b) $V_G > 0$; (c) $V_G = V_T$ (threshold), and (d) $V_G > V_T$ (inversion).

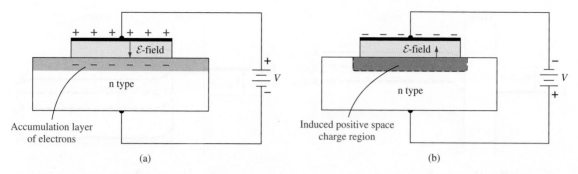

Figure 6.10 | The MOS capacitor with an n-type substrate for (a) a positive gate bias, showing an accumulation layer of electrons adjacent to the semiconductor–oxide interface, and (b) a moderate negative gate bias, showing an induced positive space charge region in the semiconductor.

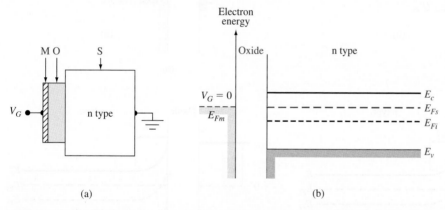

Figure 6.11 | (a) An MOS capacitor with an n-type substrate turned on its side. (b) *Idealized* energy-band diagram with n-type substrate and zero gate voltage applied.

induced with the direction shown in the figure. An accumulation layer of electrons will be induced in the n-type substrate. The case when a negative voltage is applied to the top gate is shown in Figure 6.10b. A positive space charge region is induced in the n-type semiconductor in this situation.

Figure 6.11a shows an MOS capacitor with an n-type semiconductor substrate turned on its side. The n-type substrate is at ground potential and a voltage V_G is applied to the gate terminal. Figure 6.11b is an energy-band diagram of an idealized structure. The gate voltage is $V_G = 0$ and there is no net charge in the semiconductor so that all energy bands are flat.

The energy bands and charge distributions as a function of gate voltage for the n-type substrate are very similar to the MOS capacitor with the p-type substrate except that the polarity of the gate voltage changes and the sign of the charges changes.

Figure 6.12a(i) shows the energy bands when a positive gate voltage is applied. Again, there is no current through the oxide and hence no current in the

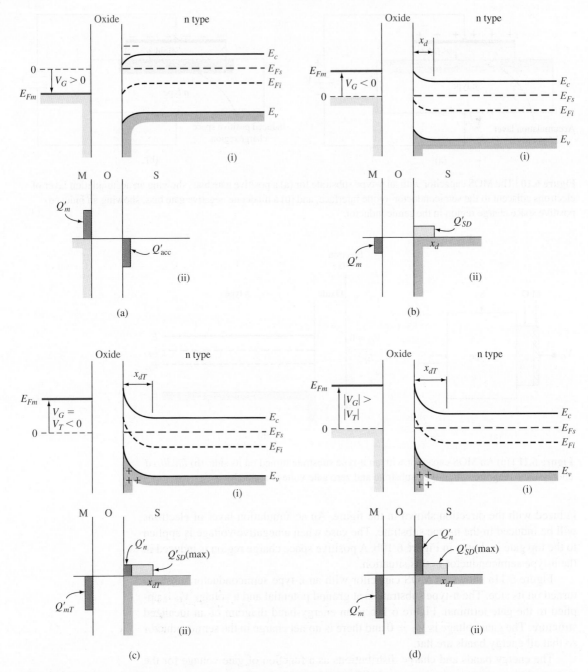

Figure 6.12 | Energy bands in the n-type semiconductor and charge distribution on the metal and in the semiconductor for (a) $V_G > 0$ (accumulation); (b) $V_G < 0$; (c) $V_G = V_T < 0$ (threshold); and (d) $|V_G| > |V_T|$, where $V_T < 0$ (inversion).

semiconductor. The semiconductor is then in thermal equilibrium and the Fermi level is constant. For a positive gate voltage, an accumulation layer of electrons is created in the semiconductor adjacent to the oxide. For this reason, the conduction-band energy moves closer to the Fermi level at the surface. Figure 6.12a(ii) shows the charge distribution through the MOS capacitor for this bias.

Accumulation layer of electrons

Figure 6.12b shows the situation when a negative gate voltage is applied. A space charge region is induced in the semiconductor. Figure 6.12c shows the condition when a larger negative gate voltage is applied. In this case, the intrinsic Fermi at the surface is now above the Fermi level. This result implies that the surface of the semiconductor adjacent to the oxide is now p type. The surface has been inverted from n type to p type. An inversion layer of holes now is created at the surface. Figure 6.12d shows the situation when a larger negative voltage is applied and a larger inversion charge is created.

Inversion layer of holes

6.2.2 Depletion Layer Thickness

We can calculate the width of the induced space charge region adjacent to the oxide–semiconductor interface. Figure 6.13 shows the space charge region in a p-type semiconductor substrate. The potential ϕ_{Fp} is the difference (in volts) between E_F and E_{Fi} and is given by

$$e\phi_{Fp} = E_F - E_{Fi} = -kT \ln\left(\frac{N_a}{n_i}\right) \tag{6.8a}$$

or

$$\phi_{Fp} = -V_t \ln\left(\frac{N_a}{n_i}\right) \tag{6.8b}$$

where N_a is the acceptor doping concentration and n_i is the intrinsic carrier concentration.

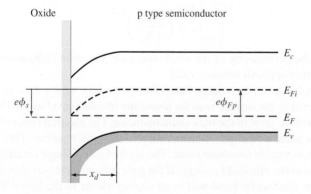

Figure 6.13 | Energy-band diagram in the p-type semiconductor, showing the potential ϕ_{Fp} and the surface potential ϕ_s.

EXAMPLE 6.1

OBJECTIVE

Determine the potential ϕ_{Fp} in silicon at $T = 300$ K for (a) $N_a = 10^{15}$ cm^{-3} and (b) $N_a = 10^{17}$ cm^{-3}.

■ **Solution**

From Equation (6.8b), we have

$$\phi_{Fp} = -V_t \ln\left(\frac{N_a}{n_i}\right) = -(0.0259) \ln\left(\frac{N_a}{1.5 \times 10^{10}}\right)$$

so for (a) $N_a = 10^{15}$ cm^{-3},

$$\phi_{Fp} = -0.288 \text{ V}$$

and for (b) $N_a = 10^{17}$ cm^{-3},

$$\phi_{Fp} = -0.407 \text{ V}$$

■ **Comment**

This simple example is intended to show the order of magnitude of ϕ_{Fp} and to show, because of the logarithm function, that ϕ_{Fp} is not a strong function of substrate doping concentration.

Exercise Problem

EX6.1 Consider p-type silicon at $T = 300$ K. Determine the semiconductor doping concentration if $\phi_{Fp} = -0.340$ V. [Ans. $N_a = 7.54 \times 10^{15}$ cm^{-3}]

The potential ϕ_s is called the surface potential; it is the difference (in volts) between E_{Fi} measured in the bulk semiconductor and E_{Fi} measured at the surface. The surface potential is the potential difference across the space charge layer. The space charge width can now be written in a form similar to that of a one-sided pn junction. We can write that

Depletion layer width

$$x_d = \left(\frac{2\epsilon_s \phi_s}{e N_a}\right)^{1/2} \qquad (6.9)$$

where ϵ_s is the permittivity of the semiconductor. Equation (6.9) assumes that the abrupt depletion approximation is valid.

Figure 6.14 shows the energy bands for the case in which $\phi_s = \phi_{sT} = 2|\phi_{Fp}|$. The Fermi level at the surface is as far above the intrinsic level as the Fermi level is below the intrinsic level in the bulk semiconductor. The electron concentration at the surface is the same as the hole concentration in the bulk material. This condition is

Threshold inversion point

Threshold voltage

known as the *threshold inversion point*. The applied gate voltage creating this condition is known as the *threshold voltage*. If the gate voltage increases above this threshold value, the conduction band will bend slightly closer to the Fermi level, but the change in the conduction band at the surface is now only a slight function of gate voltage. The electron concentration at the surface, however, is an exponential function of the surface potential. The surface potential may increase by a few (kT/e) volts,

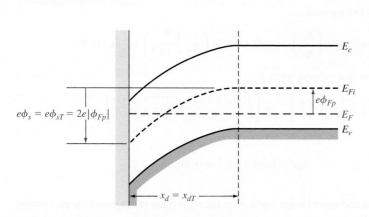

Figure 6.14 | The energy-band diagram in the p-type semiconductor at the threshold inversion point.

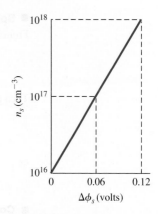

Figure 6.15 | Electron inversion charge density as a function of change in surface potential $\Delta\phi_s$.

which will change the electron concentration by orders of magnitude, but the space charge width changes only slightly.

The density of the inversion charge can be written as

$$n_s = n_i \exp\left(\frac{E_F - E_{Fi}}{kT}\right) \qquad (6.10)$$

Density of inversion charge

If $E_F - E_{Fi} = e\phi_{sT}$, then $n_s = N_a$. We can then write,

$$n_s = N_a \exp\left(\frac{\Delta\phi_s}{V_t}\right) \qquad (6.11)$$

where $\Delta\phi = \phi_s - \phi_{sT}$. Figure 6.15 is a plot of n_s versus $\Delta\phi_s$. We see that n_s increases drastically for small values of $\Delta\phi_s$.

For this reason, the space charge region has essentially reached a maximum width at threshold. The maximum space charge width, x_{dT}, at this inversion transition point can be calculated from Equation (6.9) by setting $\phi_s = \phi_{sT} = 2|\phi_{Fp}|$. Then

$$x_{dT} = \left(\frac{4\epsilon_s |\phi_{Fp}|}{e N_a}\right)^{1/2} \qquad (6.12)$$

Maximum depletion width

EXAMPLE 6.2

OBJECTIVE

Calculate the maximum space charge width given a particular semiconductor doping concentration.

Consider silicon at $T = 300$ K doped to $N_a = 10^{16}$ cm^{-3}.

■ **Solution**

From Equation (6.8b), we have

$$\phi_{Fp} = -V_t \ln\left(\frac{N_a}{n_i}\right) = -(0.0259)\ln\left(\frac{10^{16}}{1.5\times 10^{10}}\right) = -0.347 \text{ V}$$

Then the maximum space charge width is

$$x_{dT} = \left[\frac{4\epsilon_s|\phi_{Fp}|}{eN_a}\right]^{1/2} = \left[\frac{4(11.7)(8.85\times 10^{-14})(0.347)}{(1.6\times 10^{-19})(10^{16})}\right]^{1/2}$$

or

$$x_{dT} = 0.30\times 10^{-4} = 0.30 \ \mu\text{m}$$

■ **Comment**

The maximum induced space charge width is on the same order of magnitude as pn junction space charge widths.

Exercise Problem

EX6.2 (*a*) Consider as oxide-to-p-type silicon junction at $T = 300$ K. The impurity doping concentration in the silicon is $N_a = 3\times 10^{16}$ cm^{-3}. Calculate the maximum space charge width in the silicon. (*b*) Repeat part (*a*) for an impurity concentration of $N_a = 10^{15}$ cm^{-3}. [Ans. (*a*) 0.180 μm, (*b*) 0.983 μm]

We have been considering a p-type semiconductor substrate. The same maximum induced space charge region width occurs in an n-type substrate. Figure 6.16 is the energy-band diagram at the threshold voltage with an n-type substrate. We can write

$$e\phi_{Fn} = E_F - E_{Fi} = kT\ln\left(\frac{N_d}{n_i}\right) \tag{6.13a}$$

or

$$\phi_{Fn} = V_t\ln\left(\frac{N_d}{n_i}\right) \tag{6.13b}$$

Then we have

$$x_{dT} = \left(\frac{4\epsilon_s\phi_{Fn}}{eN_d}\right)^{1/2} \tag{6.14}$$

Figure 6.17 is a plot of x_{dT} at $T = 300$ K as a function of doping concentration in silicon. The semiconductor doping can be either n type or p type.

TEST YOUR UNDERSTANDING

TYU6.1 Consider an oxide-to-n-type silicon junction at $T = 300$ K. The impurity doping concentration in the silicon is $N_d = 8\times 10^{15}$ cm^{-3}. Calculate the maximum space charge width in the silicon. (Ans. 0.33 μm)

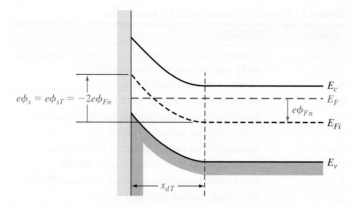

$$e\phi_s = e\phi_{sT} = -2e\phi_{Fn}$$

Figure 6.16 | Energy-band diagram in the n-type semiconductor at the threshold inversion point.

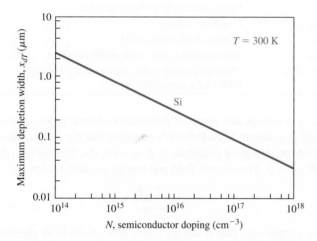

Figure 6.17 | Maximum induced space charge width in silicon versus semiconductor doping concentration.

6.3 | POTENTIAL DIFFERENCES IN THE MOS CAPACITOR

Objective: Analyze the potentials in an MOS capacitor, including work function difference, flat-band voltage, and threshold voltage.

We have considered energy bands in the semiconductor for various gate voltages. We now want to define specific gate voltages that induce specific conditions in the semiconductor. We also need to consider actual MOS structures rather than the idealized devices considered up to this point.

Table 6.1 | Summary of notation for MOS capacitor

Symbol	Definition
ϕ_{Fn}, ϕ_{Fp}	Difference, in volts, between E_F and E_{Fi} for n-type and p-type semiconductor, respectively
ϕ_m	Metal-to-vacuum work function
ϕ'_m	Metal-to-silicon dioxide work function
ϕ_{ms}	Metal–semiconductor work function difference
ϕ_s	Semiconductor surface potential
ϕ_{s0}	Semiconductor surface potential for zero bias
χ	Semiconductor-to-vacuum electron affinity
χ'	Semiconductor-to-silicon dioxide electron affinity
x_{dT}	Maximum induced depletion region
C_{ox}	Oxide capacitance per unit area
Q'_m	Charge density on metal
Q'_n	Inversion charge density
Q'_{SD}	Maximum charge density in depletion region
Q'_{ss}	Equivalent trapped charge in oxide
V_{FB}	Flat-band voltage
V_{ox}	Voltage drop across oxide
V_{ox0}	Voltage drop across oxide under zero bias
V_{TN}, V_{TP}	Threshold voltage of n-channel and p-channel MOSFETs, respectively

In addition to voltage and potential differences, electric fields are also important in the MOS device. Recall from Poisson's equation that the electric field is proportional to the rate of change of potential, or $\mathcal{E} = -d\phi/dx$. The energy of an electron is given by $E = -e\phi$. The electric field and energy are then related by

$$\mathcal{E} = \frac{1}{e}\frac{dE}{dx} \tag{6.15}$$

This equation simply says that if energy bands bend, there is an electric field, or if there is an electric field, the energy bands must bend.

In discussing the MOS capacitor, new terminology is introduced. A summary of this notation is given in Table 6.1. The reader is encouraged to refer to this table during the analysis of the MOS capacitor.

6.3.1 Work Function Differences

We have been concerned, so far, with the energy-band diagrams of the semiconductor material. Figure 6.18a shows the energy levels in the metal, silicon dioxide, and silicon relative to the vacuum level. The metal work function is ϕ_m and the electron affinity is χ. The parameter χ_i is the oxide electron affinity and, for silicon dioxide, $\chi_i = 0.9$ V.

Figure 6.18b shows the energy-band diagram of the entire metal–oxide–semiconductor structure with zero gate voltage applied. The Fermi level is a constant through the entire system at thermal equilibrium. To achieve this equilibrium

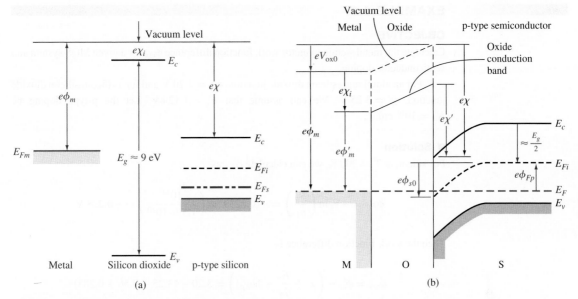

Figure 6.18 | (a) Energy levels in an MOS system prior to contact and (b) energy-band diagram through the MOS structure in thermal equilibrium after contact.

condition, we may attach a wire between the metal gate and the p-type substrate. Effectively, holes flow from the semiconductor to the metal gate increasing the potential of the gate until equilibrium is achieved. We may define ϕ'_m as a modified metal work function—the potential required to inject an electron from the metal into the conduction band of the oxide. Similarly, χ' is defined as a modified electron affinity. The voltage V_{ox0} is the potential drop across the oxide for zero applied gate voltage and is not necessarily zero because of the difference between ϕ_m and χ. The potential ϕ_{s0} is the surface potential for this case.

If we sum the energies from the Fermi level on the metal side to the Fermi level on the semiconductor side, we have

$$e\phi'_m + eV_{ox0} = e\chi' + \frac{E_g}{2} - e\phi_{s0} + e|\phi_{Fp}| \tag{6.16}$$

Equation (6.16) can be rewritten as

$$V_{ox0} + \phi_{s0} = -\left[\phi'_m - \left(\chi' + \frac{E_g}{2e} + |\phi_{Fp}|\right)\right] \tag{6.17}$$

We can define a potential ϕ_{ms} as

$$\boxed{\phi_{ms} \equiv \left[\phi'_m - \left(\chi' + \frac{E_g}{2e} + |\phi_{Fp}|\right)\right]} \tag{6.18}$$

Metal–semiconductor work function difference

which is known as the metal–semiconductor work function difference.

EXAMPLE 6.3

OBJECTIVE

Calculate the metal–semiconductor work function difference ϕ_{ms} for a given MOS system and semiconductor doping.

For an aluminum–silicon dioxide junction, $\phi'_m = 3.20$ V and for a silicon–silicon dioxide junction, $\chi' = 3.25$ V. We can assume that $E_g = 1.12$ eV. Let the p-type doping be $N_a = 10^{14}$ cm^{-3}.

■ **Solution**

For silicon at $T = 300$ K, we can calculate ϕ_{Fp} as

$$\phi_{Fp} = -V_t \ln\left(\frac{N_a}{n_i}\right) = -(0.0259)\ln\left(\frac{10^{14}}{1.5 \times 10^{10}}\right) = -0.228 \text{ V}$$

Then the work function difference is

$$\phi_{ms} = \phi'_m - \left(\chi' + \frac{E_g}{2e} + |\phi_{Fp}|\right) = 3.20 - (3.25 + 0.56 + 0.288)$$

or

$$\phi_{ms} = -0.838 \text{ V}$$

■ **Comment**

The value of ϕ_{ms} will become more negative as the doping of the p-type substrate increases.

Exercise Problem

EX6.3 Calculate the metal–semiconductor work function difference ϕ_{ms} for an aluminum–silicon dioxide–silicon device if the silicon is p type and doped to a concentration of $N_a = 10^{16}$ cm^{-3}. Assume $T = 300$ K. (Ans. $\phi_{ms} = -0.957$ V)

Degenerately doped polysilicon deposited on the oxide is also often used as the metal gate. Figure 6.19a shows the energy-band diagram of an MOS capacitor with an n^+ polysilicon gate and a p-type substrate. Figure 6.19b shows the energy-band diagram for the case of a p^+ polysilicon gate and the p-type silicon substrate. In the degenerately doped polysilicon, we will initially assume that $E_F = E_c$ for the n^+ case and $E_F = E_v$ for the p^+ case.

n-type polysilicon gate

For the n^+ polysilicon gate, the metal-semiconductor work function difference can be written as

$$\phi_{ms} = \left[\chi' - \left(\chi' + \frac{E_g}{2e} + |\phi_{Fp}|\right)\right] = -\left(\frac{E_g}{2e} + |\phi_{Fp}|\right) \quad (6.19)$$

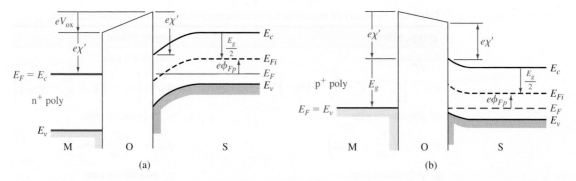

Figure 6.19 | Energy-band diagram through the MOS structure with a p-type substrate at zero gate bias for (a) an n^+ polysilicon gate and (b) a p^+ polysilicon gate. In the heavily doped polysilicon gates, the Fermi level is assumed to correspond to the conduction- and valence-band energies, respectively.

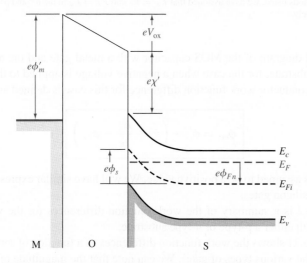

Figure 6.20 | Energy-band diagram through the MOS structure with an n-type substrate for a negative applied gate bias.

and for the p^+ polysilicon gate, we have

$$\phi_{ms} = \left[\left(\chi' + \frac{E_g}{e} \right) - \left(\chi' + \frac{E_g}{2e} + |\phi_{Fp}| \right) \right] = \left(\frac{E_g}{2e} - |\phi_{Fp}| \right) \quad (6.20)$$

However, for degenerately doped n^+ polysilicon and p^+ polysilicon, the Fermi level can be above E_c and below E_v, respectively, by 0.1 to 0.2 V. The experimental ϕ_{ms} values will then be slightly different from the values calculated by using Equations (6.19) and (6.20).

p-type polysilicon gate

We have been considering a p-type semiconductor substrate. We may also have an n-type semiconductor substrate in an MOS capacitor. Figure 6.20 shows the

Table 6.2 | Summary of equations for metal–semiconductor work function difference

p-type Silicon	n-type Silicon
Aluminum gate:	Aluminum gate:
$\phi_{ms} = \left[\phi'_m - \left(\chi' + \dfrac{E_g}{2e} + |\phi_{Fp}| \right) \right]$	$\phi_{ms} = \left[\phi'_m - \left(\chi' + \dfrac{E_g}{2e} - \phi_{Fn} \right) \right]$
n^+ polysilicon gate:	n^+ polysilicon gate:
$\phi_{ms} = - \left(\dfrac{E_g}{2e} + |\phi_{Fp}| \right)$	$\phi_{ms} = - \left(\dfrac{E_g}{2e} - \phi_{Fn} \right)$
p^+ polysilicon gate:	p^+ polysilicon gate
$\phi_{ms} = \left(\dfrac{E_g}{2e} - |\phi_{Fp}| \right)$	$\phi_{ms} = \left(\dfrac{E_g}{2e} + \phi_{Fn} \right)$

For the expressions listed, we have assumed that $E_F = E_c$ and $E_F = E_v$ in the n^+ and p^+ polysilicon gates, respectively.

energy-band diagram of the MOS capacitor with a metal gate and the n-type semi-conductor substrate, for the case when a negative voltage is applied to the gate. The metal–semiconductor work function difference for this case is defined as

$$\phi_{ms} = \phi'_m - \left(\chi' + \frac{E_g}{2e} - \phi_{Fn} \right) \tag{6.21}$$

where ϕ_{Fn} is assumed to be a positive value. We will have similar expressions for n^+ and p^+ polysilicon gates.

Table 6.2 is a summary of the work function differences for the various gate materials with either a p-type or n-type substrate.

Figure 6.21 shows the work function differences as a function of semiconductor doping for the various types of gates. We can note that the magnitude of ϕ_{ms} for the polysilicon gates are somewhat larger than Equations (6.19) and (6.20) predict. This difference again is because the Fermi level is not equal to the conduction band energy for the n^+ gate and is not equal to the valence band energy for the p^+ gate. The metal–semiconductor work function difference becomes important in the flat-band and threshold voltage parameters discussed next.

6.3.2 Oxide Charges

We have implicitly been assuming that there is zero net charge density in the oxide material. This assumption may not be valid—a net fixed charge density, usually positive, may exist in the insulator. The positive charge has been identified with broken or dangling covalent bonds near the oxide–semiconductor interface. During the thermal formation of SiO_2, oxygen diffuses through the oxide and reacts near the Si–SiO_2 interface to form the SiO_2. Silicon atoms may also break away from the silicon material just prior to reacting to form SiO_2. When the oxidation process is terminated, excess silicon may exist in the oxide near the interface, resulting in the

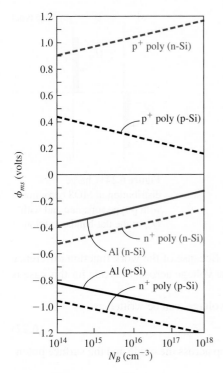

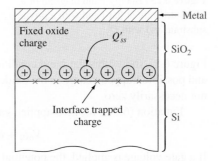

Figure 6.21 | Metal-semiconductor work function differences versus semiconductor doping concentration for aluminum, n^+ polysilicon, and p^+ polysilicon gates.

Figure 6.22 | MOS structure showing equivalent fixed positive charge Q'_{ss} in oxide adjacent to the semiconductor-oxide interface. Also shown is the interface trapped charge.

dangling bonds. The magnitude of this oxide charge seems, in general, to be a strong function of the oxidizing conditions such as oxidizing ambient and temperature. The charge density can be altered to some degree by annealing the oxide in an argon or nitrogen atmosphere. However, the charge is rarely zero.

The net fixed charge in the oxide appears to be located fairly close to the oxide–semiconductor interface. We will assume in the analysis of the MOS structure that an equivalent trapped charge per unit area, Q'_{ss}, is located in the oxide directly adjacent to the oxide–semiconductor interface. For the moment, we will ignore any other oxide-type charges that may exist in the device. The parameter Q'_{ss} is usually given in terms of number of electronic charges per unit area.

Trapped oxide charges

Figure 6.22 schematically shows the fixed oxide charge Q'_{ss} in the MOS capacitor. Interface charges also exist at the oxide–semiconductor interface. These charges will be discussed later in the chapter.

6.3.3 Flat-Band Voltage

The *flat-band voltage* is defined as the applied gate voltage such that there is no band bending in the semiconductor and, as a result, zero net space charge in this region.

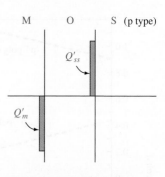

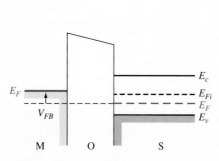

Figure 6.23 | Energy-band diagram of a MOS structure at flat-band with a p-type substrate and with Q'_{ss}.

Figure 6.24 | Charge distribution in MOS capacitor with p-type substrate and with Q'_{ss} at the flat-band condition.

Figure 6.23 shows this flat-band condition. Because of the work function difference and possible trapped charge in the oxide, the voltage across the oxide for this case is not necessarily zero.

Equation (6.17), for zero applied gate voltage, can be written as

$$V_{ox0} + \phi_{s0} = -\phi_{ms} \tag{6.22}$$

If a gate voltage is applied, the potential drop across the oxide and the surface potential will change. We can then write

$$V_G = \Delta V_{ox} + \Delta\phi_s = (V_{ox} - V_{ox0}) + (\phi_s - \phi_{s0}) \tag{6.23}$$

Using Equation (6.22), we have

$$V_G = V_{ox} + \phi_s + \phi_{ms} \tag{6.24}$$

Figure 6.24 shows the charge distribution in the MOS structure for the flat-band condition. There is zero net charge in the semiconductor and we can assume that an equivalent fixed surface charge density exists in the oxide. The charge density on the metal is Q'_m, and from charge neutrality we have

$$Q'_m + Q'_{ss} = 0 \tag{6.25}$$

We can relate Q'_m to the voltage across the oxide by

$$V_{ox} = \frac{Q'_m}{C_{ox}} \tag{6.26}$$

where C_{ox} is the oxide capacitance per unit area.[1] Substituting Equation (6.25) into Equation (6.26), we have

$$V_{ox} = \frac{-Q'_{ss}}{C_{ox}} \tag{6.27}$$

---

[1]Although we will, in general, use the primed notation for capacitance per unit area or charge per unit area, we will omit, for convenience, the prime on the oxide capacitance per unit area parameter.

In the flat-band condition, the surface potential is zero, or $\phi_s = 0$. Then from Equation (6.24), we have

$$V_G = \boxed{V_{FB} = \phi_{ms} - \frac{Q'_{ss}}{C_{ox}}} \tag{6.28}$$

Equation (6.28) is the flat-band voltage for this MOS device.

Flat-band voltage

EXAMPLE 6.4

OBJECTIVE

Calculate the flat-band voltage for a MOS capacitor with a p-type semiconductor substrate.

Consider an MOS structure with a p-type semiconductor substrate doped to $N_a = 10^{16}$ cm^{-3}, a silicon dioxide insulator with a thickness of $t_{ox} = 500$ Å, and an n$^+$ polysilicon gate. Assume that $Q'_{ss} = 10^{11}$ electronic charges per cm^2.

■ Solution

The work function difference, from Figure 6.21, is $\phi_{ms} = -1.1$ V. The oxide capacitance can be found as

$$C_{ox} = \frac{\epsilon_{ox}}{t_{ox}} = \frac{(3.9)(8.85 \times 10^{-14})}{500 \times 10^{-8}} = 6.9 \times 10^{-8} \text{ F/cm}^2$$

The equivalent oxide surface charge density is

$$Q'_{ss} = (10^{11})(1.6 \times 10^{-19}) = 1.6 \times 10^{-8} \text{ C/cm}^2$$

The flat-band voltage is then calculated as

$$V_{FB} = \phi_{ms} - \frac{Q'_{ss}}{C_{ox}} = -1.1 - \left(\frac{1.6 \times 10^{-8}}{6.9 \times 10^{-8}} \right) = -1.33 \text{ V}$$

■ Comment

The applied gate voltage required to achieve the flat-band condition for this p-type substrate is negative. If the amount of fixed oxide charge increases, the flat-band voltage becomes even more negative.

Exercise Problem

EX6.4 The silicon impurity doping concentration in an aluminum–silicon dioxide–silicon MOS structure is $N_a = 3 \times 10^{16}$ cm^{-3}. For an oxide thickness of $t_{ox} = 200$ Å and an oxide charge of $Q'_{ss} = 8 \times 10^{10}$ cm^{-2}, calculate the flat-band voltage. (Ans. $\phi_{ms} \approx -0.97$ V, $V_{FB} = -1.04$ V.)

6.3.4 Threshold Voltage

The threshold voltage was defined as the applied gate voltage required to achieve the threshold inversion point. The threshold inversion point, in turn, is defined as the condition when the surface potential is $\phi_s = 2|\phi_{Fp}|$ for the p-type semiconductor and $\phi_s = 2\phi_{Fn}$ for the n-type semiconductor. These conditions were shown in Figures 6.14 and 6.16. The threshold voltage will be derived in terms of the electrical and geometrical properties of the MOS capacitor.

Figure 6.25 shows the charge distribution through the MOS device at the threshold inversion point for a p-type semiconductor substrate. The space charge width has reached its maximum value. We will assume that there is an equivalent oxide charge Q'_{ss} and the positive charge on the metal gate at threshold is Q'_{mT}. The prime on the charge terms indicates charge per unit area. Even though we are assuming that the surface has been inverted, we will neglect the inversion layer charge at this threshold inversion point. From conservation of charge, we can write

$$Q'_{mT} + Q'_{ss} = |Q'_{SD}(\max)| \tag{6.29}$$

where

$$\boxed{|Q'_{SD}(\max)| = e N_a x_{dT}} \tag{6.30}$$

Maximum space charge density

and is the magnitude of the maximum space charge density per unit area of the depletion region.

The energy-band diagram of the MOS system with an applied positive gate voltage is shown in Figure 6.26. As we mentioned, an applied gate voltage will change the voltage across the oxide and will change the surface potential. We had from Equation (6.23) that

$$V_G = \Delta V_{\text{ox}} + \Delta \phi_s = V_{\text{ox}} + \phi_s + \phi_{ms}$$

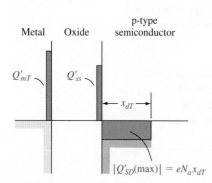

Figure 6.25 | Charge distribution in a MOS capacitor with a p-type substrate at the threshold inversion point.

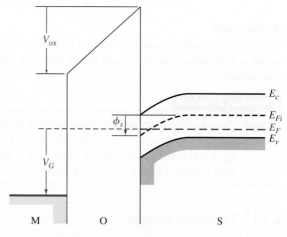

Figure 6.26 | Energy-band diagram through the MOS structure with a positive applied gate bias.

At threshold, we can define $V_G = V_{TN}$, where V_{TN} is the threshold voltage that creates the electron inversion layer charge. The surface potential is $\phi_s = 2|\phi_{Fp}|$ at threshold so Equation (6.23) can be written as

$$V_{TN} = V_{\text{ox}T} + 2|\phi_{Fp}| + \phi_{ms} \tag{6.31}$$

where $V_{\text{ox}T}$ is the voltage across the oxide at this threshold inversion point.

The voltage $V_{\text{ox}T}$ can be related to the charge on the metal and to the oxide capacitance by

$$V_{\text{ox}T} = \frac{Q'_{mT}}{C_{\text{ox}}} \tag{6.32}$$

where again C_{ox} is the oxide capacitance per unit area. Using Equation (6.29), we can write

$$V_{\text{ox}T} = \frac{Q'_{mT}}{C_{\text{ox}}} = \frac{1}{C_{\text{ox}}}(|Q'_{SD}(\text{max})| - Q'_{ss}) \tag{6.33}$$

Finally, the threshold voltage can be written as

Threshold voltage (NMOS)

$$\boxed{V_{TN} = \frac{|Q'_{SD}(\text{max})|}{C_{\text{ox}}} - \frac{Q'_{ss}}{C_{\text{ox}}} + \phi_{ms} + 2|\phi_{Fp}|} \tag{6.34a}$$

or

$$V_{TN} = (|Q'_{SD}(\text{max})| - Q'_{ss})\left(\frac{t_{\text{ox}}}{\epsilon_{\text{ox}}}\right) + \phi_{ms} + 2|\phi_{Fp}| \tag{6.34b}$$

Using the definition of flat-band voltage from Equation (6.28), we can also express the threshold voltage as

$$V_{TN} = \frac{|Q'_{SD}(\text{max})|}{C_{\text{ox}}} + V_{FB} + 2|\phi_{Fp}| \tag{6.34c}$$

For a given semiconductor material, oxide material, and gate metal, the threshold voltage is a function of semiconductor doping, oxide charge Q'_{ss}, and oxide thickness.

DESIGN EXAMPLE 6.5

OBJECTIVE

Design the oxide thickness of an MOS system to yield a specified threshold voltage.

Consider an n^+ polysilicon gate and a p-type silicon substrate doped to $N_a = 5 \times 10^{16}$ cm^{-3}. Assume $Q'_{ss} = 10^{11}$ cm^{-2}. Determine the oxide thickness such that $V_{TN} = +0.40$ V.

■ **Solution**

From Figure 6.21, the work function difference is $\phi_{ms} \approx -1.15$ V. The other various parameters can be calculated as

$$\phi_{Fp} = -V_t \ln\left(\frac{N_a}{n_i}\right) = -(0.0259)\ln\left(\frac{5 \times 10^{16}}{1.5 \times 10^{10}}\right) = -0.389 \text{ V}$$

and

$$x_{dT} = \left(\frac{4\epsilon_s|\phi_{Fp}|}{eN_a}\right)^{1/2} = \left[\frac{4(11.7)(8.85 \times 10^{-14})(0.389)}{(1.6 \times 10^{-19})(5 \times 10^{16})}\right]^{1/2} = 0.142 \text{ } \mu m$$

Then

$$|Q'_{SD}(\max)| = eN_a x_{dT} = (1.6 \times 10^{-19})(5 \times 10^{16})(0.142 \times 10^{-4})$$

or

$$|Q'_{SD}(\max)| = 1.14 \times 10^{-7} \text{ C/cm}^2$$

The oxide thickness can be determined from the threshold equation

$$V_{TN} = \left[|Q'_{SD}(\max)| - Q'_{ss}\right]\left(\frac{t_{ox}}{\epsilon_{ox}}\right) + \phi_{ms} + 2|\phi_{Fp}|$$

Then

$$0.40 = \frac{[1.14 \times 10^{-7} - (10^{11})(1.6 \times 10^{-19})]}{(3.9)(8.85 \times 10^{-14})} t_{ox} - 1.15 + 2(0.389)$$

which yields

$$t_{ox} = 272 \text{ Å}$$

■ **Comment**

Enhancement-mode device

The threshold voltage for this case is a positive quantity, which means that the MOS device is an enhancement-mode device; a gate voltage must be applied to create the inversion layer charge, which is zero for zero applied gate voltage.

Exercise Problem

EX6.5 Repeat Example 6.5 for the case when the gate material is aluminum.

(Ans. $\phi_{ms} \approx -0.98$ V, $t_{ox} = 212$ Å)

The threshold voltage must be within the voltage range of a circuit design. Although we have not yet considered the current in an MOS transistor, the threshold voltage is the point at which the transistor turns on. If a circuit is to operate between 0 and 5 V and the threshold voltage of a MOSFET is 10 V, for example, the device and circuit cannot be turned "on" and "off." The threshold voltage, then, is one of the important parameters of the MOSFET.

EXAMPLE 6.6

OBJECTIVE

Calculate the threshold voltage of an MOS system using an aluminum gate.

Consider a p-type silicon substrate at $T = 300$ K doped to $N_a = 10^{14}$ cm^{-3}. Let $Q'_{ss} = 10^{10}$ cm^{-2}, $t_{ox} = 500$ Å, and assume the oxide is silicon dioxide. From Figure 6.21, we have that $\phi_{ms} = -0.83$ V.

■ Solution

We can start calculating the various parameters as

$$\phi_{Fp} = -V_t \ln\left(\frac{N_a}{n_i}\right) = -(0.0259)\ln\left(\frac{10^{14}}{1.5 \times 10^{10}}\right) = -0.228 \text{ V}$$

and

$$x_{dT} = \left(\frac{4\epsilon_s|\phi_{Fp}|}{eN_a}\right)^{1/2} = \left[\frac{4(11.7)(8.85 \times 10^{-14})(0.228)}{(1.6 \times 10^{-19})(10^{14})}\right]^{1/2} = 2.43 \ \mu\text{m}$$

Then

$$|Q'_{SD}(\text{max})| = eN_a x_{dT} = (1.6 \times 10^{-19})(10^{14})(2.43 \times 10^{-4}) = 3.89 \times 10^{-9} \text{ C/cm}^2$$

We can now calculate the threshold voltage as

$$V_{TN} = (|Q'_{SD}(\text{max})| - Q'_{ss})\left(\frac{t_{ox}}{\epsilon_{ox}}\right) + \phi_{ms} + 2|\phi_{Fp}|$$

$$= [(3.89 \times 10^{-9}) - (10^{10})(1.6 \times 10^{-19})]\left[\frac{500 \times 10^{-8}}{(3.9)(8.85 \times 10^{-14})}\right]$$

$$- 0.83 + 2(0.228)$$

$$= -0.341 \text{ V}$$

■ Comment

In this example, the semiconductor is very lightly doped, which, in conjunction with the positive charge in the oxide and the work function potential difference, is sufficient to induce an electron inversion layer charge even with zero applied gate voltage. This condition makes the threshold voltage negative.

Exercise Problem

EX6.6 An MOS device has the following parameters: aluminum gate, p-type substrate with $N_a = 3 \times 10^{16}$ cm^{-3}, $t_{ox} = 250$ Å, and $Q'_{ss} = 10^{11}$ cm^{-2}. Determine the threshold voltage. (Ans. $\phi_{ms} \approx -0.97$ V, $V_{TN} = +0.292$ V)

A negative threshold voltage for a p-type substrate implies a depletion mode device. A negative voltage must be applied to the gate in order to make the inversion layer charge equal to zero, whereas a positive gate voltage will induce a larger inversion layer charge.

Depletion-mode device

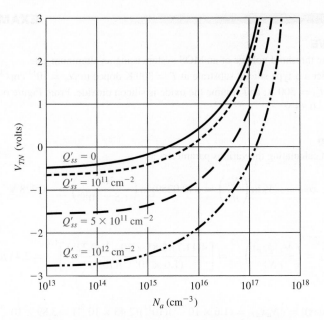

Figure 6.27 | Threshold voltage of an n-channel MOSFET versus the p-type substrate doping concentration for various values of oxide trapped charge ($t_{ox} = 500$ Å, aluminum gate).

Figure 6.27 is a plot of the threshold voltage V_{TN} as a function of the acceptor doping concentration for various positive oxide charge values. We may note that the p-type semiconductor must be somewhat heavily doped in order to obtain an enhancement mode device.

The previous derivation of the threshold voltage assumed a p-type semiconductor substrate. The same type of derivation can be done with an n-type semiconductor substrate, where a negative gate voltage can induce an inversion layer of holes at the oxide-semiconductor interface.

Figure 6.20 showed the energy-band diagram of the MOS structure with an n-type substrate and with an applied negative gate voltage. The threshold voltage for this case can be derived and is given by

Threshold voltage (PMOS)

$$V_{TP} = (-|Q'_{SD}(\text{max})| - Q'_{ss})\left(\frac{t_{ox}}{\epsilon_{ox}}\right) + \phi_{ms} - 2\phi_{Fn} \qquad (6.35)$$

where

$$\phi_{ms} = \phi'_m - \left(\chi' + \frac{E_g}{2e} - \phi_{Fn}\right) \qquad (6.36a)$$

$$|Q'_{SD}(\text{max})| = eN_d x_{dT} \qquad (6.36b)$$

$$x_{dT} = \left(\frac{4\epsilon_s \phi_{Fn}}{e N_d} \right)^{1/2}$$ (6.36c)

and

$$\phi_{Fn} = V_t \ln \left(\frac{N_d}{n_i} \right)$$ (6.36d)

We may note that x_{dT} and ϕ_{Fn} are defined as positive quantities. We may also note that the notation of V_{TP} is the threshold voltage that will induce an inversion layer of holes. We will later drop the N and P subscript notation on the threshold voltage, but, for the moment, the notation may be useful for clarity.

DESIGN EXAMPLE 6.7

OBJECTIVE

Design the semiconductor doping concentration to yield a specified threshold voltage.

Consider an aluminum–silicon dioxide–silicon MOS structure. The silicon is n type, the oxide thickness is $t_{ox} = 650 \, \text{Å}$, and the trapped charge density is $Q'_{ss} = 10^{10} \, \text{cm}^{-2}$. Determine the doping concentration such that $V_{TP} = -1.0$ V.

■ **Solution**

The solution to this design problem is not straightforward, since the doping concentration appears in the terms ϕ_{Fn}, x_{dT}, $Q'_{SD}(\text{max})$, and ϕ_{ms}. The threshold voltage, then, is a nonlinear function of N_d. Without a computer-generated solution, we resort to trial and error.

For $N_d = 2.5 \times 10^{14} \, \text{cm}^{-3}$, we find

$$\phi_{Fn} = V_t \ln \left(\frac{N_d}{n_i} \right) = 0.252 \text{ V}$$

and

$$x_{dT} = \left(\frac{4\epsilon_s \phi_{Fn}}{e N_d} \right)^{1/2} = 1.62 \ \mu\text{m}$$

Then

$$|Q'_{SD}(\text{max})| = e N_d x_{dT} = 6.48 \times 10^{-9} \text{ C/cm}^2$$

From Figure 6.21,

$$\phi_{ms} = -0.35 \text{ V}$$

The threshold voltage is

$$V_{TP} = (-|Q'_{SD}(\text{max})| - Q'_{ss}) \left(\frac{t_{ox}}{\epsilon_{ox}} \right) + \phi_{ms} - 2\phi_{Fn}$$

$$= \frac{[-(6.48 \times 10^{-9}) - (10^{10})(1.6 \times 10^{-19})](650 \times 10^{-8})}{(3.9)(8.85 \times 10^{-14})} - 0.35 - 2(0.252)$$

which yields

$$V_{TP} = -1.006 \text{ V}$$

and is essentially equal to the desired result.

■ Comment

The threshold voltage is negative, implying that this MOS capacitor, with the n-type substrate, is an enhancement mode device. The inversion layer charge is zero with zero gate voltage, and a negative gate voltage must be applied to induce the hole inversion layer.

Exercise Problem

EX6.7   Consider an MOS device with the following parameters: p^+ polysilicon gate, n-type substrate, $t_{ox} = 220$ Å, and $Q'_{ss} = 8 \times 10^{10}$ cm^{-2}. Determine the required n-type doping concentration such that the threshold voltage is in the range $-0.50 \leq V_{TP} \leq -0.30$ V.

(Ans. By trial and error, we find for $N_d = 4 \times 10^{16}$ cm^{-3}, $\phi_{ms} \approx +1.10$ V, and $V_{TP} = -0.385$ V)

Figure 6.28 is a plot of V_{TP} versus doping concentration for several values of Q'_{ss}. We can note that, for all values of positive oxide charge, this MOS capacitor is always an enhancement mode device. As the Q'_{ss} charge increases, the threshold voltage becomes more negative, which means that it takes a larger applied gate voltage to create the inversion layer of holes at the oxide–semiconductor interface.

Σ 6.3.5   Electric Field Profile

We have talked at various times about the electric fields in the MOS capacitor. We can again write Poisson's equation in the one-dimensional form as $d\mathcal{E}/dx = \rho(x)/\epsilon$, where $\rho(x)$ is the volume charge density and ϵ is the permittivity of the material. One particular result of this equation is that, if the space charge density is zero, the electric field is a constant. Another result of this equation is that, if the space charge density is a constant (uniform doping), the electric field is a linear function of distance.

We must also consider the boundary condition at the interface between the oxide and silicon. Consider the case when an equivalent surface charge density, Q'_{ss}, exists in the oxide at the oxide–silicon surface as shown in Figure 6.29. From electrostatics, we have for this one-dimensional case

$$D_s - D_{ox} = Q'_{ss} \tag{6.37}$$

where D_{ox} and D_s are the electric flux density vectors in the oxide and semiconductor, respectively. Noting that $D = \epsilon \mathcal{E}$, the boundary condition can be written as

$$\epsilon_s \mathcal{E}_s - \epsilon_{ox} \mathcal{E}_{ox} = Q'_{ss} \tag{6.38}$$

$\mathcal{E}$-field boundary conditions

where ϵ_s and ϵ_{ox} are the permittivities of the silicon and silicon dioxide, respectively.

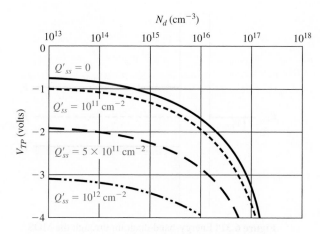

Figure 6.28 | Threshold voltage of a p-channel MOSFET versus the n-type substrate doping concentration for various values of oxide trapped charge ($t_{ox} = 500$ Å, aluminum gate).

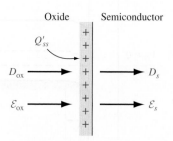

Figure 6.29 | Electric flux density and electric field vectors at the boundary between the oxide and semiconductor.

We can now consider several conditions. Figure 6.30a shows the energy-band diagrams of an MOS capacitor with an aluminum or n^+ polysilicon gate and p-type silicon with $V_G = 0$. A net negative charge exists in the depletion layer and a net positive charge exists on the metal gate. The electric field profile is shown in Figure 6.30b. The electric field is constant in the oxide and a linear function of distance in the p-type silicon (uniform doping). We can note from Equation (6.38) that, if $Q'_{ss} = 0$, then $\mathcal{E}_{ox} > \mathcal{E}_s$ at the interface since $\epsilon_s, > \epsilon_{ox}$. We can also note from the equation that, if $Q'_{ss} > 0$, and if $\mathcal{E}_s$ is held constant at the surface, then $\mathcal{E}_{ox}$ becomes smaller.

Figure 6.31 shows the energy bands at flat-band for the case when $Q'_{ss} = 0$. The flat-band voltage is negative, but all electric fields are zero.   **Ideal flat-band**

Figure 6.32 shows the energy bands at flat-band for the case when $Q'_{ss} > 0$. There is still no net charge or electric field in the p-type silicon. Now, however, there is an electric field in the oxide induced by the Q'_{ss} charge. From Equation (6.38), we see that $\mathcal{E}_{ox} = -Q'_{ss}/\epsilon_{ox}$.   **Flat-band with oxide charge**

EXAMPLE 6.8

OBJECTIVE

Calculate the electric field in and the voltage across the oxide at a flat-band condition.

Assume that $Q'_{ss} = 8 \times 10^{10}$ cm^{-2} in silicon dioxide and assume the oxide thickness is $t_{ox} = 150$ Å.

■ Solution

The electric charge density at the interface is

$$Q'_{ss} = (1.6 \times 10^{-19})(8 \times 10^{10}) = 1.28 \times 10^{-8} \text{ C/cm}^2$$

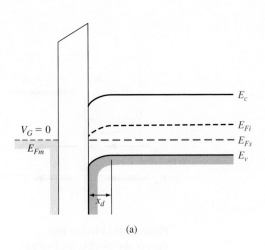

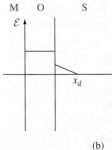

Figure 6.30 | (a) Energy-band diagram through the MOS structure with $V_G = 0$. A depletion layer is induced in the p-type substrate. (b) Electric field profile in the MOS structure; a constant electric field in the oxide and a linear electric filed in the semiconductor.

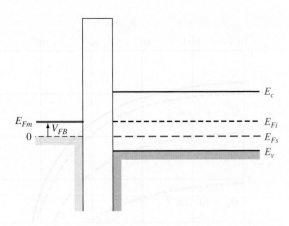

Figure 6.31 | Energy-band diagram through the MOS structure at flat-band with $Q'_{ss} = 0$.

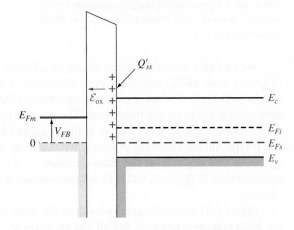

Figure 6.32 | Energy-band diagram through the MOS structure at flat-band with $Q'_{ss} > 0$.

The oxide electric field is then

$$\mathcal{E}_{ox} = \frac{-Q'_{ss}}{\epsilon_{ox}} = \frac{-1.28 \times 10^{-8}}{(3.9)(8.85 \times 10^{-14})} = -3.71 \times 10^4 \text{ V/cm}$$

Since the electric field across the oxide is a constant, the voltage across the oxide is then

$$V_{ox} = -\mathcal{E}_{ox} t_{ox} = -(-3.71 \times 10^4)(150 \times 10^{-8})$$

or

$$V_{ox} = 55.6 \text{ mV}$$

■ Comment

In the flat-band condition, an electric field exists in the oxide and a voltage exists across the oxide due to the Q'_{ss} charge.

EX6.8 Repeat Example 6.8 for the case when $Q'_{ss} = 1.2 \times 10^{11}$ cm^{-2} and $t_{ox} = 250$ Å.
(Ans. $\mathcal{E}_{ox} = -5.56 \times 10^4$ V/cm, $V_{ox} = 0.139$ V)

Now consider the case when an inversion layer has been created for an applied gate voltage of $V_{GS} > V_{TN}$. For simplicity, we will assume that the inversion charge density is a constant over a distance of d_i in the semiconductor. Figure 6.33a shows the energy bands through the MOS structure and Figure 6.33b shows the charge distribution and the electric field profiles.

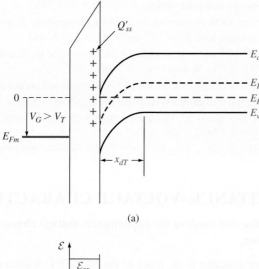

(a)

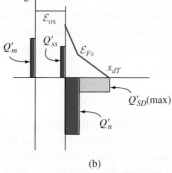

(b)

Figure 6.33 | (a) Energy-band diagram through the MOS structure for $V_G > V_T$. (b) Charge distribution and electric field profile through the MOS capacitor for $V_G > V_T$. As an approximation, the inversion charge density is assumed to be a constant over a finite distance.

TEST YOUR UNDERSTANDING

TYU6.2   The silicon impurity doping concentration in an aluminum–silicon dioxide–silicon MOS structure is $N_a = 3 \times 10^{16}$ cm^{-3}. Using the parameters in Example 6.3, determine the metal–semiconductor work function difference ϕ_{ms}. (Ans. $\phi_{ms} = -0.986$ V)

TYU6.3   Consider an n$^+$ polysilicon gate in an MOS structure with a p-type silicon substrate. The doping concentration of the silicon is $N_a = 3 \times 10^{16}$ cm^{-3}. Using Equation (6.19), find the value of ϕ_{ms}. (Ans. $\phi_{ms} = -0.936$ V)

TYU6.4   Repeat Exercise TYU6.3 for a p$^+$ polysilicon gate using Equation (6.20). (Ans. $\phi_{ms} = +0.184$ V)

TYU6.5   An MOS device has the following parameters: aluminum gate, p-type substrate with $N_a = 3 \times 10^{16}$ cm^{-3}, $t_{ox} = 250$ Å, and $Q'_{ss} = 10^{11}$ cm^{-2}. Determine the threshold voltage. (Ans. $V_{TN} = 0.726$ V)

TYU6.6   Consider an MOS device with the following parameters: p$^+$ polysilicon gate, n-type substrate with $N_d = 10^{15}$ cm^{-3}, $t_{ox} = 220$ Å, and $Q'_{ss} = 8 \times 10^{10}$ cm^{-2}. (Use Figure 6.21.) Determine the threshold voltage. (Ans. $\phi_{ms} \approx +0.98$ V, $V_{TP} = +0.235$ V)

TYU6.7   The device described in Exercise TYU6.6 is to be redesigned by changing the n-type doping concentration such that the threshold voltage is in the range $-0.50 \le V_{TP} \le -0.30$. All other parameters remain the same. (Ans. For example, for $N_d = 4 \times 10^{16}$ cm^{-3}, $\phi_{ms} \approx 1.09$ V and $V_{TP} = -0.395$ V.)

6.4 | CAPACITANCE–VOLTAGE CHARACTERISTICS

Objective: Describe and analyze the capacitance–voltage characteristics of a MOS capacitor.

The MOS capacitor structure is the heart of the MOSFET. A great deal of information about the MOS device and the oxide–semiconductor interface can be obtained from the capacitance versus voltage or C–V characteristics of the device. The capacitance of a device is defined as

$$C = \frac{dQ}{dV} \tag{6.39}$$

where dQ is the magnitude of the differential change in charge on one plate as a function of the differential change in voltage dV across the capacitor. The capacitance is a small-signal or ac parameter and is measured by superimposing a small ac voltage on an applied dc gate voltage. The capacitance, then, is measured as a function of the applied dc gate voltage.

6.4.1   Ideal C–V Characteristics

First we will consider the ideal C–V characteristics of the MOS capacitor and then discuss some of the deviations that occur from these idealized results. We will initially

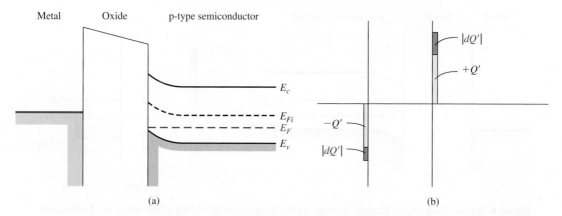

Figure 6.34 | (a) Energy-band diagram through an MOS capacitor for the accumulation mode. (b) Differential charge distribution at accumulation for a differential change in gate voltage.

assume that there is zero charge trapped in the oxide and also that there is no charge trapped at the oxide–semiconductor interface.

There are three operating conditions of interest in the MOS capacitor: accumulation, depletion, and inversion. Figure 6.34a shows the energy-band diagram of an MOS capacitor with a p-type substrate for the case when a negative voltage is applied to the gate, inducing an accumulation layer of holes in the semiconductor at the oxide–semiconductor interface. A small differential change in voltage across the MOS structure will cause a differential change in charge on the metal gate and also in the hole accumulation charge, as shown in Figure 6.34b. The differential changes in charge density occur at the edges of the oxide, as in a parallel-plate capacitor. The capacitance C' per unit area of the MOS capacitor for this accumulation mode is just the oxide capacitance, or

$$C'(\text{acc}) = C_{\text{ox}} = \frac{\epsilon_{\text{ox}}}{t_{\text{ox}}} \qquad (6.40)$$

Capacitance in accumulation mode

Figure 6.35a shows the energy-band diagram of the MOS device when a small positive voltage is applied to the gate, inducing a space charge region in the semiconductor; Figure 6.35b shows the charge distribution through the device for this condition. The oxide capacitance and the capacitance of the depletion region are in series. A small differential change in voltage across the capacitor will cause a differential change in the space charge width. The corresponding differential changes in charge densities are shown in the figure. The total capacitance of the series combination is

$$\frac{1}{C'(\text{depl})} = \frac{1}{C_{\text{ox}}} + \frac{1}{C'_{SD}} \qquad (6.41a)$$

or

$$C'(\text{depl}) = \frac{C_{\text{ox}} C'_{SD}}{C_{\text{ox}} + C'_{SD}} \qquad (6.41b)$$

Capacitance in depletion mode

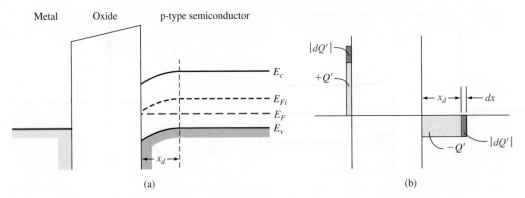

Figure 6.35 | (a) Energy-band diagram through an MOS capacitor for the depletion mode. (b) Differential charge distribution at depletion for a differential change in gate voltage.

Since $C_{\text{ox}} = \epsilon_{\text{ox}}/t_{\text{ox}}$ and $C'_{SD} = \epsilon_s/x_d$, Equation (6.41b) can be written as

$$C'(\text{depl}) = \frac{C_{\text{ox}}}{1 + \dfrac{C_{\text{ox}}}{C'_{SD}}} = \frac{\epsilon_{\text{ox}}}{t_{\text{ox}} + \left(\dfrac{\epsilon_{\text{ox}}}{\epsilon_s}\right) x_d} \tag{6.42}$$

As the space charge width increases, the total capacitance $C'(\text{depl})$ decreases.

We had defined the threshold inversion point to be the condition when the maximum depletion width is reached but there is essentially zero inversion charge density. This condition will yield a minimum capacitance C'_{min} which is given by

$$C'_{\text{min}} = \frac{\epsilon_{\text{ox}}}{t_{\text{ox}} + \left(\dfrac{\epsilon_{\text{ox}}}{\epsilon_s}\right) x_{dT}} \tag{6.43}$$

Figure 6.36a shows the energy-band diagram of this MOS device for the inversion condition. In the ideal case, a small incremental change in the voltage across the MOS capacitor will cause a differential change in the inversion-layer charge density. The space charge width does not change. If the inversion charge can respond to the change in capacitor voltage as indicated in Figure 6.36b, then the capacitance is again just the oxide capacitance, or

Ideal capacitance in inversion mode

$$C'(\text{inv}) = C_{\text{ox}} = \frac{\epsilon_{\text{ox}}}{t_{\text{ox}}} \tag{6.44}$$

Figure 6.37 shows the ideal capacitance versus gate voltage, or C–V, characteristics of the MOS capacitor with a p-type substrate. The three dashed segments correspond to the three components C_{ox}, C'_{SD}, and C'_{min}. The solid curve is the ideal net capacitance of the MOS capacitor. Moderate inversion, which is indicated in the figure, is the transition region between the point when only the space charge density changes with gate voltage and when only the inversion charge density changes with gate voltage.

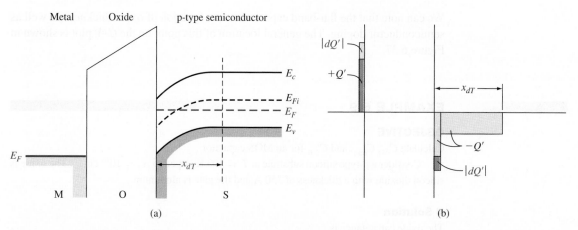

Figure 6.36 | (a) Energy-band diagram through an MOS capacitor for the inversion mode. (b) Differential charge distribution at inversion for a low-frequency differential change in gate voltage.

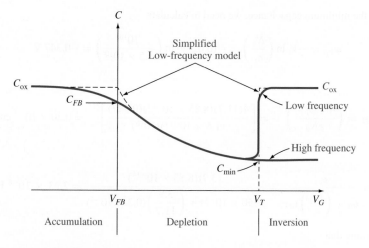

Figure 6.37 | Ideal low-frequency capacitance versus gate voltage of an MOS capacitor with a p-type substrate. Simplified ideal capacitance curve is shown by the dotted line.

The point on the curve that corresponds to the flat-band condition is of interest. The flat-band condition occurs between the accumulation and depletion conditions. The capacitance at flat band is given by

$$C'_{FB} = \cfrac{\epsilon_{ox}}{t_{ox} + \left(\cfrac{\epsilon_{ox}}{\epsilon_s}\right)\sqrt{\left(\cfrac{kT}{e}\right)\left(\cfrac{\epsilon_s}{eN_a}\right)}}$$

(6.45)   **Flat-band capacitance**

We can note that the flat-band capacitance is a function of oxide thickness as well as semiconductor doping. The general location of this point on the C–V plot is shown in Figure 6.37.

EXAMPLE 6.9

OBJECTIVE

Calculate C_{ox}, C'_{min}, and C'_{FB} for an MOS capacitor.

Consider a p-type silicon substrate at $T = 300$ K doped to $N_a = 10^{16}$ cm^{-3}. The oxide is silicon dioxide with a thickness of 550 Å and the gate is aluminum.

■ Solution

The oxide capacitance is

$$C_{ox} = \frac{\epsilon_{ox}}{t_{ox}} = \frac{(3.9)(8.85 \times 10^{-14})}{550 \times 10^{-8}} = 6.28 \times 10^{-8} \text{ F/cm}^2$$

To find the minimum capacitance, we need to calculate

$$\phi_{Fp} = -V_t \ln\left(\frac{N_a}{n_i}\right) = -(0.0259) \ln\left(\frac{10^{16}}{1.5 \times 10^{10}}\right) = -0.347 \text{ V}$$

and

$$x_{dT} = \left(\frac{4\epsilon_s |\phi_{Fp}|}{eN_a}\right)^{1/2} = \left[\frac{4(11.7)(8.85 \times 10^{-14})(0.347)}{(1.6 \times 10^{-19})(10^{16})}\right]^{1/2} = 0.30 \times 10^{-4} \text{ cm}$$

Then

$$C'_{min} = \frac{\epsilon_{ox}}{t_{ox} + \left(\dfrac{\epsilon_{ox}}{\epsilon_s}\right)x_{dT}} = \frac{(3.9)(8.85 \times 10^{-14})}{(550 \times 10^{-8}) + \left(\dfrac{3.9}{11.7}\right)(0.3 \times 10^{-4})} = 2.23 \times 10^{-8} \text{ F/cm}^2$$

We can note that

$$\frac{C'_{min}}{C_{ox}} = \frac{2.23 \times 10^{-8}}{6.28 \times 10^{-8}} = 0.355$$

The flat-band capacitance is

$$C'_{FB} = \frac{\epsilon_{ox}}{t_{ox} + \left(\dfrac{\epsilon_{ox}}{\epsilon_s}\right)\sqrt{\left(\dfrac{kT}{e}\right)\left(\dfrac{\epsilon_s}{eN_a}\right)}}$$

$$= \frac{(3.9)(8.85 \times 10^{-14})}{(550 \times 10^{-8}) + \left(\dfrac{3.9}{11.7}\right)\sqrt{(0.0259)\dfrac{(11.7)(8.85 \times 10^{-14})}{(1.6 \times 10^{-19})(10^{16})}}}$$

$$= 5.03 \times 10^{-8} \text{ F/cm}^2$$

We can also note that

$$\frac{C'_{FB}}{C_{ox}} = \frac{5.03 \times 10^{-8}}{6.28 \times 10^{-8}} = 0.80$$

■ Comment

The ratios of C'_{min} to C_{ox} and of C'_{FB} to C_{ox} are typical values obtained in C–V plots.

Exercise Problem

EX6.9 Consider an MOS device with the following parameters: aluminum gate, p-type substrate with $N_a = 3 \times 10^{16}$ cm^{-3}, $t_{ox} = 250$ Å, and $Q'_{ss} = 10^{11}$ cm^{-2}. Determine C'_{min}/C_{ox} and C'_{FB}/C_{ox}.

(Ans. $C'_{min}/C_{ox} = 0.294$, $C'_{FB}/C_{ox} = 0.761$)

If we assume values of channel length and width of 2 and 20 μm, respectively, the total gate oxide capacitance for this example is then

$$C_{oxT} = (6.28 \times 10^{-8})(2 \times 10^{-4})(20 \times 10^{-4}) = 0.025 \times 10^{-12} \text{ F} = 0.025 \text{ pF}$$

The total oxide capacitance in a typical MOS device is quite small.

The same type of ideal C–V characteristics are obtained for an MOS capacitor with an n-type substrate by changing the sign of the voltage axis. The accumulation condition is obtained for a positive gate bias and the inversion condition is obtained for a negative gate bias. This ideal curve is shown in Figure 6.38.

Σ 6.4.2 Frequency Effects

Figure 6.36a showed the MOS capacitor with a p-type substrate and biased in the inversion condition. We have argued that a differential change in the capacitor voltage in the ideal case causes a differential change in the inversion-layer charge density. However, we must consider the source of electrons that produces a change in the inversion charge density.

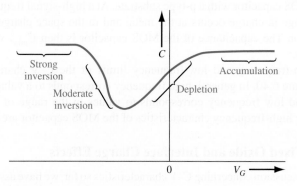

Figure 6.38 | Ideal low-frequency capacitance versus gate voltage of an MOS capacitor with an n-type substrate.

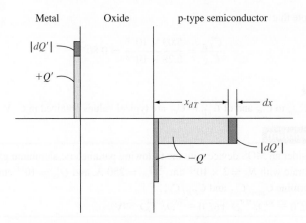

Figure 6.39 | Differential charge distribution at inversion for a high-frequency differential change in gate voltage.

There are two sources of electrons that can change the charge density of the inversion layer. The first source is by diffusion of minority carrier electrons from the p-type substrate across the space charge region. This diffusion process is the same as that in a reverse-biased pn junction that generates the ideal reverse saturation current. The second source of electrons is by thermal generation of electron–hole pairs within the space charge region. This process is again the same as that in a reverse-biased pn junction generating the reverse-biased generation current. (These processes are discussed in detail in Chapter 9 in discussing the pn junction diode.) Both of these processes generate electrons at a particular rate. The electron concentration in the inversion layer, then, cannot change instantaneously. If the ac voltage across the MOS capacitor changes rapidly, the change in the inversion-layer charge will not be able to respond. The C–V characteristics will then be a function of the frequency of the ac signal used to measure the capacitance.

C–V frequency effects

In the limit of a very high frequency, the inversion-layer charge will not respond to a differential change in capacitor voltage. Figure 6.39 shows the charge distribution in the MOS capacitor with a p-type substrate. At a high-signal frequency, the differential change in charge occurs at the metal and in the space charge width in the semiconductor. The capacitance of the MOS capacitor is then $C'_{\min}$, which we discussed earlier.

The high-frequency and low-frequency limits of the C–V characteristics are shown in Figure 6.40. In general, high frequency corresponds to a value on the order of 1 MHz and low frequency corresponds to values in the range of 5 to 100 Hz. Typically, the high-frequency characteristics of the MOS capacitor are measured.

Σ 6.4.3 Fixed Oxide and Interface Charge Effects

In all of the discussion concerning C–V characteristics so far, we have assumed an ideal oxide in which there are no fixed oxide or oxide–semiconductor interface charges. These two types of charges will change the C–V characteristics.

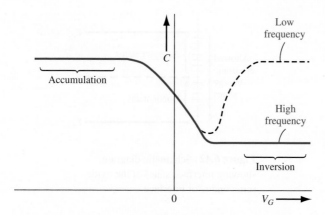

Figure 6.40 | Low-frequency and high-frequency capacitance versus gate voltage of an MOS capacitor with a p-type substrate.

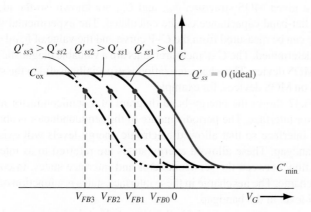

Figure 6.41 | High-frequency capacitance versus gate voltage of an MOS capacitor with a p-type substrate for several values of effective trapped oxide charge.

We previously discussed how the fixed oxide charge affects the threshold voltage. This charge will also affect the flat-band voltage. The flat-band voltage from Equation (6.28) was given by

$$V_{FB} = \phi_{ms} - \frac{Q'_{ss}}{C_{\text{ox}}}$$

where Q'_{ss} is the equivalent fixed oxide charge and ϕ_{ms} is the metal–semiconductor work function difference. The flat-band voltage shifts to more negative voltages for a positive fixed oxide charge. Since the oxide charge is not a function of gate voltage, the curves show a parallel shift with oxide charge, and the shape of the C–V curves remains the same as the ideal characteristics. Figure 6.41 shows the high-frequency

C–V effects due to oxide charges

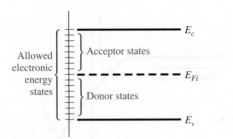

Figure 6.42 | Schematic diagram showing interface states at the oxide–semiconductor interface.

characteristics of an MOS capacitor with a p-type substrate for several values of fixed positive oxide charge.

The *C–V* characteristics can be used to determine the equivalent fixed oxide charge. For a given MOS structure, ϕ_{ms} and C_{ox} are known, so the ideal flat-band voltage and flat-band capacitance can be calculated. The experimental value of flat-band voltage can be measured from the *C–V* curve and the value of fixed oxide charge can then be determined. The *C–V* measurements are a valuable diagnostic tool to characterize an MOS device. This characterization is especially useful in the study of radiation effects on MOS devices, for example,

Figure 6.42 shows the energy-band diagram of a semiconductor at the oxide–semiconductor interface. The periodic nature of the semiconductor is abruptly terminated at the interface so that allowed electronic energy levels will exist within the forbidden bandgap. These allowed energy states are referred to as interface states. Charge can flow between the semiconductor and interface states, in contrast to the fixed oxide charge. The net charge in these interface states is a function of the position of the Fermi level in the bandgap.

In general, acceptor states exist in the upper half of the bandgap and donor states exist in the lower half of the bandgap. An acceptor state is neutral if the Fermi level is below the state, and becomes negatively charged if the Fermi level is above the state. A donor state is neutral if the Fermi level is above the state and becomes positively charged if the Fermi level is below the state. The charge of the interface states is then a function of the gate voltage applied across the MOS capacitor.

Figure 6.43a shows the energy-band diagram in a p-type semiconductor of an MOS capacitor biased in the accumulation condition. In this case, there is a net positive charge trapped in the donor states. Now let the gate voltage change to produce the energy-band diagram shown in Figure 6.43b. The Fermi level corresponds to the intrinsic Fermi level at the surface; thus, all interface states are neutral. This particular bias condition is known as *midgap*. Figure 6.43c shows the condition at inversion in which there is now a net negative charge in the acceptor states.

C–V effects due to interface states

The net charge in the interface states changes from positive to negative as the gate voltage sweeps from the accumulation, depletion, to the inversion condition. We noted that the *C–V* curves shifted in the negative gate voltage direction due to

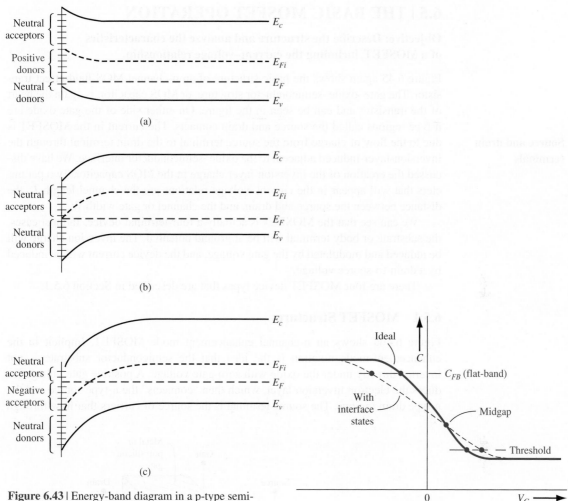

Figure 6.43 | Energy-band diagram in a p-type semi-conductor showing the charge trapped in the interface states when the MOS capacitor is biased (a) in accumulation, (b) at midgap, and (c) at inversion.

Figure 6.44 | High-frequency C–V characteristics of an MOS capacitor showing effects of interface states.

positive fixed oxide charge. When interface states are present, the amount and direction of the shift changes as we sweep through the gate voltage, since the amount and sign of the interface trapped charge changes. The C–V curves now become "smeared out," as shown in Figure 6.44.

Again, the C–V measurements can be used as a diagnostic tool in semiconductor device process control. For a given MOS device, the ideal C–V curve can be determined. Any "smearing out" in the experimental curve indicates the presence of interface states and any parallel shift indicates the presence of fixed oxide charge. The amount of smearing out can be used to determine the density of interface states.

6.5 | THE BASIC MOSFET OPERATION

**Objective: Describe the structure and analyze the characteristics
of a MOSFET, including the current–voltage relationship.**

Figure 6.45 again shows the basic structure of an n-channel MOS field-effect transistor. The gate–oxide–semiconductor structure, or MOS capacitor, is again the heart of the transistor and can be seen in the figure. On either side of the gate oxide are n-type regions called the source and drain contacts. The current in the MOSFET is due to the flow of charge from the source terminal to the drain terminal through the inversion-layer-induced adjacent to the oxide–semiconductor interface. We have discussed the creation of the inversion-layer charge in the MOS capacitor. Two parameters that will appear in the current–voltage relations are the channel length L, the distance between the source and drain, and the channel or gate width W.

We can see that the MOSFET is actually a four-terminal device. In most cases, the substrate or body terminal will be at ground potential. The inversion charge will be induced and modulated by the gate voltage, and the device current will be induced by a drain-to-source voltage.

There are four MOSFET device types that are described in Section 6.5.1.

6.5.1   MOSFET Structures

Figure 6.46a shows an n-channel enhancement mode MOSFET. Implicit in the enhancement-mode notation is the idea that the semiconductor substrate is not inverted directly under the oxide with zero gate voltage. A positive gate voltage induces the electron inversion layer, which then "connects" the n-type source and the n-type drain regions. The source terminal is the source of carriers that flow through

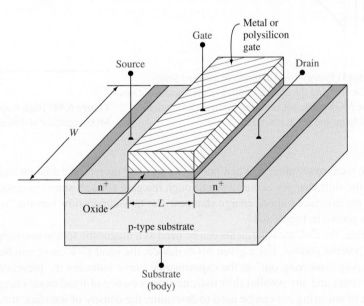

Figure 6.45 | Basic structure of an n-channel MOSFET.

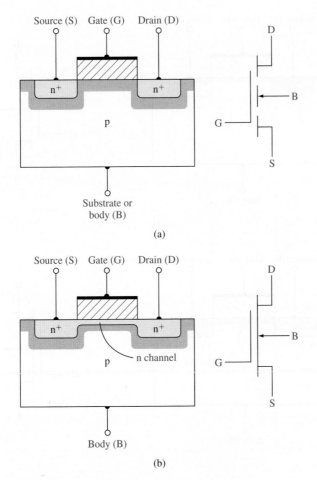

Figure 6.46 | Cross section and circuit symbol for
an n-channel (a) enhancement-mode MOSFET and
(b) depletion-mode MOSFET.

the channel to the drain terminal. For this n-channel device, electrons flow from the
source to the drain so the conventional current will enter the drain and leave the source.
The conventional circuit symbol for this n-channel enhancement mode device is also
shown in this figure.

NMOS devices

   Figure 6.46b shows an n-channel depletion mode MOSFET. An n-channel
region exists under the oxide with zero volts applied to the gate. However, we have
shown that the threshold voltage of an MOS device with a p-type substrate may
be negative; this means that an electron inversion layer already exists with zero gate
voltage applied. Such a device is also considered to be a depletion mode device. The
n-channel shown in this figure can be an electron inversion layer or an intentionally
doped n-region. The conventional circuit symbol for the n-channel depletion mode
MOSFET is also shown in the figure.

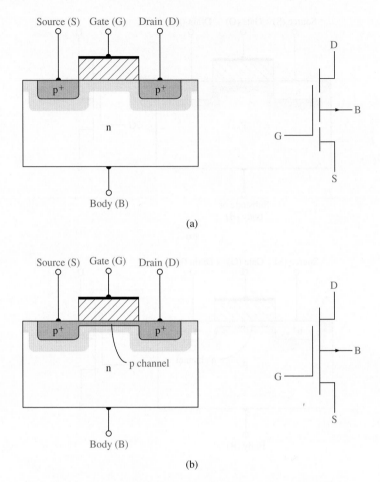

Figure 6.47 | Cross section and circuit symbol for a p-channel
(a) enhancement-mode MOSFET and (b) depletion-mode MOSFET.

PMOS devices

Figure 6.47a and 6.47b show a p-channel enhancement-mode MOSFET and a p-channel depletion mode MOSFET. In the p-channel enhancement-mode device, a negative gate voltage must be applied to create an inversion layer of holes that will "connect" the p-type source and drain regions. Holes flow from the source to the drain, so the conventional current will enter the source and leave the drain. A p-channel region exists in the depletion mode device even with zero gate voltage. The conventional circuit symbols are shown in the figure.

6.5.2 Current–Voltage Relationship—Basic Concepts

NMOS Transistor   Figure 6.48a shows an n-channel enhancement–mode MOSFET with a gate-to-source voltage that is less than the threshold voltage and with only a

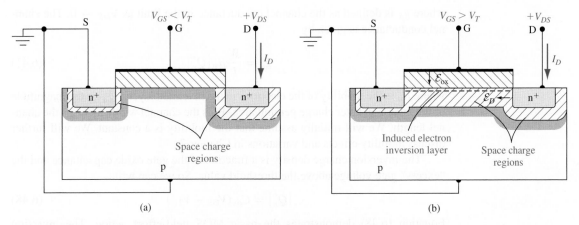

Figure 6.48 | The n-channel enhancement-mode MOSFET (a) with an applied gate voltage $V_{GS} < V_T$ and (b) with an applied gate voltage $V_{GS} > V_T$ and a small applied drain voltage V_{DS}. The vertical oxide electric field induced by the gate voltage and the horizontal electric field induced by the drain voltage are shown.

very small drain-to-source voltage. The source and substrate, or body, terminals are held at ground potential. With this bias configuration, there is no electron inversion layer, the drain-to-substrate pn junction is reverse biased, and the drain current is zero (disregarding pn junction leakage current).

Figure 6.48b shows the same MOSFET with an applied gate voltage such that $V_{GS} > V_{TN}$. An electron inversion layer has been created so that, when a small drain voltage is applied, the electrons in the inversion layer will flow from the source to the positive drain terminal. The conventional current enters the drain terminal and leaves the source terminal. In this ideal case, there is no current through the oxide to the gate terminal.

We will develop the current–voltage characteristics in a very qualitative way in this section. We will consider a *long-channel device*. Shown in Figure 6.48b are the two electric fields. The oxide electric field (vertical field) is induced by the gate voltage and creates the inversion layer of electrons. The electric field induced by the drain voltage (horizontal field) creates the force that causes the electrons in the inversion layer to flow from the source to the drain. In a long-channel device, these two electric fields can be treated independently. As the channel length decreases, the charge in the channel becomes a function of both electric fields. We will consider short-channel devices in Chapter 7. However, the results of the long-channel device enable us to investigate the basic operation and characteristics of this device. In general, a channel length greater than approximately 2 μm can be considered a long channel device.

Long-channel device

For small values of V_{DS}, the channel region has the characteristics of a resistor, so we can write

$$I_D = g_d V_{DS} \qquad (6.46)$$

where g_d is defined as the channel conductance in the limit as $V_{DS} \rightarrow 0$. The channel conductance is given by

$$g_d = \frac{W}{L} \mu_n \left| Q'_n \right| \qquad (6.47)$$

where μ_n is the mobility of the electrons in the inversion layer, $\left| Q'_n \right|$ is the magnitude of the inversion layer charge per unit area, W is the channel width, and L is the channel length. We will initially assume that the mobility is a constant. We will further discuss mobility effects and variations in Chapter 7.

The inversion charge density is a function of the gate oxide capacitance and the "excess" gate voltage above the threshold value. So we can write

$$\left| Q'_n \right| = C_{ox}(V_{GS} - V_{TN}) \qquad (6.48)$$

Equation (6.48) demonstrates the basic MOS field-effect action. The inversion charge density is a function of the gate-to-source voltage so that the channel conductance is modulated by the gate voltage.

Combining Equations (6.46) to (6.48), we can write the drain current, for small values of V_{DS}, as

$$I_D = \frac{W}{L} \cdot \mu_n C_{ox}(V_{GS} - V_{TN})V_{DS} \qquad (6.49)$$

The I_D versus V_{DS} characteristics described by Equation (6.49) are shown in Figure 6.49. When $V_{GS} < V_{TN}$, the drain current is zero. As V_{GS} becomes larger than V_{TN}, the channel inversion charge density increases, which increases the channel conductance. A larger value of g_d produces a larger initial slope on the I_D versus V_{DS} characteristic, as shown in the figure.

Figure 6.50a shows the basic MOS structure for the case when $V_{GS} > V_T$ and the applied V_{DS} voltage is small. The thickness of the inversion channel layer in the

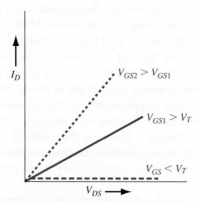

Figure 6.49 | I_D versus V_{DS} characteristics for small values of V_{DS} at three V_{GS} voltages.

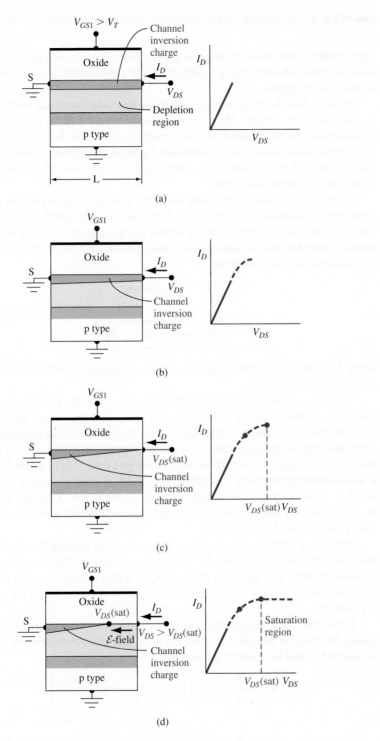

Figure 6.50 | Cross section and I_D versus V_{DS} curve when $V_{GS} < V_T$ for (a) a small V_{DS} value, (b) a larger V_{DS} value, (c) a value of $V_{DS} = V_{DS}(\text{sat})$, and (d) a value of $V_{DS} > V_{DS}(\text{sat})$.

figure qualitatively indicates the relative charge density, which is essentially constant along the entire channel length for this case. The corresponding I_D versus V_{DS} curve is shown in the figure.

Figure 6.50b shows the situation when the V_{DS} value increases. As the drain voltage increases, the voltage drop across the oxide near the drain terminal decreases, which means that the induced inversion charge density near the drain also decreases. The incremental conductance of the channel at the drain decreases, which then means that the slope of the I_D versus V_{DS} curve will decrease. This effect is shown in the I_D versus V_{DS} curve in the figure.

When V_{DS} increases to the point where the potential drop across the oxide at the drain terminal is equal to V_T, the induced inversion charge density is zero at the drain terminal. This effect is schematically shown in Figure 6.50c. At this point, the incremental conductance at the drain is zero, which means that the slope of the I_D versus V_{DS} curve is zero. We can write

$$V_{GS} - V_{DS}(\text{sat}) = V_T \qquad (6.50\text{a})$$

or

$$\boxed{V_{DS}(\text{sat}) = V_{GS} - V_T} \qquad (6.50\text{b})$$

Drain-to-source saturation voltage

where $V_{DS}(\text{sat})$ is the drain-to-source voltage producing zero inversion charge density at the drain terminal.

When V_{DS} becomes larger than the $V_{DS}(\text{sat})$ value, the point in the channel at which the inversion charge is just zero moves toward the source terminal. In this case, electrons enter the channel at the source, travel through the channel toward the drain, and then, at the point where the charge goes to zero, the electrons are injected into the space charge region where they are swept by the $\mathcal{E}$-field to the drain contact. If we assume that the change in channel length ΔL is small compared to the original length L, then the drain current will be a constant for $V_{DS} > V_{DS}(\text{sat})$. The region of the I_D versus V_{DS} characteristic is referred to as the *saturation region*. Figure 6.50d shows this region of operation.

When V_{GS} changes, the I_D versus V_{DS} curve will change. We saw that, if V_{GS} increases, the initial slope of I_D versus V_{DS} increases. We can also note from Equation (6.50b) that the value of $V_{DS}(\text{sat})$ is a function of V_{GS}. We can generate the family of curves for this n-channel enhancement mode MOSFET as shown in Figure 6.51.

Current–voltage: nonsaturation region

From this qualitative generation of the current–voltage characteristics, Equation (6.49) must be modified to show the nonlinear characteristics. We will show in Section 6.5.3, that the current is given by

$$I_D = \frac{W}{L} \mu_n C_{\text{ox}} \left[(V_{GS} - V_{TN})V_{DS} - \frac{V_{DS}^2}{2} \right] \qquad (6.51\text{a})$$

or

$$I_D = \frac{W}{L} \frac{\mu_n C_{\text{ox}}}{2} \left[2(V_{GS} - V_{TN})V_{DS} - V_{DS}^2 \right] \qquad (6.51\text{b})$$

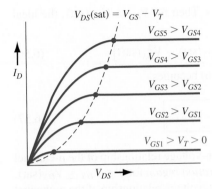

Figure 6.51 | Family of I_D versus V_{DS} curves for an n-channel enhancement-mode MOSFET.

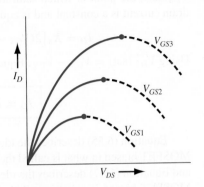

Figure 6.52 | Plots of I_D versus V_{DS} from Equation (6.55).

We can note that for very small values of V_{DS}, the V_{DS}^2 term becomes negligible, and Equation (6.51b) reduces to Equation (6.49), which we developed previously.

We can define

$$K_n = \frac{W}{L}\frac{\mu_n C_{\text{ox}}}{2} \qquad (6.52)$$

Conduction parameter

known as the conduction parameter.[2] We can also define

$$k_n' = \mu_n C_{\text{ox}} \qquad (6.53)$$

Process conduction parameter

known as the process conduction parameter. In general, the process conduction parameter, k_n', will be a constant for a given technology. We can then write

$$K_n = \frac{W}{L}\frac{k_n'}{2} \qquad (6.54)$$

Ideal current–voltage characteristics

Therefore, the width-to-length ratio, W/L, is a primary design variable that yields the desired current–voltage characteristics of a particular MOSFET.

Equation (6.51b) can now be written as

$$I_D = K_n\left[2(V_{GS} - V_{TN})V_{DS} - V_{DS}^2\right] \qquad (6.55)$$

Figure 6.52 is a plot of Equation (6.55) for three values of gate-to-source voltage. The nonlinear relation between drain current and drain-to-source voltage is obvious. We can find the value of V_{DS} at the peak current value from $\partial I_D/\partial V_{DS} = 0$. We find that the peak current occurs when $V_{DS} = V_{GS} - V_{TN}$. This value of V_{DS} is just

---

[2] In a few other texts, the conduction parameter is defined as $k_N = (\mu_n W C_{\text{ox}})/L$.

$V_{DS}(\text{sat})$, the point at which saturation occurs. Then for $V_{DS} > V_{DS}(\text{sat})$, the ideal drain current is a constant and is equal to

$$I_D = K_n\left[2(V_{GS} - V_{TN})V_{DS}(\text{sat}) - V_{DS}^2(\text{sat})\right] \tag{6.56}$$

Using $V_{DS}(\text{sat}) = V_{GS} - V_{TN}$, Equation (6.56) becomes

$$\boxed{I_D = K_n(V_{GS} - V_{TN})^2} \tag{6.57}$$

Current–voltage:
saturation region

Equation (6.55) describes the ideal current–voltage relationship of the n-channel MOSFET biased in what is called the *nonsaturation region* for $0 \leq V_{DS} \leq V_{DS}(\text{sat})$, and Equation (6.57) describes the ideal current–voltage relationship of the n-channel MOSFET biased in what is called the *saturation region* for $V_{DS} \geq V_{DS}(\text{sat})$. Figure 6.51 showed these characteristics.

EXAMPLE 6.10

OBJECTIVE

Design the width of a MOSFET such that a specified current is induced for a given applied bias.

Consider an ideal n-channel MOSFET with parameters $L = 1.25\ \mu\text{m}$, $\mu_n = 650\ \text{cm}^2/\text{V-s}$, $C_{\text{ox}} = 6.9 \times 10^{-8}\ \text{F/cm}^2$, and $V_T = 0.65\ \text{V}$. Design the channel width W such that $I_D(\text{sat}) = 4\ \text{mA}$ for $V_{GS} = 5\ \text{V}$.

■ Solution

We have, from Equations (6.51) and (6.52),

$$I_D(\text{sat}) = \frac{W\mu_n C_{\text{ox}}}{2L}(V_{GS} - V_{TN})^2$$

or

$$4 \times 10^{-3} = \frac{W(650)(6.9 \times 10^{-8})}{2(1.25 \times 10^{-4})} \cdot (5 - 0.65)^2 = 3.39W$$

Then

$$W = 11.8\ \mu\text{m}$$

■ Comment

The current capability of a MOSFET is directly proportional to the channel width W. The current handling capability can be increased by increasing W.

Exercise Problem

EX6.10 The parameters of an n-channel MOSFET are $\mu_n = 650\ \text{cm}^2/\text{V-s}$, $t_{\text{ox}} = 200\ \text{Å}$, $W/L = 50$, and $V_T = 0.40\ \text{V}$. If the transistor is biased in the saturation region, find the drain current for $V_{GS} = 1, 2$, and $3\ \text{V}$.
(Ans. $I_D = 1.01, 7.19$, and 19 mA)

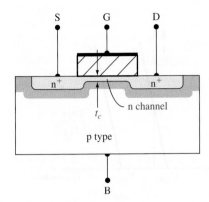

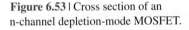

Figure 6.53 | Cross section of an
n-channel depletion-mode MOSFET.

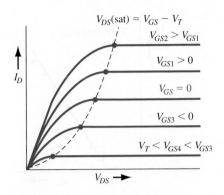

Figure 6.54 | Family of I_D versus V_{DS}
curves for an n-channel depletion-mode
MOSFET.

We implicitly assumed in the previous discussion that the MOSFET was an n-channel enhancement-mode device in which $V_{TN} > 0$. However, the same current–voltage relations apply to an n-channel depletion-mode device in which $V_{TN} < 0$.

Figure 6.53 shows an n-channel depletion mode MOSFET. If the n-channel region is actually an induced electron inversion layer created by the metal–semiconductor work function difference and fixed charge in the oxide, the current–voltage characteristics are exactly the same as we have discussed, except that V_T is a negative quantity. We can also consider the case when the n-channel region is actually an n-type semiconductor region. In this type of device, a negative gate voltage will induce a space charge region under the oxide, reducing the thickness of the n-channel region. The reduced thickness decreases the channel conductance, which reduces the drain current. A positive gate voltage will create an electron accumulation layer, which increases the drain current. One basic requirement for this device is that the channel thickness t_c must be less than the maximum induced space charge width to be able to turn the device off. The general I_D versus V_{DS} family of curves for an n-channel depletion mode MOSFET is shown in Figure 6.54.

We can use the I–V relations to experimentally determine the mobility and threshold voltage parameters. From Equation (6.51b), we can write, for very small values of V_{DS},

$$I_D = \frac{W\mu_n C_{ox}}{L}(V_{GS} - V_{TN})V_{DS} \tag{6.58}$$

Figure 6.55a shows a plot of Equation (6.58) as a function of V_{GS} for constant V_{DS}. A straight line is fitted through the points. The deviation from the straight line at low values of V_{GS} is due to subthreshold conduction and the deviation at higher values of V_{GS} is due to mobility being a function of gate voltage. Both of these effects will be considered in Chapter 7. The extrapolation of the straight line to zero current gives the threshold voltage and the slope is proportional to the inversion carrier mobility.

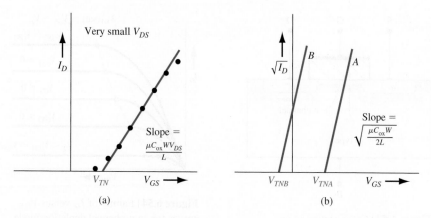

Figure 6.55 | (a) I_D versus V_{GS} (for small V_{DS}) for enhancement mode MOSFET. (b) Ideal $\sqrt{I_D}$ versus V_{GS} in saturation region for enhancement mode (curve A) and depletion mode (curve B) n-channel MOSFETs.

If we take the square root of Equation (6.57), we obtain

$$\sqrt{I_D(\text{sat})} = \sqrt{\frac{W\mu_n C_{ox}}{2L}} (V_{GS} - V_{TN}) \tag{6.59}$$

Figure 6.55b is a plot of Equation (6.59). In the ideal case, we can obtain the same information from both curves. However, as we will see in the next chapter, the threshold voltage may be a function of V_{DS} in short-channel devices. Since Equation (6.59) applies to devices biased in the saturation region, the V_{TN} parameter in this equation may differ from the extrapolated value determined in Figure 6.55a. In general, the nonsaturation current–voltage characteristics will produce the more reliable data.

EXAMPLE 6.11

OBJECTIVE

Determine the inversion carrier mobility from experimental results.

Consider an n-channel MOSFET with $W = 15\ \mu\text{m}$, $L = 2\ \mu\text{m}$, and $C_{ox} = 6.9 \times 10^{-8}$ F/cm². Assume that the drain current in the nonsaturation region for $V_{DS} = 0.10$ V is $I_D = 35\ \mu\text{A}$ at $V_{GS} = 1.5$ V and $I_D = 75\ \mu\text{A}$ at $V_{GS} = 2.5$ V.

■ **Solution**

From Equation (6.58), we can write

$$I_{D2} - I_{D1} = \frac{W\mu_n C_{ox}}{L} (V_{GS2} - V_{GS1}) V_{DS}$$

so that

$$75 \times 10^{-6} - 35 \times 10^{-6} = \left(\frac{15}{2}\right) \mu_n (6.9 \times 10^{-8})(2.5 - 1.5)(0.10)$$

which yields

$$\mu_n = 773 \text{ cm}^2/\text{V-s}$$

■ Comment

The mobility of carriers in the inversion layer is less than that in the bulk semiconductor due to the surface scattering effect. We will discuss this effect in the next chapter.

Exercise Problem

EX6.11 Consider the n-channel MOSFET described in Example 6.11. Using the results obtained in the example, determine the threshold voltage of the MOSFET.
(Ans. $V_{TN} = 0.625$ V.)

PMOS Transistor The current–voltage relationship of a p-channel MOSFET can be obtained using the same type of analysis. Figure 6.56 shows a p-channel enhancement-mode MOSFET. The voltage polarities and current directions are the reverse of those in the n-channel device. We can note the change in the subscript notation for this device. For the current direction shown in the figure, the I–V relation for the p-channel MOSFET biased in the nonsaturation region, $0 \leq V_{SD} \leq V_{SD}$ (sat), is

$$I_D = \frac{W}{L}\frac{\mu_p C_{\text{ox}}}{2}\left[2(V_{SG} + V_{TP})V_{SD} - V_{SD}^2\right] \quad (6.60a)$$

or

$$I_D = K_p\left[2(V_{SG} + V_{TP})V_{SD} - V_{SD}^2\right] \quad (6.60b)$$

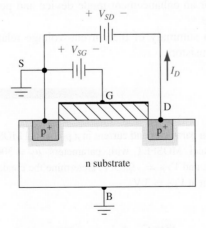

Figure 6.56 | Cross section and bias configuration for a p-channel enhancement-mode MOSFET.

Table 6.3 | Summary of ideal NMOS and PMOS current–voltage relationships

NMOS	PMOS
Transition point $V_{DS}(\text{sat}) = V_{GS} - V_{TN}$	**Transition point** $V_{SD}(\text{sat}) = V_{SG} + V_{TP}$
Nonsaturation bias $[V_{DS} \leq V_{DS}(\text{sat})]$; $I_D = K_n \left[2(V_{GS} - V_{TN})V_{DS} - V_{DS}^2 \right]$	**Nonsaturation bias** $[V_{SD} \leq V_{SD}(\text{sat})]$; $I_D = K_p \left[2(V_{SG} + V_{TP})V_{SD} - V_{SD}^2 \right]$
Saturation bias $[V_{DS} \geq V_{DS}(\text{sat})]$; $I_D = K_n (V_{GS} - V_{TN})^2$	**Saturation bias** $[V_{SD} \geq V_{SD}(\text{sat})]$; $I_D = K_p (V_{SG} + V_{TP})^2$

where K_p is the conduction parameter for the p-channel device and is defined as

$$K_p = \frac{W}{L} \frac{\mu_p C_{\text{ox}}}{2} = \frac{W}{L} \frac{k_p'}{2} \tag{6.61}$$

The parameter $k_p' = \mu_p C_{\text{ox}}$ is the process conduction parameter for the p-channel MOSFET.

When the MOSFET is biased in the saturation region, for $V_{SD} > V_{SD}(\text{sat})$, the I–V relationship is

$$I_D = K_p (V_{SG} + V_{TP})^2 \tag{6.62}$$

We have that

$$V_{SD}(\text{sat}) = V_{SG} + V_{TP} \tag{6.63}$$

We should keep in mind that the threshold voltage for the p-channel MOSFET is negative, $V_{TP} < 0$, for an enhancement-mode device and positive, $V_{TP} > 0$, for a depletion-mode device.

Table 6.3 gives a summary of the current–voltage relationships for both the NMOS and PMOS transistors.

EXAMPLE 6.12

OBJECTIVE

Determine the conduction parameter and current in a p-channel MOSFET.

Consider a p-channel MOSFET with parameters $\mu_p = 300$ cm²/V-s, $C_{\text{ox}} = 6.9 \times 10^{-8}$ F/cm, $(W/L) = 10$, and $V_{TP} = -0.65$ V. Determine the conduction parameter K_p and find the maximum current at $V_{SG} = 3$ V.

■ Solution

We have

$$K_p = \frac{W \mu_p C_{\text{ox}}}{2L} = \frac{1}{2}(10)(300)(6.9 \times 10^{-8})$$

$$= 1.04 \times 10^{-4} \text{ A/V}^2 = 0.104 \text{ mA/V}^2$$

The maximum current occurs when the transistor is biased in the saturation region, or

$$I_D = K_p(V_{SG} + V_{TP})^2 = 0.104[3 + (-0.65)]^2 = 0.574 \text{ mA}$$

■ **Comment**

The conduction parameter, for a given width-to-length ratio, of a p-channel MOSFET is approximately one-half that of an n-channel MOSFET because of the reduced hole mobility value.

Exercise Problem

EX6.12 The maximum current in a p-channel MOSFET must be $I_D = 0.85$ mA at $V_{SG} = 3$ V. If the transistor has the same electrical parameters as given in Example 6.12, determine the required width-to-length ratio of the transistor. [Ans. $(W/L) = 14.9$]

CMOS Inverter   The **c**omplementary **m**etal–**o**xide–**s**emiconductor (CMOS) inverter consists of an n-channel enhancement-mode device ($V_{TN} > 0$) in series with a p-channel enhancement-mode device ($V_{TP} < 0$) as shown in Figure 6.57. The CMOS inverter consists of two MOSFETs and a dc power supply that actually forms a circuit. However, the CMOS inverter is the basis of the CMOS digital electronics used in microprocessors, so it is worth considering the fundamentals of this circuit.

When the input voltage is in the range $0 \le V_I \le V_{TN}$, the NMOS is cutoff and the NMOS drain current is zero. Since the NMOS and PMOS devices are in series, the PMOS drain current must also be zero, so the power dissipated in the circuit is zero (neglecting leakage currents). The source-to-gate voltage of the PMOS is $V_{SGP} = V_{DD} - V_I \approx V_{DD} > |V_{TP}|$. The only condition in the PMOS, then, that can result in zero current is for $V_{SDP} = 0$, or $V_0 = V_{DD}$.

If now, the input voltage is in the range $V_{DD} - |V_{TP}| \le V_I \le V_{DD}$, the PMOS is cutoff and the PMOS drain current is zero. Again, since the NMOS and PMOS devices are in series, the NMOS drain current is also zero, so the power dissipated in the circuit is zero. The gate-to-source voltage of the NMOS is $V_{GSN} = V_I \approx V_{DD} > V_{TN}$. The only condition in the NMOS that can result in zero current is for $V_{DSN} = 0$, or $V_0 = 0$.

CMOS inverter

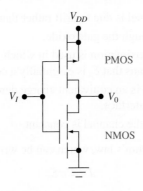

Figure 6.57 | The CMOS inverter circuit.

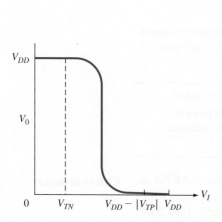

Figure 6.58 | CMOS voltage transfer characteristics.

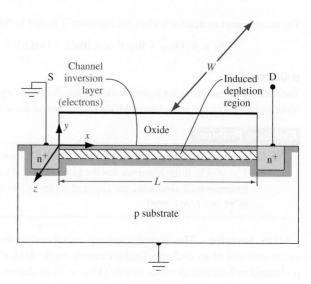

Figure 6.59 | Geometry of a MOSFET for I_D versus V_{DS} derivation.

CMOS voltage transfer characteristics

The voltage transfer characteristics (V_0 versus V_I) of the inverter are shown in Figure 6.58. The complete transfer characteristics are derived elsewhere. The important points are that when $V_I \approx$ Logic 0 ($V_I < V_{TN}$), the power dissipation is zero, and when $V_I \approx$ Logic 1 ($V_I > V_{DD} - |V_{TP}|$), the power dissipation is also zero.

Σ 6.5.3   Current–Voltage Relationship—Mathematical Derivation

In Section 6.5.2, we qualitatively discussed the current–voltage characteristics. In this section, we will derive the mathematical relation between the drain current, the gate-to-source voltage, and the drain-to-source voltage. Figure 6.59 shows the geometry of the device that we will use in this derivation.

In this analysis, we will make the following assumptions:

1. The current in the channel is due to drift rather than diffusion.
2. There is no current through the gate oxide.
3. A gradual channel approximation is used in which $\partial \mathcal{E}_y / \partial y \gg \partial \mathcal{E}_x / \partial x$. This approximation means that $\mathcal{E}_x$ is essentially a constant.
4. Any fixed oxide charge is an equivalent charge density at the oxide–semiconductor interface.
5. The carrier mobility in the channel is constant.

We start the analysis with Ohm's law, which can be written as

$$J_x = \sigma \mathcal{E}_x \qquad (6.64)$$

where σ is the channel conductivity and $\mathcal{E}_x$ is the electric field along the channel created by the drain-to-source voltage. The channel conductivity is given by $\sigma = e \mu_n n(y)$, where μ_n is the electron mobility and $n(y)$ is the electron concentration in the inversion layer.

The total channel current is found by integrating J_x over the cross-sectional area in the y and z directions. Then

$$I_x = \int_y \int_z J_x \, dy \, dz \tag{6.65}$$

We can write that

$$Q'_n = -\int en(y) \, dy \tag{6.66}$$

where Q'_n is the inversion layer charge per unit area and is a negative quantity for this case.

Equation (6.65) then becomes

$$I_x = -W\mu_n Q'_n \mathcal{E}_x \tag{6.67}$$

where W is the channel width, the result of integrating over z.

Two concepts we will use in the current–voltage derivation are charge neutrality and Gauss's law. Figure 6.60 shows the charge densities through the device for $V_{GS} > V_T$. The charges are all given in terms of charge per unit area. Using the concept of charge neutrality, we can write

$$Q'_m + Q'_{ss} + Q'_n + Q'_{SD}(\text{max}) = 0 \tag{6.68}$$

The inversion layer charge and induced space charge will be negative for this n-channel device.

Gauss's law can be written as

$$\oint_S \epsilon \mathcal{E}_n \, dS = Q_T \tag{6.69}$$

Gauss's law

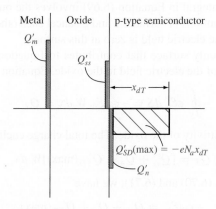

Metal   Oxide   p-type semiconductor

Q'_m

Q'_{ss}

x_{dT}

$Q'_{SD}(\text{max}) = -eN_a x_{dT}$

Q'_n

Figure 6.60 | Charge distribution in the n-channel enhancement mode MOSFET for $V_{GS} > V_T$.

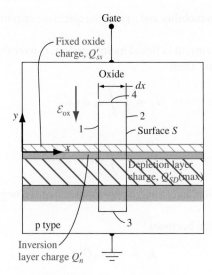

Figure 6.61 | Geometry for applying Gauss's law.

where the integral is over a closed surface. Q_T is the total charge enclosed by the surface, and $\mathcal{E}_n$ is the outward-directed normal component of the electric field crossing the surface S. Gauss's law will be applied to the surface defined in Figure 6.61. Since the surface must be enclosed, we must take into account the two end surfaces in the x-y plane. However, there is no z component of the electric field so these two end surfaces do not contribute to the integral of Equation (6.69).

Now consider the surfaces labeled 1 and 2 in Figure 6.61. From the gradual channel approximation, we will assume that $\mathcal{E}_x$ is essentially a constant along the channel length. This assumption means that $\mathcal{E}_x$ into surface 2 is the same as $\mathcal{E}_x$ out of surface 1. Since the integral in Equation (6.69) involves the outward component of the $\mathcal{E}$-field, the contributions of surfaces 1 and 2 cancel each other. Surface 3 is in the neutral p-region, so the electric field is zero at this surface.

Surface 4 is the only surface that contributes to Equation (6.69). Taking into account the direction of the electric field in the oxide, Equation (6.69) becomes

$$\oint_S \epsilon \mathcal{E}_n \, dS = -\epsilon_{ox} \mathcal{E}_{ox} W \, dx = Q_T \tag{6.70}$$

where ϵ_{ox} is the permittivity of the oxide. The total charge enclosed is

$$Q_T = [Q'_{ss} + Q'_n + Q'_{SD}(\max)] W \, dx \tag{6.71}$$

Combining Equations (6.70) and (6.71), we have

$$-\epsilon_{ox} \mathcal{E}_{ox} = Q'_{ss} + Q'_n + Q'_{SD}(\max) \tag{6.72}$$

We now need an expression for $\mathcal{E}_{ox}$. Figure 6.62a shows the oxide and channel. We will assume that the source is at ground potential. The voltage V_x is the potential

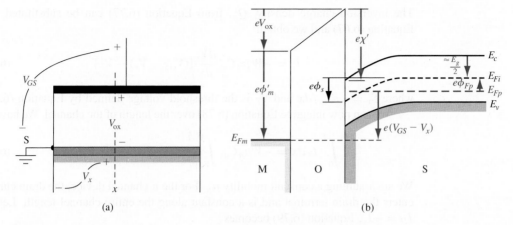

Figure 6.62 | (a) Potentials at a point x along the channel. (b) Energy-band diagram through the MOS structure at the point x.

in the channel at a point x along the channel length. The potential difference across the oxide at x is a function of V_{GS}, V_x, and the metal–semiconductor work function difference.

The energy-band diagram through the MOS structure at point x is shown in Figure 6.62b. The Fermi level in the p-type semiconductor is E_{Fp} and the Fermi level in the metal is E_{Fm}. We have

$$E_{Fp} - E_{Fm} = e(V_{GS} - V_x) \tag{6.73}$$

Considering the potential barriers, we can write

$$V_{GS} - V_x = (\phi'_m + V_{ox}) - \left(\chi' + \frac{E_g}{2e} - \phi_s + |\phi_{Fp}|\right) \tag{6.74}$$

which can also be written as

$$V_{GS} - V_x = V_{ox} + 2|\phi_{Fp}| + \phi_{ms} \tag{6.75}$$

where ϕ_{ms} is the metal–semiconductor work function difference, and $\phi_s = 2|\phi_{Fp}|$ for the inversion condition.

The electric field in the oxide is

$$\mathcal{E}_{ox} = \frac{V_{ox}}{t_{ox}} \tag{6.76}$$

Combining Equations (6.72), (6.75), and (6.76), we find that

$$-\epsilon_{ox}\mathcal{E}_{ox} = -\frac{\epsilon_{ox}}{t_{ox}}[(V_{GS} - V_x) - (\phi_{ms} + 2|\phi_{Fp}|)]$$

$$= Q'_{ss} + Q'_n + Q'_{SD}(\text{max}) \tag{6.77}$$

The inversion charge density, Q'_n, from Equation (6.77) can be substituted into Equation (6.67) and we obtain

$$I_x = -W\mu_n C_{\text{ox}}\frac{dV_x}{dx}[(V_{GS} - V_x) - V_T] \tag{6.78}$$

where $\mathcal{E}_x = -dV_x/dx$ and V_T is the threshold voltage defined by Equation (6.34).

We can now integrate Equation (6.78) over the length of the channel. We have

$$\int_0^L I_x\,dx = -W\mu_n C_{\text{ox}}\int_{V_x(0)}^{V_x(L)}[(V_{GS} - V_T) - V_x]\,dV_x \tag{6.79}$$

We are assuming a constant mobility μ_n. For the n-channel device, the drain current enters the drain terminal and is a constant along the entire channel length. Letting $I_D = -I_x$, Equation (6.79) becomes

$$I_D = \frac{W\mu_n C_{\text{ox}}}{2L}\left[2(V_{GS} - V_T)V_{DS} - V_{DS}^2\right] \tag{6.80}$$

Equation (6.80) is valid for $V_{GS} \geq V_T$ and for $0 \leq V_{DS} \leq V_{DS}(\text{sat})$.

We can find the value of V_{DS} at the peak current value from $\partial I_D/\partial V_{DS} = 0$. Then, using Equation (6.80), the peak current occurs when

$$V_{DS} = V_{GS} - V_T \tag{6.81}$$

This value of V_{DS} is just $V_{DS}(\text{sat})$, the point at which saturation occurs. For $V_{DS} > V_{DS}(\text{sat})$, the ideal drain current is a constant and is equal to

$$I_D(\text{sat}) = \frac{W\mu_n C_{\text{ox}}}{2L}\left[2(V_{GS} - V_T)V_{DS}(\text{sat}) - V_{DS}^2(\text{sat})\right] \tag{6.82}$$

Using Equation (6.81) for $V_{DS}(\text{sat})$, Equation (6.82) becomes

$$I_D(\text{sat}) = \frac{W\mu_n C_{\text{ox}}}{2L}(V_{GS} - V_T)^2 \tag{6.83}$$

Equation (6.80) is the ideal current–voltage relationship of the n-channel MOSFET in the nonsaturation region for $0 \leq V_{DS} \leq V_{DS}(\text{sat})$, and Equation (6.83) is the ideal current–voltage relationship of the n-channel MOSFET in the saturation region for $V_{DS} \geq V_{DS}(\text{sat})$. These I–V expressions were explicitly derived for an n-channel enhancement mode device. However, these same equations apply to an n-channel depletion mode MOSFET in which the threshold voltage V_T is a negative quantity.

One assumption we made in the derivation of the current–voltage relationship was that the charge neutrality condition given by Equation (6.68) was valid over the entire length of the channel. We implicitly assumed that $Q'_{SD}(\text{max})$ was constant along the length of the channel. The space charge width, however, varies between source and drain due to the drain-to-source voltage; it is widest at the drain when $V_{DS} > 0$. A change in the space charge density along the channel length must be balanced by a corresponding change in the inversion-layer charge. An increase in the space charge width means that the inversion-layer charge is reduced, implying that the drain current and drain-to-source saturation voltage are less than the ideal values. The actual saturation drain current may be as much as 20 percent less than the predicted value due to this bulk charge effect.

6.5.4 Substrate Bias Effects

In all of our analyses so far, the substrate, or body, has been connected to the source and held at ground potential. In MOSFET circuits, the source and body may not be at the same potential. Figure 6.63a shows an n-channel MOSFET and the associated double-subscripted voltage variables. The source-to-substrate pn junction must always be zero or reverse biased, so V_{SB} must always be greater than or equal to zero.

If $V_{SB} = 0$, threshold is defined as the condition when $\phi_s = 2|\phi_{Fp}|$ as we discussed previously and as shown in Figure 6.63b. When $V_{SB} > 0$ the surface will still try to invert when $\phi_s = 2|\phi_{Fp}|$. However, these electrons are at a higher potential energy than are the electrons in the source. The newly created electrons will move laterally and flow out of the source terminal. When $\phi_s = 2|\phi_{Fp}| + V_{SB}$, the surface reaches an equilibrium inversion condition. The energy-band diagram for this condition is shown in Figure 6.63c. The curve represented as E_{Fn} is the Fermi level from the p substrate through the reverse-biased source–substrate junction to the source contact.

The space charge region width under the oxide increases from the original x_{dT} value when a reverse-biased source–substrate junction voltage is applied. With an applied $V_{SB} > 0$, there is more charge associated with this region. Considering the charge neutrality condition through the MOS structure, the positive charge on the top metal gate must increase to compensate for the increased negative space charge in order to reach the threshold inversion point. So when $V_{SB} > 0$, the threshold voltage of the n-channel MOSFET increases.

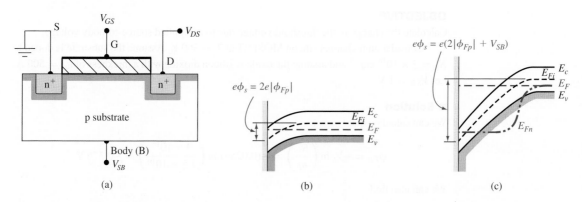

Figure 6.63 | (a) Applied voltages on an n-channel MOSFET. (b) Energy-band diagram at inversion point when $V_{SB} = 0$. (c) Energy-band diagram at inversion point when $V_{SB} > 0$ is applied.

When $V_{SB} = 0$, we had

$$Q'_{SD}(\text{max}) = -eN_a x_{dT} = -\sqrt{2e\epsilon_s N_a(2|\phi_{Fp}|)} \qquad (6.84)$$

When $V_{SB} > 0$, the space charge width increases and we now have

$$Q'_{SD} = -eN_a x_d = -\sqrt{2e\epsilon_s N_a(2|\phi_{Fp}| + V_{SB})} \qquad (6.85)$$

The change in the space charge density is then

$$\Delta Q'_{SD} = -\sqrt{2e\epsilon_s N_a}\left[\sqrt{2|\phi_{Fp}| + V_{SB}} - \sqrt{2|\phi_{Fp}|}\right] \qquad (6.86)$$

To reach the threshold condition, the applied gate voltage must be increased. The change in threshold voltage can be written as

Substrate bias effects

$$\boxed{\Delta V_T = -\frac{\Delta Q'_{SD}}{C_{\text{ox}}} = \frac{\sqrt{2e\epsilon_s N_a}}{C_{\text{ox}}}\left[\sqrt{2|\phi_{Fp}| + V_{SB}} - \sqrt{2|\phi_{Fp}|}\right]} \qquad (6.87)$$

where $\Delta V_T = V_T(V_{SB} > 0) - V_T(V_{SB} = 0)$. We may note that V_{SB} must always be positive so that, for the n-channel device, ΔV_T is always positive. The threshold voltage of the n-channel MOSFET will increase as a function of the source–substrate junction voltage.

If a body or substrate bias is applied to a p-channel device, the threshold voltage is shifted to more negative values. Because the threshold voltage of a p-channel enhancement mode MOSFET is negative, a body voltage will increase the applied negative gate voltage required to create inversion. The same general observation was made for the n-channel MOSFET.

EXAMPLE 6.13

OBJECTIVE

Calculate the change in the threshold voltage due to an applied source-to-body voltage.

Consider an n-channel silicon MOSFET at $T = 300$ K. Assume the substrate is doped to $N_a = 3 \times 10^{16}$ cm^{-3} and assume the oxide is silicon dioxide with a thickness of $t_{\text{ox}} = 500$ Å. Let $V_{SB} = 1$ V.

■ Solution

We can calculate that

$$\phi_{Fp} = -V_t \ln\left(\frac{N_a}{n_i}\right) = -(0.0259) \ln\left(\frac{3 \times 10^{16}}{1.5 \times 10^{10}}\right) = -0.376 \text{ V}$$

We can also find

$$C_{\text{ox}} = \frac{\epsilon_{\text{ox}}}{t_{\text{ox}}} = \frac{(3.9)(8.85 \times 10^{-14})}{500 \times 10^{-8}} = 6.9 \times 10^{-8} \text{ F/cm}^2$$

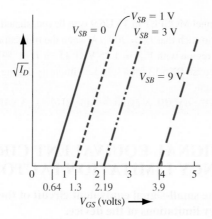

Figure 6.64 | Plots of $\sqrt{I_D}$ versus V_{GS} at several values of V_{SB} for an n-channel MOSFET.

Then from Equation (6.87), we can obtain

$$\Delta V_T = \frac{[2(1.6 \times 10^{-19})(11.7)(8.85 \times 10^{-14})(3 \times 10^{16})]^{1/2}}{6.9 \times 10^{-8}}$$

$$\times \{[2(0.376) + 1]^{1/2} - [2(0.376)]^{1/2}\}$$

or

$$\Delta V_T = 1.445(1.324 - 0.867) = 0.66 \text{ V}$$

■ **Comment**

Figure 6.64 shows plots of $\sqrt{I_D(\text{sat})}$ versus V_{GS} for various values of applied V_{SB}. The original threshold voltage, V_{T0}, is 0.64 V.

Exercise Problem

EX6.13 A silicon MOS device has the following parameters: $N_a = 10^{16}$ cm^{-3} and $t_{\text{ox}} = 200$ Å. Calculate (a) the body-effect coefficient $\gamma = \sqrt{2e\epsilon_s N_a}/C_{\text{ox}}$ and (b) the change in threshold voltage for (i) $V_{SB} = 1$ V and (ii) $V_{SB} = 2$ V.
[Ans. (a) $\gamma = 0.333$ V$^{1/2}$, (b) (i) $\Delta V_T = 0.156$ V, (ii) $\Delta V_T = 0.269$ V]

TEST YOUR UNDERSTANDING

TYU6.8 The n-channel MOSFET in EX6.10 is to be redesigned by changing the W/L ratio such that $I_D = 100$ μA when the transistor is biased in the saturation region with $V_{GS} = 1.75$ V. (Ans. $W/L = 0.976$)

TYU6.9 The parameters of a p-channel MOSFET are $\mu_p = 310$ cm^2/V-s, $t_{\text{ox}} = 220$ Å, $W/L = 60$, and $V_T = -0.40$ V. If the transistor is biased in the saturation region, find the drain current for $V_{SG} = 1$, 1.5, and 2 V.
(Ans. $I_D = 0.526$, 1.77 and 3.74 mA)

TYU6.10   The p-channel MOSFET in TYU6.9 is to be redesigned by changing the (W/L) ratio such that $I_D = 200\ \mu$A when the transistor is biased in the saturation region with $V_{SG} = 1.25$ V. (Ans. $W/L = 11.4$.)

TYU6.11   Repeat exercise EX6.13 for a substrate impurity doping concentration of $N_a = 10^{15}$ cm^{-3}.
[Ans. $(a)\ \gamma = 0.105$ V$^{1/2}$, $(b)\ (i)\ \Delta V_T = 0.052$ V, $(ii)\ \Delta V_T = 0.0888$ V]

6.6 | SMALL-SIGNAL EQUIVALENT CIRCUIT AND FREQUENCY LIMITATION FACTORS

Objective: Derive the small-signal equivalent circuit of the MOSFET and analyze the frequency limitations of the device.

In many applications, the MOSFET is used in a linear amplifier circuit. A small-signal equivalent circuit for the MOSFET is needed to mathematically analyze the electronic circuit. The equivalent circuit contains capacitances and resistances that introduce frequency effects. We will initially develop a small-signal equivalent circuit and then discuss the physical factors that limit the frequency response of the MOSFET. A transistor cutoff frequency, which is a figure of merit, will then be defined and an expression derived for this factor.

6.6.1 Transconductance

The MOSFET transconductance is defined as the change in drain current with respect to the corresponding change in gate voltage, or

$$g_m = \frac{\partial I_D}{\partial V_{GS}} \tag{6.88}$$

The transconductance is sometimes referred to as the transistor gain.

If we consider an n-channel MOSFET operating in the nonsaturation region, then, using Equation (6.51b), we have

$$g_{mL} = \frac{\partial I_D}{\partial V_{GS}} = \frac{\partial}{\partial V_{GS}} \left\{ \frac{W}{L} \frac{\mu_n C_{ox}}{2} \left[2(V_{GS} - V_{TN})V_{DS} - V_{DS}^2 \right] \right\} \tag{6.89a}$$

or

$$g_{mL} = \frac{W \mu_n C_{ox}}{L} V_{DS} \tag{6.89b}$$

The transconductance increases linearly with V_{DS} but is independent of V_{GS} in the nonsaturation region.

The I–V characteristics of an n-channel MOSFET in the saturation region were given by Equation (6.57). The transconductance in this region of operation is given by

$$g_{ms} = \frac{\partial I_D}{\partial V_{GS}} = \frac{\partial}{\partial V_{GS}} \left[\frac{W}{L} \frac{\mu_n C_{ox}}{2} (V_{GS} - V_{TN})^2 \right] \tag{6.90a}$$

or

$$g_{ms} = \frac{W\mu_n C_{ox}}{L}(V_{GS} - V_{TN}) \qquad (6.90b)$$

In the saturation region, the transconductance is a linear function of V_{GS} and is independent of V_{DS}.

The transconductance is a function of the geometry of the device as well as of carrier mobility and threshold voltage. The transconductance increases as the width of the device increases, and it also increases as the channel length and oxide thickness decrease. In the design of MOSFET circuits, the size of the transistor, in particular the channel width W, is an important engineering design parameter.

6.6.2 Small-Signal Equivalent Circuit

The small-signal equivalent circuit of the MOSFET is constructed from the basic MOSFET geometry. A model based on the inherent capacitances and resistances within the transistor structure, along with elements that represent the basic device equations, is shown in Figure 6.65. One simplifying assumption we will make in the equivalent circuit is that the source and substrate are both tied to ground potential.

Two of the capacitances connected to the gate are inherent in the device. These capacitances are C_{gs} and C_{gd}, which represent the interaction between the gate and the channel charge near the source and drain terminals, respectively. The remaining two gate capacitances, C_{gsp} and C_{gdp}, are parasitic or overlap capacitances. In real devices, the gate oxide will overlap the source and drain contacts because of tolerance or fabrication factors. As we will see, the drain overlap capacitance—C_{gdp}, in particular—will lower the frequency response of the device. The parameter C_{ds} is the drain-to-substrate pn junction capacitance, and r_s and r_d are the series resistances

Overlap capacitance

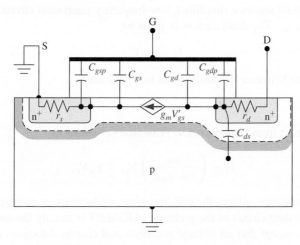

Figure 6.65 | Inherent resistances and capacitances in the n-channel MOSFET structure.

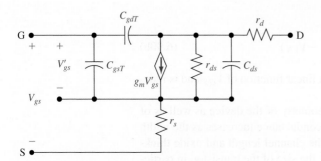

Figure 6.66 | Small-signal equivalent circuit of a common-source n-channel MOSFET.

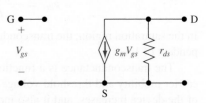

Figure 6.67 | Simplified, low-frequency small-signal equivalent circuit of a common-source n-channel MOSFET.

associated with the source and drain terminals. The small-signal channel current is controlled by the internal gate-to-source voltage through the transconductance.

The small-signal equivalent circuit for the n-channel common-source MOSFET is shown in Figure 6.66. The voltage V'_{gs} is the internal gate-to-source voltage that controls the channel current. The parameters C_{gsT} and C_{gdT} are the total gate-to-source and total gate-to-drain capacitances. One parameter, r_{ds}, shown in Figure 6.66, is not shown in Figure 6.65. This resistance is associated with the slope I_D versus V_{DS}. In the ideal MOSFET biased in the saturation region, I_D is independent of V_{DS} so that r_{ds} would be infinite. In short-channel-length devices, in particular, r_{ds} is finite because of channel length modulation, which we will consider in Chapter 7.

A simplified small-signal equivalent circuit valid at low frequency is shown in Figure 6.67. The series resistances, r_s and r_d, have been neglected, so the drain current is essentially only a function of the gate-to-source voltage through the transconductance. The input gate impedance is infinite in this simplified model.

The source resistance r_s can have a significant effect on the transistor characteristics. Figure 6.68 shows a simplified, low-frequency equivalent circuit including r_s but neglecting r_{ds}. The drain current is given by

$$I_d = g_m V'_{gs} \tag{6.91}$$

and the relation between V_{gs} and V'_{gs} can be found from

$$V_{gs} = V'_{gs} + (g_m V'_{gs})r_s = (1 + g_m r_s)V'_{gs} \tag{6.92}$$

The drain current from Equation (6.91) can now be written as

$$I_d = \left(\frac{g_m}{1 + g_m r_s} \right) V_{gs} = g'_m V_{gs} \tag{6.93}$$

The source resistance reduces the effective transconductance or transistor gain.

The equivalent circuit of the p-channel MOSFET is exactly the same as that of the n-channel except that all voltage polarities and current directions are reversed. The same capacitances and resistances that are in the n-channel model apply to the p-channel model.

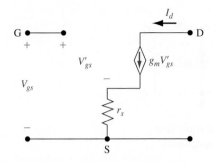

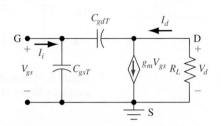

Figure 6.68 | Simplified, low-frequency small-signal equivalent circuit of common-source n-channel MOSFET including source resistance r_s.

Figure 6.69 | High-frequency small-signal equivalent circuit of common-source n-channel MOSFET.

6.6.3 Frequency Limitation Factors and Cutoff Frequency

There are two basic frequency limitation factors in the MOSFET. The first factor is the channel transit time. If we assume that carriers are traveling at their saturation drift velocity v_{sat}, then the transit time is $\tau_t = L/v_{\text{sat}}$, where L is the channel length. If $v_{\text{sat}} = 10^7$ cm/s and $L = 1\ \mu$m, then $\tau_t = 10$ ps, which translates into a maximum frequency of 100 GHz. This frequency is much larger than the typical maximum frequency response of a MOSFET. The transit time of carriers through the channel is usually not the limiting factor in the frequency responses of MOSFETs.

The second limiting factor is the gate or capacitance charging time. If we neglect r_s, r_d, r_{ds}, and C_{ds}, the resulting equivalent small-signal circuit is shown in Figure 6.69 where R_L is a load resistance.

The input gate impedance in this equivalent circuit is no longer infinite. Summing currents at the input gate node, we have

$$I_i = j\omega C_{gsT} V_{gs} + j\omega C_{gdT}(V_{gs} - V_d) \tag{6.94}$$

where I_i is the input current. Likewise, summing currents at the output drain node, we have

$$\frac{V_d}{R_L} + g_m V_{gs} + j\omega C_{gdT}(V_d - V_{gs}) = 0 \tag{6.95}$$

Combining Equations (6.94) and (6.95) to eliminate the voltage variable V_d, we can determine the input current as

$$I_i = j\omega \left[C_{gsT} + C_{gdT}\left(\frac{1 + g_m R_L}{1 + j\omega R_L C_{gdT}} \right) \right] V_{gs} \tag{6.96}$$

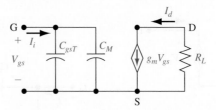

Figure 6.70 | Small-signal equivalent circuit including Miller capacitance.

Normally, $\omega R_L C_{gdT}$ is much less than unity; therefore we can neglect the $(j\omega R_L C_{gdT})$ term in the denominator. Equation (6.96) then simplifies to

$$I_i = j\omega[C_{gsT} + C_{gdT}(1 + g_m R_L)]V_{gs} \tag{6.97}$$

Miller capacitance

Figure 6.70 shows the equivalent circuit with the equivalent input impedance described by Equation (6.97). The parameter C_M is the Miller capacitance and is given by

$$C_M = C_{gdT}(1 + g_m R_L) \tag{6.98}$$

The serious effect of the drain overlap capacitance now becomes apparent. When the transistor is operating in the saturation region, C_{gd} essentially becomes zero, but C_{gdp} is a constant. This parasitic capacitance is multiplied by the gain of the transistor and can become a significant factor in the input impedance.

The cutoff frequency f_T is defined to be the frequency at which the magnitude of the current gain of the device is unity, or when the magnitude of the input current I_i is equal to the ideal load current I_d. From Figure 6.70, we can see that

$$I_i = j\omega(C_{gsT} + C_M)V_{gs} \tag{6.99}$$

and the ideal load current is

$$I_d = g_m V_{gs} \tag{6.100}$$

The magnitude of the current gain is then

$$\left|\frac{I_d}{I_i}\right| = \frac{g_m}{2\pi f(C_{gsT} + C_M)} \tag{6.101}$$

Setting the magnitude of the current gain equal to unity at the cutoff frequency, we find

$$f_T = \frac{g_m}{2\pi(C_{gsT} + C_M)} = \frac{g_m}{2\pi C_G} \tag{6.102}$$

where C_G is the equivalent input gate capacitance.

In the ideal MOSFET, the overlap or parasitic capacitances, C_{gsp} and C_{gdp}, are zero. Also, when the transistor is biased in the saturation region, C_{gd} approaches zero and C_{gs} is approximately $C_{ox}WL$. The transconductance of the ideal MOSFET biased in the saturation region and assuming a constant mobility was given by

Equation (6.90b) as

$$g_{ms} = \frac{W\mu_n C_{\text{ox}}}{L}(V_{GS} - V_{TN})$$

Then, for this ideal case, the cutoff frequency is

Cutoff frequency

$$f_T = \frac{g_m}{2\pi C_G} = \frac{\dfrac{W\mu_n C_{\text{ox}}}{L}(V_{GS} - V_{TN})}{2\pi(C_{\text{ox}}WL)} = \frac{\mu_n(V_{GS} - V_{TN})}{2\pi L^2} \qquad (6.103)$$

EXAMPLE 6.14

OBJECTIVE

Calculate the cutoff frequency of an ideal MOSFET with a constant mobility.

Assume that the electron mobility in an n-channel device is $\mu_n = 400$ cm^2/V-s and that the channel length is $L = 1.2$ μm. Also assume that $V_{TN} = 0.5$ V and let $V_{GS} = 2.2$ V.

■ **Solution**

From Equation (6.103), the cutoff frequency is

$$f_T = \frac{\mu_n(V_{GS} - V_{TN})}{2\pi L^2} = \frac{(400)(2.2 - 0.5)}{2\pi(1.2 \times 10^{-4})^2} = 7.52 \text{ GHz}$$

■ **Comment**

In an actual MOSFET, the effect of parasitic capacitance will substantially reduce the cutoff frequency from that calculated in this example.

Exercise Problem

EX6.14 An n-channel MOSFET has the following parameters: $\mu_n = 400$ cm^2/V-s, $t_{\text{ox}} = 200$ Å, $W/L = 20$, $L = 0.5$ μm, and $V_{TN} = 0.4$ V. The transistor is biased at $V_{GS} = 2.5$ V in the saturation region and is connected to an effective load of $R_L = 100$ kΩ. (*a*) Calculate the ratio of Miller capacitance C_M to gate-to-drain capacitance C_{gd}. (*b*) Determine the cutoff frequency. [Ans. (*a*) 291, (*b*) 53.5 GHz]

TEST YOUR UNDERSTANDING

TYU6.12 An n-channel MOSFET has the following parameters: $\mu_n = 400$ cm^2/V-s, $t_{\text{ox}} = 200$ Å, $W/L = 20$, and $V_T = 0.4$ V. The transistor is biased at $V_{GS} = 2.5$ V in the saturation region and is connected to an effective load of $R_L = 100$ kΩ. Calculate the ratio of Miller capacitance C_M to gate-to-drain capacitance C_{gdT}. (Ans. 292)

TYU6.13 An n-channel MOSFET has the same parameters as described in TYU6.12. The channel length is $L = 0.5$ μm. Determine the cutoff frequency. (Ans. 53.5 GHz)

Σ 6.7 I DEVICE FABRICATION TECHNIQUES

Objective: Describe a few of the MOSFET fabrication techniques including the gate oxide, gate "metallization," and the CMOS technology.

We will list some of the very basic steps in the fabrication of an NMOS transistor, and then also discuss the fabrication techniques used in the fabrication of CMOS.

6.7.1   Fabrication of an NMOS Transistor

The starting material is a lightly doped, (100) oriented, p-type wafer. The (100) surface is preferred because the interface–trap density at the interface between the oxide and semiconductor is far less than the (111) surface. The first step is to form a channel stop, as shown in Figure 6.71a. A film of silicon dioxide has been grown and a film of silicon nitride deposited on top of that. The active device region has been defined by the photoresist. Boron is then implanted through the silicon dioxide and silicon nitride into the silicon substrate. This implant forms a highly doped p-type surface so that this region cannot be inverted and prevents conduction between devices. After etching the silicon nitride over the channel stop region, a field oxide is then grown over this region.

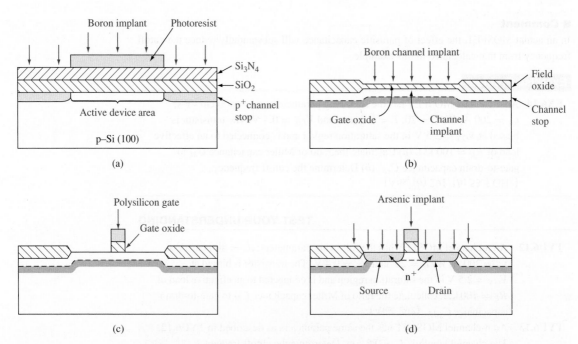

Figure 6.71 I Basic NMOS fabrication steps: (a) Formation of p$^+$ channel stops. (b) Threshold voltage adjust by channel ion implant. (c) Formation of gate. (d) Source- and drain-region implants.

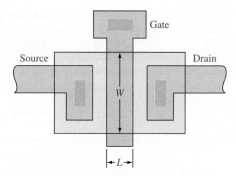

Figure 6.72 | Top view of NMOS transistor showing source, drain, and gate connections.

The next step is to grow the gate oxide and to adjust the threshold voltage by ion implantation. The silicon dioxide and silicon nitride over the active region are removed. A thin gate oxide (typically less than 100 Å) is then grown over the active region. For an enhancement-mode device, boron atoms are implanted in the channel region, as shown in Figure 6.71b, to achieve a specified threshold voltage. For a depletion-mode device, arsenic atoms are implanted in the channel region.

    A polysilicon layer is then deposited and is heavily doped by either diffusion or ion implantation. The gate is then patterned by photolithography as shown in Figure 6.71c. Arsenic atoms are now implanted, as shown in Figure 6.71d, to form the source and drain regions. The polysilicon gate acts as a mask to the implant atoms, so the source and drain regions are self-aligned with respect to the gate. This self-alignment process then minimizes the overlap capacitance. Low-temperature anneal steps minimize any lateral diffusion.

    The final step is metallization. Normally, a phosphorus-doped oxide is deposited over the entire wafer to protect the surface. Contact windows over the source, drain, and gate regions are then defined and etched. Metal is then deposited and patterned so that contact can be made to the NMOS terminals.

    A top view of the NMOS device is shown in Figure 6.72. The channel length and width are shown, and the source, drain, and gate contacts are also shown.

Threshold adjustment by ion implantation

6.7.2   The CMOS Technology

Since CMOS is so pervasive in digital electronics, it is worth considering, briefly, this fabrication technology. Since both NMOS and PMOS devices are used in CMOS, isolated p- and n-substrate regions must be formed to accommodate each type of device. The p-well process has been a commonly used technique for CMOS circuits. The process starts with a fairly low-doped n-type silicon substrate in which the p-channel MOSFET will be fabricated. A diffused p region, called a p well, is formed in which the n-channel MOSFET will be fabricated. In most cases, the p-type substrate doping level must be larger than the n-type substrate doping level to obtain the desired threshold voltages. The larger p doping can easily compensate the initial

p-well process

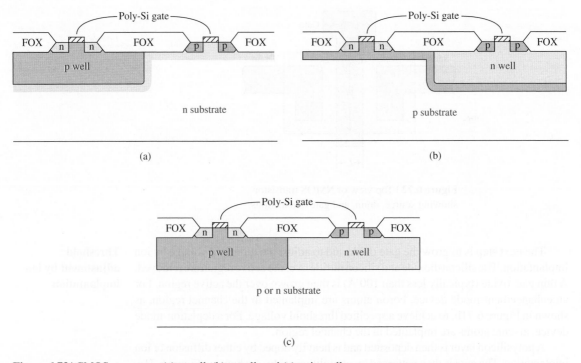

Figure 6.73 | CMOS structures: (a) p well, (b) n well, and (c) twin well.

n doping to form the p well. A simplified cross section of the p-well CMOS structure is shown in Figure 6.73a. The notation FOX stands for field oxide, which is a relatively thick oxide separating the devices. The field oxide prevents either the n or p substrate from becoming inverted and helps maintain isolation between the two devices. In practice, additional processing steps must be included; for example, providing connections so that the p well and n substrate can be electrically connected to the appropriate voltages. The n substrate must always be at a higher potential than the p well; therefore, this pn junction will always be reverse biased.

n-well process   With ion implantation now being extensively used for threshold voltage control, both the n-well CMOS process and twin-well CMOS process can be used. The n-well CMOS process, shown in Figure 6.73b, starts with an optimized p-type substrate that is used to form the n-channel MOSFETs. (The n-channel MOSFETs, in general, have superior characteristics, so this starting point should yield excellent n-channel devices.) The n well is then added, in which the p-channel devices are fabricated. The n-well doping can be controlled by ion implantation.

Twin-well process   The twin-well CMOS process, shown in Figure 6.73c, allows both the p-well and n-well regions to be optimally doped to control the threshold voltage and transconductance of each transistor. The twin-well process allows a higher packing density because of self-aligned channel stops.

6.8 | SUMMARY

1. The basic structure of an MOS field-effect transistor was given and the basic operation of the device was qualitatively discussed.

2. A. The heart of the MOSFET is the MOS capacitor. The energy bands in the semiconductor adjacent to the oxide–semiconductor interface bend, depending on the voltage applied to the gate terminal. The position of the conduction and valence bands relative to the Fermi level at the surface is a function of the MOS capacitor voltage.

   B. The semiconductor surface at the oxide–semiconductor interface can be inverted from p type to n type by applying a positive gate voltage, or from n type to p type by applying a negative gate voltage. Thus, an inversion layer of mobile charge can be created adjacent to the oxide. The basic MOS field-effect action is the modulation of the inversion charge density, or channel conductance, by the gate voltage.

3. A. The potential differences across the MOS capacitor were investigated. The first potential difference considered was the metal–semiconductor work function difference. The metal–semiconductor work-function difference is a function of the metal gate material and the semiconductor substrate doping.

   B. The flat-band voltage is the gate voltage that must be applied to achieve the flat-band condition, in which the conduction and valence bands in the semiconductor do not bend and there is no space charge region in the semiconductor. The flat-band voltage is a function of the metal-semiconductor work function difference and the amount of fixed trapped oxide charge.

   C. The threshold voltage is the applied gate voltage required to reach the threshold inversion point, which is the condition at which the inversion charge density is equal in magnitude to the semiconductor doping concentrations. The threshold voltage is a function of the flat-band voltage, semiconductor doping concentration, and oxide thickness.

4. The capacitance–voltage characteristics of the MOS capacitor were analyzed. The flat-band voltage, amount of fixed oxide charge, and interface charge density can be determined from the capacitance–voltage characteristics.

5. A. The current in a MOSFET is due to the flow of carriers in the inversion layer between the source and drain terminals. The inversion layer charge density and channel conductance are controlled by the gate voltage (this is the field-effect), which means that the channel current is also controlled by the gate voltage.

   B. When the transistor is biased in the nonsaturation region [$V_{DS} < V_{DS}(\text{sat})$], the inversion charge density extends completely across the channel from the source to the drain terminals. The drain current is a function of both the gate-to-source and drain-to-source voltages. When the transistor is biased in the saturation region [$V_{DS} > V_{DS}(\text{sat})$], the inversion charge density is pinched off near the drain terminal, and the ideal drain current is only a function of the gate-to-source voltage.

   C. The MOSFET is actually a four-terminal device, with the substrate of body being the fourth terminal. As the magnitude of the reverse-bias source-to-substrate voltage increases, the magnitude of the threshold voltage increases. The substrate bias effect may become important in integrated circuits in which the source and substrate are not electrically tied together.

6. A. A small-signal equivalent circuit, including capacitances, of the MOSFET was developed. The various physical factors in the MOSFET that affect the frequency limitations were considered. In particular, the drain overlap capacitance may be a limiting factor in the frequency response of the MOSFET because of the Miller effect.

   B. The cutoff frequency, a figure of merit for the frequency response of the device, is inversely proportional to channel length; thus, a reduction in channel length results in an increased frequency capability of the MOSFET.

7. A. The basic process of fabricating an NMOS transistor was presented including the use of channel stops and self-aligned source and drain contacts with respect to the gate.

   B. The various CMOS fabrication technologies were discussed including the p-well, n-well, and twin-well structures.

CHECKPOINT

After studying this chapter, the reader should have the ability to

1. A. Sketch the cross section of an n-channel MOSFET.
   B. Qualitatively describe the operation of the device.

2. A. Sketch the energy-band diagrams in the semiconductor of the MOS capacitor under various bias conditions.
   B. Describe the process by which an inversion layer of charge is created in an MOS capacitor.
   C. Discuss the reason the space charge region width reaches a maximum value once the inversion layer is formed.

3. A. Discuss what is meant by the metal–semiconductor work-function difference and discuss why this value is different between aluminum, n^+ polysilicon, and p^+ polysilicon gates.
   B. Describe the condition of flat-band.
   C. Define threshold voltage.

4. A. Sketch the C–V characteristics of an MOS capacitor with p- and n-type semiconductor substrates under high- and low-frequency conditions.
   B. Discuss the effects of fixed trapped oxide charge and interface states on the C–V characteristics.

5. A. Sketch the cross-sections of n- and p-channel MOSFET structures.
   B. Explain the basic operation of the MOSFET.
   C. Discuss the I–V characteristics of the MOSFET when biased in the nonsaturation and saturation regions.
   D. Describe the substrate bias effects on the threshold voltage.

6. A. Sketch the small-signal equivalent circuit, including capacitances, of the MOSFET, and explain the physical origin of each capacitance.
   B. Define the condition that defines the cutoff frequency of a MOSFET.

7. A. Describe the basic fabrication procedure of an NMOS transistor.
   B. Describe the differences between p-well, n-well, and twin-well structures in the CMOS fabrication procedure.

REVIEW QUESTIONS

1. A. Describe the concept of "field effect."
   B. Describe how a MOSFET can amplify a time-varying input signal.
2. A. Sketch the energy-band diagrams in an MOS capacitor with an n-type substrate in accumulation, depletion, and inversion modes.
   B. Describe what is meant by an inversion layer of charge. Describe how an inversion layer of charge can be formed in an MOS capacitor with a p-type substrate.
   C. Why does the space charge region in the semiconductor of an MOS capacitor essentially reach a maximum width once the inversion layer is fomed?
3. A. Define electron affinity in the semiconductor of an MOS capacitor.
   B. Sketch the energy-band diagram through an MOS structure with a p-type substrate and an n^+ polysilicon gate under zero bias.
   C. Define flat-band voltage.
   D. Define threshold voltage.
4. A. Sketch the $C-V$ characteristics of an MOS capacitor with an n-type substrate under the low-frequency condition. How and why do the characteristics change for the high-frequency condition?
   B. Indicate the approximate capacitance at flat-band on the $C-V$ characteristic of an MOS capacitor with a p-type substrate under the high-frequency condition.
   C. What is the effect on the $C-V$ characteristics of an MOS capacitor with a p-type substrate if the amount of positive trapped charge in the oxide increases?
5. A. Qualitatively sketch the inversion charge density in the channel region when the transistor is biased in the nonsaturation region. Repeat for the case when the transistor is biased in the saturation region.
   B. Define $V_{DS}(\text{sat})$.
   C. Define enhancement mode and depletion mode for both n- and p-channel devices.
   D. Define the conduction parameter. What is the primary parameter that a device designer has control of in the design of a MOSFET?
6. A. Sketch the basic small-signal equivalent circuit of the MOSFET.
   B. State the condition that defines the cutoff frequency of a MOSFET.
7. A. What is a channel stop in an NMOS transistor?
   B. What is meant by self-aligned source and drain contacts?
   C. Sketch the p-well configuration in the CMOS structure.

PROBLEMS

Section 6.2   The Two-Terminal MOS Capacitor

6.1 The dc charge distributions of four ideal MOS capacitors are shown in Figure P6.1. For each case: (*a*) Is the semiconductor n or p type? (*b*) Is the device biased in the accumulation, depletion, or inversion mode? (*c*) Draw the energy-band diagram in the semiconductor region.

6.2 (*a*) Calculate the maximum space charge width x_{dT} and the maximum space charge density $|Q'_{SD}(\text{max})|$ in p-type silicon, gallium arsenide, and germanium semiconductors of an MOS structure. Let $T = 300$ K and assume $N_a = 10^{16}$ cm^{-3}. (*b*) Repeat part (*a*) if $T = 200$ K.

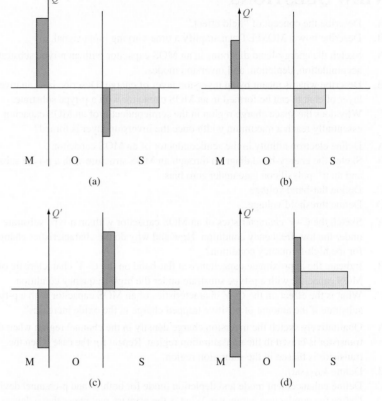

Figure P6.1 | Figure for Problem 6.1.

6.3   (*a*) Consider n-type silicon in an MOS structure. Let $T = 300$ K. Determine the semiconductor doping so that $|Q'_{SD}(\text{max})| = 7.5 \times 10^{-9}$ C/cm^2. (*b*) Determine the surface potential that results in the maximum space charge width.

Section 6.3   Potential Differences in the MOS Capacitor

[Note: Use Figure 6.21 to determine ϕ_{ms} unless otherwise stated.]

6.4   Determine the metal–semiconductor work function difference ϕ_{ms} in an MOS structure with p-type silicon for the case when the gate is (*a*) aluminum, (*b*) n$^+$ polysilicon, and (*c*) p$^+$ polysilicon. Let $N_a = 6 \times 10^{15}$ cm^{-3}.

6.5   Consider an MOS structure with n-type silicon. A metal–semiconductor work function difference of $\phi_{ms} = -0.35$ V is required. Determine the silicon doping required to meet this specification when the gate is (*a*) n$^+$ polysilicon, (*b*) p$^+$ polysilicon, and (*c*) aluminum. If a particular gate cannot meet this requirement, explain why.

6.6   Consider an n$^+$ polysilicon–silicon dioxide–n-type silicon MOS capacitor. Let $N_d = 10^{15}$ cm^{-3}. Calculate the flat-band voltage for (*a*) $t_{\text{ox}} = 400$ Å when Q'_{ss} is (*i*) 10^{10} cm^{-2} and (*ii*) 10^{11} cm^{-2}. (*b*) Repeat part (*a*) when $t_{\text{ox}} = 200$ Å.

6.7 Consider an aluminum gate–silicon dioxide–p-type silicon MOS structure with $t_{ox} = 450$ Å. The silicon doping is $N_a = 2 \times 10^{16}$ cm^{-3} and the flat-band voltage is $V_{FB} = -1.0$ V. Determine the fixed oxide charge Q'_{ss}.

6.8 An MOS transistor is fabricated on a p-type silicon substrate with $N_a = 2 \times 10^{15}$ cm^{-3}. The oxide thickness is $t_{ox} = 450$ Å and the equivalent fixed oxide charge is $Q'_{ss} = 5 \times 10^{10}$ cm^{-2}. Calculate the threshold voltage for (a) an aluminum gate, (b) an n$^+$ polysilicon gate, and (c) a p$^+$ polysilicon gate.

6.9 Repeat Problem 6.8 for an n-type silicon substrate with $N_d = 10^{15}$ cm^{-3}.

6.10 A 400 Å oxide is grown on p-type silicon with $N_a = 5 \times 10^{15}$ cm^{-3}. The flat-band voltage is -0.9 V. Calculate the surface potential at the threshold inversion point as well as the threshold voltage assuming negligible oxide charge. Also find the maximum space charge width for this device.

*6.11 An MOS transistor with an aluminum gate is fabricated on a p-type silicon substrate. The oxide thickness is $t_{ox} = 450$ Å, and the equivalent fixed oxide charge is $Q'_{ss} = 8 \times 10^{10}$ cm^{-2}. The measured threshold voltage is $V_T = +0.80$ V. Determine the p-type doping concentration.

*6.12 Repeat Problem 6.11 for an n-type silicon substrate if the measured threshold voltage is $V_T = -1.15$ V. Determine the n-type doping concentration.

6.13 An Al–silicon dioxide–silicon MOS capacitor has an oxide thickness of 450 Å and a doping of $N_a = 10^{15}$ cm^{-3}. The oxide charge density is $Q'_{ss} = 3 \times 10^{11}$ cm^{-2}. Calculate (a) the flat-band voltage and (b) the threshold voltage. Sketch the electric field through the structure at the onset of inversion.

6.14 An n-channel depletion mode MOSFET with an n$^+$ polysilicon gate is shown in Figure 6.46b. The n-channel doping is $N_d = 10^{15}$ cm^{-3}, and the oxide thickness is $t_{ox} = 500$ Å. The equivalent fixed oxide charge is $Q'_{ss} = 10^{10}$ cm^{-2}. The n-channel thickness t_c is equal to the maximum induced space charge width. (Disregard the space charge region at the n-channel–p-substrate junction.) (a) Determine the channel thickness t_c, and (b) calculate the threshold voltage.

6.15 Consider an MOS capacitor with an n$^+$ polysilicon gate and n-type silicon substrate. Assume $N_a = 10^{16}$ cm^{-3} and let $E_F - E_c = 0.2$ eV in the n$^+$ polysilicon. Assume the oxide has a thickness of $t_{ox} = 300$ Å. Also assume that χ' (polysilicon) $= \chi'$ (single-crystal silicon). (a) Sketch the energy-band diagrams (i) for $V_G = 0$ and (ii) at flat band. (b) Calculate the metal–semiconductor work function difference. (c) Calculate the threshold voltage for the ideal case of zero fixed oxide charge and zero interface states.

6.16 The threshold voltage of an n-channel MOSFET is given by Equation (6.34a). Plot V_T versus temperature over the range $200 \le T \le 480$ K. Consider both an aluminum gate and an n$^+$ polysilicon gate. Assume the work functions are independent of temperature and use device parameters similar to those in Example 6.5.

6.17 Plot the threshold voltage of an n-channel MOSFET versus p-type substrate doping concentration similar to Figure 6.27. Consider both n$^+$ and p$^+$ polysilicon gates. Use reasonable device parameters.

6.18 Plot the threshold voltage of a p-channel MOSFET versus n-type substrate doping concentration similar to Figure 6.28. Consider both n$^+$ and p$^+$ polysilicon gates. Use reasonable device parameters.

6.19 Consider an NMOS device with the parameters given in Problem 6.10. Plot V_T versus t_{ox} over the range $20 \le t_{ox} \le 500$ Å.

Section 6.4   Capacitance–Voltage Characteristics

6.20   An ideal MOS capacitor with an aluminum gate has a silicon dioxide thickness of $t_{ox} = 400$ Å on a p-type silicon substrate doped with an acceptor concentration of $N_a = 10^{16}$ cm^{-3}. Determine the capacitances C_{ox}, C'_{FB}, C'_{min}, and $C'(\text{inv})$ at (a) $f = 1$ Hz and (b) $f = 1$ MHz. (c) Determine V_{FB} and V_T. Sketch C'/C_{ox} versus V_G for parts (a) and (b).

6.21   Repeat Problem 6.20 for an n-type silicon substrate doped with a donor concentration of $N_d = 5 \times 10^{14}$ cm^{-3}.

*6.22   Using superposition, show that the shift in the flat-band voltage due to a fixed charge distribution $\rho(x)$ in the oxide is given by

$$\Delta V_{FB} = -\frac{1}{C_{ox}} \int_0^{t_{ox}} \frac{x\rho(x)}{t_{ox}} \, dx$$

*6.23   Using the results of Problem 6.22, calculate the shift in the flat-band voltage for the following oxide charge distributions: (a) $Q'_{ss} = 5 \times 10^{11}$ cm^{-2} is entirely located at the oxide–semiconductor interface. Let $t_{ox} = 750$ Å. (b) $Q'_{ss} = 5 \times 10^{11}$ cm^{-2} is uniformly distributed throughout the oxide, which has a thickness of $t_{ox} = 750$ Å. (c) $Q'_{ss} = 5 \times 10^{11}$ cm^{-2} forms a triangular distribution with the peak at $x = t_{ox} = 750$ Å (the oxide–semiconductor interface) and which goes to zero at $x = 0$ (the metal–oxide interface).

6.24   An ideal MOS capacitor is fabricated by using intrinsic silicon and an n$^+$ polysilicon gate. (a) Sketch the energy-band diagram through the MOS structure under flat-band conditions. (b) Sketch the low-frequency C–V characteristics from negative to positive gate voltage.

6.25   Consider an MOS capacitor with a p-type substrate. Assume that donor-type interface traps exist only at midgap (i.e., at E_{Fi}). Sketch the high-frequency C–V curve from accumulation to inversion. Compare this sketch to the ideal C–V plot.

6.26   Consider an SOS capacitor as shown in Figure P6.26. Assume the SiO$_2$ is ideal (no trapped charge) and has a thickness of $t_{ox} = 500$ Å. The doping concentrations are $N_d = 10^{16}$ cm^{-3} and $N_a = 10^{16}$ cm^{-3}, (a) Sketch the energy band diagram through the device for (i) flat-band, (ii) $V_G = +3$ V, and (iii) $V_G = -3$ V. (b) Calculate the flat-band voltage. (c) Estimate the voltage across the oxide for (i) $V_G = +3$ V and (ii) $V_G = -3$ V. (d) Sketch the high-frequency C–V characteristic curve.

6.27   The high-frequency C–V characteristic curve of an MOS capacitor is shown in Figure P6.27. The area of the device is 2×10^{-3} cm^2. The metal–semiconductor work function difference is $\phi_{ms} = -0.50$ V, the oxide is SiO$_2$, the semiconductor is silicon, and the semiconductor doping concentration is 2×10^{16} cm^{-3}. (a) Is the semiconductor n or p type? (b) What is the oxide thickness? (c) What is the equivalent trapped oxide charge density? (d) Determine the flat-band capacitance.

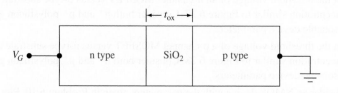

Figure P6.26 | Figure for Problem 6.26.

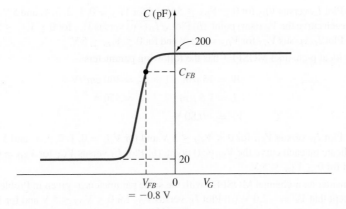

Figure P6.27 | Figure for Problem 6.27.

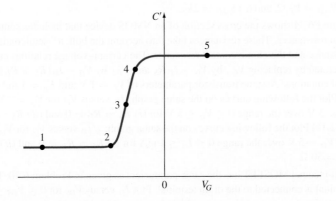

Figure P6.28 | Figure for Problem 6.28.

6.28 Consider the high-frequency C–V plot shown in Figure P6.28. (*a*) Indicate which points correspond to flat-band, inversion, accumulation, threshold, and depletion mode. (*b*) Sketch the energy-band diagram in the semiconductor for each condition.

Section 6.5   The Basic MOSFET Operation

6.29 An expression that includes the inversion charge density was given by Equation (6.77). Consider the definition of threshold voltage and show that the inversion charge density goes to zero at the drain terminal at saturation. [Hint: Let $V_x = V_{DS} = V_{DS}(\text{sat}).$]

6.30 An ideal n-channel MOSFET has the following parameters:

$$W = 30 \ \mu\text{m} \qquad \mu_n = 450 \ \text{cm}^2/\text{V-s}$$
$$L = 2 \ \mu\text{m} \qquad t_{\text{ox}} = 350 \ \text{Å}$$
$$V_T = +0.80 \ \text{V}$$

(a) Plot I_D versus V_{DS} for $0 \leq V_{DS} \leq 5$ V and for $V_{GS} = 0, 1, 2, 3, 4,$ and 5 V. Indicate on each curve the $V_{DS}(\text{sat})$ point. (b) Plot $\sqrt{I_D(\text{sat})}$ versus V_{GS} for $0 \leq V_{GS} \leq 5$ V. (c) Plot I_D versus V_{GS} for $V_{DS} = 0.1$ V and for $0 \leq V_{GS} \leq 5$ V.

6.31   An ideal p-channel MOSFET has the following parameters:

$$W = 15 \; \mu\text{m} \qquad \mu_p = 300 \; \text{cm}^2/\text{V-s}$$
$$L = 1.5 \; \mu\text{m} \qquad t_{\text{ox}} = 350 \; \text{Å}$$
$$V_T = -0.80 \; \text{V}$$

(a) Plot I_D versus V_{SD} for $0 \leq V_{SD} \leq 5$ V and for $V_{SG} = 0, 1, 2, 3, 4,$ and 5 V. Indicate on each curve the $V_{SD}(\text{sat})$ point. (b) Plot I_D versus V_{SG} for $V_{SD} = 0.1$ V and for $0 \leq V_{SG} \leq 5$ V.

6.32   Consider an n-channel MOSFET with the same parameters as given in Problem 6.30 except that $V_T = -2.0$ V. (a) Plot I_D versus V_{DS} for $0 \leq V_{DS} \leq 5$ V and for $V_{GS} = -2, -1, 0, +1,$ and $+2$ V. (b) Plot $\sqrt{I_D(\text{sat})}$ versus V_{GS} for $-2 \leq V_{GS} \leq +3$ V.

6.33   Consider an n-channel enhancement mode MOSFET biased as shown in Figure P6.33. Sketch the current–voltage characteristics, I_D versus V_{DS}, for (a) $V_{GD} = 0$, (b) $V_{GD} = V_T/2$, and (c) $V_{GD} = 2V_T$.

6.34   Figure P6.34 shows the cross section of an NMOS device that includes source and drain resistances. These resistances take into account the bulk n^+ semiconductor resistance and the ohmic contact resistance. The current–voltage relations can be generated by replacing V_{GS} by $V_G - I_D R_S$ and V_{DS} by $V_D - I_D(R_S + R_D)$ in the ideal equations. Assume transistor parameters of $V_T = 1$ V and $K_n = 1$ mA/V^2. (a) Plot the following curves on the same graph: I_D versus V_D for $V_G = 2$ V and $V_G = 3$ V over the range $0 \leq V_D \leq 5$ V for (i) $R_S = R_D = 0$ and (ii) $R_S = R_D = 50 \; \Omega$. (b) Plot the following curves on the same graph: $\sqrt{I_D}$ versus V_G for $V_D = 0.1$ V and $V_D = 5$ V over the range $0 \leq I_D \leq 1$ mA for (i) $R_S = R_D = 0$ and (ii) $R_S = R_D = 50 \; \Omega$.

6.35   An n-channel MOSFET has the same parameters as given in Problem 6.30. The gate terminal is connected to the drain terminal. Plot I_D versus V_{DS} for $0 \leq V_{DS} \leq 5$ V. Determine the range of V_{DS} over which the transistor is biased in the nonsaturation and saturation regions.

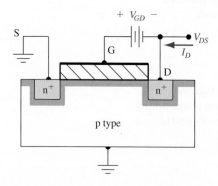

Figure P6.33 | Figure for Problem 6.33.

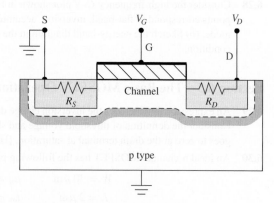

Figure P6.34 | Figure for Problem 6.34.

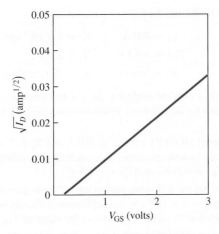

Figure P6.37 | Figure for Problem 6.37.

6.36 The channel conductance for a p-channel MOSFET is defined as

$$g_d = \frac{\partial I_D}{\partial V_{SD}}\bigg|_{V_{SD}\to 0}$$

Plot the channel conductance for the p-channel MOSFET in Problem 6.31 for $0 \le V_{SG} \le 5$ V.

6.37 The experimental characteristics of an ideal n-channel MOSFET biased in the saturation region are shown in Figure P6.37. If $W/L = 10$ and $t_{ox} = 425$ Å, determine V_T and μ_n.

6.38 One curve of an n-channel MOSFET is characterized by the following parameters: $I_D(\text{sat}) = 2 \times 10^{-4}$ A, $V_{DS}(\text{sat}) = 4$ V, and $V_T = 0.8$ V.

(a) What is the gate voltage?
(b) What is the value of the conduction parameter?
(c) If $V_G = 2$ V and $V_{DS} = 2$ V, determine I_D.
(d) If $V_G = 3$ V and $V_{DS} = 1$ V, determine I_D.
(e) For each of the conditions given in (c) and (d), sketch the inversion charge density and depletion region through the channel.

6.39 (a) An ideal n-channel MOSFET has an inversion carrier mobility $\mu_n = 525$ cm²/V-s, a threshold voltage $V_T = +0.75$ V, and an oxide thickness $t_{ox} = 400$ Å. When biased in the saturation region, the required rated current is $I_D(\text{sat}) = 6$ mA when $V_{GS} = 5$ V. Determine the required W/L ratio. (b) A p-channel MOSFET has the same requirements when $V_{GS} = 5$ V and has the same parameters as part (a) except $\mu_p = 300$ cm²/V-s and $V_T = -0.75$ V. Determine the W/L ratio.

6.40 Consider the transistor described in Problem 6.30. (a) Calculate g_{mL} for $V_{DS} = 0.5$ V. (b) Calculate g_{ms} for $V_{GS} = 4$ V.

6.41 Consider the transistor described in Problem 6.31. (a) Calculate g_{mL} for $V_{SD} = 0.5$ V. (b) Calculate g_{ms} for $V_{SG} = 4$ V.

6.42 An n-channel MOSFET has the following parameters:

$$t_{ox} = 400 \text{ Å} \qquad N_a = 5 \times 10^{16} \text{ cm}^{-3}$$
$$V_{FB} = -0.5 \text{ V} \qquad L = 2 \text{ } \mu\text{m}$$
$$W = 10 \text{ } \mu\text{m} \qquad \mu_n = 450 \text{ cm}^2/\text{V-s}$$

Plot $\sqrt{I_D}$ versus V_{GS} over the range $0 \leq I_D \leq 1$ mA when the transistor is biased in the saturation region for the following values of source-to-body voltage: $V_{SB} = 0, 1, 2,$ and 4 V.

6.43 Consider a p-channel MOSFET with $t_{ox} = 600 \text{ Å}$ and $N_d = 5 \times 10^{15} \text{ cm}^{-3}$. Determine the body-to-source voltage, V_{BS}, such that the shift in threshold voltage, ΔV_T, from the $V_{BS} = 0$ curve is $\Delta V_T = -1.5$ V.

6.44 An NMOS device has the following parameters: n^+ poly gate, $t_{ox} = 400 \text{ Å}$, $N_a = 10^{15} \text{ cm}^{-3}$, and $Q'_{ss} = 5 \times 10^{10} \text{ cm}^{-2}$. (a) Determine V_T. (b) Is it possible to apply a V_{SB} voltage such that $V_T = 0$? If so, what is the value of V_{SB}?

6.45 Investigate the threshold voltage shift due to substrate bias. The threshold shift is given by Equation (6.87). Plot ΔV_T versus V_{SB} over the range $0 \leq V_{SB} \leq 5$ V for several values of N_a and t_{ox}. Determine the conditions for which ΔV_T is limited to a maximum value of 0.7 V over the range of V_{SB}.

Section 6.6   Small-Signal Equivalent Circuit and Frequency Limitations Factors

6.46 Consider an ideal n-channel MOSFET with a width-to-length ratio of $(W/L) = 10$, an electron mobility of $\mu_n = 400 \text{ cm}^2/\text{V-s}$, an oxide thickness of $t_{ox} = 475 \text{ Å}$, and a threshold voltage of $V_T = +0.65$ V. (a) Determine the maximum value of source resistance so that the saturation transconductance g_{ms} is reduced by no more than 20 percent from its ideal value when $V_{GS} = 5$ V. (b) Using the value of r_s calculated in part (a), how much is g_{ms} reduced from its ideal value when $V_{GS} = 3$ V?

6.47 An n-channel MOSFET has the following parameters:

$$\mu_n = 400 \text{ cm}^2/\text{V-s} \qquad t_{ox} = 500 \text{ Å}$$
$$L = 2 \text{ } \mu\text{m} \qquad W = 20 \text{ } \mu\text{m}$$
$$V_T = +0.75 \text{ V}$$

Assume the transistor is biased in the saturation region at $V_{GS} = 4$ V. (a) Calculate the ideal cutoff frequency. (b) Assume that the gate oxide overlaps both the source and drain contacts by 0.75 μm. If a load resistance of $R_L = 10$ kΩ is connected to the output, calculate the cutoff frequency.

6.48 Repeat Problem 6.47 for the case when the electrons are traveling at a saturation velocity of $v_{sat} = 4 \times 10^6$ cm/s.

Summary and Review

*6.49 Design an ideal silicon n-channel MOSFET with a polysilicon gate to have a threshold voltage of $V_T = 0.65$ V. Assume an oxide thickness of $t_{ox} = 300 \text{ Å}$, a channel length of $L = 1.25 \text{ } \mu\text{m}$, and a nominal value of $Q'_{ss} = 1.5 \times 10^{11} \text{ cm}^{-2}$. It is desired to have a drain current of $I_D = 50 \text{ } \mu\text{A}$ at $V_{GS} = 2.5$ V and $V_{DS} = 0.1$ V. Determine the substrate doping concentration, channel width, and type of gate required.

*6.50 Design an ideal silicon n-channel depletion mode MOSFET with a polysilicon gate to have a threshold voltage of $V_T = -0.65$ V. Assume an oxide thickness of $t_{ox} = 300$ Å, a channel length of $L = 1.25$ μm, and a nominal value of $Q'_{ss} = 1.5 \times 10^{11}$ cm^{-2}. It is desired to have a drain current of I_D (sat) $= 50$ μA at $V_{GS} = 0$. Determine the type of gate, substrate doping concentration, and channel width required.

*6.51 Consider the CMOS inverter circuit shown in Figure 6.57. Ideal n- and p-channel devices are to be designed with channel lengths of $L = 2.5$ μm and oxide thicknesses of $t_{ox} = 450$ Å. Assume the inversion channel mobilities are one-half the bulk values. The threshold voltages of the n- and p-channel transistors are to be $+0.5$ V and -0.5 V, respectively. The drain current is to be $I_D = 0.256$ mA when the input voltage to the inverter is 1.5 V and 3.5 V with $V_{DD} = 5$ V. The gate material is to be the same in each device. Determine the type of gate, substrate doping concentrations, and channel widths.

*6.52 A complementary pair of ideal n-channel and p-channel MOSFETs are to be designed to produce the same *I–V* characteristics when they are equivalently biased. The devices are to have the same oxide thickness of 250 Å and the same channel length of $L = 2$ μm. Assume the SiO$_2$ layer is ideal. The n-channel device is to have a channel width of $W = 20$ μm. Assume constant inversion layer mobilities of $\mu_n = 600$ cm^2/V-s and $\mu_p = 220$ cm^2/V-s. (*a*) Determine p-type and n-type substrate doping concentrations. (*b*) What are the threshold voltages? (*c*) What is the width of the p-channel device?

READING LIST

1. Dimitrijev, S. *Understanding Semiconductor Devices*. New York: Oxford University Press, 2000.
2. Kano, K. *Semiconductor Devices*. Upper Saddle River, NJ: Prentice-Hall, 1998.
3. Muller, R. S., T. I. Kamins, and W. Chan. *Device Electronics for Integrated Circuits*, 3rd ed. New York: John Wiley and Sons, 2003.
4. Neamen, D. A. *Semiconductor Physics and Devices: Basic Principles,* 3rd ed. New York: McGraw-Hill, 2003.
5. Ng, K. K. *Complete Guide to Semiconductor Devices*. New York: McGraw-Hill, 1995.
6. Nicollian, E. H., and J. R. Brews. *MOS Physics and Technology*. New York: Wiley, 1982.
7. Ong, D. G. *Modern MOS Technology: Processes, Devices, and Design*. New York: McGraw-Hill, 1984.
8. Pierret, R. F. *Semiconductor Device Fundamentals*. Reading, MA: Addison-Wesley, 1996.
9. Roulston, D. J. *An Introduction to the Physics of Semiconductor Devices*. New York: Oxford University Press, 1999.
10. Schroder, D. K. *Advanced MOS Devices, Modular Series on Solid State Devices*. Reading, MA: Addison-Wesley, 1987.
11. Shur, M. *Introduction to Electronic Devices*. New York: John Wiley & Sons, Inc., 1996.
*12. Shur, M. *Physics of Semiconductor Devices*. Englewood Cliffs, NJ: Prentice-Hall, 1990.

13. Singh, J. *Semiconductor Devices: An Introduction.* New York: McGraw-Hill, 1994.

14. Singh, J. *Semiconductor Devices: Basic Principles.* New York: Wiley, 2001.

15. Streetman, B. G., and S. Banerjee. *Solid State Electronic Devices.* 5th ed. Upper Saddle River, NJ: Prentice-Hall, 2000.

16. Sze, S. M. *High-Speed Semiconductor Devices.* New York: Wiley, 1990.

17. Sze, S. M. *Physics of Semiconductor Devices.* 2nd ed. New York: Wiley, 1981.

*18. Taur, Y., and T. H. Ning. *Fundamentals of Modern VLSI Devices.* New York: Cambridge University Press, 1998.

*19. Tsividis, Y. *Operation and Modeling of the MOS Transistor.* 2nd ed. Burr Ridge, IL.: McGraw-Hill, 1999.

20. Werner, W. M. "The Work Function Difference of the MOS System with Aluminum Field Plates and Polycrystalline Silicon Field Plates." *Solid State Electronics* 17 (1974), pp. 769–75.

21. Wolf, S. *Silicon Processing for the VLSI Era: Volume 3—The Submicron MOSFET.* Sunset Beach, CA: Lattice Press, 1995.

22. Yamaguchi, T., S. Morimoto, G. H. Kawamoto, and J. C. DeLacy. "Process and Device Performance of 1 μm-Channel n-Well CMOS Technology." *IEEE Transactions on Electron Devices* ED-31 (February 1984), pp. 205–14.

23. Yang, E. S. *Microelectronic Devices.* New York: McGraw-Hill, 1988.

7

Metal–Oxide–Semiconductor Field-Effect Transistor: Additional Concepts

I n this chapter we present additional concepts that are commonly encountered in metal–oxide–semiconductor field-effect transistors. The channel length of MOSFETs is now, in general, less than 1 micrometer, so these devices are referred to as submicron MOSFETs. These devices exhibit "short-channel" effects that differ from the "long-channel" characteristics discussed in Chapter 6. We will initially consider the parameters of the device that are scaled when designing the short-channel devices. Because of the small size, mobility, threshold voltage, and breakdown voltage characteristics must be analyzed for these devices. Many additional details can be found in more advanced texts.

7.0 | PREVIEW

In this chapter, we will

1. Discuss how the various dimensions and parameters in a MOSFET are scaled when the channel length is reduced.

2. Analyze various nonideal electrical effects in short-channel MOSFETs.

3. Analyze the change in threshold voltage as the dimensions of the MOSFETs are reduced.

4. Discuss additional electrical effects, such as threshold adjustment by ion implantation, in MOSFETs.

5. Consider the fabrication and characteristics of a few specialized MOSFET devices.

Historical Insights

Since the development of the first MOSFET, the MOS technology has been growing at an incredible rate. A basic law described by Gordon Moore, the cofounder of Intel, states that the number of active elements on a chip doubles every 18 months. This law has been experimentally realized for the last three decades. At the same time, the cost per function has decreased every year by about 25 percent.

In some cases, large-power devices are required. The HEXFET power device was developed in 1979 by H. Collins and B. Pelley. Also, silicon-on-insulator structures have been proposed and fabricated to reduce parasitic capacitances. In 1977, the first buried oxide layer (SIMOX) process was proposed. In addition, the first non-volatile MOS memory device was proposed by D. Kahng and S. Sze in 1967.

Present-Day Insight

The MOSFET technology (in particular, CMOS) continues to be the core of digital integrated circuits. One aim is to make smaller devices so that more devices can be fabricated on a single chip, so that switching times can be made smaller, and so that power dissipation per device can be reduced. However, these very small devices have led to nonideal effects compared to the long-channel MOSFETs. These nonideal effects must be considered in the design of MOSFET ICs. Changes in the fabrication technology have been necessary to improve the transistor characteristics.

7.1 | MOSFET SCALING

Objective: Discuss how the various dimensions and parameters in a MOSFET are scaled when the channel length is reduced.

As we noted in Chapter 6, the frequency response of MOSFETs increases as the channel length decreases. The driving force in CMOS technology evolution in the last couple of decades has been reduced channel lengths. Channel lengths of 0.25 μm down to 0.13 μm are now the norm. One question that must be considered is what other device parameters must be changed as the channel length is scaled down.

7.1.1 Constant-Field Scaling

The principle of constant-field scaling is that device dimensions and device voltages be scaled such that electric fields (both horizontal and vertical) remain essentially constant. To ensure that the reliability of the scaled device is not compromised, the electric fields in the scaled device must not increase.

Figure 7.1a shows the cross section and parameters of an original NMOS device and Figure 7.1b shows the scaled device, where the scaling parameter is k. Typically, $k \approx 0.7$ per generation of a given technology.

Channel length scaling

As seen in the figure, the channel length is scaled from L to kL. To maintain a constant horizontal electric field, the drain voltage must also be scaled from V_D to kV_D. The maximum gate voltage will also be scaled from V_G to kV_G so that the gate

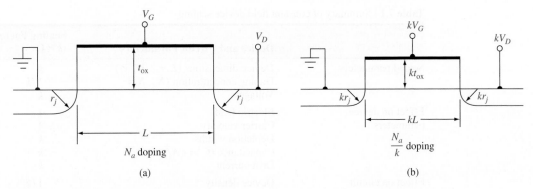

Figure 7.1 | Cross section of (a) original NMOS transistor and (b) scaled NMOS transistor.

and drain voltages remain compatible. To maintain a constant vertical electric field, the oxide thickness then must also be scaled from t_{ox} to kt_{ox}.

The maximum depletion width at the drain terminal, for a one-sided pn junction, is

$$x_D = \sqrt{\frac{2\epsilon(V_{bi} + V_D)}{eN_a}} \qquad (7.1)$$

Since the channel length is being reduced, the depletion widths also need to be reduced. If the substrate doping concentration is increased by the factor $(1/k)$, then the depletion width is reduced by approximately the factor k since V_D is reduced by k.

The drain current per channel width, for the transistor biased in the saturation region, can be written as[1]

$$\frac{I_D}{W} = \frac{\mu_n \epsilon_{ox}}{2t_{ox}L}(V_G - V_T)^2 \rightarrow \frac{\mu_n \epsilon_{ox}}{2(kt_{ox})(kL)}(kV_G - V_T)^2 \approx \text{constant} \qquad (7.2)$$

The drift current per channel width remains essentially a constant, so if the channel width is reduced by k, then the drain current is also reduced by k. The area of the device, $A \approx WL$, is then reduced by k^2 and the power, $P = IV$, is also reduced by k^2. The power density in the chip remains unchanged.

Table 7.1 summarizes the device scaling and the effect on circuit parameters. Keep in mind that the width and length of interconnect lines are also assumed to be reduced by the same scaling factor.

7.1.2 Threshold Voltage—First Approximation

In constant-field scaling, the device voltages are reduced by the scaling factor k. It would seem appropriate that the threshold voltage should also be scaled by the same

---

[1]The threshold voltage will simply be denoted as V_T.

Table 7.1 | Summary of constant field device scaling

	Device and Circuit Parameters	Scaling Factor ($k < 1$)
Scaled parameters	Device dimensions (L, t_{ox}, W, x_j)	k
	Doping concentration (N_a, N_d)	$1/k$
	Voltages	k
Effect on device parameters	Electric field	1
	Carrier velocity	1
	Depletion widths	k
	Capacitance ($C = \epsilon A / t$)	k
	Drift current	k
Effect on circuit parameters	Device density	$1/k^2$
	Power density	1
	Power dissipation per device ($P = VI$)	k^2
	Circuit delay time ($\approx CV/I$)	k
	Power-delay product ($P\tau$)	k^3

Source: Taur and Ning (1998) [23].

factor. The threshold voltage, for a uniformly doped substrate, can be written as

$$V_T = V_{FB} + 2|\phi_{Fp}| + \frac{\sqrt{2\epsilon e N_a (2|\phi_{Fp}|)}}{C_{ox}} \qquad (7.3)$$

The first two terms in Equation (7.3) are functions of material parameters that do not scale and are only very slight functions of doping concentration. The last term is approximately proportional to $\sqrt{k}$, so the threshold voltage does not scale directly with the scaling factor k.

The effect of short channels on the threshold voltage will be discussed further in Section 7.3 of this chapter.

7.1.3   Generalized Scaling

In constant-field scaling, the applied voltages are scaled with the same scaling factor k as the device dimensions. However, in actual technology evolution, voltages have not been reduced with the same scaling factor. There has been reluctance, for example, to change standardized power supply levels that have been used in previous circuits. In addition, other factors that do not scale, such as threshold voltage and subthreshold currents, have made the reduction in applied voltages less desirable. As a consequence, electric fields in MOS devices have tended to increase as device dimensions shrink.

Consequences of increased electric fields are reduced reliability and increased power density. As the power density increases, the device temperature may increase. Increased temperature may affect the device reliability. As the oxide thickness is reduced and the electric field is increased, gate oxides are closer to breakdown and oxide integrity may be more difficult to maintain. In addition, direct tunneling of carriers through the oxide may be more likely to occur. Increased electric fields may also increase the chances of hot-electron effects, which are discussed later in the chapter. Reducing device dimensions, then, can introduce challenging problems that must be solved.

TEST YOUR UNDERSTANDING

TYU7.1 An NMOS transistor has the following parameters: $L = 1\ \mu$m, $W = 10\ \mu$m, $t_{ox} = 250$ Å, $N_a = 5 \times 10^{15}$ cm^{-3}, and applied voltages of 3 V. If the device is to be scaled using constant-field scaling, determine the new device parameters for a scaling factor of $k = 0.7$.

(Ans. $L = 0.7\ \mu$m, $W = 7\ \mu$m, $t_{ox} = 175$ Å, $N_a = 7.14 \times 10^{15}$ cm^{-3}, and applied voltages of 2.1 V.)

7.2 | NONIDEAL EFFECTS

Objective: Analyze various nonideal electrical effects in short-channel MOSFETs.

As with any semiconductor device, the experimental characteristics of MOSFETs deviate to some degree from the ideal relations that have been theoretically derived using the various assumptions and approximations. In this section, we will consider four effects that cause deviations from the assumptions used in the ideal derivations. These effects are subthreshold conduction, channel length modulation, mobility variations, and velocity saturation.

7.2.1 Subthreshold Conduction

The ideal current–voltage relationship predicts zero drain current when the gate-to-source voltage is less than or equal to the threshold voltage. Experimentally, I_D is not zero when $V_{GS} \le V_T$. Figure 7.2 shows a comparison between the ideal characteristic that was derived and the experimental results. The drain current, which exists for $V_{GS} \le V_T$, is known as the *subthreshold current*.

Figure 7.3 shows the energy-band diagram of an MOS structure with a p-type substrate biased so that $\phi_s < 2|\phi_{Fp}|$. At the same time, the Fermi level is closer to the conduction band than the valence band, so the semiconductor surface develops the characteristics of a lightly doped n-type material. We would expect, then, to observe some conduction between the n$^+$ source and drain contacts through this weakly inverted channel. The condition for $|\phi_{Fp}| < \phi_s < 2|\phi_{Fp}|$ is known as *weak inversion*.

Figure 7.4 shows the surface potential along the length of the channel at accumulation, weak inversion, and threshold for the case when a small drain voltage is applied. The bulk p substrate is assumed to be at zero potential. Figures 7.4b and 7.4c are the accumulation and weak inversion cases. There is a potential barrier between the n$^+$ source and channel region, which the electrons must overcome to generate a channel current. A comparison of these barriers with those in pn junctions would suggest that the channel current is an exponential function of V_{GS}. In the inversion

Subthreshold current

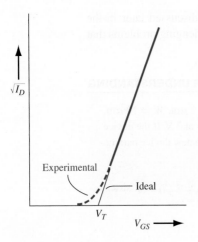

Figure 7.2 | Comparison of ideal and experimental plots of $\sqrt{I_D}$ versus V_{GS}.

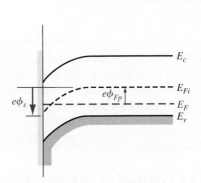

Figure 7.3 | Energy-band diagram when $|\phi_{Fp}| < \phi_s < 2|\phi_{Fp}|$.

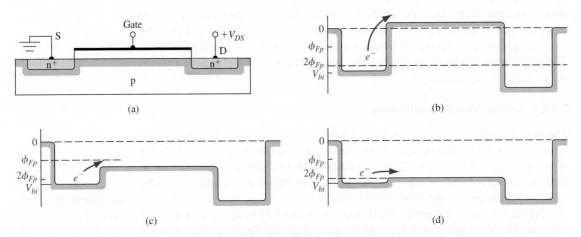

Figure 7.4 | (a) Cross section along channel length of n-channel MOSFET. Energy-band diagrams along channel length at (b) accumulation, (c) weak inversion, and (d) inversion.

mode, shown in Figure 7.4d, the barrier is so small that we lose the exponential dependence, since the junction is more like an ohmic contact.

The actual derivation of the subthreshold current is beyond the scope of this text. We can write that

$$I_D(\text{sub}) \propto \left[\exp\left(\frac{V_G - V_T}{V_t} \right) \right] \left[1 - \exp\left(\frac{-V_{DS}}{V_t} \right) \right] \tag{7.4}$$

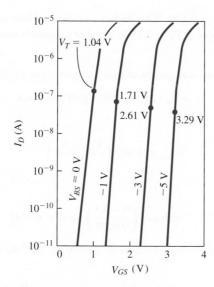

Figure 7.5 | Subthreshold current–
voltage characteristics for several values
of substrate voltage (the threshold
voltage is indicated on each curve).
(From Schroder [16].)

If V_{DS} is larger than a few (kT/e) volts, then the subthreshold current is independent
of V_{DS}.

Figure 7.5 shows the exponential behavior of the subthreshold current for
several body-to-source voltages. Also shown on the curves are the threshold voltage
values. Ideally, a change in gate voltage of approximately 60 mV produces an order
of magnitude change in the subthreshold current. A detailed analysis of the subthreshold condition shows that the slope of the $\ln I_D$ versus V_{DS} curve is a function
of the semiconductor doping and is also a function of the interface state density. The
measurement of the slope of these curves has been used to experimentally determine
the oxide–semiconductor interface state density.

If a MOSFET is biased at or even slightly below the threshold voltage, the drain
current is not zero. The subthreshold current may add significantly to power dissipation in a large-scale integrated circuit in which millions of MOSFETs are used. The
circuit design must include the subthreshold current or ensure that the MOSFET is
biased sufficiently below the threshold voltage in the "off" state.

EXAMPLE 7.1

OBJECTIVE

Determine the total bias current on an IC due to subthreshold currents.

Assume there are 10^7 n-channel transistors on a single chip, all biased at $V_{GS} = 0$ and
$V_{DS} = 2$ V. Assume $I_{sub} = 10^{-10}$ A for each transistor for this bias condition and for a

threshold voltage of $V_T = 0.5$ V. What happens to the total bias current on the IC if the threshold voltage is reduced to $V_T = 0.25$ V, all other parameters remaining the same.

■ **Solution**

The total bias current is the bias current of each transistor times the number of transistors, or

$$I_T = I_{\text{sub}}(10^7) = (10^{-10})(10^7) \Rightarrow 1 \text{ mA}$$

We can write

$$I_{\text{sub}} \approx I_0 \exp\left(\frac{V_{GS} - V_T}{V_t}\right)$$

so

$$10^{-10} = I_0 \exp\left(\frac{0 - 0.5}{0.0259}\right) \Rightarrow I_0 = 0.0242$$

Now, if the threshold voltage changes to $V_T = 0.25$, then the subthreshold current at $V_{GS} = 0$ becomes

$$I_{\text{sub}} = I_0 \exp\left(\frac{V_{GS} - V_T}{V_t}\right) = (0.0242) \exp\left(\frac{0 - 0.25}{0.0259}\right)$$

or

$$I_{\text{sub}} = 1.56 \times 10^{-6} \text{ A}$$

Now, the total bias current for this IC chip would be

$$I_T = (1.56 \times 10^{-6})(10^7) = 15.6 \text{ A}$$

■ **Comment**

This example is intended to show that, taking into account subthreshold currents, the threshold voltage must be designed to be a "reasonable" value such that the zero-bias gate currents are not excessive.

Exercise Problem

EX7.1   Repeat Example 7.1 if the threshold voltage is reduced from $V_T = 0.5$ V to $V_T = 0.35$ V. (Ans. $I_T = 327$ mA)

7.2.2   Channel Length Modulation

Recall that, as the drain voltage of a MOSFET increases, the inversion charge density at the drain terminal decreases since the voltage across the oxide is decreasing. At $V_{DS}(\text{sat}) = V_{GS} - V_T$, the inversion charge density at the drain terminal becomes zero, and for $V_{DS} > V_{DS}(\text{sat})$, the point in the channel at which the inversion charge is zero moves toward the source terminal.

We assumed in the derivation of the ideal current–voltage relationship that the channel length L was a constant. However, when the MOSFET is biased in the saturation region, the depletion region at the drain terminal extends laterally into the

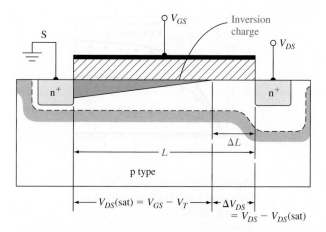

Figure 7.6 | Cross section of an n-channel MOSFET showing the channel length modulation effect.

channel, reducing the effective channel length. Since the depletion region width is bias dependent, the effective channel length is also bias dependent and is modulated by the drain-to-source voltage. This channel length modulation effect is shown in Figure 7.6 for an n-channel MOSFET.

The depletion width extending into the p region of a pn junction under zero bias can be written as

$$x_p = \sqrt{\frac{2\epsilon_s |\phi_{Fp}|}{eN_a}} \tag{7.5}$$

For a one-sided n^+p junction, essentially all of the applied reverse-bias voltage is across the low-doped p region. The space charge width of the drain–substrate junction is approximately

$$x_p = \sqrt{\frac{2\epsilon_s}{eN_a}(|\phi_{Fp}| + V_{DS})} \tag{7.6}$$

However, the space charge region defined by ΔL, as shown in Figure 7.6, does not begin to form until $V_{DS} > V_{DS}(\text{sat})$. As a first approximation, we can write that ΔL is the total space charge width minus the space charge width that exists when $V_{DS} = V_{DS}$ (sat), or

$$\Delta L = \sqrt{\frac{2\epsilon_s}{eN_a}} \left[\sqrt{|\phi_{Fp}| + V_{DS}(\text{sat}) + \Delta V_{DS}} - \sqrt{|\phi_{Fp}| + V_{DS}(\text{sat})} \right] \tag{7.7}$$

Channel length modulation

where

$$\Delta V_{DS} = V_{DS} - V_{DS}(\text{sat}) \tag{7.8}$$

The applied drain-to-source voltage is V_{DS} and we are assuming that $V_{DS} > V_{DS}(\text{sat})$.

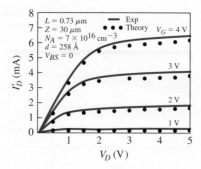

Figure 7.7 | Current–voltage characteristics of a MOSFET showing short-channel effects.
(From Sze [21].)

Other models used to determine ΔL include the negative charges due to the drain current and also include two-dimensional effects. These models will not be considered here.

Since the drain current is inversely proportional to the channel length, we can write

$$I'_D = \left(\frac{L}{L - \Delta L} \right) I_D \qquad (7.9)$$

where I'_D is the actual drain current and I_D is the ideal drain current. Since ΔL is a function of V_{DS}, I'_D is now also a function of V_{DS} even though the transistor is biased in the saturation region. Figure 7.7 shows some typical I'_D versus V_{DS} curves with positive slopes in the saturation region due to channel length modulation. As the MOSFET dimensions become smaller, the change in the channel length ΔL becomes a larger fraction of the original length L, and the channel length modulation becomes more severe.

EXAMPLE 7.2

OBJECTIVE

To determine the effect of channel length modulation on the value of drain current.

Consider an n-channel MOSFET with a substrate impurity doping concentration of $N_a = 2 \times 10^{16} \ \text{cm}^{-3}$, a threshold voltage of $V_T = 0.4$ V, and a channel length of $L = 1 \ \mu\text{m}$. The device is biased at $V_{GS} = 1$ V and $V_{DS} = 2.5$ V.

■ Solution

We find that

$$\phi_{Fp} = -V_t \ln \left(\frac{N_a}{n_i} \right) = -(0.0259) \ln \left(\frac{2 \times 10^{16}}{1.5 \times 10^{10}} \right) = -0.365 \ \text{V}$$

and

$$V_{DS}(\text{sat}) = V_{GS} - V_T = 1 - 0.4 = 0.6 \text{ V}$$

Now,

$$\Delta L = \left[\frac{2(11.7)(8.85 \times 10^{-14})}{(1.6 \times 10^{-19})(2 \times 10^{16})} \right]^{1/2}$$

$$\times \left[\sqrt{0.365 + 0.6 + (2.5 - 0.6)} - \sqrt{0.365 + 0.6} \right]$$

or

$$\Delta L = 0.181 \ \mu\text{m}$$

We can write

$$\frac{I'_D}{I_D} = \frac{L}{L - \Delta L} = \frac{1}{1 - 0.181}$$

or

$$\frac{I'_D}{I_D} = 1.22$$

■ Comment

Due to channel length modulation, the drain current is 22 percent larger than the ideal long channel value.

Exercise Problem

EX7.2 An n-channel MOSFET has the same parameters as described in Example 7.2 except for the channel length. The transistor is biased at $V_{GS} = 0.8$ V and $V_{DS} = 2.5$ V. Find the minimum channel length such that the ratio of actual drain current to the ideal long-channel value due to channel length modulation is no larger than 1.30. (Ans. $L = 0.901 \ \mu\text{m}$)

7.2.3 Mobility Variation

In the derivation of the ideal *I–V* relationship, we explicitly assumed that the mobility was a constant. However, this assumption must be modified for two reasons. The first effect to be considered is the variation in mobility with gate voltage. The second reason for a mobility variation is that the effective carrier mobility decreases as the carrier approaches the velocity saturation limit. This effect will be discussed in Section 7.2.4.

The inversion layer charge is induced by a vertical electric field, which is shown in Figure 7.8 for an n-channel device. A positive gate voltage produces a force on the electrons in the inversion layer toward the surface. As the electrons travel through the channel toward the drain, they are attracted to the surface, but then are repelled by localized coulombic forces. This effect, schematically shown in Figure 7.9, is called *surface scattering*. The surface scattering effect reduces mobility. If there is a positive

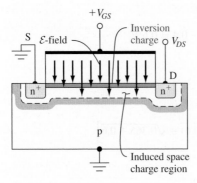

Figure 7.8 | Vertical electric field in an n-channel MOSFET.

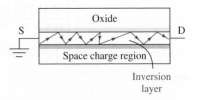

Figure 7.9 | Schematic of carrier surface scattering effects.

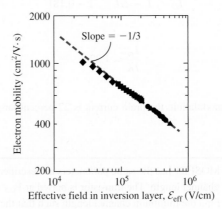

Figure 7.10 | Measured inversion layer electron mobility versus electric field at the inversion layer.
(From Yang [26].)

fixed oxide charge near the oxide–semiconductor interface, the mobility will be further reduced due to the additional coulomb interaction.

The relationship between the inversion charge mobility and the transverse electric field is usually measured experimentally. An effective transverse electric field can be defined as

Effective surface electric field

$$\mathcal{E}_{\text{eff}} = \frac{1}{\epsilon_s} \left(|Q'_{SD}(\text{max})| + \frac{1}{2} Q'_n \right) \tag{7.10}$$

The effective inversion charge mobility can be determined from the channel conductance as a function of gate voltage. Figure 7.10 shows the effective electron mobility at $T = 300$ K for different doping levels and different oxide thicknesses. The effective mobility is only a function of the electric field at the inversion layer and is independent of oxide thickness. The effective mobility may be represented by

Effective mobility

$$\mu_{\text{eff}} = \mu_0 \left(\frac{\mathcal{E}_{\text{eff}}}{\mathcal{E}_0} \right)^{-1/3} \tag{7.11}$$

where μ_0 and $\mathcal{E}_0$ are constants determined from experimental results.

The effective inversion charge mobility is a strong function of temperature because of lattice scattering. As the temperature is reduced, the mobility increases. The effective mobility is a function of gate voltage through the inversion charge density in Equation (7.10). As the gate voltage increases, the carrier mobility decreases even further.

EXAMPLE 7.3

OBJECTIVE

To calculate the effective electric field at threshold for a given semiconductor doping.

Consider a p-type silicon substrate at $T = 300$ K and doped to $N_a = 3 \times 10^{16}$ cm^{-3}.

■ Solution

From Equation (6.8b) in Chapter 6, we can calculate

$$\phi_{Fp} = -V_t \ln \left(\frac{N_a}{n_i} \right) = -(0.0259) \ln \left(\frac{3 \times 10^{16}}{1.5 \times 10^{10}} \right) = -0.376 \text{ V}$$

and

$$x_{dT} = \left[\frac{4\epsilon_s |\phi_{Fp}|}{eN_a} \right]^{1/2} = \left[\frac{4(11.7)(8.85 \times 10^{-14})(0.376)}{(1.6 \times 10^{-19})(3 \times 10^{16})} \right]^{1/2}$$

which is $x_{dT} = 0.18$ μm. Then

$$|Q'_{SD}(\text{max})| = eN_a x_{dT} = 8.64 \times 10^{-8} \text{ C/cm}^2$$

At the threshold inversion point, we may assume that $Q'_n = 0$, so the effective electric field from Equation (7.10) is found as

$$\mathcal{E}_{\text{eff}} = \frac{1}{\epsilon_s} |Q'_{SD}(\text{max})| = \frac{8.64 \times 10^{-8}}{(11.7)(8.85 \times 10^{-14})} = 8.34 \times 10^4 \text{ V/cm}$$

■ Comment

We can see, from Figure 7.10, that this value of effective transverse electric field at the surface is sufficient for the effective inversion charge mobility to be significantly less than the bulk semiconductor value.

Exercise Problem

EX7.3 Using the results of Example 7.3 and Figure 7.10, determine the effective electron mobility. (Ans. $\mu_n \approx 700$ cm^2/V-s)

7.2.4 Velocity Saturation

In the analysis of the long-channel MOSFET, we assumed the mobility to be constant, which means that the drift velocity increases without limit as the electric field increases. In this ideal case, the carrier velocity increases until the ideal current is attained. However, we have seen that the carrier velocity saturates with increasing electric field. Velocity saturation will become more prominent in shorter-channel devices since the corresponding horizontal electric field is generally larger.

In the ideal I–V relationship, current saturation occurred when the inversion charge density became zero at the drain terminal, or when

$$V_{DS} = V_{DS}(\text{sat}) = V_{GS} - V_T \tag{7.12}$$

for the n-channel MOSFET. However, velocity saturation can change this saturation condition. Velocity saturation will occur when the horizontal electric field is approximately 10^4 V/cm. If $V_{DS} = 5$ volts in a device with a channel length of $L = 1\ \mu\text{m}$, the average electric field is 5×10^4 V/cm. Velocity saturation, then, is very likely to occur in short-channel devices.

The modified $I_D(\text{sat})$ characteristics are described approximately by

Drain current with velocity saturation

$$I_D(\text{sat}) = WC_{\text{ox}}(V_{GS} - V_T)v_{\text{sat}} \tag{7.13}$$

where v_{sat} is the saturation velocity (approximately 10^7 cm/s for electrons in bulk silicon) and C_{ox} is the gate oxide capacitance per cm^2. The saturation velocity will decrease somewhat with applied gate voltage because of the vertical electric field and surface scattering. Velocity saturation will yield an $I_D(\text{sat})$ value smaller than that predicted by the ideal relation, and it will yield a smaller $V_{DS}(\text{sat})$ value than predicted. The $I_D(\text{sat})$ current is also approximately linear with V_{GS}, instead of having the ideal square law dependence predicted previously.

If we take the ratio of the drain current under the velocity saturation condition to the ideal long-channel value, we obtain

$$\frac{I_D|_{v,\text{sat}}}{I_D|_{\text{ideal}}} = \frac{WC_{\text{ox}}(V_{GS} - V_T)v_{\text{sat}}}{\dfrac{W}{L}\dfrac{\mu_n C_{\text{ox}}}{2}(V_{GS} - V_T)^2} = \frac{2L}{\mu_n}\frac{v_{sat}}{(V_{GS} - V_T)} \tag{7.14}$$

Figure 7.11 shows a comparison of drain current versus drain-to-source voltage characteristics for constant mobility and for field-dependent mobility. The smaller values of $I_D(\text{sat})$ and the approximate linear dependence on V_{GS} may be noted for the field-dependent mobility curves.

The transconductance is found from

$$g_{ms} = \frac{\partial I_D(\text{sat})}{\partial V_{GS}} = WC_{\text{ox}}v_{\text{sat}} \tag{7.15}$$

which is now independent of V_{GS} and V_{DS} when velocity saturation occurs. The drain current is saturated by the velocity saturation effect, which leads to a constant transconductance.

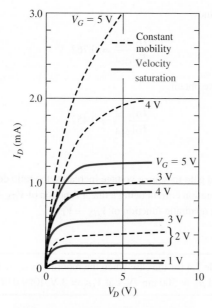

Figure 7.11 | Comparison of I_D versus V_D characteristics for constant mobility (dashed curves) and for field-dependent mobility and velocity saturation effects (solid curves).
(From Sze [21].)

When velocity saturation occurs, the cutoff frequency is given by

$$f_T = \frac{g_m}{2\pi C_G} = \frac{W C_{\text{ox}} v_{\text{sat}}}{2\pi (C_{\text{ox}} W L)} = \frac{v_{\text{sat}}}{2\pi L} \qquad (7.16) \qquad \textbf{Cutoff frequency}$$

where the parasitic capacitances are assumed to be negligible.

EXAMPLE 7.4

OBJECTIVE

To determine the ratio of drain current under the velocity saturation condition to the ideal long-channel value.

Assume an n-channel MOSFET with a channel length $L = 0.8\ \mu$m, a threshold voltage of $V_T = 0.5$ V, an electron mobility of $\mu_n = 700$ cm^2/V-s, and $v_{\text{sat}} = 5 \times 10^6$ cm/s. Assume that the transistor is biased at (a) $V_{GS} = 2$ V and (b) $V_{GS} = 3$ V.

■ **Solution**

We can write

$$\frac{I_D|_{v,\text{sat}}}{I_D|_{\text{ideal}}} = \frac{2L}{\mu_n} \frac{v_{\text{sat}}}{V_{GS} - V_T} = \frac{2(0.8 \times 10^{-4})}{700} \frac{5 \times 10^6}{V_{GS} - 0.5}$$

For (a) $V_{GS} = 2$ V, we find

$$\left.\frac{I_D|_{v,\text{sat}}}{I_D|_{\text{ideal}}}\right. = 0.762$$

and for (b) $V_{GS} = 3$ V, we obtain

$$\left.\frac{I_D|_{v,\text{sat}}}{I_D|_{\text{ideal}}}\right. = 0.457$$

■ **Comment**

We see that as the applied gate-to-source voltage increases, the ratio decreases. This effect is a result of the velocity saturation current being a linear function of $V_{GS} - V_T$, whereas the ideal long-channel current is a quadratic function of $V_{GS} - V_T$.

Exercise Problem

EX7.4 Repeat Example 7.4 for the case when the mobility is $\mu_n = 600\,\text{cm}^2/\text{V-s}$ at $V_{GS} = 2$ V and $\mu_n = 500\,\text{cm}^2/\text{V-s}$ at $V_{GS} = 3$ V. [Ans. (a) 0.889, (b) 0.640]

TEST YOUR UNDERSTANDING

TYU7.2 Consider a MOSFET biased in the subthreshold region with $V_D \gg kT/e$. For the ideal relationship given, what change in gate-to-source voltage produces a factor of 10 change in drain current? (Ans. $\Delta V_{GS} = 59.6$ mV)

TYU7.3 Consider an NMOS transistor with the following parameters: $\mu_n = 1000\,\text{cm}^2/\text{V-s}$, $C_{ox} = 10^{-8}$ F/cm^2, $W = 10\,\mu$m, $L = 1\,\mu$m, $V_T = 0.4$ V, and $v_{\text{sat}} = 5 \times 10^6$ cm/s. Plot on the same graph $I_D(\text{sat})$ versus V_{GS} over the range $0 \leq V_{GS} \leq 4$ V for the case (a) of an ideal transistor (Equation (6.57) and (b) when velocity saturation occurs (Equation (7.13)). [Ans. (a) $I_D(\text{sat}) = 50(V_{GS} - 0.4)^2\,\mu$A. (b) $I_D(\text{sat}) = 50(V_{GS} - 0.4)\,\mu$A]

7.3 | THRESHOLD VOLTAGE MODIFICATIONS

Objective: Analyze the change in threshold voltage as the dimensions of the MOSFETs are reduced.

We derived the ideal MOSFET relations in Chapter 6 including expressions for threshold voltage and for the current–voltage characteristics. We have now considered some of the nonideal effects including channel length modulation. Additional effects on threshold voltage occur as the devices shrink in size. A reduction in channel length will increase the transconductance and frequency response of the MOSFET, and a reduction in channel width will increase the packing density in an integrated circuit. A reduction in either or both the channel length and channel width can affect the threshold voltage.

7.3.1 Short-Channel Effects

For the ideal MOSFET, we derived the threshold voltage using the concept of charge neutrality in which the sum of charges in the metal–oxide inversion layer and semiconductor space charge region is zero. We also assumed that the gate area was the same as the active area in the semiconductor. Using this assumption, we considered only equivalent surface charge densities and neglected any effects on threshold voltage that might occur due to source and drain space charge regions that extend into the active channel region.

Figure 7.12a shows the cross section of a long n-channel MOSFET at flat band, with zero source and drain voltage applied. The space charge regions at the source and drain extend into the channel region, but occupy only a small fraction of the entire channel region. The gate voltage, then, will control essentially all of the space charge induced in the channel region at inversion as shown in Figure 7.12b.

As the channel length decreases, the fraction of charge in the channel region controlled by the gate decreases. This effect can be seen in Figure 7.13 for the flat-band condition. As the drain voltage increases, the reverse-biased space charge region at the drain extends farther into the channel area and the gate will control even less bulk charge. The amount of charge in the channel region, $Q'_{SD}(\max)$, controlled by the gate, affects the threshold voltage as can be seen from Equation (7.17):

Charge sharing

$$V_{TN} = (|Q'_{SD}(\max)| - Q'_{ss})\left(\frac{t_{ox}}{\epsilon_{ox}}\right) + \phi_{ms} + 2|\phi_{Fp}| \qquad (7.17)$$

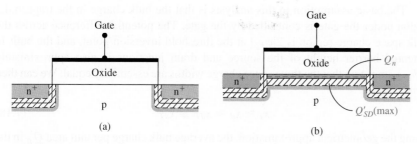

(a)   (b)

Figure 7.12 | Cross section of a long n-channel MOSFET (a) at flat band and (b) at inversion.

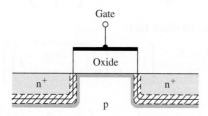

Figure 7.13 | Cross section of a short n-channel MOSFET at flat band.

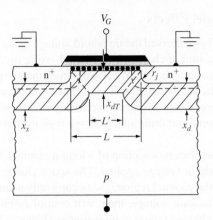

Figure 7.14 | Charge sharing in the short-channel threshold voltage model.
(From Yau [27].)

We can quantitatively determine the short-channel effects on the threshold voltage by considering the parameters shown in Figure 7.14. The source and drain junctions are characterized by a diffused junction depth r_j. We will assume that the lateral diffusion distance under the gate is the same as the vertical diffusion distance. This assumption is a reasonably good approximation for diffused junctions but becomes less accurate for ion-implanted junctions. We will initially consider the case when the source, drain, and body contacts are all at ground potential.

The basic assumption in this analysis is that the bulk charge in the trapezoidal region under the gate is controlled by the gate. The potential difference across the bulk space charge region is $2|\phi_{Fp}|$ at the threshold inversion point, and the built-in potential barrier height of the source and drain junctions is also approximately $2|\phi_{Fp}|$, implying that the three space charge widths are essentially equal. We can then write

$$x_s \approx x_d \approx x_{dT} \equiv x_{dT} \tag{7.18}$$

Using the geometrical approximation, the average bulk charge per unit area Q'_B in the trapezoid is

$$|Q'_B| \cdot L = eN_a x_{dT}\left(\frac{L + L'}{2}\right) \tag{7.19}$$

From the geometry, we can show that

$$\frac{L + L'}{2L} = \left[1 - \frac{r_j}{L}\left(\sqrt{1 + \frac{2x_{dT}}{r_j}} - 1\right)\right] \tag{7.20}$$

Then

$$|Q'_B| = eN_a x_{dT}\left[1 - \frac{r_j}{L}\left(\sqrt{1 + \frac{2x_{dT}}{r_j}} - 1\right)\right] \tag{7.21}$$

Equation (7.21) is now used in place of $|Q'_{SD}(\text{max})|$ in the expression for the threshold voltage.

Since $|Q'_{SD}(\text{max})| = eN_a x_{dT}$, we can find ΔV_T as

$$\boxed{\Delta V_T = -\frac{eN_a x_{dT}}{C_{ox}}\left[\frac{r_j}{L}\left(\sqrt{1+\frac{2x_{dT}}{r_j}}-1\right)\right]} \qquad (7.22)$$

Threshold voltage shift—short channel

where

$$\Delta V_T = V_{T(\text{short channel})} - V_{T(\text{long channel})} \qquad (7.23)$$

As the channel length decreases, the threshold voltage shifts in the negative direction so that an n-channel MOSFET shifts toward depletion mode.

EXAMPLE 7.5

OBJECTIVE

Calculate the threshold voltage shift due to short-channel effects.

Consider an n-channel MOSFET with $N_a = 5 \times 10^{16}$ cm^{-3} and $t_{ox} = 200$ Å. Let $L = 0.8$ μm and assume that $r_j = 0.4$ μm.

■ **Solution**

We can determine the oxide capacitance to be

$$C_{ox} = \frac{\epsilon_{ox}}{t_{ox}} = \frac{(3.9)(8.85 \times 10^{-14})}{200 \times 10^{-8}} = 1.73 \times 10^{-7} \text{ F/cm}^2$$

and can calculate the potential as

$$\phi_{Fp} = -V_t \ln\left(\frac{N_a}{n_i}\right) = -(0.0259)\ln\left(\frac{5 \times 10^{16}}{1.5 \times 10^{10}}\right) = -0.389 \text{ V}$$

The maximum space charge width is found as

$$x_{dT} = \left(\frac{4\epsilon_s|\phi_{Fp}|}{eN_a}\right)^{1/2} = \left[\frac{4(11.7)(8.85 \times 10^{-14})(0.389)}{(1.6 \times 10^{-19})(5 \times 10^{16})}\right]^{1/2} = 0.142 \text{ μm}$$

Finally, the threshold voltage shift, from Equation (7.22), is

$$\Delta V_T = -\frac{(1.6 \times 10^{-19})(5 \times 10^{16})(0.142 \times 10^{-4})}{1.73 \times 10^{-7}}\left[\frac{0.4}{0.8}\left(\sqrt{1+\frac{2(0.142)}{0.4}}-1\right)\right]$$

or

$$\Delta V_T = -0.101 \text{ V}$$

■ **Comment**

If the threshold voltage of this n-channel MOSFET is to be $V_T = 0.40$ V, for example, a shift of $\Delta V_T = -0.101$ V due to short-channel effects is significant and needs to be taken into account in the design of this device.

Exercise Problem

EX7.5 Repeat Example 7.5 if the device parameters are $N_a = 3 \times 10^{16}\,\text{cm}^{-3}$, $t_{ox} = 300$ Å, $L = 0.8\,\mu\text{m}$, and $r_j = 0.3\,\mu\text{m}$. (Ans. $\Delta V_T = -0.136$ V)

The effect of short channels becomes more pronounced as the channel length is reduced further.

The shift in threshold voltage with channel length for an n-channel MOSFET is shown in Figure 7.15. As the substrate doping increases, the initial threshold voltage increases, as we saw in Chapter 6, and the short-channel threshold shift also becomes larger. The short-channel effects on threshold voltage do not become significant until the channel length becomes less than approximately 2 μm. The threshold voltage shift also becomes smaller as the diffusion depth r_j becomes smaller so that very shallow junctions reduce the threshold voltage dependence on channel length.

Equation (7.22) was derived using the assumption that the source, channel, and drain space charge widths were all equal. If we now apply a drain voltage, the space charge width at the drain terminal widens, which makes L' smaller, and the amount of bulk charge controlled by the gate voltage decreases. This effect makes the threshold voltage a function of drain voltage. As the drain voltage increases, the threshold voltage of an n-channel MOSFET decreases. The threshold voltage versus channel length is plotted in Figure 7.16 for two values of drain-to-source voltage and two values of body-to-source voltage.

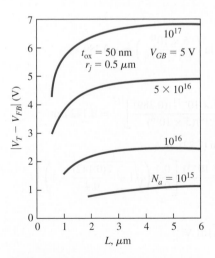

Figure 7.15 | Threshold voltage versus channel length for various substrate dopings.
(From Yau [27].)

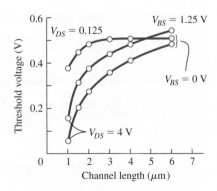

Figure 7.16 | Threshold voltage versus channel length for two values of drain-to-source and body-to-source voltage.
(From Yang [26].)

7.3.2 Narrow-Channel Effects

Figure 7.17 shows the cross section along the channel width of an n-channel MOSFET biased at inversion. The current is perpendicular to the channel width through the inversion charge. We can note in the figure that there is an additional space charge region at each end of the channel width. This additional charge is controlled by the gate voltage but was not included in the derivation of the ideal threshold voltage relation. The threshold voltage expression must be modified to include this additional charge.

If we neglect short-channel effects, the gate-controlled bulk charge can be written as

$$Q_B = Q_{B0} + \Delta Q_B \qquad (7.24)$$

where Q_B is the total bulk charge, Q_{B0} is the ideal bulk charge, and ΔQ_B is the additional bulk charge at the ends of the channel width. For a uniformly doped p-type semiconductor biased at the threshold inversion point, we may write

$$|Q_{B0}| = e N_a W L x_{dT} \qquad (7.25)$$

and

$$\Delta Q_B = e N_a L x_{dT} (\xi x_{dT}) \qquad (7.26) \qquad \textbf{Charge sharing}$$

where ξ is a fitting parameter that accounts for the lateral space charge width. The lateral space charge width may not be the same as the vertical width x_{dT} due to the thicker field oxide at the ends, and/or due to the nonuniform semiconductor doping created by an ion implantation. If the ends were a semicircle, then $\xi = \pi/2$.

We can now write

$$|Q_B| = |Q_{B0}| + |\Delta Q_B| = e N_a W L x_{dT} + e N_a L x_{dT} (\xi x_{dT})$$

$$= e N_a W L x_{dT} \left(1 + \frac{\xi x_{dT}}{W} \right) \qquad (7.27)$$

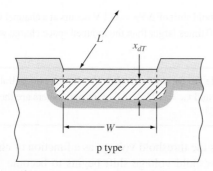

Figure 7.17 | Cross section of an n-channel MOSFET showing the depletion region along the width of the device.

The effect of the end space charge regions becomes significant as the width W decreases and the factor (ξx_{dT}) becomes a significant fraction of the width W.

The change in threshold voltage due to the additional space charge is

Threshold voltage shift—narrow channel

$$\Delta V_T = \frac{eN_a x_{dT}}{C_{ox}} \left(\frac{\xi x_{dT}}{W} \right) \tag{7.28}$$

The shift in threshold voltage due to a narrow channel is in the positive direction for the n-channel MOSFET. As the width W becomes smaller, the shift in threshold voltage becomes larger.

EXAMPLE 7.6

OBJECTIVE

Design the channel width that will limit the threshold shift because of narrow channel effects to a specified value.

Consider an n-channel MOSFET with $N_a = 5 \times 10^{16}$ cm^{-3} and $t_{ox} = 200$ Å. Let $\xi = \pi/2$. Assume that we want to limit the threshold shift to $\Delta V_T = 0.1$ V.

■ **Solution**

From Example 7.5, we have

$$C_{ox} = 1.73 \times 10^{-7} \text{ F/cm}^2 \quad \text{and} \quad x_{dT} = 0.142 \text{ } \mu\text{m}$$

From Equation (7.28), we can express the channel width as

$$W = \frac{eN_a \left(\xi x_{dT}^2 \right)}{C_{ox}(\Delta V_T)} = \frac{(1.6 \times 10^{-19})(5 \times 10^{16}) \left(\frac{\pi}{2} \right) (0.142 \times 10^{-4})^2}{(1.73 \times 10^{-7})(0.1)}$$

or

$$W = 1.46 \text{ } \mu\text{m}$$

■ **Comment**

We can note that the threshold shift of $\Delta V_T = 0.1$ V occurs at a channel width of $W = 1.46 \text{ } \mu$m, which is approximately 10 times larger than the induced space charge width x_{dT}.

Exercise Problem

EX7.6 Repeat Example 7.6 for the case when the doping concentration is $N_a = 6 \times 10^{16}$ cm^{-3} and $t_{ox} = 125$ Å. All other parameters are the same. (Ans. 0.923 μm)

Figure 7.18 shows the threshold voltage as a function of channel width. We can again note that the threshold voltage shift begins to become apparent for channel widths that are large compared to the induced space charge width.

Figures 7.19a and 7.19b show qualitatively the threshold voltage shifts due to short-channel and narrow-channel effects, respectively, in n-channel MOSFETs.

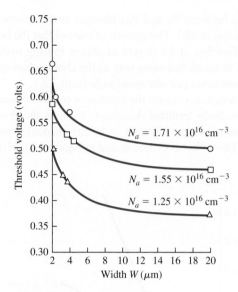

Figure 7.18 | Threshold voltage versus
channel width (solid curves, theoretical;
points, experimental).
(From Akers [1].)

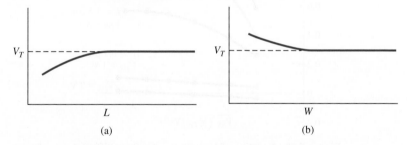

Figure 7.19 | Qualitative variation of threshold voltage (a) with channel length and
(b) with channel width.

The narrow-channel device produces a larger threshold voltage; the short-channel
device produces a smaller threshold voltage. For devices exhibiting both short-
channel and narrow-channel effects, the two models need to be combined into a
three-dimensional volume approximation of the space charge region controlled by
the gate.

7.3.3 Substrate Bias Effects

As discussed in Chapter 6, the threshold voltage is a function of the body-to-source
voltage V_{BS}. Equation (6.87) described the relationship. This expression is for the
long-channel, uniformly doped MOSFET.

The relationship between V_T and V_{BS} changes as the channel length decreases. Figure 7.20 shows some results. The amount of control that the body-to-source voltage has on V_T is a function of the degree of charge sharing with the drain-to-body space charge region in much that same way as the charge sharing between the gate-substrate and drain-substrate just discussed in Section 7.3.1.

As the channel length decreases, the amount of p-type substrate under the channel controlled by the body terminal decreases. Also, as the drain-to-body voltage increases, the amount of p-type substrate under the channel controlled by the body terminal decreases. This effect is demonstrated in Figure 7.21. Hence, as the channel

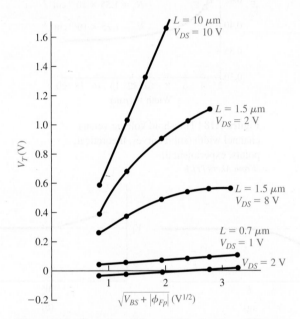

Figure 7.20 | Variation of V_T with V_{BS} for three different channel lengths and different values of V_{DS}.

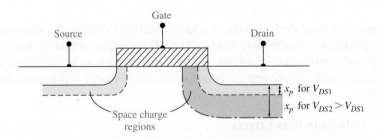

Figure 7.21 | Short-channel MOSFET showing effect of increasing V_{DS}. With an increase in V_{Ds}, there is less channel charge that is controlled by the substrate voltage.

length decreases and/or as the drain-to-substrate voltage increases, the threshold voltage becomes less dependent on the body-to-source voltage.

7.4 | ADDITIONAL ELECTRICAL CHARACTERISTICS

Objective: Discuss additional electrical effects, such as threshold adjustment by ion implantation, in MOSFETs.

There is a tremendous volume of information on MOSFETs that cannot be included in an introductory text on semiconductor physics and devices. However, two additional topics should be included here: breakdown voltage and threshold adjustment by ion implantation.

7.4.1 Oxide Breakdown

We have assumed that the oxide is a perfect insulator. However, if the electric field in the oxide becomes large enough, breakdown can occur, which can lead to a catastrophic failure. In silicon dioxide, the electric field at breakdown is on the order of 6×10^6 V/cm. This breakdown field is larger than that in silicon, but the gate oxides are also quite thin. A gate voltage of approximately 30 volts would produce breakdown in an oxide with a thickness of 500 Å. However, a safety margin of a factor of 3 is common, so that the maximum safe gate voltage with $t_{ox} = 500$ Å would be 10 V. A safety margin is necessary since there may be defects in the oxide that lower the breakdown field. Oxide breakdown is normally not a serious problem except in power devices and ultrathin oxide devices.

7.4.2 Near Punch-Through or Drain-Induced Barrier Lowering

Drain-induced barrier lowering

Punch-through is the condition at which the drain-to-substrate space charge region extends completely across the channel region to the source-to-substrate space charge region. In this situation, the barrier between the source and drain is completely eliminated and a very large drain current would exist.

However, the drain current will begin to increase rapidly before the actual punch-through condition is reached. This characteristic is referred to as the near punch-through condition. Figure 7.22a shows the ideal energy-band diagram from source to drain for a long n-channel MOSFET for the case when $V_{GS} < V_T$ and when the drain-to-source voltage is relatively small. The large potential barriers prevent significant current between the drain and source. Figure 7.22b shows the energy-band diagram when a relatively large drain voltage V_{DS2} is applied. The space charge region near the drain terminal is beginning to interact with the source space charge region and the potential barrier is being lowered. Since the current is an exponential function of barrier height, the current will increase very rapidly with drain voltage once this near punch-through condition has been reached. Figure 7.23 shows some typical characteristics of a short-channel device with a near punch-through condition.

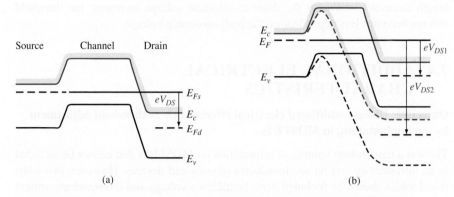

Figure 7.22 | (a) Equipotential plot along the surface of a long-channel MOSFET. (b) Equipotential plot along the surface of a short-channel MOSFET before and after punch-through.

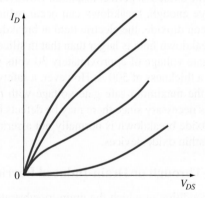

Figure 7.23 | Typical I–V characteristics of a MOSFET exhibiting punch-through effects.

EXAMPLE 7.7

OBJECTIVE

Calculate the theoretical punch-through voltage assuming the abrupt junction approximation.

Consider an n-channel MOSFET with source and drain doping concentrations of $N_d = 10^{19}$ cm^{-3} and a channel region doping of $N_a = 10^{16}$ cm^{-3}. Assume a channel length of $L = 1.2$ μm, and assume the source and body are at ground potential.

■ **Solution**

The pn junction built-in potential barrier is given by

$$V_{bi} = V_t \ln\left(\frac{N_a N_d}{n_i^2}\right) = (0.0259) \ln\left[\frac{(10^{16})(10^{19})}{(1.5 \times 10^{10})^2}\right] = 0.874 \text{ V}$$

The zero-biased source–substrate pn junction width is

$$x_{d0} = \left(\frac{2\epsilon_s V_{bi}}{e N_a} \right)^{1/2} = \left[\frac{2(11.7)(8.85 \times 10^{-14})(0.874)}{(1.6 \times 10^{-19})(10^{16})} \right]^{1/2} = 0.336 \ \mu m$$

The reverse-biased drain-substrate pn junction width is given by

$$x_d = \left[\frac{2\epsilon_s (V_{bi} + V_{DS})}{e N_a} \right]^{1/2}$$

At punch-through, we will have

$$x_{d0} + x_d = L \quad \text{or} \quad 0.336 + x_d = 1.2$$

which gives $x_d = 0.864 \ \mu m$ at the punch-through condition. We can then find

$$V_{bi} + V_{DS} = \frac{x_d^2 e N_a}{2\epsilon_s} = \frac{(0.864 \times 10^{-4})^2 (1.6 \times 10^{-19})(10^{16})}{2(11.7)(8.85 \times 10^{-14})}$$

$$= 5.77 \ V$$

The punch-through voltage is then found as

$$V_{DS} = 5.77 - 0.874 = 4.9 \ V$$

■ Comment

As the two space charge regions approach punch-through, the abrupt junction approximation is no longer a good assumption.

Exercise Problem

EX7.7 Repeat Example 7.7 for the case when $N_a = 3 \times 10^{16} \ cm^{-3}$ and $L = 0.6 \ \mu m$. All other parameters are the same. (Ans. $V_{DS} = 2.86 \ V$)

For a doping of $10^{16} \ cm^{-3}$, the two space charge regions will begin to interact when the abrupt depletion layers are approximately $0.25 \ \mu m$ apart. The drain voltage at which this near punch-through condition, also known as drain-induced barrier lowering, occurs is significantly less than the ideal punch-through voltage such as calculated in Example 7.7.

7.4.3 Hot Electron Effects

As the drain-to-source voltage increases, the electric field in the space charge region at the drain increases. At high electric fields, electron–hole pairs can be generated in the space charge region by impact ionization. The generated electrons tend to be swept to the drain and generated holes swept into the substrate in an n-channel MOSFET.

Some of the electrons generated in the space charge region are attracted to the oxide due to the electric field induced by a positive gate voltage; this effect is shown in Figure 7.24. These generated electrons have energies far greater than the thermal-equilibrium value and are called hot electrons. If the electrons have energies on the order of 1.5 eV, they may be able to tunnel into the oxide; or in some cases they may be able to overcome the silicon oxide potential barrier and produce a gate current,

Hot electrons

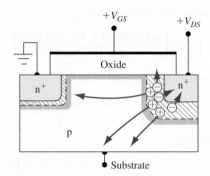

Figure 7.24 | Hot carrier generation, current components, and electron injection into the oxide.

which may be in the range of femtoampere (fA) $(10^{-15}$ A) or perhaps picoamperes (pA) $(10^{-12}$ A). A fraction of the electrons traveling through the oxide may be trapped, producing a net negative charge density in the oxide. The probability of electron trapping is usually less than that of hole trapping; but a hot-electron–induced gate current may exist over a long period of time, therefore the negative charging effect may build up. The negative oxide charge trapping will cause a local positive shift in the threshold voltage.

The energetic electrons, as they cross the Si–SiO$_2$ interface, can generate additional interface states. The probable cause of interface state generation is due to the breaking of silicon–hydrogen bonds–a dangling silicon bond is produced, which acts as an interface state. The charge trapping in interface states causes a shift in threshold voltage, additional surface scattering, and reduced mobility. The hot electron charging effects are continuous processes, so the device degrades over a period of time. This degradation is obviously an undesirable effect and may tend to limit the useful life of the device.

7.4.4 Threshold Adjustment by Ion Implantation

Several factors, such as fixed oxide charge, metal–semiconductor work function difference, oxide thickness, and semiconductor doping, influence the threshold voltage. All of these parameters may be fixed in a particular design and fabrication process, although the resulting threshold voltage may not be acceptable for all applications. Ion implantation can be used to change and adjust the substrate doping near the oxide–semiconductor surface to provide the desired threshold voltage. In addition, ion implantation is used for more than doping the channel. It is used extensively as a standard part of device fabrication; for example, it is used to form the source and drain regions of the transistor.

To change the doping and thereby change the threshold voltage, a precise, controlled number of either donor or acceptor ions are implanted into the semiconductor near the oxide surface. When an MOS device is biased in either depletion or inversion

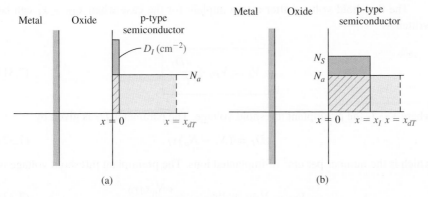

Figure 7.25 | (a) Ion-implanted profile approximated by a delta function. (b) Ion-implanted profile approximated by a step function, in which the depth x_I is less than the space charge width x_{dT}.

and when the implanted dopant atoms are within the induced space charge region, then the ionized dopant charge adds to (or subtracts from) the maximum space charge density, which controls the threshold voltage. An implant of acceptor ions into either a p- or n-type substrate will shift the threshold voltage to more positive values, while an implant of donor ions will shift the threshold voltage to more negative values.

As a first approximation, assume that D_I acceptor atoms per cm^2 are implanted into a p-type substrate directly adjacent to the oxide-semiconductor interface as shown in Figure 7.25a. (The parameter D_I is called the *implant dose*.) The shift in threshold voltage due to the implant dose is

$$\Delta V_T = +\frac{eD_I}{C_{\text{ox}}} \qquad (7.29)$$

Threshold shift by ion implantation

If donor atoms were implanted into the p-type substrate, the space charge density would be reduced; thus, the threshold voltage would shift in the negative voltage direction.

A second type of implant approximation is the step junction, shown in Figure 7.25b. If the induced space charge width at the threshold inversion point is less than x_I, then the threshold voltage is determined on the basis of a semiconductor with a uniform doping concentration of N_s atoms per cm^3. On the other hand, if the induced space charge width is greater than x_I at the threshold inversion point, then a new expression for x_{dT} must be derived. We can apply Poisson's equation and show that the maximum induced space charge width after the step implant is

$$x_{dT} = \sqrt{\frac{2\epsilon_s}{eN_a}\left[2|\phi_{Fp}| - \frac{ex_I^2}{2\epsilon_s}(N_s - N_a)\right]^{1/2}} \qquad (7.30)$$

The threshold voltage after a step implant for the case when $x_{dT} > x_I$ can be written as

$$V_T = V_{T0} + \frac{eD_I}{C_{ox}} \qquad (7.31)$$

where V_{T0} is the preimplant threshold voltage. The parameter D_I is given by

$$D_I = (N_s - N_a)x_I \qquad (7.32)$$

which is the number per cm^2 of implanted ions. The preimplant threshold voltage is

$$V_{T0} = V_{FB0} + 2|\phi_{Fp0}| + \frac{eN_a x_{dT0}}{C_{ox}} \qquad (7.33)$$

where the subscript 0 indicates the preimplant values.

EXAMPLE 7.8

OBJECTIVE
Design the ion implant dose required to adjust the threshold voltage to a specified value.

Consider an n-channel MOSFET with a doping of $N_a = 5 \times 10^{15}$ cm^{-3}, an oxide thickness of $t_{ox} = 500$ Å, and an initial flat-band voltage of $V_{FBO} = -1.25$ V. Determine the ion implantation dose such that a threshold voltage of $V_T = +0.70$ V is obtained.

■ Solution
We may calculate the necessary parameters as

$$\phi_{Fp0} = -V_t \ln\left(\frac{N_a}{n_i}\right) = -(0.0259)\ln\left(\frac{5 \times 10^{15}}{1.5 \times 10^{10}}\right) = -0.329 \text{ V}$$

$$x_{dT0} = \left(\frac{4\epsilon_s|\phi_{Fp0}|}{eN_a}\right)^{1/2} = \left[\frac{4(11.7)(8.85 \times 10^{-14})(0.329)}{(1.6 \times 10^{-19})(5 \times 10^{15})}\right]^{1/2} = 0.413 \ \mu\text{m}$$

$$C_{ox} = \frac{\epsilon_{ox}}{t_{ox}} = \frac{(3.9)(8.85 \times 10^{-14})}{500 \times 10^{-8}} = 6.9 \times 10^{-8} \text{ F/cm}^2$$

The initial pre-implant threshold voltage is

$$V_{T0} = V_{FBO} + 2|\phi_{Fp0}| + \frac{eN_a x_{dT0}}{C_{ox}}$$

$$= -1.25 + 2(0.329) + \frac{(1.6 \times 10^{-19})(5 \times 10^{15})(0.413 \times 10^{-4})}{6.9 \times 10^{-8}}$$

$$= -0.113 \text{ V}$$

The threshold voltage after implant, from Equation (7.31), is

$$V_T = V_{T0} + \frac{eD_I}{C_{ox}}$$

so that

$$+0.70 = -0.113 + \frac{(1.6 \times 10^{-19})D_I}{6.9 \times 10^{-8}}$$

which gives

$$D_I = 3.51 \times 10^{11} \text{ cm}^{-2}$$

If the uniform step implant extends to a depth of $x_I = 0.15 \ \mu$m, for example, then the equivalent acceptor concentration at the surface is

$$N_s - N_a = \frac{D_I}{x_I} = \frac{3.51 \times 10^{11}}{0.15 \times 10^{-4}} = 2.34 \times 10^{16} \text{ cm}^{-3}$$

or

$$N_s = 2.84 \times 10^{16} \text{ cm}^{-3}$$

■ **Comment**

The required implant dose to achieve the desired threshold voltage is $D_I = 3.51 \times 10^{11} \text{ cm}^{-2}$. This calculation has assumed that the induced space charge width in the channel region is greater than the ion implant depth x_I. We can show that this requirement is indeed satisfied in this example.

Exercise Problem

EX7.8 An MOS transistor has the following parameters: $N_a = 10^{15} \text{ cm}^{-3}$, $t_{ox} = 200 \text{ Å}$, $Q'_{ss}/e = 5 \times 10^{10} \text{ cm}^{-2}$, p$^+$ poly gate. A final threshold voltage of $V_T = +0.40 \text{ V}$ is to be achieved using an idealized delta function ion implant profile as shown in Figure 7.25a. (*a*) What type (acceptor or donor) ion should be implanted? (*b*) Determine the ion dose D_I required.

[Ans. (*a*) Donor, (*b*) $D_I = 6.03 \times 10^{11} \text{ cm}^{-2}$]

The actual implant dose versus distance is neither a delta function nor a step function; it tends to be a Gaussian-type distribution. The threshold shift due to a nonuniform ion implant density may be defined as the shift in curves of N_{inv} versus V_G where N_{inv} is the inversion carrier density per cm^2. This shift corresponds to an experimental shift of drain current versus V_G when the transistor is biased in the linear mode. The criteria of the threshold inversion point as $\phi_s = 2|\phi_{Fp}|$ in the implanted devices have an uncertain meaning because of the nonuniform doping in the substrate. The determination of the threshold voltage becomes more complicated and will not be done here.

7.5 | DEVICE FABRICATION TECHNIQUES: SPECIALIZED DEVICES

Objective: Consider the fabrication and characteristics of a few specialized MOSFET devices.

In this section, we will consider a few specialized MOSFET structures. So, rather than actually discussing fabrication techniques, we will be discussing specialized fabricated devices.

7.5.1 Lightly Doped Drain Transistor

The junction breakdown voltage is a function of the maximum electric field. As the channel length becomes smaller, the bias voltages may not be scaled down accordingly, so the junction electric fields become larger. As the electric field increases, near avalanche breakdown and near punch-through effects become more serious. In addition, as device geometries are scaled down, the parasitic bipolar device becomes more dominant and breakdown effects are enhanced.

Lightly doped drain transistor

One approach that reduces these breakdown effects is to alter the doping profile of the drain contact. The lightly **d**oped **d**rain (LDD) design and doping profiles are shown in Figure 7.26a, the conventional MOSFET and doping profiles are shown in Figure 7.26b for comparison. By introducing the lightly doped region, the peak electric field in the space charge region is reduced and the breakdown effects are minimized. The peak electric field at the drain junction is a function of the semiconductor doping as well as the curvature of the n^+ drain region. Figure 7.27 shows the physical geometries of a conventional n^+ drain contact and an LDD structure superimposed on the same plot. The magnitude of the electric field at the oxide–semiconductor interface in the LDD structure is less than in the conventional structure. The electric field in the conventional device peaks approximately at the metallurgical junction and drops quickly to zero in the drain because no field can exist in the highly conductive n^+ region. On the other hand, the electric field in the LDD device extends across the n-region before dropping to zero at the drain. This effect will minimize breakdown and the hot electron effects, which were discussed in Section 7.4.3.

Two disadvantages of the LDD device are an increase in both fabrication complexity and drain resistance. The added processing steps, however, produce a device with significant improvements in performance. The cross section of the LDD device

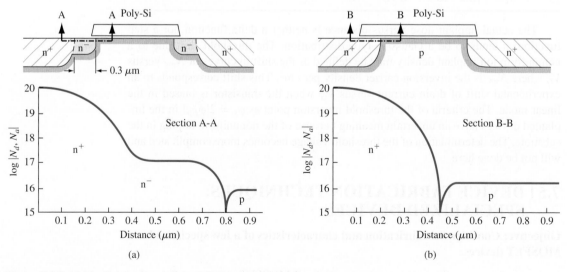

Figure 7.26 | (a) The lightly doped drain (LDD) structure. (b) Conventional structure. *(From Ogura et al. [11].)*

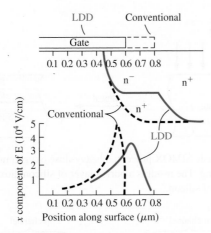

Figure 7.27 | Magnitude of the electric field at the Si–SiO$_2$ interface as a function of distance; $V_{DS} = 10$ V, $V_{SB} = 2$ V, $V_{GS} = V_T$. *(From Ogura et al. [11].)*

shown in Figure 7.26 indicates a lightly doped n region at the source terminal also. The inclusion of this region does not improve device performance, but does reduce the fabrication complexity as much as possible. The added series resistances will increase power dissipation in the device; this must be taken into account in high-power devices.

7.5.2 The MOSFET on Insulator

Up to this point, we have considered the situation where the MOSFET is fabricated on a silicon wafer and the substrate becomes the fourth terminal of the device. There are certain applications in which it is advantageous to fabricate the MOSFET in a thin film of silicon on an insulating substrate. If the thin film of silicon is a single-crystal material, we refer to these devices as silicon-on-insulator (SOI) devices.

Silicon-on-Sapphire Heteroepitaxial silicon-on-insulator films are obtained by epitaxially growing a silicon layer on a single-crystal insulator. A silicon film is deposited using the pyrolysis of silane at temperatures between 900 and 1000°C. Due to lattice and thermal mismatch, the defect density in the films is quite high, especially in thin films. As a result, the electron mobility in SOS devices is smaller than that in bulk silicon. SOS devices are used in applications where radiation hardness is required.

SOS

SIMOX The acronym SIMOX stands for "separation by **im**planted **ox**ygen." The principle of SIMOX is the formation of a buried layer of SiO$_2$ by ion implantation beneath the surface of a silicon wafer. Figure 7.28 shows the basic process. Oxygen ions are implanted into the surface of a silicon wafer. To form SiO$_2$, there must be

SIMOX

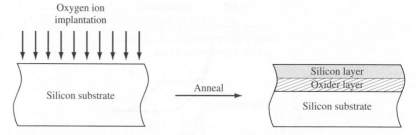

Figure 7.28 | The basic SIMOX process: a heavy-dose oxygen implant into silicon followed by annealing. The result is a buried layer of silicon dioxide below a thin, single-crystal layer of silicon.

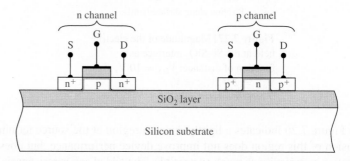

Figure 7.29 | A simplified cross section of an n-channel and p-channel (CMOS) MOSFET on a SIMOX wafer. The thin layer of silicon is etched around each device, providing isolation and reducing capacitance.

two oxygen atoms for every silicon atom. Therefore, O^+ implant doses greater than 10^{18} cm^{-2} are commonly used. After the implant process, a thermal annealing process is necessary to activate the SiO_2 and to anneal the damage in the silicon layer at the surface.

SOI

The MOSFET Structure on Insulator   The two basic SOI structures that have been used are silicon-on-sapphire (SOS) and silicon-on-oxide. Figure 7.29 shows a simplified cross section of CMOS devices fabricated in silicon-on-silicon dioxide (the SIMOX process).

The isolation of the devices simply involves etching the thin silicon film between the devices down to the insulator. Complicated well structures are not necessary, so the packing density of the SOI devices can be increased. In addition, junction capacitances at the source and drain regions are substantially reduced in the SOI structure, so there is potential for increased speed.

One aspect of the SOI MOSFET is that the substrate is floating. When a high drain voltage is applied, impact ionization may occur in the drain-to-substrate junction. Holes that are created will be accelerated toward the p-type substrate in an n-channel device. Since there is no substrate contact, these positive charges will cause

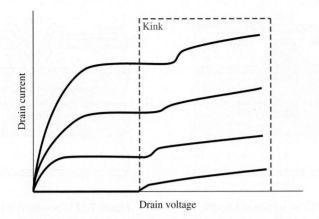

Figure 7.30 | Drain current versus drain voltage illustrating the kink effect in the characteristics of an n-channel SOI MOSFET.

the p-type substrate potential to increase. The increase in substrate potential results in a reduction in threshold voltage. This reduction in threshold voltage causes the current to increase. This floating body effect produces a "kink" effect as shown in Figure 7.30. The kink effect occurs at a particular drain voltage. The kink effect can be eliminated by forming an electrical contact between the substrate and source. However, the device layout would have to be changed and the device size would increase.

Kink effect

7.5.3 The Power MOSFET

The basic operation of the power MOSFET is the same as that of any MOSFET. However, the current handling capability of these devices is usually in the ampere range, and the drain-to-source blocking voltage may be in the range of 50 to 100 V or even higher. One big advantage that a power MOSFET has over a bipolar power device is that the control signal is applied to the gate whose input impedance is extremely large. Even during switching between on and off states, the gate current is small, so that relatively large currents can be switched with very small control currents.

Power Transistor Structures Large currents can be obtained in a MOSFET with a very large channel width. To achieve a large channel width device with good characteristics, power MOSFETs are fabricated with a repetitive pattern of small cells operating in parallel. To achieve a large blocking voltage, a vertical structure is used. There are two basic power MOSFET structures. The first is called a *DMOS* device and is shown in Figure 7.31. The DMOS device uses a double diffusion process: The p base or the p-substrate region and the n^+ source contact are diffused through a common window defined by the edge of the gate. The p-base region is diffused deeper than the n^+ source, and the difference in the lateral diffusion distance between the p base and the n^+ source defines the surface channel length.

DMOS power transistor

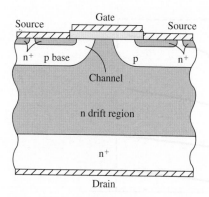

Figure 7.31 | Cross section of a double-diffused MOS (DMOS) transistor.

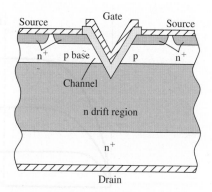

Figure 7.32 | Cross section of a vertical channel MOS (VMOS) transistor.

Electrons enter the source terminal and flow laterally through the inversion layer under the gate to the n-drift region. The electrons then flow vertically through the n-drift region to the drain terminal. The conventional current direction is from the drain to the source. The n-drift region must be moderately doped so that the drain breakdown voltage is sufficiently large. However, the thickness of the n drift region should also be as thin as possible to minimize drain resistance.

VMOS power transistor

The second power MOSFET structure, shown in Figure 7.32, is a *VMOS* structure. The vertical channel or VMOS power device is a nonplanar structure that requires a different type of fabrication process. In this case, a p-base or p-"substrate" diffusion is performed over the entire surface followed by the n+ source diffusion. A V-shaped groove is then formed, extending through the n drift region. Is has been found that certain chemical solutions etch the (111) planes in silicon at a much slower rate than the other planes. If (100)-oriented silicon is etched through a window at the surface, these chemical etches will create a V-shaped groove. A gate oxide is then grown in the V groove and the metal gate material is deposited. An electron inversion layer is formed in the base or substrate so that current is again essentially a vertical current between the source and drain. The relatively low doped n drift region supports the drain voltage since the depletion region extends mainly into this low-doped region.

HEXFET structure

We mentioned that many individual MOSFET cells are connected in parallel to fabricate a power MOSFET with the proper width-to-length ratio. Figure 7.33 shows a HEXFET structure. Each cell is a DMOS device with an n+ polysilicon gate. The HEXFET has a very high packing density—it may be on the order of 10^5 cells per cm^2. In the VMOS structure, the anisotropic etching of the grooves must be along the [110] direction on the (100) surface. This constraint limits the design options available for this type of device.

Power MOSFET Characteristics   Table 7.2 lists the basic parameters of two n-channel power MOSFETs. The drain currents are in the ampere range and the breakdown voltages are in the hundreds of volts range.

Table 7.2 | Characteristics of two power MOSFETs

Parameter	2N6757	2N6792
V_{DS}(max) (V)	150	400
I_D(max) (A) (at $T = 25°C$)	8	2
P_D (W)	75	20

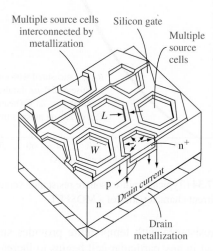

Figure 7.33 | A HEXFET structure.

An important parameter of a power MOSFET is the *on resistance,* which can be written as

$$R_{on} = R_S + R_{CH} + R_D \qquad (7.34)$$

where R_S is the resistance associated with the source contact, R_{CH} is the channel resistance, and R_D is the resistance associated with the drain contact. The R_S and R_D resistance values are not necessarily negligible in power MOSFETs, since small resistances and high currents can produce considerable power dissipation.

In the linear region of operation, we may write the channel resistance as

$$R_{CH} = \frac{L}{W \mu_n C_{ox}(V_{GS} - V_T)} \qquad (7.35) \qquad \textbf{Channel resistance}$$

We have noted in previous chapters that mobility decreases with increasing temperature. The threshold voltage varies only slightly with temperature so that, as current in a device increases and produces additional power dissipation, the temperature of the device increases, the carrier mobility decreases, and R_{CH} increases, which inherently limits the channel current. The resistances R_S and R_D are proportional to semiconductor resistivity and so are also inversely proportional to mobility and have the same temperature characteristics as R_{CH}. Figure 7.34 shows a typical "on-resistance" characteristic as a function of drain current.

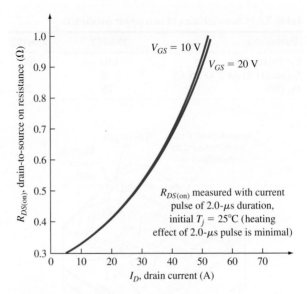

Figure 7.34 | Typical drain-to-source resistance versus drain current characteristics of a MOSFET.

The increase in resistance with temperature provides stability for the power MOSFET. If the current in any particular cell begins to increase, the resulting temperature rise will increase the on resistance, thus limiting the current. With this particular characteristic, the total current in a power MOSFET tends to be evenly distributed among the parallel cells, not concentrated in any single cell, a condition that can cause burn-out.

Power MOSFETs differ from bipolar power transistors both in operating principles and performance. The superior performance characteristics of power MOSFETs are: faster switching times, no second breakdown, and stable gain and response time over a wide temperature range. Figure 7.35a shows the transconductance of the 2N6757 versus temperature. The variation with temperature of the MOSFET transconductance is less than the variation in the BJT current gain. Figure 7.35b is a plot of drain current versus gate-to-source voltage at three different temperatures. We can note that at high current, the current decreases with temperature at a constant gate-to-source voltage, providing the stability that has been discussed.

7.5.4   MOS Memory Device

A nonvolatile memory device can be formed by adding a second floating gate to the MOS structure. The first nonvolatile memory device was proposed in 1967. Since then, various device structures have been proposed and fabricated.

The basic structure is shown in Figure 7.36. Charges are injected from the silicon substrate or the drain terminal into the floating gate through the first oxide adjacent to the silicon. The stored charge on the floating gate changes the threshold voltage of the device.

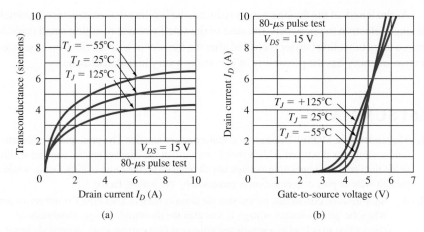

Figure 7.35 | Typical characteristics for high-power MOSFETs at various temperatures: (a) transconductance versus drain current; (b) drain current versus gate-to-source voltage.

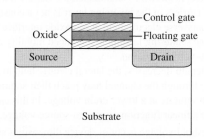

Figure 7.36 | Cross section of an example of a floating-gate nonvolatile memory.

Prior to programming the device (initially there is zero charge on the floating gate), a moderate operating voltage on the control gate will turn on the MOSFET. When the device is to be programmed, a large control gate voltage and drain voltage are applied. Electrons near the drain terminal can gain enough energy to tunnel through the thin oxide into the floating gate. The floating gate then becomes negatively charged. When the control voltage is set equal to zero, the floating gate effectively produces a relatively large negative threshold voltage and the device is turned off. Now, even when a moderate operating voltage is applied to the control gate, the negative threshold voltage is not overcome and the device remains off.

Floating-gate memory MOSFET

Various structures have been designed and fabricated such that the charge on the floating gate can be erased. In an erasable programmable read only memory (EPROM), erasing is accomplished by UV light. However, in electrically erasable PROM (EEPROM) devices, individual transistors can be erased using a tunneling process. Once the devices have been erased, they can be reprogrammed.

As the length of the floating gate is reduced, the limiting device structure becomes the single-electron memory cell. Because of the small size and resulting small capacitance, a large tunneling barrier is created after the transfer of a single electron. A single-electron memory has the possibility of becoming a very high dense memory.

7.6 | SUMMARY

1. The tendency in MOSFET design is to make devices smaller. The principle of constant-field scaling was discussed. This principle means that the channel length, channel width, oxide thickness, and operating voltage are all reduced by the same scaling factor, while the substrate doping concentration is increased by the scaling factor.

2. A. Subthreshold conduction means that the drain current in a MOSFET is not zero even when the gate-to-source voltage is less than the threshold voltage. Subthreshold conduction may lead to a significant quiescent bias current in an integrated circuit.

   B. The effective channel length decreases with an increase in drain voltage when the MOSFET is biased in the saturation region since the depletion region at the drain extends into the channel. The drain current becomes a function of drain-to-source voltage. This effect is known as channel length modulation.

   C. The mobility of carriers in the inversion layer is not a constant. As the gate voltage increases, the transverse electric field at the oxide interface increases, causing additional surface scattering leading to a reduced mobility and a deviation from the ideal current–voltage relation.

   D. As the channel length decreases, the lateral electric field in general increases. Carriers flowing through the channel may reach their saturation velocity; the drain current will then saturate at a lower drain voltage. In this case, the drain current tends to become a linear function of gate-to-source voltage.

3. Modifications in threshold voltage occur as device dimensions shrink. Because of charge-sharing effects in the substrate, the threshold voltage decreases as channel length decreases and increases as channel width decreases.

4. A. Oxide breakdown must be considered as device dimensions shrink. In addition, near punch-through or drain-induced barrier lowering may become a problem as device size becomes smaller.

   B. Hot electron effects were discussed and may become a problem as device sizes become smaller.

   C. Various semiconductor and device parameters may be fixed in a particular design and fabrication process. However, the final threshold voltage may not be acceptable. Ion implantation can be used as essentially a final step to change and adjust the substrate doping concentration in the channel region to provide the desired threshold voltage. This process is referred to as threshold voltage adjustment by ion implantation and is extensively used in device fabrication.

5. A few specialized MOS device structures were discussed.

   A. The lightly doped drain transistor incorporates lightly doped regions directly adjacent to the drain terminal in the channel region to increase breakdown voltage.

   B. MOSFETs can be fabricated on insulators to reduce the device volume and capacitances. Increased packing density and increased speed generally result from this fabrication process.

   C. The power MOSFET structure and device characteristics were discussed.

D. The operation and characteristics of the floating-gate, nonvolatile MOS memory device were discussed.

CHECKPOINT

After studying this chapter, the reader should have the ability to

1. Determine how the various parameters in a MOSFET change in constant-field scaling.

2. A. Describe the mechanism and consequence of subthreshold conduction.

    B. Discuss the source and consequence of channel-length modulation.

    C. Discuss the effect of a variable mobility on the $I-V$ characteristics of a MOSFET.

    D. Determine the effect on the $I-V$ characteristics of a MOSFET of carrier saturation velocity.

3. A. Describe the effect on threshold voltage as the channel length decreases.

    B. Describe the effect on threshold voltage as the channel width decreases.

4. A. Describe drain-induced barrier lowering and its effect on the $I-V$ characteristics of a MOSFET.

    B. Describe why threshold adjustment by ion implantation may be required.

5. A. Describe the device structure of a lightly doped drain transistor.

    B. Discuss the basic structure of a MOSFET on insulator.

    C. Describe the device structure of a power MOSFET.

    D. Discuss the operation of a floating gate nonvolatile MOS memory device.

REVIEW QUESTIONS

1. If the channel length is reduced by the constant k in constant-field scaling, what is the thickness of the oxide in the new device? What should be the doping concentration of the substrate?

2. A. What is subthreshold current?

    B. What is the effect on the $I-V$ characteristics in a MOSFET of channel-length modulation? What is the mechanism of channel-length modulation?

    C. Why is the mobility of channel carriers not a constant? How does this variable mobility change the $I-V$ characteristics?

    D. What is carrier velocity saturation and how does this effect the $I-V$ characteristics?

3. A. Discuss the effect of charge sharing on the threshold voltage as the channel length decreases.

    B. Discuss the effect of charge sharing on the threshold voltage as the channel width decreases.

4. A. What is drain-induced barrier lowering?

    B. If the threshold voltage of an NMOS device needs to be increased, what type of impurity atom should be implanted to adjust the threshold voltage?

5. A. What is the advantage of a lightly doped drain transistor?

    B. What is the floating-substrate effect in a MOSFET fabricated on an insulator?

    C. Describe the double-diffused power MOSFET device. What are the advantages of this structure?

    D. Sketch the cross section of a floating-gate nonvolatile MOS memory device. Discuss the device operation.

PROBLEMS

Section 7.1   MOSFET Scaling

7.1   Apply constant-field scaling to the ideal current–voltage relations in both the saturation and nonsaturation bias regions. (*a*) How does the drain current scale in each bias region? (*b*) How does the power dissipation per device scale in each bias region?

7.2   Consider a MOSFET biased such that carriers are traveling at their saturated velocity in the n channel. If constant-field scaling is applied to the device, how does the drain current scale?

7.3   Consider an NMOS transistor with parameters $K_n = 0.1$ mA/V^2 and $V_{TN} = 0.8$ V. Assume operating voltages of 5 V. Assume a constant-field scaling factor of $k = 0.6$ is applied but assume V_{TN} remains constant. (*a*) Determine the maximum drain current in the (*i*) original device and in the (*ii*) scaled device. (*b*) Determine the maximum power dissipation in the (*i*) original device and in the (*ii*) scaled device. (*c*) What is the actual scaling factor for the drain current in part (*a*) and the maximum power dissipation in part (*b*)?

Section 7.2   Nonideal Effects

7.4   Assume that the subthreshold current of a MOSFET is given by

$$I_D = 10^{-15} \exp\left(\frac{V_{GS}}{(2.1)V_t}\right)$$

over the range $0 \le V_{GS} \le 1$ volt and where the factor 2.1 takes into account the effect of interface states. Assume that 10^6 identical transistors on a chip are all biased at the same V_{GS} and at $V_{DD} = 5$ volts. (*a*) Calculate the total current that must be supplied to the chip at $V_{GS} = 0.5, 0.7,$ and 0.9 V. (*b*) Calculate the total power dissipated in the chip for the same V_{GS} values.

7.5   A silicon n-channel MOSFET has an acceptor doping of $N_a = 10^{16}$ cm^{-3} and a threshold voltage of $V_T = +0.75$ V. (*a*) Determine the minimum channel length so that the incremental change ΔL is no more than 10 percent of the original length L when $V_{DS} = 5$ V and $V_{GS} = 5$ V. (*b*) Repeat part (*a*) for $V_{GS} = 2$ V.

7.6   Consider an n-channel MOSFET with $N_a = 4 \times 10^{16}$ cm^{-3}, $t_{ox} = 400$ Å, $Q'_{ss} = 3 \times 10^{10}$ cm^{-2}, and $\phi_{ms} = 0$, biased at $V_{GS} = 5$ V and $V_{SB} = 0$. (*a*) Considering channel length modulation, plot ΔL versus V_{DS} over the range $V_{DS}(\text{sat}) \le V_{DS} \le V_{DS}(\text{sat}) + 5$. (*b*) Determine the minimum length L such that the maximum $\Delta L/L$ is 10 percent over the voltage range considered.

7.7   (a) Consider an n-channel MOSFET with parameters described in Example 6.10 of Chapter 6. Taking into account channel length modulation effects [Equations (7.7) and (7.9)], plot I_D versus ΔV_{DS} for $V_{GS} = 1, 2, 3,$ and 4 volts, and over the range $0 \le \Delta V_{DS} \le 3$ volts. (*b*) Repeat part (*a*) for $L = 1.0$ μm and $L = 0.8$ μm.

7.8   Consider a MOSFET with a substrate doping concentration of $N_a = 10^{16}$ cm^{-3} and $V_{DS}(\text{sat}) = 2$ V. Using Equation (7.7), plot ΔL versus ΔV_{DS} over the range $0 \le \Delta V_{DS} \le 3$ V.

7.9   Consider the n-channel MOSFET described in Problem 6.30 of Chapter 6. Let $N_a = 3 \times 10^{16}$ cm^{-3}. (*a*) Using Equations (7.9) and (7.7), calculate the output conductance defined as $g_0 = \partial I'_D/\partial V_{DS}$ for $V_{GS} = 2$ V and $\Delta V_{DS} = 1$ V. (*b*) Repeat part (*a*) if the channel length is reduced to $L = 1$ μm.

7.10 (a) Consider an n-channel enhancement mode MOSFET with $(W/L) = 10$, $C_{ox} = 6.9 \times 10^{-8}$ F/cm^2, and $V_T = +1$ V. Assume a constant mobility of $\mu_n = 500$ cm^2/V-s. Plot $\sqrt{I_D}$ versus V_{GS} for $0 \le V_{GS} \le 5$ V when the transistor is biased in the saturation region. (b) Now assume that the effective mobility in the channel is given by

$$\mu_{eff} = \mu_0 \left(\frac{\mathcal{E}_{eff}}{\mathcal{E}_c} \right)^{-1/3}$$

where $\mu_0 = 1000$ cm^2/V-s and $\mathcal{E}_c = 2.5 \times 10^4$ V/cm. As a first approximation, let $\mathcal{E}_{eff} = V_{GS}/t_{ox}$. Using μ_{eff} in place of μ_n in the $\sqrt{I_D}$ versus V_{GS} relation, plot $\sqrt{I_D}$ versus V_{GS} over the same V_{GS} range as in part (a). (c) Plot the curves from parts (a) and (b) on the same graph. What can be said about the slopes of the two curves?

7.11 One model used to describe the variation in electron mobility in an NMOS device is

$$\mu_{eff} = \frac{\mu_0}{1 + \theta(V_{GS} - V_{TN})}$$

where θ is called the mobility degradation parameter. Assume the following parameters: $C_{ox} = 10^{-8}$ F/cm^2, $(W/L) = 25$, $\mu_0 = 800$ cm^2/V-s, and $V_{TN} = 0.5$ V. Plot, on the same graph, $\sqrt{I_D}$ versus V_{GS} for the NMOS device biased in the saturation region over the range $0 \le V_{GS} \le 3$ V for (a) $\theta = 0$ (ideal case) and (b) $\theta = 0.5$ V^{-1}.

7.12 An n-channel enhancement mode MOSFET has the following parameters:

$$t_{ox} = 400 \text{ Å} \qquad N_a = 5 \times 10^{16} \text{ cm}^{-3}$$
$$V_{FB} = -1.2 \text{ V} \qquad L = 2 \ \mu\text{m}$$
$$W = 20 \ \mu\text{m}$$

(a) Assuming a constant mobility of $\mu_n = 400$ cm^2/V-s, plot I_D versus V_{DS} for $V_{GS} - V_T = 1$ V and $V_{GS} - V_T = 2$ V over the range $0 \le V_{DS} \le 5$ V. (b) Consider the piecewise linear model of the carrier velocity versus V_{DS} shown in Figure P7.12. Again plot I_D versus V_{DS} for the same voltage values given in part (a). Compare the $V_{DS}(\text{sat})$ values for the curves in parts (a) and (b).

7.13 Consider an NMOS transistor with a threshold voltage of $V_{TN} = 0.4$ V. Plot, on the same graph, $V_{DS}(\text{sat})$ over the range $0 \le V_{GS} \le 3$ V for (a) an ideal MOSFET - (constant mobility) and (b) a device whose drift velocity is given in Figure P7.12.

Section 7.3 Threshold Voltage Modifications

7.14 Consider an n-channel MOSFET with $N_a = 10^{16}$ cm^{-3} and $t_{ox} = 450$ Å. If $r_j = 0.3 \ \mu$m and $L = 1 \ \mu$m, determine the threshold shift due to the short channel effect.

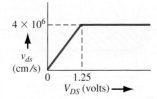

Figure P7.12 | Figure for Problems 7.12 and 7.13.

7.15   An n-channel MOSFET is doped to $N_a = 3 \times 10^{16}$ cm^{-3} and has an oxide thickness of $t_{ox} = 800$ Å. The diffused junction radius is $r_j = 0.60$ μm . If the threshold shift due to short-channel effects is to be no more than $\Delta V_T = -0.20$ V, determine the minimum channel length L.

*7.16   The shift in threshold voltage due to short-channel effects given by Equation (7.22) assumed all space charge regions were of equal width. If a drain voltage is applied, this condition is no longer valid. Using the same trapezoidal approximation, show that the threshold voltage shift is given by

$$\Delta V_T = -\frac{eN_a x_{dT}}{C_{ox}} \cdot \frac{rj}{2L}\left[\left(\sqrt{1 + \frac{2x_{ds}}{r_j} + \alpha^2} - 1\right) + \left(\sqrt{1 + \frac{2x_{dD}}{r_j} + \beta^2} - 1\right)\right]$$

where

$$\alpha^2 = \frac{x_{ds}^2 - x_{dT}^2}{r_j^2} \qquad \beta^2 = \frac{x_{dD}^2 - x_{dT}^2}{r_j^2}$$

and where x_{ds} and x_{dD} are the source and drain space charge widths, respectively.

*7.17   The threshold voltage shift due to short channel effects, given by Equation (7.22), was derived assuming L is large enough so that a trapezoidal charge region could be defined as shown in Figure 7.14. Derive the expression for ΔV_T for the case when L becomes small enough such that the trapezoid becomes a triangle. Assume punch-through does not occur.

7.18   Consider the short channel effect. Plot $V_T - V_{FB}$ versus L as shown in Figure 7.15 over the range $0.5 \le L \le 6$ μm. Use the parameters given in the figure and assume $V_{SB} = 0$.

7.19   Repeat Problem 7.18 at $N_a = 10^{16}$ and 10^{17} cm^{-3} for $V_{SB} = 0, 2, 4,$ and 6 V.

7.20   Equation (7.22) describes the shift in threshold voltage due to short channel effects. If constant-field scaling is applied, what is the scaling factor in ΔV_T?

7.21   An n-channel MOSFET has a substrate doping of $N_a = 10^{16}$ cm^{-3} and an oxide thickness of $t_{ox} = 450$ Å. The channel width is $W = 2.5$ μm. Neglecting short-channel effects, calculate the threshold voltage shift due to narrow-channel effects. (Assume the fitting parameter is $\xi = \pi/2$.)

7.22   Consider an n-channel MOSFET with $N_a \approx 3 \times 10^{16}$ cm^{-3} and $t_{ox} = 800$ Å. The depletion regions at the end of the channel width can be approximated by triangular regions shown in Figure P7.22. Assume both the lateral and vertical depletion widths

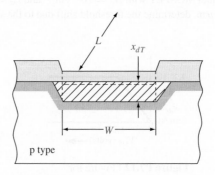

Figure P7.22 | Figure for Problem 7.22.

are equal to x_{dT}. If the threshold shift due to narrow-channel effects is $\Delta V_T = +0.25$ V, calculate the channel width W.

7.23 Consider the narrow channel effect. Use the transistor parameters described in Example 7.6. Plot $V_T - V_{FB}$ over the range $0.5 \leq W \leq 5\,\mu m$ for a long-channel device.

7.24 Equation (7.28) describes the shift in threshold voltage due to narrow channel effects. If constant-field scaling is applied, what is the scaling factor in ΔV_T?

Section 7.4 Additional Electrical Characteristics

7.25 An MOS device has a silicon dioxide gate insulator with a thickness of $t_{ox} = 250$ Å. (a) Calculate the ideal oxide breakdown voltage. (b) If a safety factor of 3 is required, determine the maximum safe gate voltage that may be applied.

7.26 In a power MOS device, a maximum gate voltage of 20 V is to be applied. If a safety factor of three is specified, determine the minimum thickness necessary for the silicon dioxide gate insulator.

7.27 Near punch-through occurs when the two depletion regions are within approximately six Debye lengths of each other. The extrinsic Debye length L_D is defined as

$$L_D = \left\{ \frac{\epsilon_s(kT/e)}{eN_a} \right\}^{1/2}$$

Consider the n-channel MOSFET in Example 7.7. Calculate the near punch-through voltage. How does this voltage compare to the ideal punch-through voltage determined in the example?

7.28 The near punch-through voltage (see Problem 7.27) of an n-channel MOSFET is to be no less than $V_{DS} = 5$ V. The source and drain regions are doped $N_d = 10^{19}$ cm^{-3}, and the channel region is doped $N_a = 3 \times 10^{16}$ cm^{-3}. The source and body are at ground potential. Determine the minimum channel length.

7.29 Repeat Problem 7.27 if a source–substrate voltage $V_{SB} = 2$ V is applied.

7.30 Consider an n-channel MOSFET with an n$^+$ polysilicon gate and with $N_a = 2 \times 10^{15}$ cm^{-3}, $t_{ox} = 650$ Å, and $Q'_{ss} = 2 \times 10^{11}$ cm^{-2}. (a) Calculate the threshold voltage. (b) The desired threshold voltage is $V_T = +0.80$ volt. Determine the type and ion implant density required to achieve this specification. Assume the implant is directly adjacent to the oxide-semiconductor interface.

7.31 An MOS transistor with an aluminum gate is fabricated on an n-type semiconductor substrate. The doping is $N_d = 10^{16}$ cm^{-3}, the oxide thickness is $t_{ox} = 750$ Å, and the equivalent fixed oxide charge is $Q'_{ss} = 5 \times 10^{11}$ cm^{-2}. (a) Calculate the threshold voltage. (b) The desired threshold voltage is $V_T = -0.50$ V. Determine the type and ion implant density required to achieve this specification. Assume the implant is directly adjacent to the oxide–semiconductor interface.

7.32 Consider an n-channel MOSFET with a doping of $N_a = 10^{15}$ cm^{-3}, an oxide thickness of $t_{ox} = 750$ Å, and an initial flat-band voltage of $V_{FB} = -1.50$ V. (a) Calculate the threshold voltage. (b) Determine the type and the ion implant density D_I required to achieve a threshold voltage of $V_T = +0.90$ V with zero volts applied to the substrate. (c) Use the results of part (b) and determine the threshold voltage if a source-to-body voltage $V_{SB} = 2$ V is applied.

7.33 The channel of a device with $t_{ox} = 500$ Å and a p-type substrate with $N_a = 10^{14}$ cm^{-3} is implanted with acceptors using an effective dose of $D_I = 2 \times 10^{11}$ cm^{-2}. The implant is approximated as a step function with $x_I = 0.2\ \mu$m. Calculate the shift in threshold voltage due to back bias effects for $V_{SB} = 1$, 3, and 5 V.

7.34   A MOSFET has the following parameters: n^+ poly gate, $t_{ox} = 80$ Å, $N_d = 10^{17}$ cm^{-3}, and $Q'_{ss} = 5 \times 10^{10}$ cm^{-2}. (*a*) What is the threshold voltage of this MOSFET? Is the device enhancement- or depletion-mode? (*b*) What type of implant and dose are required such that $V_T = 0$?

7.35   The threshold voltage of an NMOS device with $t_{ox} = 400$ Å needs to be shifted in the negative direction by 1.4 V. Determine the type and dose of ion implant required.

Section 7.5   Device Fabrication Techniques

7.36   Three MOSFETs are to be used in parallel to sink 5 A of load current when they are on. (*a*) The on resistances of the three devices are $R_{on1} = 1.8\ \Omega$, $R_{on2} = 2\ \Omega$, and $R_{on3} = 2.2\ \Omega$. Calculate the current in each device and the power dissipated in each device. (*b*) For some unknown reason, the on resistance of the second device increases on $R_{on2} = 3.6\ \Omega$. Recalculate the current in each device and the power dissipated in each device.

Summary and Review

*7.37   Reconsider Problem 6.49 in Chapter 6 taking into account short-channel effects.

*7.38   A particular process produces an n-channel MOSFET with the following properties:

$$t_{ox} = 325\ \text{Å} \qquad L = 0.8\ \mu\text{m}$$
$$N_a = 10^{16}\ \text{cm}^3 \qquad W = 20\ \mu\text{m}$$
$$n^+ \text{ polysilicon gate} \qquad r_j = 0.35\ \mu\text{m}$$
$$Q'_{ss} = 10^{11}\ \text{cm}^{-2}$$

The desired threshold voltage is $V_T = 0.35$ V at $T = 300$ K. Design an additional process to achieve this objective by using ion implantation, which produces a step function profile that is 0.35 μm deep.

*7.39   A CMOS inverter is to be designed in which both the n-channel and p-channel devices have the same magnitude of doping concentration equal to 10^{16} cm^{-3}, equal oxide thickness of $t_{ox} = 150$ Å, equal oxide trapped charge of $Q'_{ss} = +8 \times 10^{10}$ cm^{-2}. The gate of the n channel is p^+ poly and the gate of the p channel is n^+ poly. Determine the type of ion implant and the implant dose in each device such that the final threshold voltages are $V_{TN} = +0.5$ V and $V_{TP} = -0.5$ V.

READING LIST

1.   Akers, L. A., and J. J. Sanchez. "Threshold Voltage Models of Short, Narrow, and Small Geometry MOSFETs: A Review." *Solid State Electronics* 25 (July 1982), pp. 621–41.

2.   Baliga, B. J. *Power Semiconductor Devices.* Boston: PWS Publishing Co., 1996.

3.   Brews, J. R. "Threshold Shifts Due to Nonuniform Doping Profiles in Surface Channel MOSFETs." *IEEE Transactions on Electron Devices* ED-26 (November 1979), pp. 1696–1710.

4.   Dimitrijev, S. *Understanding Semiconductor Devices.* New York: Oxford University Press, 2000.

5. Kano, K. *Semiconductor Devices.* Upper Saddle River, NJ: Prentice-Hall, 1998.

6. Klaassen, F. M., and W. Hes. "On the Temperature Coefficient of the MOSFET Threshold Voltage." *Solid State Electronics* 29 (August 1986), pp. 787–89.

7. Muller, R. S., T. I. Kamins, and W. Chan. *Device Electronics for Integrated Circuits,* 3rd ed. New York: John Wiley and Sons, 2003.

8. Neamen, D. A. *Semiconductor Physics and Devices: Basic Principles,* 3rd ed. New York: McGraw-Hill, 2003.

*9. Nicollian, E. H., and J. R. Brews. *MOS Physics and Technology.* New York: Wiley, 1982.

10. Ning, T. H., P. W. Cook, R. H. Dennard, C. M. Osburn, S. E. Schuster, and H. N. Yu. "1 μm MOSFET VLSI Technology: Part IV—Hot Electron Design Constraints." *IEEE Transactions on Electron Devices* ED-26 (April 1979), pp. 346–53.

11. Ogura, S., P. J. Tsang, W. W. Walker, D. L. Critchlow, and J. F. Shepard. "Design and Characteristics of the Lightly Doped Drain-Source (LDD) Insulated Gate Field-Effect Transistor." *IEEE Transactions on Electron Devices* ED-27 (August 1980), pp. 1359–67.

12. Ong, D. G. *Modern MOS Technology: Processes, Devices, and Design.* New York: McGraw-Hill, 1984.

13. Pierret, R. F. *Semiconductor Device Fundamentals.* Reading, MA: Addison-Wesley, 1996.

14. Roulston, D. J. *An Introduction to the Physics of Semiconductor Devices.* New York: Oxford University Press, 1999.

15. Sanchez, J. J., K. K. Hsueh, and T. A. DeMassa. "Drain-Engineered Hot-Electron-Resistant Device Structures: A Review." *IEEE Transactions on Electron Devices* ED-36 (June 1989), pp. 1125–32.

16. Schroder, D. K. *Advanced MOS Devices, Modular Series on Solid State Devices.* Reading, MA: Addison-Wesley, 1987.

17. Shur, M. *Introduction to Electronic Devices.* New York: John Wiley and Sons, Inc., 1996.

*18. Shur, M. *Physics of Semiconductor Devices.* Englewood Cliffs, NJ: Prentice-Hall, 1990.

19. Singh, J. *Semiconductor Devices: Basic Principles.* New York: Wiley, 2001.

20. Streetman, B. G., and S. Banerjee. *Solid State Electronic Devices.* 5th ed. Upper Saddle River, NJ: Prentice-Hall, 2000.

21. Sze, S. M. *Physics of Semiconductor Devices.* 2nd ed. New York: Wiley, 1981.

22. Sze, S. M. *Semiconductor Devices: Physics and Technology,* 2nd ed. New York: John Wiley and Sons, 2002.

*23. Taur, Y., and T. H. Ning. *Fundamentals of Modern VLSI Devices.* New York: Cambridge University Press, 1998.

*24. Tsividis, Y. *Operation and Modeling of the MOS Transistor,* 2nd ed. Burr Ridge, IL: McGraw-Hill, 1999.

25. Wolf, S. *Silicon Processing for the VLSI Era: Volume 3, The Submicron MOSFET.* Sunset Beach, CA: Lattice Press, 1995.

26. Yang, E. S. *Microelectronic Devices.* New York: McGraw-Hill, 1988.

27. Yau, L. D. "A Simple Theory to Predict the Threshold Voltage of Short-Channel IGFETs." *Solid-State Electronics* 17 (October 1974), pp. 1059–63.

8

Nonequilibrium Excess Carriers in Semiconductors

Our discussion of the physics of semiconductors in Chapter 3 was based on thermal equilibrium. When a voltage is applied or a current exists in a semiconductor device, the semiconductor is operating under nonequilibrium conditions. In our discussion of current transport, drift and diffusion, in Chapter 4, we implicitly assumed that equilibrium was not significantly disturbed. Also, our analysis of the MOS capacitor, the heart of the MOSFET, assumed thermal equilibrium existed in the semiconductor since there was no current through the oxide.

Excess electrons in the conduction band and excess holes in the valence band may exist in addition to the thermal-equilibrium concentrations if an external excitation is applied to the semiconductor. In this chapter, we will discuss the behavior of these nonequilibrium excess carriers as functions of time and space coordinates. This analysis is necessary for the study of the forward-biased pn junction and the bipolar transistor considered in the following chapters.[1]

8.0 | PREVIEW

In this chapter, we will

1. Review generation and recombination of excess carriers.
2. Derive the continuity and time-dependent diffusion equations that describe the behavior of excess carriers.
3. Define ambipolar transport, describe the ambipolar transport equation, and consider several applications of this equation.

---

[1]Σ Because of time constraints, the reader may study the following chapters simply using the results of this chapter.

4. Define and describe quasi-Fermi energy levels.
5. Analyze excess carrier recombination.
6. Qualitatively describe surface effects on excess carrier recombination.

Historical Insight

The characteristics of excess carriers were experimentally determined by J. Haynes and W. Shockley in 1951. The theory of excess electron–hole recombination was published by R. Hall and also by W. Shockley and W. Read in 1952. The solar cell was described in 1954 by Chapin, Fuller, and Pearson and operates by the interaction of light with the semiconductor creating excess electrons and holes.

Present-Day Insight

The characteristics of excess electrons and holes continue to be the basis of the operation of many semiconductor devices. The generation process of creating excess carriers is fundamental to the operation of solar cells and photodetectors. The recombination process is fundamental to the characteristics of forward-biased pn junctions, bipolar transistors, and light-emitting diodes.

8.1 | CARRIER GENERATION AND RECOMBINATION

Objective: Review generation and recombination of excess carriers.

We introduced the concepts of excess carrier generation and recombination in Chapter 4. Just to repeat briefly, carrier generation and recombination can be defined as

> *Generation*—the process whereby electrons and holes (carriers) are created.
>
> *Recombination*—the process whereby electrons and holes (carriers) are annihilated.

We discussed several mechanisms by which carriers can be generated or annihilated. In this chapter, we will discuss how these excess carriers behave as a function of time and as a function of space coordinates.

Excess electrons and holes are generated by external forces at a particular rate. Let g'_n and g'_p be the generation rates of excess electrons and holes, respectively. These generation rates have units of #/cm^3-s. Excess electrons and holes are usually generated in pairs so that

$$g'_n = g'_p \tag{8.1}$$

When excess electrons and holes are created, the concentration of electrons in the conduction band and holes in the valence band increase above their thermal equilibrium values. We can write

$$n = n_0 + \delta n \tag{8.2a}$$

Carrier generation

Carrier recombination

Excess carrier generation rate

Excess electrons and holes

Table 8.1 | Relevant notation used in Chapter 8

Symbol	Definition
n_0, p_0	Thermal-equilibrium electron and hole concentrations (independent of time and also usually position).
n, p	Total electron and hole concentrations (may be functions of time and/or position).
$\delta n = n - n_0$ $\delta p = p - p_0$	Excess electron and hole concentrations (may be functions of time and/or position).
g_n', g_p'	Excess electron and hole generation rates.
R_n', R_p'	Excess electron and hole recombination rates.
τ_{n0}, τ_{p0}	Excess minority-carrier electron and hole lifetimes.

and

$$p = p_0 + \delta p \tag{8.2b}$$

where n_0 and p_0 are the thermal equilibrium values, and where δn and δp are the excess electron and hole concentrations, respectively.

We found that electrons and holes recombine at a particular rate (#/cm³-s). We can write the recombination rates of electrons and holes as

$$R_n = \frac{n}{\tau_n} \tag{8.3a}$$

and

$$R_p = \frac{p}{\tau_p} \tag{8.3b}$$

where τ_n and τ_p are the electron and hole lifetimes, respectively.

We now want to analyze the behavior of these excess carriers. Since additional notation is used in the analysis of excess carriers, Table 8.1 lists some of the more pertinent symbols used throughout the chapter.

8.2 | ANALYSIS OF EXCESS CARRIERS

Objective: Derive the continuity and time-dependent diffusion equations that describe the behavior of excess carriers.

The generation and recombination rates of excess carriers are important parameters, but how the excess carriers behave with time and in space in the presence of electric fields and density gradients is of equal importance. As mentioned in the preview section, the excess electrons and holes do not move independently of each other, but they diffuse and drift with the same effective diffusion coefficient and with the same effective mobility. This phenomenon is called ambipolar transport. The question that must be answered is what is the effective diffusion coefficient and what is the effective mobility that characterizes the behavior of these excess carriers? To answer these questions, we must develop the continuity equations for the carriers and then develop the ambipolar transport equations.

The final results show that, for an extrinsic semiconductor under low injection (this concept will be defined in the analysis), the effective diffusion coefficient and mobility parameters are those of the minority carrier. This result is thoroughly developed in the following derivations. As will be seen in the following chapters, the behavior of the excess carriers has a profound impact on the characteristics of semiconductor devices.

8.2.1 Continuity Equations

The continuity equations for electrons and holes are developed in this section. Figure 8.1 shows a differential volume element in which a one-dimensional hole–particle flux is entering the differential element at x and is leaving the element at $x + dx$. The parameter F_{px}^+ is the hole-particle flux, or flow, and has units of number of holes/cm^2-s. For the x component of the particle current density shown, we may write

$$F_{px}^+(x + dx) = F_{px}^+(x) + \frac{\partial F_{px}^+}{\partial x} \cdot dx \tag{8.4}$$

This equation is a Taylor expansion of $F_{px}^+(x + dx)$, where the differential length dx is small, so that only the first two terms in the expansion are significant. The net increase in the number of holes per unit time within the differential volume element due to the x component of hole flux is given by

$$\frac{\partial p}{\partial t} \, dx \, dy \, dz = \left[F_{px}^+(x) - F_{px}^+(x + dx) \right] dy \, dz = -\frac{\partial F_{px}^+}{\partial x} \, dx \, dy \, dz \tag{8.5}$$

If $F_{px}^+(x) > F_{px}^+(x + dx)$, for example, there will be a net increase in the number of holes in the differential volume element with time. If we generalize to a three-dimensional hole flux, then the right side of Equation (8.5) can be written as $-\nabla \cdot F_p^+ \, dx \, dy \, dz$, where $\nabla \cdot F_p^+$ is the divergence of the flux vector. We will limit ourselves to a one-dimensional analysis.

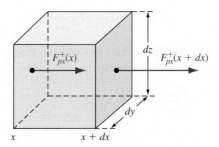

Figure 8.1 | Differential volume showing x component of the hole–particle flux.

The generation rate and recombination rate of holes will also affect the hole concentration in the differential volume. The net increase in the number of holes per unit time in the differential volume element is then given by

$$\frac{\partial p}{\partial t} \, dx \, dy \, dz = -\frac{\partial F_p^+}{\partial x} \, dx \, dy \, dz + g_p \, dx \, dy \, dz - \frac{p}{\tau_{pt}} \, dx \, dy \, dz \tag{8.6}$$

where p is the density of holes. The first term on the right side of Equation (8.6) is the increase in the number of holes per unit time due to the hole flux, the second term is the increase in the number of holes per unit time due to the generation of holes, and the last term is the decrease in the number of holes per unit time due to the recombination of holes. The recombination rate for holes is given by p/τ_{pt}, where τ_{pt} includes the thermal equilibrium carrier lifetime and the excess carrier lifetime.

If we divide both sides of Equation (8.6) by the differential volume $dx \, dy \, dz$, the net increase in the hole concentration per unit time is

$$\frac{\partial p}{\partial t} = -\frac{\partial F_p^+}{\partial x} + g_p - \frac{p}{\tau_{pt}} \tag{8.7}$$

Continuity equation for holes

Equation (8.7) is known as the continuity equation for holes.

Similarly, the one-dimensional continuity equation for electrons is given by

Continuity equation for electrons

$$\frac{\partial n}{\partial t} = -\frac{\partial F_n^-}{\partial x} + g_n - \frac{n}{\tau_{nt}} \tag{8.8}$$

where F_n^- is the electron-particle flow, or flux, also given in units of number of electrons/cm^2-s.

8.2.2 Time-Dependent Diffusion Equations

In Chapter 4, we derived the hole and electron current densities, which are given, in one dimension, by

$$J_p = e\mu_p p \mathcal{E} - eD_p \frac{\partial p}{\partial x} \tag{8.9}$$

and

$$J_n = e\mu_n n \mathcal{E} + eD_n \frac{\partial n}{\partial x} \tag{8.10}$$

If we divide the hole current density by $(+e)$ and the electron current density by $(-e)$, we obtain each particle flux. These equations become

$$\frac{J_p}{(+e)} = F_p^+ = \mu_p p \mathcal{E} - D_p \frac{\partial p}{\partial x} \tag{8.11}$$

and

$$\frac{J_n}{(-e)} = F_n^- = -\mu_n n \mathcal{E} - D_n \frac{\partial n}{\partial x} \tag{8.12}$$

Taking the divergence of Equations (8.11) and (8.12), and substituting back into the continuity equations of (8.7) and (8.8), we obtain

$$\frac{\partial p}{\partial t} = -\mu_p \frac{\partial (p\mathcal{E})}{\partial x} + D_p \frac{\partial^2 p}{\partial x^2} + g_p - \frac{p}{\tau_{pt}} \tag{8.13}$$

and

$$\frac{\partial n}{\partial t} = +\mu_n \frac{\partial (n\mathcal{E})}{\partial x} + D_n \frac{\partial^2 n}{\partial x^2} + g_n - \frac{n}{\tau_{nt}} \tag{8.14}$$

Keeping in mind that we are limiting ourselves to a one-dimensional analysis, we can expand the derivative of the product as

$$\frac{\partial (p\mathcal{E})}{\partial x} = \mathcal{E} \frac{\partial p}{\partial x} + p \frac{\partial \mathcal{E}}{\partial x} \tag{8.15}$$

In a more generalized three-dimensional analysis, Equation (8.15) would have to be replaced by a vector identity. Equations (8.13) and (8.14) can be written in the form

$$D_p \frac{\partial^2 p}{\partial x^2} - \mu_p \left(\mathcal{E} \frac{\partial p}{\partial x} + p \frac{\partial \mathcal{E}}{\partial x} \right) + g_p - \frac{p}{\tau_{pt}} = \frac{\partial p}{\partial t} \tag{8.16}$$

and

$$D_n \frac{\partial^2 n}{\partial x^2} + \mu_n \left(\mathcal{E} \frac{\partial n}{\partial x} + n \frac{\partial \mathcal{E}}{\partial x} \right) + g_n - \frac{n}{\tau_{nt}} = \frac{\partial n}{\partial t} \tag{8.17}$$

Equations (8.16) and (8.17) are the time-dependent diffusion equations for holes and electrons, respectively. Since both the hole concentration p and the electron concentration n contain the excess concentrations, Equations (8.16) and (8.17) describe the space and time behavior of the excess carriers.

The hole and electron concentrations are functions of both the thermal equilibrium and the excess values are given in Equation (8.2a) and (8.2b). The thermal-equilibrium concentrations, n_0 and p_0, are not functions of time. For the special case of a homogeneous semiconductor, n_0 and p_0 are also independent of the space coordinates. Equations (8.16) and (8.17) may then be written in the form

$$D_p \frac{\partial^2 (\delta p)}{\partial x^2} - \mu_p \left(\mathcal{E} \frac{\partial (\delta p)}{\partial x} + p \frac{\partial \mathcal{E}}{\partial x} \right) + g_p - \frac{p}{\tau_{pt}} = \frac{\partial (\delta p)}{\partial t} \tag{8.18}$$

Time-dependent diffusion equations

and

$$D_n \frac{\partial^2 (\delta n)}{\partial x^2} + \mu_n \left(\mathcal{E} \frac{\partial (\delta n)}{\partial x} + n \frac{\partial \mathcal{E}}{\partial x} \right) + g_n - \frac{n}{\tau_{nt}} = \frac{\partial (\delta n)}{\partial t} \tag{8.19}$$

Note that the Equations (8.18) and (8.19) contain terms involving the total concentrations, p and n, and terms involving only the excess concentrations, δp and δn.

8.3 | AMBIPOLAR TRANSPORT

Objective: Define ambipolar transport, describe the ambipolar transport equation, and consider several applications of this equation.

Originally, we assumed that the electric field in the current Equations (8.9) and (8.10) was an applied electric field. This electric field term appears in the time-dependent diffusion equations given by Equations (8.18) and (8.19). If a pulse of excess electrons and a pulse of excess holes are created at a particular point in a semiconductor with an applied electric field, the excess holes and electrons *will tend* to drift in opposite directions. However, because the electrons and holes are charged particles, any separation will induce an internal electric field between the two sets of particles. This internal electric field will create a force attracting the electrons and holes back toward each other. This effect is shown in Figure 8.2. The electric field term in Equations (8.18) and (8.19) is then composed of the externally applied field plus the induced internal field. This $\mathcal{E}$-field may be written as

$$\mathcal{E} = \mathcal{E}_{\text{app}} + \mathcal{E}_{\text{int}} \tag{8.20}$$

where $\mathcal{E}_{\text{app}}$ is the applied electric field and $\mathcal{E}_{\text{int}}$ is the induced internal electric field.

Since the internal $\mathcal{E}$-field creates a force attracting the electrons and holes, this $\mathcal{E}$-field will hold the pulses of excess electrons and excess holes together. The negatively charged electrons and positively charged holes then will drift or diffuse together with a single effective mobility or diffusion coefficient. This phenomenon is

Ambipolar transport   called *ambipolar diffusion* or *ambipolar transport*.

8.3.1 Derivation of the Ambipolar Transport Equation

The time-dependent diffusion Equations (8.18) and (8.19) describe the behavior of the excess carriers. However, a third equation is required to relate the excess electron and hole concentrations to the internal electric field. This relation is Poisson's equation, which can be written as

$$\nabla \cdot \mathcal{E}_{\text{int}} = \frac{e(\delta p - \delta n)}{\epsilon_s} = \frac{\partial \mathcal{E}_{\text{int}}}{\partial x} \tag{8.21}$$

where ϵ_s is the permittivity of the semiconductor material.

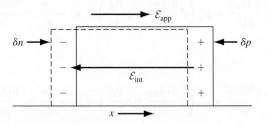

Figure 8.2 | The creation of an internal electric field as excess electrons and holes *tend* to separate.

To make the solution of Equations (8.18), (8.19), and (8.21) more tractable, we need to make some approximations. We can show that only a relatively small internal electric field is sufficient to keep the excess electrons and holes drifting and diffusing together. Hence, we can assume that

$$|\mathcal{E}_{\text{int}}| \ll |\mathcal{E}_{\text{app}}| \tag{8.22}$$

However, the $\nabla \cdot \mathcal{E}_{\text{int}}$ term may not be negligible. We will impose the condition of charge neutrality: We will assume that the excess electron concentration is just balanced by an equal excess hole concentration at any point in space and time. If this assumption were exactly true, there would be no induced internal electric field to keep the two sets of particles together. However, only a very small difference in the excess electron concentration and excess hole concentration will set up an internal $\mathcal{E}$-field sufficient to keep the particles diffusing and drifting together. We can show that a 1 percent difference in δp and δn, for example, will result in nonnegligible values of the $\nabla \cdot \mathcal{E} = \nabla \cdot \mathcal{E}_{\text{int}}$ term in Equations (8.18) and (8.19).

We can combine Equations (8.18) and (8.19) to eliminate the $\nabla \cdot \mathcal{E}$ term. In general, we can assume that electrons and holes are generated in pairs, so the generation rates are equal. We then have

$$g_n = g_p \equiv g \tag{8.23}$$

In addition, electrons and holes generally recombine in pairs so that the recombination rates are equal. We can then write

$$R_n = \frac{n}{\tau_{nt}} = R_p = \frac{p}{\tau_{pt}} \equiv R \tag{8.24}$$

The lifetimes in Equation (8.24) include the thermal-equilibrium carrier lifetimes and the excess-carrier lifetimes. If we impose the charge neutrality condition, then $\delta n \approx \delta p$. We will denote both the excess electron and excess hole concentrations in Equations (8.18) and (8.19) by δn. We may then rewrite Equations (8.18) and (8.19) as

$$D_p \frac{\partial^2 (\delta n)}{\partial x^2} - \mu_p \left(\mathcal{E} \frac{\partial (\delta n)}{\partial x} + p \frac{\partial \mathcal{E}}{\partial x} \right) + g - R = \frac{\partial (\delta n)}{\partial t} \tag{8.25}$$

and

$$D_n \frac{\partial^2 (\delta n)}{\partial x^2} + \mu_n \left(\mathcal{E} \frac{\partial (\delta n)}{\partial x} + n \frac{\partial \mathcal{E}}{\partial x} \right) + g - R = \frac{\partial (\delta n)}{\partial t} \tag{8.26}$$

If we multiply Equation (8.25) by $\mu_n n$, multiply Equation (8.26) by $\mu_p p$, and add the two equations, the $\nabla \cdot \mathcal{E} = \partial \mathcal{E}/\partial x$ term will be eliminated. The result of this addition gives

$$(\mu_n n D_p + \mu_p p D_n) \frac{\partial^2 (\delta n)}{\partial x^2} + (\mu_n \mu_p)(p - n)\mathcal{E} \frac{\partial (\delta n)}{\partial x}$$

$$+ (\mu_n n + \mu_p p)(g - R) = (\mu_n n + \mu_p p) \frac{\partial (\delta n)}{\partial t} \tag{8.27}$$

If we divide Equation (8.27) by the term $(\mu_n n + \mu_p p)$, this equation becomes

Ambipolar transport equation

$$D' \frac{\partial^2 (\delta n)}{\partial x^2} + \mu' \mathcal{E} \frac{\partial (\delta n)}{\partial x} + g - R = \frac{\partial (\delta n)}{\partial t} \qquad (8.28)$$

where

$$D' = \frac{\mu_n n D_p + \mu_p p D_n}{\mu_n n + \mu_p p} \qquad (8.29)$$

and

$$\mu' = \frac{\mu_n \mu_p (p - n)}{\mu_n n + \mu_p p} \qquad (8.30)$$

Equation (8.28) is called the *ambipolar transport equation* and describes the behavior of the excess electrons and holes in time and space. The parameter D' is called

Ambipolar mobility

the *ambipolar diffusion coefficient* and μ' is called the *ambipolar mobility*.

The Einstein relation relates the mobility and diffusion coefficient by

$$\frac{\mu_n}{D_n} = \frac{\mu_p}{D_p} = \frac{e}{kT} \qquad (8.31)$$

Ambipolar diffusion coefficient

Using these relations, the ambipolar diffusion coefficient can be written in the form

$$D' = \frac{D_n D_p (n + p)}{D_n n + D_p p} \qquad (8.32)$$

The ambipolar diffusion coefficient, D', and the ambipolar mobility, μ', are functions of the electron and hole concentrations, n and p, respectively. Since both n and p contain the excess carrier concentration δn, the coefficient in the ambipolar transport equation are not constants. The ambipolar transport equation, given by Equation (8.28), then, is a nonlinear differential equation.

8.3.2 Limits of Extrinsic Doping and Low Injection

The ambipolar transport equation can be simplified and linearized by considering an extrinsic semiconductor and by considering low-level injection. The ambipolar diffusion coefficient, from Equation (8.32), can be written as

$$D' = \frac{D_n D_p [(n_0 + \delta n) + (p_0 + \delta n)]}{D_n (n_0 + \delta n) + D_p (p_0 + \delta n)} \qquad (8.33)$$

where n_0 and p_0 are the thermal-equilibrium electron and hole concentrations, respectively, and δn is the excess carrier concentration. If we consider a p-type semi-

Low injection

conductor, we can assume that $p_0 \gg n_0$. The condition of low-level injection, or just low injection, means that the excess carrier concentration is much smaller than the thermal-equilibrium majority-carrier concentration. For the p-type semiconductor, then, low injection implies that $\delta n \ll p_0$. Assuming that $n_0 \ll p_0$ and $\delta n \ll p_0$, and assuming that D_n and D_p are on the same order of magnitude, the ambipolar diffusion coefficient from Equation (8.33) reduces to

$$D' = D_n \tag{8.34}$$

If we apply the conditions of an extrinsic p-type semiconductor and low injection to the ambipolar mobility, Equation (8.30) reduces to

$$\mu' = \mu_n \tag{8.35}$$

It is important to note that for an extrinsic p-type semiconductor under low injection, the ambipolar diffusion coefficient and the ambipolar mobility coefficient reduce to the minority-carrier electron parameter values, which are constants. The ambipolar transport equation reduces to a linear differential equation with constant coefficients.

If we now consider an extrinsic n-type semiconductor under low injection, we can assume that $p_0 \ll n_0$ and $\delta n \ll n_0$. The ambipolar diffusion coefficient from Equation (8.32) reduces to

$$D' = D_p \tag{8.36}$$

and the ambipolar mobility from Equation (8.30) reduces to

$$\mu' = -\mu_p \tag{8.37}$$

The ambipolar parameters again reduce to the minority-carrier values, which are constants. Note that, for the n-type semiconductor, the ambipolar mobility is a negative value. The ambipolar mobility term is associated with carrier drift; therefore, the sign of the drift term depends on the charge of the particle. The equivalent ambipolar particle is negatively charged, as one can see by comparing Equations (8.19) and (8.28). If the ambipolar mobility reduces to that of a positively charged hole, a negative sign is introduced as shown in Equation (8.37).

The remaining terms we need to consider in the ambipolar transport equation are the generation rate and the recombination rate. We can show that, in Equation (8.28) for a p-type material, we obtain

$$g - R = g'_n - \frac{\delta n}{\tau_n} \tag{8.38}$$

and for an n-type material, we obtain

$$g - R = g'_p - \frac{\delta p}{\tau_p} \tag{8.39}$$

where τ_n and τ_p are the lifetimes of the excess electrons and excess holes, respectively. The terms are usually referred to as the excess minority-carrier electron and excess minority-carrier hole lifetimes.

The generation rate for excess electrons must equal the generation rate for excess holes. We may then define a generation rate for excess carriers as g', so that $g_n' = g_p' \equiv g'$. We also determined that the minority-carrier lifetime is essentially a constant for low injection. Then the term $g - R$ in the ambipolar transport equation may be written in terms of the minority-carrier parameters.

Ambipolar transport equation for p type

The ambipolar transport equation, given by Equation (8.28), for a p-type semiconductor under low injection then becomes

$$D_n \frac{\partial^2 (\delta n)}{\partial x^2} + \mu_n \mathcal{E} \frac{\partial (\delta n)}{\partial x} + g' - \frac{\delta n}{\tau_{n0}} = \frac{\partial (\delta n)}{\partial t} \qquad (8.40)$$

The parameter δn is the excess minority-carrier electron concentration, the parameter τ_{n0} is the minority-carrier lifetime under low injection, and the other parameters are the usual minority-carrier electron parameters.

Ambipolar transport equation for n type

Similarly, for an extrinsic n-type semiconductor under low injection, the ambipolar transport equation becomes

$$D_p \frac{\partial^2 (\delta p)}{\partial x^2} - \mu_p \mathcal{E} \frac{\partial (\delta p)}{\partial x} + g' - \frac{\delta p}{\tau_{p0}} = \frac{\partial (\delta p)}{\partial t} \qquad (8.41)$$

The parameter δp is the excess minority-carrier hole concentration, the parameter τ_{p0} is the minority-carrier hole lifetime under low injection, and the other parameters are the usual minority-carrier hole parameters.

It is extremely important to note that the transport and recombination parameters in Equations (8.40) and (8.41) are those of the minority carrier. *Equations (8.40) and (8.41) describe the drift, diffusion, and recombination of excess minority carriers as a function of spatial coordinates and as a function of time.* Recall that we had imposed the condition of charge neutrality; the excess minority-carrier concentration is equal to the excess majority-carrier concentration. The excess majority carriers, then, diffuse and drift with the excess minority carriers; thus, the behavior of the excess majority carrier is determined by the minority carrier parameters. This ambipolar phenomenon is extremely important in semiconductor physics, and is the basis for describing the characteristics and behavior of semiconductor devices.

Ambipolar transport phenomenon

8.3.3 Applications of the Ambipolar Transport Equation

We will solve the ambipolar transport equation for several problems. These examples will help illustrate the behavior of excess carriers in a semiconductor material, and the results will be used later in the discussion of the pn junction and the other semiconductor devices.

Examples 8.1 through 8.4 use several common simplifications in the solution of the ambipolar transport equation. Table 8.2 summarizes these simplifications and their effects.

Table 8.2 | Common ambipolar transport equation simplifications

Specification	Effect
Steady state	$\dfrac{\partial(\delta n)}{\partial t} = 0, \quad \dfrac{\partial(\delta p)}{\partial t} = 0$
Uniform distribution of excess carriers (uniform generation rate)	$D_n \dfrac{\partial^2(\delta n)}{\partial x^2} = 0, \quad D_p \dfrac{\partial^2(\delta n)}{\partial x^2} = 0$
Zero electric field	$\mathcal{E} \dfrac{\partial(\delta n)}{\partial x} = 0, \quad \mathcal{E} \dfrac{\partial(\delta p)}{\partial x} = 0$
No excess carrier generation	$g' = 0$
No excess carrier recombination (infinite lifetime)	$\dfrac{\delta n}{\tau_{n0}} = 0, \quad \dfrac{\delta p}{\tau_{p0}} = 0$

EXAMPLE 8.1

OBJECTIVE

To determine the time behavior of excess carriers as a semiconductor returns to thermal equilibrium.

Consider an infinitely large, homogeneous n-type semiconductor with zero applied electric field. Assume that at time $t = 0$, a uniform concentration of excess carriers exists in the crystal, but assume that $g' = 0$ for $t > 0$. If we assume that the concentration of excess carriers is much smaller than the thermal-equilibrium electron concentration, then the low-injection condition applies. Calculate the excess carrier concentration as a function of time for $t \geq 0$.

■ **Solution**

For the n-type semiconductor, we need to consider the ambipolar transport equation for the minority-carrier holes, which was given by Equation (8.41). The equation is

$$D_p \frac{\partial^2(\delta p)}{\partial x^2} - \mu_p \mathcal{E} \frac{\partial(\delta p)}{\partial x} + g' - \frac{\delta p}{\tau_{p0}} = \frac{\partial(\delta p)}{\partial t}$$

We are assuming a uniform concentration of excess holes so that $\partial^2(\delta p)/\partial x^2 = \partial(\delta p)/\partial x = 0$. For $t > 0$, we are also assuming that $g' = 0$. Equation (8.41) reduces to

$$\frac{d(\delta p)}{dt} = -\frac{\delta p}{\tau_{p0}} \qquad (8.42)$$

Since there is no spatial variation, the total time derivative may be used. At low injection, the minority-carrier hole lifetime, τ_{p0}, is a constant. The solution to Equation (8.42) is

$$\boxed{\delta p(t) = \delta p(0)e^{-t/\tau_{p0}}} \qquad (8.43)$$

where $\delta p(0)$ is the uniform concentration of excess carriers that exists at time $t = 0$. The concentration of excess holes decays exponentially with time, with a time constant equal to the minority-carrier hole lifetime.

From the charge-neutrality condition, we have that $\delta n = \delta p$, so the excess electron concentration is given by

$$\delta n(t) = \delta p(0)e^{-t/\tau_{p0}} \tag{8.44}$$

■ Numerical Calculation

Consider n-type gallium arsenide doped at $N_d = 10^{16}$ cm^{-3}. Assume that 10^{14} electron-hole pairs per cm^3 have been created at $t = 0$, and assume the minority-carrier hole lifetime is $\tau_{p0} = 10$ ns.

We can note that $\delta p(0) \ll n_0$, so low injection applies. Then from Equation (8.43) we can write

$$\delta p(t) = 10^{14}e^{-t/10^{-8}} \text{ cm}^{-3}$$

The excess hole and excess electron concentrations will decay to $1/e$ of their initial value in 10 ns.

■ Comment

The excess electrons and holes recombine at the rate determined by the excess minority-carrier hole lifetime in the n-type semiconductor. This decay in the minority-carrier concentration is shown in Figure 8.3 for the 10-ns lifetime given in Example 8.1 (solid curve). Also shown are curves for lifetimes of 5 ns and 20 ns.

EX8.1   Silicon at $T = 300$ K has been doped with boron atoms to a concentration of $N_a = 5 \times 10^{16}$ cm^{-3}. Excess carriers have been generated in the uniformly doped material to a concentration of 10^{15} cm^{-3}. The minority-carrier lifetime is 5 μs. (a) What carrier type is the minority carrier? (b) Assuming $g' = \mathcal{E} = 0$ for $t > 0$, determine the minority-carrier concentration for $t > 0$.

[Ans. (a) electrons, (b) $10^{15}e^{-t/5\times10^{-6}}$ cm^{-3}]

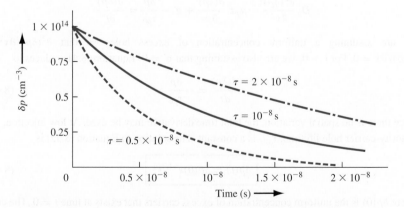

Figure 8.3 | Exponential decay of excess carriers, as described in Example 8.1 for a lifetime of $\tau = 10^{-8}$ s. Also shown, for comparison purposes, are the exponential decay curves for lifetimes of 5 ns and 20 ns.

EXAMPLE 8.2

OBJECTIVE

To determine the time dependence of excess carriers in reaching a steady-state condition.

Again consider an infinitely large, homogeneous n-type semiconductor with a zero applied electric field. Assume that, for $t < 0$, the semiconductor is in thermal equilibrium and that, for $t \geq 0$, a uniform generation rate exists in the crystal. Calculate the excess carrier concentration as a function of time assuming the condition of low injection.

■ Solution

The condition of a uniform generation rate and a homogeneous semiconductor again implies that $\partial^2(\delta p)/\partial x^2 = \partial(\delta p)/\partial x = 0$ in Equation (8.41). The equation, for this case, reduces to

$$g' - \frac{\delta p}{\tau_{p0}} = \frac{d(\delta p)}{dt} \tag{8.45}$$

The solution to this differential equation is

$$\boxed{\delta p(t) = g'\tau_{p0}(1 - e^{-t/\tau_{p0}})} \tag{8.46}$$

■ Numerical Calculation

Consider n-type silicon at $T = 300$ K doped at $N_d = 2 \times 10^{16}$ cm^{-3}. Assume that $\tau_{p0} = 10^{-7}$ s and $g' = 5 \times 10^{21}$ cm^{-3} s^{-1}. From Equation (8.46) we can write

$$\delta p(t) = (5 \times 10^{21})(10^{-7})[1 - e^{-t/10^{-7}}] = 5 \times 10^{14}[1 - e^{-t/10^{-7}}]\ \text{cm}^{-3}$$

■ Comment

We can note that for $t \to \infty$, we create a steady-state excess hole and electron concentration of 5×10^{14} cm^{-3}. We can note that $\delta p \ll n_0$ so that low injection is valid. The exponential and steady-state behavior in the excess minority-carrier concentration is shown in Figure 8.4 for

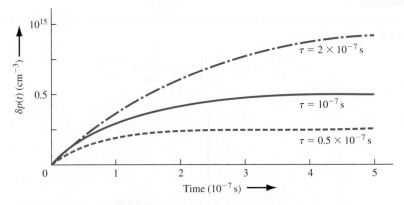

Figure 8.4 | Exponential and steady-state behavior of the excess carrier concentration as described in Example 8.2 for a lifetime of $\tau = 10^{-7}$ s. Also shown, for comparison purposes, are the curves for lifetimes of 0.5×10^{-7} s and 2×10^{-7} s.

the lifetime of 10^{-7} s (solid curve). Also shown are curves for lifetimes of 0.5×10^{-7} s and 2×10^{-7} s. Note that, as the lifetime changes, the steady-state value of the excess carrier concentration and the time to reach steady state changes.

Exercise Problem

EX8.2 Consider silicon with the same parameters as given in Ex8.1. The material is in thermal equilibrium for $t < 0$. At $t = 0$, a source generating excess carriers is turned on, producing a generation rate of $g' = 10^{20}$ cm^{-3}-s^{-1}. (a) What carrier type is the minority carrier? (b) Determine the minority carrier concentration for $t > 0$. (c) What is the minority carrier concentration as $t \to \infty$?

[Ans. (a) electrons, (b) $5 \times 10^{14}[1 - e^{-t/5 \times 10^{-6}}]$ cm^{-3}, (c) 5×10^{14} cm^{-3}]

The excess minority-carrier hole concentration increases with time with the same time constant τ_{p0}, which is the excess minority-carrier lifetime. The excess carrier concentration reaches a steady-state value as time goes to infinity, even though a steady-state generation of excess electrons and holes exists. This steady-state effect can be seen from Equation (8.45) by setting $d(\delta p)/dt = 0$. The remaining terms simply state that, in steady state, the generation rate is equal to the recombination rate.

EXAMPLE 8.3

OBJECTIVE

To determine the steady-state spatial dependence of the excess carrier concentration.

Consider a p-type semiconductor that is homogeneous and infinite in extent. Assume a zero applied electric field. For a one-dimensional crystal, assume that excess carriers are being generated at $x = 0$ only, as indicated in Figure 8.5. The excess carriers being generated at $x = 0$ will begin diffusing in both the $+x$ and $-x$ directions. Calculate the steady-state excess carrier concentration as a function of x.

■ Solution

The ambipolar transport equation for excess minority-carrier electrons was given by Equation (8.40), and is written as

$$D_n \frac{\partial^2(\delta n)}{\partial x^2} + \mu_n \mathcal{E} \frac{\partial(\delta n)}{\partial x} + g' - \frac{\delta n}{\tau_{n0}} = \frac{\partial(\delta n)}{\partial t}$$

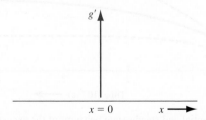

Figure 8.5 | Steady-state generation rate at $x = 0$.

From our assumptions, we have $\mathcal{E} = 0$, $g' = 0$ for $x \neq 0$, and $\partial(\delta n)/\partial t = 0$ for steady state. Assuming a one-dimensional crystal, Equation (8.40) reduces to

$$D_n \frac{d^2(\delta n)}{dx^2} - \frac{\delta n}{\tau_{n0}} = 0 \tag{8.47}$$

Dividing by the diffusion coefficient, Equation (8.47) can be written as

$$\frac{d^2(\delta n)}{dx^2} - \frac{\delta n}{D_n \tau_{n0}} = \frac{d^2(\delta n)}{dx^2} - \frac{\delta n}{L_n^2} = 0 \tag{8.48}$$

where we have defined $L_n^2 = D_n \tau_{n0}$. The parameter L_n has the unit of length and is called the minority-carrier electron diffusion length. The general solution to Equation (8.48) is

Minority-carrier diffusion length

$$\delta n(x) = A e^{-x/L_n} + B e^{x/L_n} \tag{8.49}$$

As the minority-carrier electrons diffuse away from $x = 0$, they will recombine with the majority-carrier holes. The minority-carrier electron concentration will then decay toward zero at both $x = +\infty$ and $x = -\infty$. These boundary conditions mean that $B \equiv 0$ for $x > 0$ and $A \equiv 0$ for $x < 0$. The solution to Equation (8.48) can then be written as

$$\boxed{\delta n(x) = \delta n(0) e^{-x/L_n} \qquad x \geq 0} \tag{8.50a}$$

and

$$\boxed{\delta n(x) = \delta n(0) e^{+x/L_n} \qquad x \leq 0} \tag{8.50b}$$

where $\delta n(0)$ is the value of the excess electron concentration at $x = 0$. The steady-state excess electron concentration decays exponentially with distance away from the source at $x = 0$.

■ Numerical Calculation

Consider p-type silicon at $T = 300\,\text{K}$ doped at $N_a = 5 \times 10^{16}$ cm^{-3}. Assume that $\tau_{n0} = 5 \times 10^{-7}$ s, $D_n = 25$ cm^2/s, and $\delta n(0) = 10^{15}$ cm^{-3}.

The minority-carrier diffusion length is

$$L_n = \sqrt{D_n \tau_{n0}} = \sqrt{(25)(5 \times 10^{-7})} = 35.4 \; \mu\text{m}$$

Then for $x \geq 0$, we have

$$\delta n(x) = 10^{15} e^{-x/35.4 \times 10^{-4}} \; \text{cm}^{-3}$$

■ Comment

Figure 8.6 shows the results of this example. We can note that the steady-state excess concentration decays to $1/e$ of its value at $x = L_n = 35.4 \; \mu\text{m}$. We can also note that the majority-carrier (holes) concentration barely changes under this low-injection condition. However, the minority-carrier (electron) concentration may change by orders of magnitude.

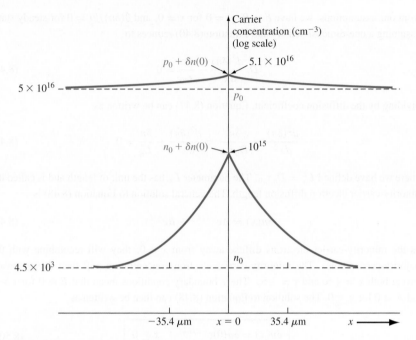

Figure 8.6 | Steady-state electron and hole concentrations for the case when excess electrons and holes are generated at $x = 0$.

Exercise Problem

EX8.3 Excess electrons and holes are generated at the end of a silicon bar ($x = 0$). The silicon is doped with phosphorus atoms to a concentration of $N_d = 10^{17}$ cm^{-3}. The minority-carrier lifetime is 1 μs, the electron diffusion coefficient is $D_n = 25$ cm^2/s, and the hole diffusion coefficient is $D_p = 10$ cm^2/s. If $\delta n(0) = \delta p(0) = 10^{15}$ cm^{-3}, determine the steady-state electron and hole concentrations in the silicon for $x > 0$. [Ans. $\delta n(x) = \delta p(x) = 10^{15} e^{-x/3.16 \times 10^{-3}}$ cm^{-3}, where x is in cm.]

Examples 8.1 through 8.3, which applied the ambipolar transport equation to specific situations, assumed either a homogeneous or a steady-state condition; only the time variation or the spatial variation was considered. Now consider an example in which both the time and spatial dependence are considered in the same problem.

EXAMPLE 8.4

OBJECTIVE

To determine both the time dependence and spatial dependence of the excess carrier concentration.

Assume that a finite number of electron–hole pairs is generated instantaneously at time $t = 0$ and at $x = 0$, but assume $g' = 0$ for $t > 0$. Assume we have an n-type semiconductor with a constant applied electric field equal to $\mathcal{E}_0$, which is applied in the $+x$ direction. Calculate the excess carrier concentration as a function of x and t.

■ **Solution**

The one-dimensional ambipolar transport equation for the minority-carrier holes can be written from Equation (8.41) as

$$D_p \frac{\partial^2(\delta p)}{\partial x^2} - \mu_p \mathcal{E}_0 \frac{\partial(\delta p)}{\partial x} - \frac{\delta p}{\tau_{p0}} = \frac{\partial(\delta p)}{\partial t} \tag{8.51}$$

The solution to this partial differential equation is of the form

$$\delta p(x, t) = p'(x, t)e^{-t/\tau_{p0}} \tag{8.52}$$

By substituting Equation (8.52) into Equation (8.51), we are left with the partial differential equation

$$D_p \frac{\partial^2 p'(x, t)}{\partial x^2} - \mu_p \mathcal{E}_0 \frac{\partial p'(x, t)}{\partial x} = \frac{\partial p'(x, t)}{\partial t} \tag{8.53}$$

Equation (8.53) is normally solved using Laplace transform techniques. The solution, without going through the mathematical details, is

$$p'(x, t) = \frac{1}{(4\pi D_p t)^{1/2}} \exp\left[\frac{-(x - \mu_p \mathcal{E}_0 t)^2}{4 D_p t}\right] \tag{8.54}$$

The total solution, from Equations (8.52) and (8.54), for the excess minority-carrier hole concentration is

$$\delta p(x, t) = \frac{e^{-t/\tau_{p0}}}{(4\pi D_p t)^{1/2}} \exp\left[\frac{-(x - \mu_p \mathcal{E}_0 t)^2}{4 D_p t}\right] \tag{8.55}$$

■ **Comment**

We could show that Equation (8.55) is a solution by direct substitution back into the partial differential equation, Equation (8.51).

Exercise Problem

EX8.4 As a good approximation, the peak value of a normalized excess carrier concentration, given by Equation (8.55), occurs at $x = \mu_p \mathcal{E}_0 t$. Assume the following parameters: $\tau_{p0} = 5 \ \mu s$, $D_p = 10 \ cm^2/s$, $\mu_p = 386 \ cm^2/V\text{-}s$, and $\mathcal{E}_0 = 10 \ V/cm$. Calculate the peak value at times of (a) $t = 1 \ \mu s$, (b) $t = 5 \ \mu s$, (c) $t = 15 \ \mu s$, and (d) $t = 25 \ \mu s$. What are the corresponding values of x for parts (a) to (d)?

[Ans. (a) $73.0, x = 38.6 \ \mu m$; (b) $14.7, x = 193 \ \mu m$; (c) $1.15, x = 579 \ \mu m$; (d) $0.120, x = 965 \ \mu m$]

Equation (8.55) can be plotted as a function of distance x, for various times. Figure 8.7 shows such a plot for the case when the applied electric field is zero. For $t > 0$, the excess minority-carrier holes diffuse in both the $+x$ and $-x$ directions. During this time, the excess majority-carrier electrons, which were generated, diffuse at exactly the same rate as the holes. As time proceeds, the excess holes recombine with the excess electrons so that at $t = \infty$ the excess hole concentration is zero.

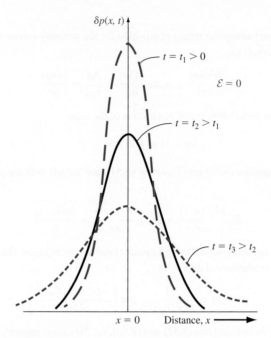

Figure 8.7 | Excess-hole concentration versus distance at various times for zero applied electric field.

In this particular example, both diffusion and recombination processes are occurring at the same time.

Figure 8.8 shows a plot of Equation (8.55) as a function of distance x at various times for the case when the applied electric field is not zero. In this case, the pulse of excess minority-carrier holes is drifting in the $+x$ direction, which is the direction of the electric field. We still have the same diffusion and recombination processes as we had before. An important point to consider is that, with charge neutrality, $\delta n = \delta p$ at any instant of time and at any point in space. The excess-electron concentration is equal to the excess-hole concentration. In this case, then, the excess-electron pulse is moving in the same direction as the applied electric field even though the electrons have a negative charge. In the ambipolar transport process, the excess carriers are characterized by the minority-carrier parameters. In this example, the excess carriers behave according to the minority-carrier hole parameters, which include D_p, μ_p, and τ_{p0}. The excess majority-carrier electrons are being pulled along by the excess minority-carrier holes.

Ambipolar transport process

8.3.4 Dielectric Relaxation Time Constant

We have assumed in the previous analysis that a quasi-neutrality conditions exists—that is, the concentration of excess holes is balanced by an equal concentration of excess electrons. Suppose that we have a situation as shown in Figure 8.9, in which a

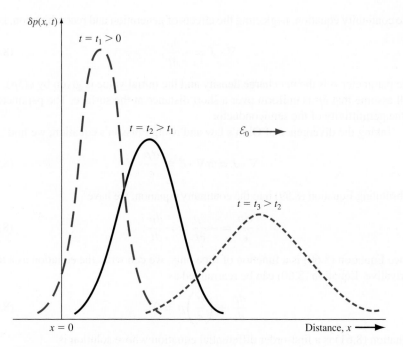

Figure 8.8 | Excess-hole concentration versus distance at various times for a constant applied electric field.

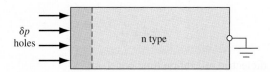

Figure 8.9 | The injection of a concentration of holes into a small region at the surface of an n-type semiconductor.

uniform concentration of holes δp is suddenly injected into a portion of the surface of a semiconductor. We will instantly have a concentration of excess holes and a net positive charge density that is not balanced by a concentration of excess electrons. How is charge neutrality achieved and how fast?

There are three defining equations to be considered. Poisson's equation is

$$\nabla \cdot \mathcal{E} = \frac{\rho}{\epsilon} \tag{8.56}$$

The current equation, Ohm's law, is

$$J = \sigma \mathcal{E} \tag{8.57}$$

The continuity equation, neglecting the effects of generation and recombination, is

$$\nabla \cdot J = -\frac{\partial \rho}{\partial t} \tag{8.58}$$

The parameter ρ is the net charge density and the initial value is given by $e(\delta p)$. We will assume that δp is uniform over a short distance at the surface. The parameter ϵ is the permittivity of the semiconductor.

Taking the divergence of Ohm's law and using Poisson's equation, we find

$$\nabla \cdot J = \sigma \nabla \cdot \mathcal{E} = \frac{\sigma \rho}{\epsilon} \tag{8.59}$$

Substituting Equation (8.59) into the continuity equation, we have

$$\frac{\sigma \rho}{\epsilon} = -\frac{\partial \rho}{\partial t} = -\frac{d\rho}{dt} \tag{8.60}$$

Since Equation (8.60) is a function of time only, we can write the equation as a total derivative. Equation (8.60) can be rearranged as

$$\frac{d\rho}{dt} + \left(\frac{\sigma}{\epsilon}\right)\rho = 0 \tag{8.61}$$

Equation (8.61) is a first-order differential equation whose solution is

$$\rho(t) = \rho(0)e^{-(t/\tau_d)} \tag{8.62}$$

where

$$\tau_d = \frac{\epsilon}{\sigma} \tag{8.63}$$

Dielectric relaxation time constant

and is called the dielectric relaxation time constant.

EXAMPLE 8.5

OBJECTIVE

To calculate the dielectric relaxation time constant for a particular semiconductor.

Consider n-type silicon at $T = 300$ K with an impurity concentration of $N_d = 10^{16}$ cm^{-3}.

■ **Solution**

The conductivity is found as

$$\sigma \approx e\mu_n N_d = (1.6 \times 10^{-19})(1200)(10^{16}) = 1.92 \ (\Omega\text{-cm})^{-1}$$

where the value of mobility is the approximate value found from Figure 4.3. The permittivity of silicon is

$$\epsilon = \epsilon_r \epsilon_0 = (11.7)(8.85 \times 10^{-14}) \ \text{F/cm}$$

The dielectric relaxation time constant is then

$$\tau_d = \frac{\epsilon}{\sigma} = \frac{(11.7)(8.85 \times 10^{-14})}{1.92} = 5.39 \times 10^{-13} \text{ s}$$

or

$$\tau_d = 0.539 \text{ ps}$$

■ **Comment**

Equation (8.62) then predicts that in approximately four time constants, or in approximately 2 ps, the net charge density is essentially zero; that is, quasi-neutrality has been achieved. Since the continuity equation, Equation (8.58), used in this analysis does not contain any generation or recombination terms, the initial positive charge is then neutralized by pulling in electrons from the bulk n-type material to create excess electrons. This process occurs very quickly compared to the normal excess carrier lifetimes of approximately 0.1 μs. The condition of quasi-charge neutrality is then justified.

Exercise Problem

EX8.5 Repeat Example 8.5 for the case of n-type GaAs doped to an impurity concentration of $N_d = 5 \times 10^{16}$ cm^{-3}.

(sd 6Z0'0 = $^{p}\tau$'s-A/$_z$ɯɔ 000ϛ ≈ $^u\eta$ əɯnss∀ ˙su∀)

8.3.5   Haynes–Shockley Experiment

We have derived the mathematics describing the behavior of excess carriers in a semiconductor. The Haynes–Shockley experiment was one of the first experiments to actually measure excess carrier behavior.

Figure 8.10 shows the basic experimental arrangement. The voltage source V_1 establishes an applied electric field $\mathcal{E}_0$ in the $+x$ direction in the n-type semiconductor sample. Excess carriers are effectively injected into the semiconductor at

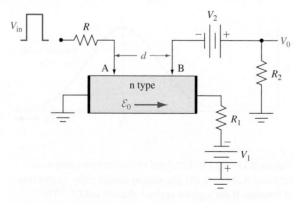

Figure 8.10 | The basic Haynes–Shockley experimental arrangement.

contact A. Contact B is a rectifying contact that is under reverse bias by the voltage source V_2. The contact B will collect a fraction of the excess carriers as they drift through the semiconductor. The collected carriers will generate an output voltage, V_0.

This experiment corresponds to the problem we discussed in Example 8.4. Figure 8.11 shows the excess carrier concentrations at contacts A and B for two conditions. Figure 8.11a shows the idealized excess carrier pulse at contact A at time $t = 0$. For a given electric field $\mathcal{E}_{01}$, the excess carriers will drift along the semiconductor producing an output voltage as a function of time given in Figure 8.11b. The peak of the pulse will arrive at contact B at time t_0. If the applied electric field is

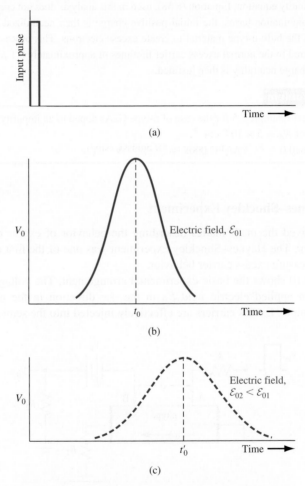

(a)

(b)

(c)

Figure 8.11 | (a) The idealized excess carrier pulse at terminal A at $t = 0$. (b) The excess carrier pulse versus time at terminal B for a given applied electric field. (c) The excess carrier pulse versus time at terminal B for a smaller applied electric field.

reduced to a value $\mathcal{E}_{02}$, $\mathcal{E}_{02} < \mathcal{E}_{01}$, the output voltage response at contact B will look approximately as shown in Figure 8.11c. For the smaller electric field, the drift velocity of the pulse of excess carriers is smaller, and so it will take a longer time for the pulse to reach the contact B. During this longer time period, there is more diffusion and more recombination. The excess carrier pulse shapes shown in Figure 8.11b and 8.11c are different for the two electric field conditions.

The minority-carrier mobility, lifetime, and diffusion coefficient can be determined from this single experiment. As a good first approximation, the peak of the minority-carrier pulse will arrive at contact B when the exponent involving distance and time in Equation (8.55) is zero, or

$$x - \mu_p \mathcal{E}_0 t = 0 \qquad (8.64a)$$

In this case $x = d$, where d is the distance between contacts A and B, and $t = t_0$, where t_0 is the time at which the peak of the pulse reaches contact B. The mobility may be calculated as

$$\mu_p = \frac{d}{\mathcal{E}_0 t_0} \qquad (8.64b)$$

Figure 8.12 again shows the output response as a function of time. At times t_1 and t_2, the magnitude of the excess concentration is e^{-1} of its peak value. If the time difference between t_1 and t_2 is not too large, $e^{-t/\tau_{p0}}$ and $(4\pi D_p t)^{1/2}$ do not change appreciably during this time; then the equation

$$(d - \mu_p \mathcal{E}_0 t)^2 = 4 D_p t \qquad (8.65)$$

is satisfied at both $t = t_1$ and $t = t_2$. If we set $t = t_1$ and $t = t_2$ in Equation (8.65) and add the two resulting equations, we can show that the diffusion coefficient is given by

$$D_p = \frac{(\mu_p \mathcal{E}_0)^2 (\Delta t)^2}{16 t_0} \qquad (8.66)$$

where

$$\Delta t = t_2 - t_1 \qquad (8.67)$$

The area S under the curve shown in Figure 8.12 is proportional to the number of excess holes that have not recombined with majority-carrier electrons. We may

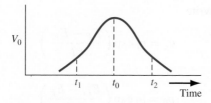

Figure 8.12 | The output excess carrier pulse versus time to determine the diffusion coefficient.

write

$$S = K \exp\left(\frac{-t_0}{\tau_{p0}}\right) = K \exp\left(\frac{-d}{\mu_p \mathcal{E}_0 \tau_{p0}}\right) \tag{8.68}$$

where K is a constant. By varying the electric field, the area under the curve will change. A plot of $\ln(S)$ as a function of $(d/\mu_p \mathcal{E}_0)$ will yield a straight line whose slope is $(1/\tau_{p0})$, so the minority-carrier lifetime can also be determined from this experiment.

The Haynes–Shockley experiment is elegant in the sense that the three basic processes of drift, diffusion, and recombination are all observed in a single experiment. The determination of mobility is straightforward and can yield accurate values. The determination of the diffusion coefficient and lifetime is more complicated and may lead to some inaccuracies.

TEST YOUR UNDERSTANDING

TYU8.1   Using the parameters given in Ex8.2, calculate the electron and hole diffusion current densities at $x = 10 \ \mu$m.

        (Ans. $J_p = +0.369$ A/cm^2, $J_n = -0.369$ A/cm^2.)

TYU8.2   The excess carrier concentration, given by Equation (8.55), is to be calculated at distances of one diffusion length away from the peak value. Using the parameters given in Ex8.4, calculate the values of δp for (a) $t = 1 \ \mu$s at (i) 1.093×10^{-2} cm and (ii) $x = -3.21 \times 10^{-3}$ cm; (b) $t = 5 \ \mu$s at (i) $x = 2.64 \times 10^{-2}$ cm and (ii) $x = 1.22 \times 10^{-2}$ cm; (c) $t = 15 \ \mu$s at (i) $x = 6.50 \times 10^{-2}$ cm and (ii) $x = 5.08 \times 10^{-2}$ cm.

        [Ans. (a) 20.9, (i) 20.9; (b) 11.4, (i) 11.4, (ii) 1.05, 1.05 (ii) (c)]

TYU8.3   Using the parameters given in TYU8.2, (a) plot $\delta p(x, t)$ from Equation (8.55) versus x for (i) $t = 1 \ \mu$s, (ii) $t = 5 \ \mu$s, and (iii) $t = 15 \ \mu$s, and (b) plot $\delta p(x, t)$ versus time for (i) $x = 10^{-2}$ cm, (ii) $x = 3 \times 10^{-2}$ cm, and (iii) $x = 6 \times 10^{-2}$ cm.

8.4 | QUASI-FERMI ENERGY LEVELS

Objective: Define and describe quasi-Fermi energy levels.

The thermal-equilibrium electron and hole concentrations are functions of the Fermi energy level. We can write

$$n_0 = n_i \exp\left(\frac{E_F - E_{Fi}}{kT}\right) \tag{8.69a}$$

and

$$p_0 = n_i \exp\left(\frac{E_{Fi} - E_F}{kT}\right) \tag{8.69b}$$

where E_F and E_{Fi} are the Fermi energy and intrinsic Fermi energy, respectively, and n_i is the intrinsic carrier concentration. Figure 8.13a shows the energy-band diagram

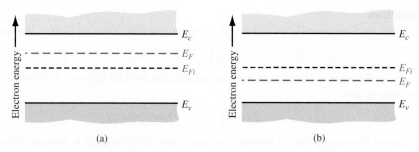

Figure 8.13 | Thermal-equilibrium energy-band diagrams for (a) n-type semiconductor and (b) p-type semiconductor.

for an n-type semiconductor in which $E_F > E_{Fi}$. For this case, we can note from Equation (8.69a) and (8.69b) that $n_0 > n_i$ and $p_0 < n_i$, as we would expect. Similarly, Figure 8.13b shows the energy-band diagram for a p-type semiconductor in which $E_F < E_{Fi}$. Again we can note from Equation (8.69a) and (8.69b) that $n_0 < n_i$ and $p_0 > n_i$, as we would expect for the p-type material. These results are for thermal equilibrium.

If excess carriers are created in a semiconductor, we are no longer in thermal equilibrium and the Fermi energy is strictly no longer defined. However, we can define a quasi-Fermi level for electrons and a quasi-Fermi level for holes that apply for nonequilibrium. If δn and δp are the excess electron and hole concentrations, respectively, we can write

$$n_0 + \delta n = n_i \exp\left(\frac{E_{Fn} - E_{Fi}}{kT}\right)$$ (8.70a)

Quasi-Fermi level for electrons

and

$$p_0 + \delta p = n_i \exp\left(\frac{E_{Fi} - E_{Fp}}{kT}\right)$$ (8.70b)

Quasi-Fermi level for holes

where E_{Fn} and E_{Fp} are the quasi-Fermi energy levels for electrons and holes, respectively. The total electron concentration and the total hole concentration are functions of the quasi-Fermi levels.

EXAMPLE 8.6

OBJECTIVE
To calculate the quasi-Fermi energy levels.

Consider an n-type semiconductor at $T = 300$ K with carrier concentrations of $n_0 = 10^{15}$ cm^{-3}, $n_i = 10^{10}$ cm^{-3}, and $p_0 = 10^5$ cm^{-3}. In nonequilibrium, assume that the excess carrier concentrations are $\delta n = \delta p = 10^{13}$ cm^{-3}.

■ **Solution**

The Fermi level for thermal equilibrium can be determined from Equation (8.69a). We have

$$E_F - E_{Fi} = kT \ln\left(\frac{n_0}{n_i}\right) = 0.2982 \text{ eV}$$

We can use Equation (8.70a) to determine the quasi-Fermi level for electrons in nonequilibrium. We can write

$$E_{Fn} - E_{Fi} = kT \ln\left(\frac{n_0 + \delta n}{n_i}\right) = 0.2984 \text{ eV}$$

Equation (8.70b) can be used to calculate the quasi-Fermi level for holes in nonequilibrium. We can write

$$E_{Fi} - E_{Fp} = kT \ln\left(\frac{p_0 + \delta p}{n_i}\right) = 0.179 \text{ eV}$$

■ **Comment**

We may note that the quasi-Fermi level for electrons is above E_{Fi} while the quasi-Fermi level for holes is below E_{Fi}.

Exercise Problem

EX8.6 Silicon at $T = 300$ K is doped at impurity concentrations of $N_d = 10^{16}$ cm^{-3} and $N_a = 0$. Excess carriers are generated such that the steady-state values are $\delta n = \delta p = 5 \times 10^{14}$ cm^{-3}. (a) Calculate the thermal equilibrium Fermi level with respect to E_{Fi}. (b) Determine E_{Fn} and E_{Fp} with respect to E_{Fi}.
[Ans. (a) $E_F - E_{Fi} = 0.3473$ eV;
(b) $E_{Fn} - E_{Fi} = 0.3486$ eV, $E_{Fi} - E_{Fp} = 0.2697$ eV]

Figure 8.14a shows the energy-band diagram with the Fermi energy level corresponding to thermal equilibrium. Figure 8.14b now shows the energy-band diagram under the nonequilibrium condition. Since the majority-carrier electron concentration does not change significantly for this low-injection condition, the quasi-Fermi level for electrons is not much different from the thermal-equilibrium Fermi level. The quasi-Fermi energy level for the minority-carrier holes is significantly different

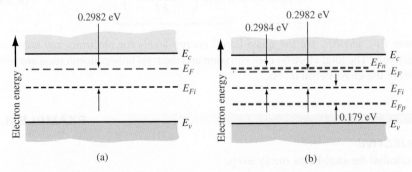

(a)   (b)

Figure 8.14 | (a) Thermal-equilibrium energy-band diagram for $N_d = 10^{15}$ cm^{-3} and $n_i = 10^{10}$ cm^{-3}. (b) Quasi-Fermi levels for electrons and holes if 10^{13} cm^{-3} excess carriers are present.

from the Fermi level and illustrates the fact that we have deviated from thermal equilibrium significantly. Since the electron concentration has increased, the quasi-Fermi level for electrons has moved slightly closer to the conduction band. The hole concentration has increased significantly so that the quasi-Fermi level for holes has moved much closer to the valence band. We will consider the quasi-Fermi energy levels again when we discuss forward-biased pn junctions.

TEST YOUR UNDERSTANDING

TYU8.4   Impurity concentrations of $N_d = 10^{15}$ cm^{-3} and $N_a = 6 \times 10^{15}$ cm^{-3} are added to silicon at $T = 300$ K. Excess carriers are generated in the material such that the steady-state concentrations are $\delta n = \delta p = 2 \times 10^{14}$ cm^{-3}.

(a) Find the thermal equilibrium Fermi level with respect to E_{Fi}.

(b) Calculate E_{Fn} and E_{Fp} with respect to E_{Fi}.

[Ans. (a) $E_{Fi} - E_F = 0.3294$ eV;

(b) $E_{Fn} - E_{Fi} = 0.2460$ eV, $E_{Fi} - E_{Fp} = 0.3304$ eV]

8.5 | EXCESS CARRIER LIFETIME

Objective: Analyze excess carrier recombination.

The rate at which excess electrons and holes recombine is an important characteristic of the semiconductor and influences many of the device characteristics, as we will see in Chapters 9 and 10. We considered recombination briefly at the beginning of this chapter and argued that the recombination rate is inversely proportional to the mean carrier lifetime. We have assumed up to this point that the mean carrier lifetime is simply a parameter of the semiconductor material.

We have been considering an ideal semiconductor in which electronic energy states do not exist within the forbidden-energy bandgap. This ideal effect is present in a perfect single-crystal material with an ideal periodic-potential function. In a real semiconductor material, defects occur within the crystal and disrupt the perfect periodic-potential function. If the density of these defects is not too great, the defects will create discrete electronic energy states within the forbidden-energy band. These allowed energy states may be the dominant effect in determining the mean carrier lifetime. The mean carrier lifetime may be determined from the Shockley–Read–Hall theory of recombination.

8.5.1 Shockley–Read–Hall Theory of Recombination

An allowed energy state, also called a *trap,* within the forbidden bandgap may act as a *recombination center,* capturing both electrons and holes with almost equal probability. This equal probability of capture means that the capture cross sections for electrons and holes are approximately equal. The Shockley–Read–Hall theory of recombination assumes that a single recombination center, or trap, exists at an energy E_t within the bandgap. There are four basic processes, shown in Figure 8.15,

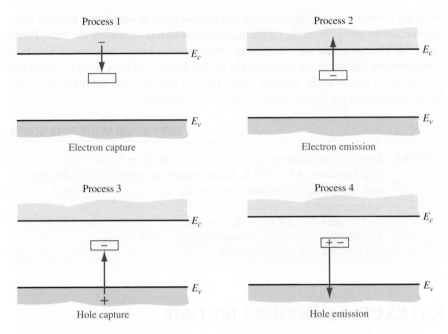

Figure 8.15 | The four basic trapping and emission processes for the case of an acceptor-type trap.

that may occur at this single trap. We will assume that the trap is an acceptor-type trap; that is, it is negatively charged when it contains an electron and is neutral when it does not contain an electron.

The four basic processes are as follows:

Process 1: The capture of an electron from the conduction band by an initially neutral empty trap.

Process 2: The inverse of process 1—the emission of an electron that is initially occupying a trap level back into the conduction band.

Process 3: The capture of a hole from the valence band by a trap containing an electron. (Or we can consider the process to be the emission of an electron from the trap into the valence band.)

Process 4: The inverse of process 3—the emission of a hole from a neutral trap into the valence band. (Or we can consider this process to be the capture of an electron from the valence band.)

The recombination rate of electrons and holes due to the recombination center at $E = E_t$ is given by

$$R_n = R_p \equiv R = \frac{C_n C_p N_t (np - n_i^2)}{C_n (n + n') + C_p (p + p')} \quad (8.71)$$

where C_n is a constant proportional to the electron-capture rate, C_p is a constant proportional to the hole-capture rate, and N_t is the total concentration of trapping centers. The parameters n' and p' are related to the position of the trap within the bandgap. If the trap is near midgap, then $n' \approx p' \approx n_i$.

If we consider thermal equilibrium, then $np = n_0 p_0 = n_i^2$, so that $R_n = R_p = 0$. Equation (8.71), then, is the recombination rate of excess electrons and holes. Since R in Equation (8.71) is the recombination rate of excess carriers, we can write

$$R = \frac{\delta n}{\tau} \tag{8.72}$$

where δn is the excess carrier concentration and τ is the lifetime of the excess carriers.

8.5.2 Limits of Extrinsic Doping and Low Injection

We simplified the ambipolar transport equation, Equation (8.28), from a nonlinear differential equation to a linear differential equation by applying limits of extrinsic doping and low injection. We can apply these same limits to the recombination rate equation.

Consider an n-type semiconductor under low injection. Then

$$n_0 \gg p_0, \quad n_0 \gg \delta p, \quad n_0 \gg n', \quad n_0 \gg p'$$

where δp is the excess minority-carrier hole concentration. The assumptions of $n_0 \gg n'$ and $n_0 \gg p'$ imply that the trap level energy is near midgap so that n' and p' are not too different from the intrinsic carrier concentration. With these assumptions, Equation (8.71) reduces to

$$R = C_p N_t \delta p \tag{8.73}$$

The recombination rate of excess carriers in the n-type semiconductor is a function of the parameter C_p, which is related to the minority carrier hole capture cross section. The recombination rate, then, is a function of the minority-carrier parameter in the same way that the ambipolar transport parameters reduced to their minority-carrier values.

The recombination rate is related to the mean carrier lifetime. Comparing Equations (8.72) and (8.73), we can write

Excess carrier hole lifetime

$$R = \frac{\delta n}{\tau} = C_p N_t \delta p \equiv \frac{\delta p}{\tau_{p0}} \tag{8.74}$$

where

$$\tau_{p0} = \frac{1}{C_p N_t} \tag{8.75}$$

and where τ_{p0} is defined as the excess minority-carrier hole lifetime. If the trap concentration increases, the probability of excess carrier recombination increases; thus, the excess minority-carrier lifetime decreases.

Similarly, if we have a strongly extrinsic p-type material under low injection, we can assume that

$$p_0 \gg n_0, \quad p_0 \gg \delta n, \quad p_0 \gg n', \quad p_0 \gg p'$$

Excess carrier electron lifetime

The lifetime then becomes that of the excess minority-carrier electron lifetime, or

$$\tau_{n0} = \frac{1}{C_n N_t} \tag{8.76}$$

Again note that for the n-type material, the lifetime is a function of C_p, which is related to the capture rate of the minority carrier hole. And for the p-type material, the lifetime is a function of C_n, which is related to the capture rate of the minority-carrier electron. The excess carrier lifetime for an extrinsic material under low injection reduces to that of the minority carrier.

EXAMPLE 8.7

OBJECTIVE
To determine the excess carrier lifetime in an intrinsic semiconductor.

If we substitute the definitions of excess carrier lifetimes from Equations (8.75) and (8.76) into Equation (8.71), the recombination rate can be written as

$$R = \frac{(np - n_i^2)}{\tau_{p0}(n + n') + \tau_{n0}(p + p')} \tag{8.77}$$

Consider an intrinsic semiconductor containing excess carriers. Then $n = n_i + \delta n$ and $p = n_i + \delta n$. Also assume that $n' = p' = n_i$.

■ Solution
Equation (8.77) now becomes

$$R = \frac{2n_i \delta n + (\delta n)^2}{(2n_i + \delta n)(\tau_{p0} + \tau_{n0})}$$

If we also assume very low injection, so that $\delta n \ll 2n_i$, then we can write

$$R = \frac{\delta n}{\tau_{p0} + \tau_{n0}} = \frac{\delta n}{\tau}$$

where τ is the excess carrier lifetime. We see that $\tau = \tau_{p0} + \tau_{n0}$ in the intrinsic material.

■ Comment
The excess carrier lifetime increases as we change from an extrinsic to an intrinsic semiconductor.

Exercise Problem

EX8.7   Consider silicon at $T = 300$ K doped at concentrations of $N_d = 10^{15}$ cm^{-3} and $N_a = 0$. Assume that $n' = p' = n_i$ in the excess carrier recombination rate equation and assume parameter values of $\tau_{n0} = \tau_{p0} = 5 \times 10^{-7}$ s. Calculate the recombination rate of excess carriers if $\delta n = \delta p = 10^{14}$ cm^{-3}.

(Ans. 1.83×10^{20} cm^{-3} s^{-1})

Intuitively, we can see that the number of majority carriers that are available for recombining with excess minority carriers decreases as the extrinsic semiconductor becomes intrinsic. Since there are fewer carriers available for recombining in the intrinsic material, the mean lifetime of an excess carrier increases.

8.6 | SURFACE EFFECTS

Objective: Qualitatively describe surface effects on excess carrier recombination.

In all previous discussions, we have implicitly assumed the semiconductors were infinite in extent; thus, we were not concerned with any boundary conditions at a semiconductor surface. In any real application of semiconductors, the material is not infinitely large and therefore surfaces do exist between the semiconductor and an adjacent medium.

8.6.1 Surface States

When a semiconductor is abruptly terminated, the perfect periodic nature of the idealized single-crystal lattice ends abruptly at the surface. The disruption of the periodic-potential function results in allowed electronic energy states within the energy bandgap. In Section 8.5, we argued that simple defects in the semiconductor would create discrete energy states within the bandgap. The abrupt termination of the periodic potential at the surface results in a distribution of allowed energy states within the bandgap, shown schematically in Figure 8.16 along with the discrete energy states in the bulk semiconductor.

The Shockley–Read–Hall recombination theory shows that the excess minority-carrier lifetime is inversely proportional to the density of trap states. We can argue that, since the density of traps at the surface is larger than in the bulk, the excess minority-carrier lifetime at the surface will be smaller than the corresponding lifetime in the bulk material. If we consider an extrinsic n-type semiconductor, for example, the recombination rate of excess carriers in the bulk, given by Equation (8.74), is

$$R = \frac{\delta p}{\tau_{p0}} \equiv \frac{\delta p_B}{\tau_{p0}} \tag{8.78}$$

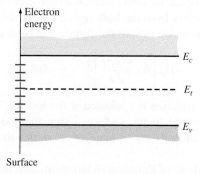

Figure 8.16 | Distribution of surface states within the forbidden bandgap.

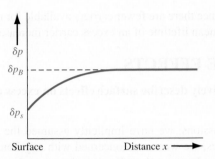

Figure 8.17 | Steady-state excess hole concentration versus distance from a semiconductor surface.

where δp_B is the concentration of excess minority carrier holes in the bulk material. We can write a similar expression for the recombination rate of excess carriers at the surface as

$$R_s = \frac{\delta p_s}{\tau_{p0s}} \tag{8.79}$$

where δp_s is the excess minority-carrier hole concentration at the surface and τ_{p0s} is the excess minority-carrier hole lifetime at the surface.

Assume that excess carriers are being generated at a constant rate throughout the entire semiconductor material. We showed that, in steady state, the generation rate is equal to the recombination rate for the case of a homogeneous, infinite semiconductor. Using this argument, the recombination rates at the surface and in the bulk material must be equal. Since $\tau_{p0s} < \tau_{p0}$, the excess minority-carrier concentration at the surface is smaller than the excess minority-carrier concentration in the bulk region, or $\delta p_s < \delta p_B$. Figure 8.17 shows an example of the excess carrier concentration plotted as a function of distance from the semiconductor surface.

8.6.2   Surface Recombination Velocity

A gradient in the excess carrier concentration exists near the surface as shown in Figure 8.17; excess carriers from the bulk region diffuse toward the surface where they recombine. This diffusion toward the surface can be described by the equation

$$-D_p \left[\hat{n} \cdot \frac{d(\delta p)}{dx} \right]\bigg|_{\text{surf}} = s\delta p|_{\text{surf}} \tag{8.80}$$

where each side of the equation is evaluated at the surface. The parameter $\hat{n}$ is the unit outward vector normal to the surface. Using the geometry of Figure 8.17, $d(\delta p)/dx$ is a positive quantity and $\hat{n}$ is negative, so that the parameter s is a positive quantity.

A dimensional analysis of Equation (8.80) shows that the parameter s has units of cm/sec, or velocity. The parameter s is called the *surface recombination velocity*. If the excess concentrations at the surface and in the bulk region were equal, then the gradient term would be zero and the surface recombination velocity would be zero. As the excess concentration at the surface becomes smaller, the gradient term becomes larger, and the surface recombination velocity increases. If the excess carrier concentration at the surface were to become zero, the surface recombination velocity would be infinite. The surface recombination velocity gives some indication of the surface characteristics as compared with the bulk region.

8.7 | SUMMARY

1. The processes of excess electron and hole generation and recombination were reviewed. The excess carrier generation and recombination rates were defined. The recombination rate can be written as $R = \delta n / \tau$, where δn is the excess carrier concentration and τ is the excess carrier lifetime.

2. The continuity equations and the time-dependent diffusion equations were derived. These equations describe the behavior of excess carriers in a semiconductor.

3. A. Excess electrons and holes do not move independently of each other, but move together. This common movement is called ambipolar transport.
   B. The ambipolar transport equation was derived and limits of low-injection and extrinsic doping were applied to the coefficients. Under these conditions, the excess electrons and holes diffuse and drift together with the characteristics of the minority carrier, a result that is fundamental to the behavior of semiconductor devices.
   C. The concept of excess carrier lifetime was developed.
   D. Examples of excess carrier behavior as a function of time, as a function of space, and as a function of both time and space were examined.

4. The quasi-Fermi level for electrons and quasi-Fermi level for holes were defined. These parameters characterize the total electron and hole concentrations in a semiconductor in nonequilibrium.

5. The Shockley–Read–Hall theory of recombination was considered. Expressions for the excess minority-carrier lifetime were developed.

6. The effect of a semiconductor surface influences the behavior of excess electrons and holes. The surface recombination velocity was defined.

CHECKPOINT

After studying this chapter, the reader should have the ability to

1. Discuss the processes of excess electron and hole generation and recombination, and define the excess carrier recombination rate.

2. Describe, qualitatively, the method of deriving the continuity equations and the time-dependent diffusion equations.

3. A. Describe the concept of ambipolar transport.
   B. Define the concept of low-injection and the concept of extrinsic doping.
   C. Describe the concept of excess minority-carrier lifetime.
   D. Describe the behavior of excess carriers under various boundary conditions.

4. Define the quasi-Fermi level for electrons and quasi-Fermi level for holes.

5. Describe the basic idea of the Shockley–Read–Hall theory of recombination.

6. Describe, qualitatively, the effect of a surface on the excess carrier concentration.

REVIEW QUESTIONS

1. A.   Define the excess carrier recombination rate in terms of the excess carrier concentration and lifetime.

    B.   Discuss the process by which an allowed electronic energy state near midgap can aid the process of electron–hole generation and electron–hole recombination.

2. Discuss the process by which the continuity equation for holes is derived.

3. A.   What is the concept of ambipolar transport?

    B.   Define the concept of low injection and the concept of extrinsic doping for a p-type material.

    C.   Describe the behavior of uniformly generated excess holes in a p-type material for $t > 0$ if an external source is applied at $t = 0$. What is the excess carrier concentration for $t = \infty$?

    D.   Describe the behavior of excess holes generated at $x = 0$ and $t = 0$ in a p-type semiconductor with an applied electric field in the positive x direction.

4. Define the quasi-Fermi level for electrons and the quasi-Fermi level for holes.

5. The excess carrier hole recombination rate in an n-type semiconductor is a function of three parameters. What are these three parameters?

6. Why is the recombination rate of excess carriers at a surface greater, in general, than the recombination rate in the bulk semiconductor?

PROBLEMS

(*Note:* Use the semiconductor parameters listed in Appendix B if they are not specifically given in a problem. Assume $T = 300$ K.)

Section 8.1   Carrier Generation and Recombination

8.1   Consider a semiconductor in which $n_0 = 10^{15}$ cm^{-3} and $n_i = 10^{10}$ cm^{-3}. Assume that the excess carrier lifetime is 10^{-6} s. Determine the electron–hole recombination rate if the excess hole concentration is $\delta p = 5 \times 10^{13}$ cm^{-3}.

8.2   A semiconductor, in thermal equilibrium, has a hole concentration of $p_0 = 10^{16}$ cm^{-3} and an intrinsic concentration of $n_i = 10^{10}$ cm^{-3}. The minority-carrier lifetime is 2×10^{-7} s. (*a*) Determine the thermal-equilibrium recombination rate of electrons. (*b*) Determine the change in the recombination rate of electrons if an excess electron concentration of $\delta n = 10^{12}$ cm^{-3} exists.

Section 8.2   Analysis of Excess Carriers

8.3   Derive Equation (8.16) from Equations (8.7) and (8.9).

8.4   Consider a one-dimensional hole flux as shown in Figure 8.1. If the generation rate of holes in this differential volume is $g_p = 10^{20}$ cm^{-3}-s^{-1} and the recombination rate is 2×10^{19} cm^{-3}-s^{-1}, what must be the gradient in the particle current density to maintain a steady-state hole concentration?

8.5   Repeat Problem 8.4 if the generation rate becomes zero.

Section 8.3   Ambipolar Transport

8.6   Starting with the continuity equations given by Equations (8.18) and (8.19), derive the ambipolar transport equation given by Equation (8.28).

8.7   A sample of Ge at $T = 300$ K has a uniform donor concentration of 2×10^{13} cm^{-3}. The excess carrier lifetime is found to be $\tau_{p0} = 24$ μs. Determine the ambipolar diffusion coefficient and the ambipolar mobility. What are the electron and hole lifetimes?

8.8   Assume that an n-type semiconductor is uniformly illuminated, producing a uniform excess generation rate g'. Show that in steady state the change in the semiconductor conductivity is given by

$$\Delta\sigma = e(\mu_n + \mu_p)\tau_{p0}g'$$

8.9   Light is incident on a silicon sample starting at $t = 0$ and generating excess carriers uniformly throughout the silicon for $t > 0$. The generation rate is $g' = 5 \times 10^{21}$ cm^{-3} s^{-1}. The silicon ($T = 300$ K) is n type with $N_d = 5 \times 10^{16}$ cm^{-3} and $N_a = 0$. Let $n_i = 1.5 \times 10^{10}$ cm^{-3}, $\tau_{n0} = 10^{-6}$ s, and $\tau_{p0} = 10^{-7}$ s. Also let $\mu_n = 1000$ cm^2/V-s and $\mu_p = 420$ cm^2/V-s. Determine the conductivity of the silicon as a function of time for $t \geq 0$.

8.10   An n-type gallium arsenide semiconductor is doped with $N_d = 10^{16}$ cm^{-3} and $N_a = 0$. The minority-carrier lifetime is $\tau_{p0} = 2 \times 10^{-7}$ s. Calculate the steady-state increase in conductivity and the steady-state excess carrier recombination rate if a uniform generation rate, $g' = 2 \times 10^{21}$ cm^{-3}-s^{-1}, is incident on the semiconductor.

8.11   A silicon sample at $T = 300$ K is n type with $N_d = 5 \times 10^{16}$ cm^{-3} and $N_a = 0$. The sample has a length of 0.1 cm and a cross-sectional area of 10^{-4} cm^2. A voltage of 5 V is applied between the ends of the sample. For $t < 0$, the sample has been illuminated with light, producing an excess carrier generation rate of $g' = 5 \times 10^{21}$ cm^{-3}-s^{-1} uniformly throughout the entire silicon. The minority-carrier lifetime is $\tau_{p0} = 3 \times 10^{-7}$ s. At $t = 0$, the light is turned off. Derive the expression for the current in the sample as a function of time $t \geq 0$. (Neglect surface effects.)

8.12   Consider a homogeneous gallium arsenide semiconductor at $T = 300$ K with $N_a = 10^{16}$ cm^{-3} and $N_d = 0$. A light source is turned on at $t = 0$ producing a uniform generation rate of $g' = 10^{20}$ cm^{-3}-s^{-1}. The electric field is zero. (a) Derive the expression for the excess carrier concentration and excess carrier recombination rate as a function of time. (b) If the maximum, steady-state, excess carrier concentration is to be 1×10^{14} cm^{-3}, determine the maximum value of the minority-carrier lifetime. (c) Determine the times at which the excess minority-carrier concentration will be equal to (i) three-fourths, (ii) one-half, and (iii) one-fourth of the steady-state value.

8.13   In a silicon semiconductor material at $T = 300$ K, the doping concentrations are $N_d = 10^{15}$ cm^{-3} and $N_a = 0$. The equilibrium recombination rate is $R_{p0} = 10^{11}$ cm^{-3}-s^{-1}. A uniform generation rate produces an excess carrier concentration of $\delta n = \delta p = 10^{14}$ cm^{-3}. (a) By what factor does the total recombination rate increase? (b) What is the excess carrier lifetime?

8.14   Consider a silicon material doped with 3×10^{16} cm^{-3} donor atoms. At $t = 0$, a light source is turned on, producing a uniform generation rate of $g' = 2 \times 10^{20}$ cm^{-3}-s^{-1}. At $t = 10^{-7}$ s, the light source is turned off. Determine the excess minority-carrier concentration as a function of t for $0 \leq t \leq \infty$. Let $\tau_{p0} = 10^{-7}$ s. Plot the excess minority-carrier concentration as a function of time.

8.15   A semiconductor has the following properties:

$$D_n = 25 \text{ cm}^2/\text{s} \qquad \tau_{n0} = 10^{-6} \text{ s}$$
$$D_p = 10 \text{ cm}^2/\text{s} \qquad \tau_{p0} = 10^{-7} \text{ s}$$

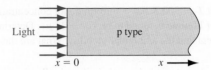

Figure P8.16 | Figure for Problems 8.16 and 8.18.

The semiconductor is a homogeneous, p-type ($N_a = 10^{17}$ cm^{-3}) material in thermal equilibrium for $t \leq 0$. At $t = 0$, an external source is turned on, which produces excess carriers uniformly at the rate of $g' = 10^{20}$ cm^{-3}-s^{-1}. At $t = 2 \times 10^{-6}$ s, the external source is turned off. (a) Derive the expression for the excess electron concentration as a function of time for $0 \leq t \leq \infty$. (b) Determine the value of the excess electron concentration at (i) $t = 0$, (ii) $t = 2 \times 10^{-6}$ s, and (iii) $t = \infty$. (c) Plot the excess electron concentration as a function of time.

8.16 Consider a bar of p-type silicon material that is homogeneously doped to a value of 3×10^{15} cm^{-3} at $T = 300$ K. The applied electric field is zero. A light source is incident on the end of the semiconductor as shown in Figure P8.16. The excess carrier concentration generated at $x = 0$ is $\delta p(0) = \delta n(0) = 10^{13}$ cm^{-3}. Assume the following parameters (neglect surface effects):

$$\mu_n = 1200 \text{ cm}^2/\text{V-s} \qquad \tau_{n0} = 5 \times 10^{-7} \text{ s}$$
$$\mu_p = 400 \text{ cm}^2/\text{V-s} \qquad \tau_{p0} = 1 \times 10^{-7} \text{ s}$$

(a) Calculate the steady-state excess electron and hole concentrations as a function of distance into the semiconductor. (b) Calculate the electron diffusion current density as a function of x.

8.17 The $x = 0$ end of an $N_a = 1 \times 10^{14}$ cm^{-3} doped semi-infinite ($x \geq 0$) bar of silicon maintained at $T = 300$ K is attached to a "minority carrier digester" which makes $n_p = 0$ at $x = 0$ (n_p is the minority-carrier electron concentration in a p-type semiconductor). The electric field is zero. (a) Determine the thermal-equilibrium values of n_{p0} and p_{p0}. (b) What is the excess minority-carrier concentration at $x = 0$? (c) Derive the expression for the steady-state excess minority-carrier concentration as a function of x.

8.18 In a p-type silicon semiconductor, excess carriers are being generated at the end of the semiconductor bar at $x = 0$ as shown in Figure P8.16. The doping concentration is $N_a = 5 \times 10^{16}$ cm^{-3} and $N_d = 0$. The steady-state excess carrier concentration at $x = 0$ is 10^{15} cm^{-3}. (Neglect surface effects.) The applied electric field is zero. Assume that $\tau_{n0} = \tau_{p0} = 8 \times 10^{-7}$ s. (a) Calculate δn, and the electron and hole diffusion current densities at $x = 0$. (b) Repeat part (a) for $x = L_n$.

*8.19 Consider an n-type silicon sample. Excess carriers are generated at $x = 0$ such as shown in Figure 8.5. A constant electric field $\mathcal{E}_0$ is applied in the $+x$ direction. Show that the steady-state excess carrier concentration is given by

$$\delta p(x) = A \exp (s_- x) \qquad x > 0 \qquad \text{and} \qquad \delta p(x) = A \exp (s_+ x) \qquad x < 0$$

where

$$s_\mp = \frac{1}{L_p} \left[\beta \mp \sqrt{1 + \beta^2} \right]$$

and

$$\beta = \frac{\mu_p L_p \mathcal{E}_0}{2D_p}$$

8.20 Plot the excess carrier concentration $\delta p(x)$ versus x from Problem 8.19 for (a) $\mathcal{E}_0 = 0$ and (b) $\mathcal{E}_0 = 10$ V/cm. Assume $L_p = 10\,\mu$m.

*8.21 Consider the semiconductor described in Problem 8.16. Assume a constant electric field $\mathcal{E}_0$ is applied in the $+x$ direction. (a) Derive the expression for the steady-state excess-electron concentration. (Assume the solution is of the form e^{-ax}.) (b) Plot δn versus x for (i) $\mathcal{E}_0 = 0$ and (ii) $\mathcal{E}_0 = 12$ V/cm. (c) Explain the general characteristics of the two curves plotted in part (b).

8.22 Assume that a p-type semiconductor is in thermal equilibrium for $t < 0$ and has an infinite minority-carrier lifetime. Also assume that the semiconductor is uniformly illuminated, resulting in a uniform generation rate, $g'(t)$, which is given by

$$\begin{aligned} g'(t) &= G_0' \qquad \text{for } 0 < t < T \\ g'(t) &= 0 \qquad \text{for } t < 0 \text{ and } t > T \end{aligned}$$

where G_0' is a constant. Find the excess minority-carrier concentration as a function of time.

*8.23 Consider the n-type semiconductor shown in Figure P8.23. Illumination produces a constant excess carrier generation rate, G_0', in the region $-L < x < +L$. Assume that the minority-carrier lifetime is infinite and assume that the excess minority-carrier hole concentration is zero at $x = -3L$ and at $x = +3L$. Find the steady-state excess minority-carrier concentration versus x, for the case of low injection and for zero applied electric field.

8.24 An n-type germanium sample is used in the Haynes–Shockley experiment. The length of the sample is 1 cm and the applied voltage is $V_1 = 2.5$ V. The contacts A and B are separated by 0.75 cm. The peak of the pulse arrives at contact B 160 μs after carrier injection at contact A. The width of the pulse is $\Delta t = 75.5\,\mu$s. Determine the hole mobility and diffusion coefficient. Compare the results with the Einstein relation.

8.25 Consider the function $f(x, t) = (4\pi Dt)^{-1/2} \exp\left(-x^2/4Dt\right)$. (a) Show that this function is a solution to the differential equation $D(\partial^2 f/\partial x^2) = \partial f/\partial t$. (b) Show that the integral of the function $f(x, t)$ over x from $-\infty$ to $+\infty$ is unity for all values of time. (c) Show that this function approaches a δ function as t approaches zero.

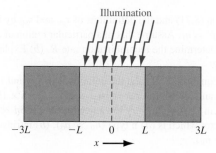

Figure P8.23 | Figure for Problem 8.23.

8.26   The basic equation in the Haynes–Shockley experiment is given by Equation (8.55). (a) Plot $\delta p(x, t)$ versus x for various values of t and for $\mathcal{E}_0 = 0$ as well as for $\mathcal{E}_0 \neq 0$. (b) Plot $\delta p(x, t)$ versus t for various values of x and for $\mathcal{E}_0 = 0$ as well as for $\mathcal{E}_0 \neq 0$.

Section 8.4   Quasi-Fermi Energy Levels

8.27   An n-type silicon sample with $N_d = 10^{16}$ cm^{-3} is steadily illuminated such that $g' = 10^{21}$ cm^{-3}-s^{-1}. If $\tau_{n0} = \tau_{p0} = 10^{-6}$ s, calculate the position of the quasi-Fermi levels for electrons and holes with respect to the intrinsic level (assume that $n_i = 1.5 \times 10^{10}$ cm^{-3}). Plot these levels on an energy-band diagram.

8.28   Consider a p-type silicon semiconductor at $T = 300$ K doped at $N_a = 5 \times 10^{15}$ cm^{-3}. (a) Determine the position of the Fermi level with respect to the intrinsic Fermi level. (b) Excess carriers are generated such that the excess carrier concentration is 10 percent of the thermal-equilibrium majority-carrier concentration. Determine the quasi-Fermi levels with respect to the intrinsic Fermi level. (c) Plot the Fermi level and quasi-Fermi levels with respect to the intrinsic level.

8.29   Consider an n-type gallium arsenide semiconductor at $T = 300$ K doped at $N_d = 5 \times 10^{16}$ cm^{-3}. (a) Determine $E_{Fn} - E_F$ if the excess carrier concentration is 0.1 N_d. (b) Determine $E_{Fi} - E_{Fp}$.

8.30   A p-type gallium arsenide semiconductor at $T = 300$ K is doped at $N_a = 10^{16}$ cm^{-3}. The excess carrier concentration varies linearly from 10^{14} cm^{-3} to zero over a distance of 50 μm. Plot the position of the quasi-Fermi levels with respect to the intrinsic Fermi level versus distance.

8.31   Consider p-type silicon at $T = 300$ K doped to $N_a = 5 \times 10^{14}$ cm^{-3}. Assume excess carriers are present and assume that $E_F - E_{Fp} = (0.01)kT$. (a) Does this condition correspond to low injection? Why or why not? (b) Determine $E_{Fn} - E_{Fi}$.

8.32   An n-type silicon sample is doped with donors at a concentration of $N_d = 10^{16}$ cm^{-3}. Excess carriers are generated such that the excess hole concentration is given by $\delta p(x) = 10^{14} \exp{(-x/10^{-4})}$ cm^{-3}. Plot the function $E_{Fi} - E_{Fp}$ versus x over the range $0 \leq x \leq 4 \times 10^{-4}$.

8.33   For a p-type silicon material doped at $N_a = 10^{16}$ cm^{-3}, plot $E_{Fn} - E_F$ versus δn over the range $0 \leq \delta n \leq 10^{14}$ cm^{-3}. Use a log scale for δn.

Section 8.5   Excess Carrier Lifetime

8.34   Consider Equation (8.71) and the definitions of τ_{p0} and τ_{n0} by Equations (8.75) and (8.76). Let $n' = p' = n_i$. Assume that in a particular region of a semiconductor, $n = p = 0$. (a) Determine the recombination rate R. (b) Explain what this result means physically.

8.35   Again consider Equation (8.71) and the definitions of τ_{p0} and τ_{n0} given by Equations (8.75) and (8.76). Let $\tau_{p0} = 10^{-7}$ s and $\tau_{n0} = 5 \times 10^{-7}$ s. Also let $n' = p' = n_i = 10^{10}$ cm^{-3}. Assume very low injection so that $\delta n \ll n_i$. Calculate $R/\delta n$ for a semiconductor which is (a) n type ($n_0 \gg p_0$), (b) intrinsic ($n_0 = p_0 = n_i$), and (c) p type ($p_0 \gg n_0$).

READING LIST

1. Brennan, K. F. *The Physics of Semiconductors with Applications to Optoelectronic Devices.* New York: Cambridge University Press, 1999.

2. Bube, R. H. *Photoelectronic Properties of Semiconductors,* New York: Cambridge University Press, 1992.

*3. deCogan, D. *Solid State Devices: A Quantum Physics Approach.* New York: Springer-Verlag, 1987.

4. Hall, R. H. "Electron-Hole Recombination." *Physical Review* 87, no. 2 (July 15, 1952), p. 387.

5. Haynes, J. R., and W. Shockley. "The Mobility and Life of Injected Holes and Electrons in Germanium." *Physical Review* 81, no. 5 (March 1, 1951), pp. 835–43.

*6. Hess, K. *Advanced Theory of Semiconductor Devices.* Englewood Cliffs, NJ: Prentice-Hall, 1988.

7. Kano, K. *Semiconductor Devices.* Upper Saddle River, NJ: Prentice-Hall, 1998.

8. Kingston, R. H. *Semiconductor Surface Physics.* Philadelphia: University of Pennsylvania Press, 1957.

9. McKelvey, J. P. *Solid State Physics for Engineering and Materials Science.* Malabar, FL.: Krieger Publishing, 1993.

10. Neamen, D. A. *Semiconductor Physics and Devices: Basic Principles,* 3rd ed. New York: McGraw-Hill, 2003.

11. Pierret, R. F. *Semiconductor Device Fundamentals.* Reading, MA: Addison-Wesley, 1996.

12. Shockley, W., and W. T. Read, Jr. "Statistics of the Recombinations of Holes and Electrons." *Physical Review* 87, no. 5 (September 1, 1952), pp. 835–42.

13. Singh, J. *Semiconductor Devices: An Introduction.* New York: McGraw-Hill, 1994.

14. Singh, J. *Semiconductor Devices: Basic Principles.* New York: John Wiley and Sons, 2001.

15. Streetman, B. G., and S. Banerjee. *Solid State Electronic Devices.* 5th ed. Upper Saddle River, NJ: Prentice-Hall, 2000.

*16. Wang, S. *Fundamentals of Semiconductor Theory and Device Physics.* Englewood Cliffs, NJ: Prentice-Hall, 1989.

9

The pn Junction and Schottky Diodes

I n Chapter 5, we discussed the electrostatics of the pn junction and Schottky barrier junction in thermal equilibrium and under reverse bias. We determined the built-in potential barrier at thermal equilibrium, calculated the electric field in the space charge region, and determined space charge widths. We also considered the junction capacitance. In this chapter, we will consider the pn and Schottky barrier junctions with a forward-bias voltage applied. The potential barrier of the junction is lowered when a forward-bias voltage is applied, allowing carriers to flow across the space charge region. When holes diffuse from the p region across the space charge region of the pn junction into the n region, they become excess minority carrier holes and are subject to the excess minority carrier diffusion, drift, and recombination processes discussed in Chapter 8—ambipolar transport. Likewise, when electrons from the n region diffuse across the space charge region of the pn junction into the p region, they become excess minority-carrier electrons and are subject to these same ambipolar transport processes. We will develop the current–voltage relationship of the forward-biased pn junction as well as the Schottky barrier junction.

9.0 | PREVIEW

In this chapter, we will

1. Revisit the pn junction and Schottky barrier structures and the characteristics of the zero- and reverse-biased junctions.
2. Derive the ideal current–voltage relationship of the pn junction diode.
3. Develop the ideal current–voltage relationship of the Schottky barrier diode.
4. Develop the small-signal equivalent circuit of the pn junction diode.

5. Analyze the generation and recombination currents in the space charge region of the pn junction diode.

6. Discuss the breakdown voltage in the diode.

7. Consider the switching characteristics of the diode.

Historical Insight

A key motivation for research in semiconductors came during World War II from the radar project. A key component of the radar system was a device that could detect a microwave signal. Eventually, germanium diodes were mass-produced and used in the radar systems. Work on semiconductor devices increased as a result of this success.

Present-Day Insight

The pn junction continues to be a basic building block in semiconductor devices, and the theory of the pn junction is still fundamental in the physics of semiconductor devices. The pn junction by itself performs nonlinear rectification. Other semiconductor devices are formed by combining two or more pn junctions in various configurations.

9.1 | THE pn AND SCHOTTKY BARRIER JUNCTIONS REVISITED

Objective: Revisit the pn junction and Schottky barrier structures and the characteristics of the zero- and reverse-biased junctions.

The structures of the pn and Schottky barrier junctions were presented in Chapter 5. The zero- and reverse-biased characteristics of the devices were analyzed. In this chapter we develop the forward-biased characteristics of these devices.

9.1.1 The pn Junction

Figure 9.1a shows a simplified geometry of a pn junction. Keep in mind that, in general, the entire semiconductor is a single-crystal lattice with one region doped with acceptors to form the p region and the adjacent region doped with donors to form the n region. In most cases, we will assume that each region is uniformly doped. As discussed in Chapter 5, a space charge region is formed on either side of the metallurgical junction, as shown in Figure 9.1b. Electrons have diffused from the n region and uncovered positively charged donor ions while holes have diffused from the p region and uncovered negatively charged acceptor ions. There is a separation of charge within the space charge region so an electric field is created. Since the charge is uniform in each region, the electric field is a linear function of distance. The maximum electric field occurs at the metallurgical junction.

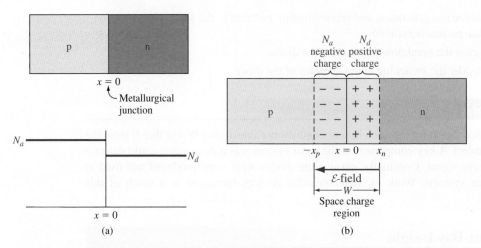

Figure 9.1 | (a) Simplified geometry of a pn junction showing uniformly doped regions. (b) The pn junction showing depletion regions, space charge, and electric field.

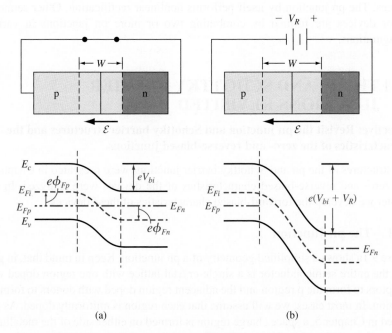

Figure 9.2 | The pn junction and energy-band diagrams for (a) zero bias and (b) reverse bias.

Figure 9.2a shows the energy-band diagram of a pn junction in thermal equilibrium (zero bias). As shown previously, the Fermi energy is a constant through the entire structure. A built-in potential barrier is formed between the n and p regions that establishes thermal equilibrium. Majority-carrier electrons in the n region and majority carrier holes in the p region are held back so there is no net flow of carriers for this condition.

From the figure, we see that the built-in potential barrier is given by

$$V_{bi} = |\phi_{Fp}| + |\phi_{Fn}| \tag{9.1}$$

and using results from Chapter 3, we find

$$V_{bi} = V_t \ln\left(\frac{N_a N_d}{n_i^2}\right) \tag{9.2}$$

Figure 9.2b shows the energy band diagram when the pn junction is reverse biased (n region positive with respect to the p region). The total barrier height between the two regions has increased. Since the barrier has increased, there is still essentially no net flow of carriers across the junction. We will modify this statement slightly as we continue our study of the pn junction in this chapter.

The space charge width increases with an applied reverse bias voltage. Since additional charges in the space charge region are uncovered with an increase in reverse bias voltage, a capacitance exists across the junction. This capacitance is called the junction or depletion capacitance.

Figure 9.3 shows the energy-band diagram when the pn junction is forward biased (p region positive with respect to the n region). In this case, the barrier height between the two regions is reduced. A reduction in the barrier height upsets the thermal-equilibrium condition so that, now, electrons can diffuse from the n region across the space charge region into the p region. Likewise, holes can now diffuse from

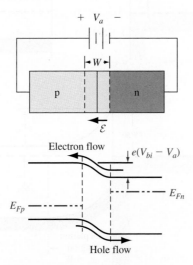

Figure 9.3 | The pn junction and energy-band diagram with a forward bias. The electron and hole diffusion across the space charge region is shown.

the p region across the space charge region into the n region. A net flow of charge means that a current exists in the device in the direction from the p region to the n region. We will derive the ideal current–voltage relation in Section 9.2.

9.1.2   The Schottky Barrier Junction

The ideal energy-band diagram for a particular metal and n-type semiconductor before making contact is shown in Figure 9.4a. The vacuum level is used as a reference level. The parameter ϕ_m is the metal work function (measured in volts), ϕ_s is the semiconductor work function, and χ is known as the *electron affinity*. The work functions of various metals and the electron affinities of several semiconductors were given in Chapter 5. In Figure 9.4a, we have assumed that $\phi_m > \phi_s$. The ideal thermal-equilibrium metal–semiconductor energy-band diagram, for this situation, is shown in Figure 9.4b. Before contact, the Fermi level in the semiconductor was above that in the metal. In order for the Fermi level to become a constant through the system in thermal equilibrium, electrons from the semiconductor flow into the lower energy

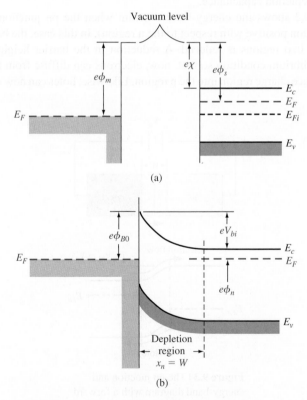

Figure 9.4 | (a) Energy-band diagram of a metal and semiconductor before contact; (b) ideal energy-band diagram of a metal–n-semiconductor junction for $\phi_m > \phi_s$.

states in the metal. Positively charged donor atoms remain in the semiconductor, creating a space charge region.

The parameter ϕ_{B0} is the ideal barrier height of the semiconductor contact, the potential barrier seen by electrons in the metal trying to move into the semiconductor. This barrier is known as the *Schottky barrier* and is given, ideally, by

Schottky barrier height

$$\boxed{\phi_{B0} = (\phi_m - \chi)} \tag{9.3}$$

On the semiconductor side, V_{bi} is the built-in potential barrier. This barrier, similar to the case of the pn junction, is the barrier seen by electrons in the conduction band trying to move into the metal. The built-in potential barrier is given by

Built-in potential barrier

$$\boxed{V_{bi} = \phi_{B0} - \phi_n} \tag{9.4}$$

which makes V_{bi} a slight function of the semiconductor doping, as was the case in a pn junction.

If we apply a positive voltage to the semiconductor with respect to the metal, the semiconductor-to-metal barrier height increases, while ϕ_{B0} remains constant in this idealized case. This bias condition is the reverse bias. If a positive voltage is applied to the metal with respect to the semiconductor, the semiconductor-to-metal barrier V_{bi} is reduced while ϕ_{B0} again remains essentially constant. In this situation, electrons can more easily flow from the semiconductor into the metal since the barrier has been reduced. This bias condition is the forward bias. The energy-band diagram for the forward bias is shown in Figure 9.5.

The current transport in a metal–semiconductor junction is due primarily to majority carriers as opposed to the diffusion of minority carriers in a pn junction. The basic process in the rectifying contact with an n-type semiconductor is by transport of electrons over the potential barrier, which can be described by the thermionic emission theory.

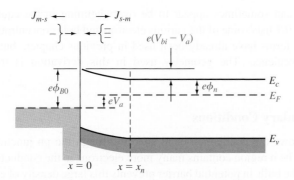

Figure 9.5 | Energy-band diagram of a forward-biased metal–semiconductor rectifying contact showing electron flow and current directions.

9.2 | THE pn JUNCTION—IDEAL CURRENT–VOLTAGE RELATIONSHIP

Objective: Derive the ideal current–voltage relationship of the pn junction diode.

We have indicated that, when the pn junction is forward biased, there is a net diffusion of carriers across the space charge region. Holes from the p region diffuse across the space charge region into the n region and electrons from the n region diffuse across the space charge region into the p region. We can then consider minority-carrier holes being injected into the n region and minority-carrier electrons being injected into the p region. The behavior of excess minority carriers is described by the ambipolar transport equation that was discussed in Chapter 8. There will be diffusion as well as recombination of excess minority carriers in each region. The diffusion of carriers implies that diffusion currents exist. The mathematical derivation of the excess minority-carrier concentrations and the current–voltage relationship is now considered.

The ideal current–voltage relationship of a pn junction is derived on the basis of four assumptions. (The last assumption has three parts, but each part deals with current.) They are

1. The abrupt depletion layer approximation applies. The space charge regions have abrupt boundaries and the semiconductor is neutral outside of the depletion region.
2. The Maxwell–Boltzmann approximation applies to carrier statistics.
3. The concept of low injection applies.
4a. The total current is a constant throughout the entire pn structure.
4b. The individual electron and hole currents are continuous functions through the pn structure.
4c. The individual electron and hole currents are constant throughout the depletion region.

Notation can sometimes appear to be overwhelming in the equations in this chapter. Table 9.1 lists some of the various electron and hole concentration terms that appear. Many terms have already been used in previous chapters but are repeated here for convenience. The geometry used in this derivation is that shown in Figure 9.1b.

9.2.1 Boundary Conditions

Figure 9.6 shows the conduction-band energy through the pn junction in thermal equilibrium. The n region contains many more electrons in the conduction band than the p region; the built-in potential barrier prevents this large density of electrons from flowing into the p region. The built-in potential barrier maintains equilibrium between the carrier distributions on either side of the junction.

Table 9.1 | Commonly used terms and notation for this chapter

Term	Meaning
N_a	Acceptor concentration in the p region of the pn junction
N_d	Donor concentration in the n region of the pn junction
$n_{n0} = N_d$	Thermal equilibrium majority-carrier electron concentration in the n region
$p_{p0} = N_a$	Thermal equilibrium majority-carrier hole concentration in the p region
$n_{p0} = n_i^2/N_a$	Thermal equilibrium minority-carrier electron concentration in the p region
$p_{n0} = n_i^2/N_d$	Thermal equilibrium minority-carrier hole concentration in the n region
n_p	Total minority-carrier electron concentration in the p region
p_n	Total minority-carrier hole concentration in the n region
$n_p(-x_p)$	Minority-carrier electron concentration in the p region at the space charge edge
$p_n(x_n)$	Minority-carrier hole concentration in the n region at the space charge edge
$\delta n_p = n_p - n_{p0}$	Excess minority-carrier electron concentration in the p region
$\delta p_n = p_n - p_{n0}$	Excess minority-carrier hole concentration in the n region

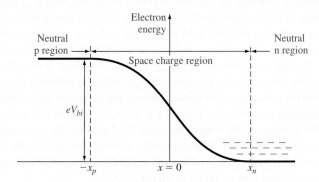

Figure 9.6 | Conduction-band energy through a pn junction showing the potential barrier and depletion widths.

An expression for the built-in potential barrier was derived previously and is given by

$$V_{bi} = V_t \ln\left(\frac{N_a N_d}{n_i^2}\right)$$

If we divide the equation by $V_t = kT/e$, take the exponential of both sides, and then take the reciprocal, we obtain

$$\frac{n_i^2}{N_a N_d} = \exp\left(\frac{-V_{bi}}{V_t}\right) = \exp\left(\frac{-eV_{bi}}{kT}\right) \tag{9.5}$$

If we assume complete ionization, we can write

$$n_{n0} \approx N_d \tag{9.6}$$

where n_{n0} is the thermal-equilibrium concentration of majority-carrier electrons in the n region. In the p region, we can write

$$n_{p0} = \frac{n_i^2}{N_a} \tag{9.7}$$

where n_{p0} is the thermal-equilibrium concentration of minority-carrier electrons. Substituting Equations (9.6) and (9.7) into Equation (9.5) yields

$$n_{p0} = n_{n0} \exp\left(\frac{-eV_{bi}}{kT}\right) \tag{9.8}$$

This equation relates the minority-carrier electron concentration on the p side of the junction to the majority-carrier electron concentration on the n side of the junction in thermal equilibrium.

If a positive voltage is applied to the p region with respect to the n region, the potential barrier is reduced. Figure 9.7a shows a pn junction with an applied voltage V_a. The electric field in the bulk p and n regions is normally very small. Essentially all of the applied voltage is across the junction region. The electric field $\mathcal{E}_{app}$ induced by the applied voltage is in the opposite direction to the thermal equilibrium space charge electric field, so the net electric field in the space charge region is reduced below the equilibrium value. The delicate balance between diffusion and the $\mathcal{E}$-field force achieved at thermal equilibrium is upset. The electric field force that prevented majority carriers from crossing the space charge region is reduced; majority-carrier electrons from the n side are now injected across the depletion region into the p material, and majority-carrier holes from the p side are injected across the depletion region into the n material. As long as the bias V_a is applied, the injection of carriers across the space charge region continues and a current is created in the pn junction. This bias condition is known as forward bias; the energy-band diagram of the forward-biased pn junction is shown in Figure 9.7b.

Forward bias

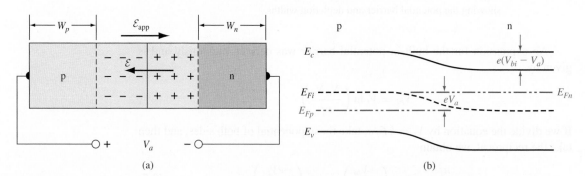

(a)   (b)

Figure 9.7 | (a) A pn junction with an applied forward-bias voltage showing the directions of the electric field induced by V_a and the space charge electric field. (b) Energy-band diagram of the forward-biased pn junction.

The potential barrier V_{bi} in Equation (9.8) can be replaced by $(V_{bi} - V_a)$ when the junction is forward biased. Equation (9.8) becomes

$$n_p = n_{n0} \exp\left(\frac{-e(V_{bi} - V_a)}{kT}\right) = n_{n0} \exp\left(\frac{-eV_{bi}}{kT}\right) \exp\left(\frac{+eV_a}{kT}\right) \quad (9.9)$$

If we assume low injection, the majority-carrier electron concentration n_{n0}, for example, does not change significantly. However, the minority-carrier concentration, n_p, can deviate from its thermal-equilibrium value n_{p0} by orders of magnitude. Using Equation (9.8), we can write Equation (9.9) as

$$n_p = n_{p0} \exp\left(\frac{eV_a}{kT}\right) \quad (9.10)$$

When a forward-bias voltage is applied to the pn junction, the junction is no longer in thermal equilibrium. The left side of Equation (9.10) is the total minority-carrier electron concentration in the p region, which is now greater than the thermal equilibrium value. The forward-bias voltage lowers the potential barrier so that majority-carrier electrons from the n region are injected across the junction into the p region, thereby increasing the minority-carrier electron concentration. We have produced excess minority-carrier electrons in the p region.

Carrier injection

When the electrons are injected into the p region, these excess carriers are subject to the diffusion and recombination processes we discussed in Chapter 8. Equation (9.10), then, is the expression for the minority-carrier electron concentration at the edge of the space charge region in the p region.

Exactly the same process occurs for majority-carrier holes in the p region, which are injected across the space charge region into the n region under a forward-bias voltage. We can write that

$$p_n = p_{n0} \exp\left(\frac{eV_a}{kT}\right) \quad (9.11)$$

where p_n is the concentration of minority carrier holes at the edge of the space charge region in the n region. Figure 9.8 shows these results. By applying a forward-bias voltage, we create excess minority carriers in each region of the pn junction.

EXAMPLE 9.1

OBJECTIVE

Calculate the minority-carrier concentration at the edge of the space charge region of a pn junction when a forward-bias voltage is applied.

Consider a silicon pn junction at $T = 300$ K. Assume the n-type doping is $N_d = 10^{16}$ cm^{-3} and assume that a forward bias of 0.60 V is applied to the pn junction. Calculate the minority-carrier hole concentration at the edge of the space charge region.

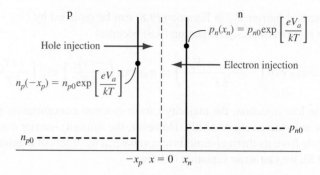

Figure 9.8 | Excess minority-carrier concentrations at the space charge edges generated by the forward-bias voltage.

■ Solution

The thermal-equilibrium minority-carrier hole concentration in the n region is

$$p_{n0} = \frac{n_i^2}{N_d} = \frac{(1.5 \times 10^{10})^2}{10^{16}} = 2.25 \times 10^4 \text{ cm}^{-3}$$

From Equation (9.11), we have

$$p_n(x_n) = p_{n0} \exp\left(\frac{eV_a}{kT}\right) = (2.25 \times 10^4) \exp\left(\frac{0.60}{0.0259}\right)$$

or

$$p_n(x_n) = 2.59 \times 10^{14} \text{ cm}^{-3}$$

■ Comment

The minority-carrier concentration can increase by many orders of magnitude when a relatively small forward-bias voltage is applied. Low injection still applies, however, since the excess electron concentration (equal to the excess hole concentration to maintain charge neutrality) is much less than the thermal-equilibrium electron concentration.

Exercise Problem

EX9.1 A silicon pn junction at $T = 300$ K is doped with impurity concentrations of $N_d = 5 \times 10^{16}$ cm^{-3} and $N_a = 2 \times 10^{16}$ cm^{-3}. The junction is forward biased at $V_a = 0.610$ V. Determine the minority-carrier concentrations at the space charge edges. [Ans. $p_n(x_n) = 7.62 \times 10^{13}$ cm^{-3}, $n_p(-x_p) = 1.90 \times 10^{14}$ cm^{-3}.]

The minority-carrier concentrations at the space charge edges, given by Equations (9.10) and (9.11), were derived assuming a forward-bias voltage ($V_a > 0$) was applied across the pn junction. However, nothing in the derivation prevents V_a from being negative (reverse bias). If a reverse-bias voltage greater than a few tenths of a volt is applied to the pn junction, then we see from Equations (9.10) and (9.11) that the minority-carrier concentrations at the space charge edge are essentially zero. The

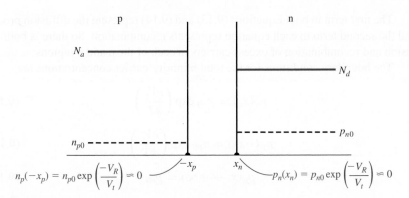

Figure 9.9 | Excess minority-carrier concentrations at the space charge edges generated by a reverse-bias voltage. For a reverse-bias voltage of $V_R \geq 0.25 \, \text{V}$, the minority-carrier concentrations at the space charge edges are essentially zero.

minority-carrier concentrations for the reverse-bias condition drop below the thermal-equilibrium values, as shown in Figure 9.9.

9.2.2 Minority-Carrier Distribution

We developed, in Chapter 8, the ambipolar transport equation for excess minority-carrier holes in an n region. This equation, in one dimension, is

$$D_p \frac{\partial^2 (\delta p_n)}{\partial x^2} - \mu_p \mathcal{E} \frac{\partial (\delta p_n)}{\partial x} + g' - \frac{\delta p_n}{\tau_{p0}} = \frac{\partial (\delta p_n)}{\partial t} \tag{9.12}$$

where $\delta p_n = p_n - p_{n0}$ is the excess minority-carrier hole concentration and is the difference between the total and thermal equilibrium minority-carrier concentrations. The ambipolar transport equation describes the behavior of excess carriers as a function of time and spatial coordinates.

In Chapter 4, we calculated drift current densities in a semiconductor. We determined that relatively large currents could be created with fairly small electric fields. As a first approximation, we will assume that the electric field is zero in both the neutral p and n regions. In the n region for $x > x_n$, we have that $\mathcal{E} = 0$ and $g' = 0$. If we also assume steady state so $\partial (\delta p_n)/\partial t = 0$, then Equation (9.12) reduces to

$$\frac{d^2 (\delta p_n)}{dx^2} - \frac{\delta p_n}{L_p^2} = 0 \qquad (x > x_n) \tag{9.13}$$

where $L_p^2 = D_p \tau_{p0}$. For the same set of conditions, the excess minority-carrier electron concentration in the p region is determined from

$$\frac{d^2 (\delta n_p)}{dx^2} - \frac{\delta n_p}{L_n^2} = 0 \qquad (x < x_p) \tag{9.14}$$

where $L_n^2 = D_n \tau_{n0}$. The constants L_p and L_n are called the minority-carrier hole and electron diffusion lengths, respectively.

The first term in both Equations (9.13) and (9.14) represent the diffusion process and the second term in each equation represents recombination. So there is both diffusion and recombination of excess carriers in each of the p and n regions.

The boundary conditions for the total minority-carrier concentrations are

$$p_n(x_n) = p_{n0} \exp\left(\frac{eV_a}{kT}\right) \tag{9.15a}$$

$$n_p(-x_p) = n_{p0} \exp\left(\frac{eV_a}{kT}\right) \tag{9.15b}$$

$$p_n(x \to +\infty) = p_{n0} \tag{9.15c}$$

$$n_p(x \to -\infty) = n_{p0} \tag{9.15d}$$

Long pn junction

As minority carriers diffuse from the space charge edge into the neutral semiconductor regions, they will recombine with majority carriers. We will assume that the lengths W_n and W_p shown in Figure 9.7a are very long, meaning in particular that $W_n \gg L_p$ and $W_p \gg L_n$. The excess minority-carrier concentrations must approach zero at distances far from the space charge region. The structure is referred to as a long pn junction.

The general solution to Equation (9.13) is

$$\delta p_n(x) = p_n(x) - p_{n0} = Ae^{x/L_p} + Be^{-x/L_p} \qquad (x \geq x_n) \tag{9.16}$$

and the general solution to Equation (9.14) is

$$\delta n_p(x) = n_p(x) - n_{p0} = Ce^{x/L_n} + De^{-x/L_n} \qquad (x \leq -x_p) \tag{9.17}$$

Excess carrier concentrations

Applying the boundary conditions from Equation (9.15c) and (9.15d), the coefficients A and D must be zero. The coefficients B and C can be determined from the boundary conditions given by Equation (9.15a) and (9.15b). The excess carrier concentrations are then found to be, for $(x \geq x_n)$,

$$\delta p_n(x) = p_n(x) - p_{n0} = p_{n0}\left[\exp\left(\frac{eV_a}{kT}\right) - 1\right]\exp\left(\frac{x_n - x}{L_p}\right) \tag{9.18}$$

and, for $(x \leq -x_p)$,

$$\delta n_p(x) = n_p(x) - n_{p0} = n_{p0}\left[\exp\left(\frac{eV_a}{kT}\right) - 1\right]\exp\left(\frac{x_p + x}{L_n}\right) \tag{9.19}$$

The minority-carrier concentrations decay exponentially with distance away from the junction to their thermal-equilibrium values. Figure 9.10 shows these results. Again, we have assumed that both the n-region and the p-region lengths are long compared to the minority-carrier diffusion lengths.

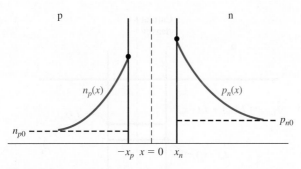

Figure 9.10 | Steady-state minority-carrier concentrations in a pn junction under forward bias.

To review, a forward-bias voltage lowers the built-in potential barrier of a pn junction so that electrons from the n region diffuse across the space charge region, creating excess minority carriers in the p region. These excess electrons begin diffusing into the bulk p region where they can recombine with majority-carrier holes. The excess minority-carrier electron concentration then decreases with distance from the junction. The same discussion applies to holes diffusing across the space charge region into the n region.

9.2.3   Ideal pn Junction Current

The approach we use to determine the current in a pn junction is based on the three parts of the fourth assumption stated earlier in this section. The total current in the junction is the sum of the individual electron and hole currents, which are constant through the depletion region. Since the electron and hole currents are continuous functions through the pn junction, the total pn junction current will be the minority-carrier hole diffusion current at $x = x_n$ plus the minority-carrier electron diffusion current at $x = -x_p$. The gradients in the minority carrier concentrations, as shown in Figure 9.10, produce diffusion currents, and since we are assuming the electric field to be zero at the space charge edges, we can neglect any minority-carrier drift current component. This approach in determining the pn junction current is shown in Figure 9.11.

We can calculate the minority-carrier hole diffusion current density at $x = x_n$ from the relation

$$J_p(x_n) = -eD_p\frac{dp_n(x)}{dx}\bigg|_{x=x_n} \tag{9.20}$$

Since we are assuming uniformly doped regions, the thermal-equilibrium carrier concentration is constant, so the hole diffusion current density can be written as

$$J_p(x_n) = -eD_p\frac{d(\delta p_n(x))}{dx}\bigg|_{x=x_n} \tag{9.21}$$

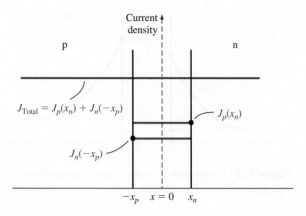

Figure 9.11 | Electron and hole current densities through the space charge region of a pn junction.

Taking the derivative of Equation (9.18) and substituting into Equation (9.21), we obtain

$$J_p(x_n) = \frac{eD_p p_{n0}}{L_p}\left[\exp\left(\frac{eV_a}{kT}\right) - 1\right] \qquad (9.22)$$

Hole current density The hole current density for this forward-bias condition is in the $+x$ direction, which is from the p to the n region.

Similarly, we can calculate the electron diffusion current density at $x = -x_p$. This can be written as

$$J_n(-x_p) = eD_n\frac{d(\delta n_p(x))}{dx}\bigg|_{x=-x_p} \qquad (9.23)$$

Using Equation (9.19), we obtain

$$J_n(-x_p) = \frac{eD_n n_{p0}}{L_n}\left[\exp\left(\frac{eV_a}{kT}\right) - 1\right] \qquad (9.24)$$

Electron current density The electron current density is also in the $+x$ direction.

An assumption we made at the beginning was that the individual electron and hole currents were continuous functions and constant through the space charge region. The total current is the sum of the electron and hole currents and is constant through the entire junction. Figure 9.11 again shows a plot of the magnitudes of these currents.

The total current density in the pn junction is then

$$J = J_p(x_n) + J_n(-x_p) = \left(\frac{eD_p p_{n0}}{L_p} + \frac{eD_n n_{p0}}{L_n}\right)\left[\exp\left(\frac{eV_a}{kT}\right) - 1\right] \qquad (9.25)$$

Equation (9.25) is the ideal current–voltage relationship of a pn junction.

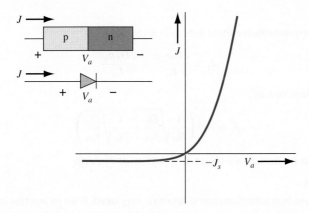

Figure 9.12 | Ideal *I–V* characteristic of a pn junction diode.

We can define a parameter J_s as

$$J_s = \left(\frac{e D_p p_{n0}}{L_p} + \frac{e D_n n_{p0}}{L_n} \right) \qquad (9.26)$$

Reverse-saturation current density

so that Equation (9.25) can be written as

$$J = J_s \left[\exp\left(\frac{e V_a}{kT} \right) - 1 \right] \qquad (9.27)$$

Equation (9.27), known as the ideal-diode equation, gives a good description of the current–voltage characteristics of the pn junction over a wide range of currents and voltages. Although Equation (9.27) was derived assuming a forward-bias voltage ($V_a > 0$), there is nothing to prevent V_a from being negative (reverse bias). Equation (9.27) is plotted in Figure 9.12 as a function of forward-bias voltage V_a. If the voltage V_a becomes negative (reverse bias) by a few kT/e V, then the reverse-bias current density becomes independent of the reverse-bias voltage. The parameter J_s is then referred to as the reverse-saturation current density. The current–voltage characteristics of the pn junction diode are obviously not bilateral.

Ideal diode equation

EXAMPLE 9.2

OBJECTIVE

Determine the ideal reverse-saturation current density in a silicon pn junction at $T = 300\,\text{K}$.
    Consider the following parameters in a silicon pn junction:

$$N_a = N_d = 10^{16} \text{ cm}^{-3} \qquad n_i = 1.5 \times 10^{10} \text{ cm}^{-3}$$
$$D_n = 25 \text{ cm}^2/\text{s} \qquad \tau_{p0} = \tau_{n0} = 5 \times 10^{-7} \text{ s}$$
$$D_p = 10 \text{ cm}^2/\text{s} \qquad \epsilon_r = 11.7$$

■ Solution

The ideal reverse-saturation current density is given by

$$J_s = \frac{e D_n n_{p0}}{L_n} + \frac{e D_p p_{n0}}{L_p}$$

which can be rewritten as

$$J_s = e n_i^2 \left(\frac{1}{N_a} \sqrt{\frac{D_n}{\tau_{n0}}} + \frac{1}{N_d} \sqrt{\frac{D_p}{\tau_{p0}}} \right)$$

Substituting the parameters, we obtain $J_s = 4.15 \times 10^{-11}$ A/cm^2.

■ Comment

The ideal reverse-bias saturation current density is very small. If the pn junction cross-sectional area were A $= 10^{-4}$ cm^2, for example, then the ideal reverse-bias diode current would be $I_s = 4.15 \times 10^{-15}$ A.

Exercise Problem

EX9.2 Consider a GaAs pn junction at $T = 300$ K with the following parameters: $N_a = N_d = 10^{16}$ cm^{-3}, $D_n = 200$ cm^2/s, $D_p = 8$ cm^2/s, and $\tau_{n0} = \tau_{p0} = 5 \times 10^{-7}$ s. Calculate the reverse-saturation current if the cross-sectional area is $A = 10^{-4}$ cm^2. (Ans. $I_s = 1.24 \times 10^{-22}$ A.)

EXAMPLE 9.3

OBJECTIVE

Calculate the forward-bias pn junction current.

Consider the pn junction described in Example 9.2 with a junction area of $A = 10^{-4}$ cm^2. Calculate the current for forward-bias voltages of $V_a = 0.5$, 0.6, and 0.7 V.

■ Solution

For forward-bias voltages, we can write

$$I = J A = J_S A \left[\exp\left(\frac{V_a}{V_t} \right) - 1 \right] \approx J_S A \exp\left(\frac{V_a}{V_t} \right)$$

For $V_a = 0.5$ V, we obtain

$$I = (4.15 \times 10^{-11})(10^{-4}) \exp\left(\frac{0.5}{0.0259} \right) \Rightarrow 1.0 \; \mu A$$

For $V_a = 0.6$ V, we find

$$I = (4.15 \times 10^{-11})(10^{-4}) \exp\left(\frac{0.6}{0.0259} \right) \Rightarrow 47.7 \; \mu A$$

For $V_a = 0.7$ V, we have

$$I = (4.15 \times 10^{-11})(10^{-4}) \exp\left(\frac{0.7}{0.0259} \right) \Rightarrow 2.27 \; mA$$

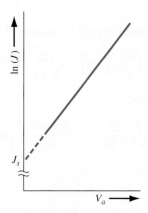

Figure 9.13 | Ideal I–V characteristic of a pn junction diode with the current plotted on a log scale.

■ Comment

We see, from this example, that significant pn junction currents can be induced for relatively small forward-bias voltages even though the reverse-saturation current is very small.

Exercise Problem

EX9.3 Consider the GaAs pn junction described in Exercise Problem EX9.2. Determine the forward-bias current for applied voltages of $V_a = 1.0$, 1.1, and 1.2 V.
(Ans. 7.27 μA, 0.345 mA, 16.4 mA)

If the forward-bias voltage in Equation (9.27) is positive by more than a few kT/e V, then the (-1) term in Equation (9.27) becomes negligible. Figure 9.13 shows the forward-bias current–voltage characteristic when the current is plotted on a log scale. Ideally, this plot yields a straight line when V_a is greater than a few kT/e V. The forward-bias current is an exponential function of the forward-bias voltage.

EXAMPLE 9.4

OBJECTIVE

Design a pn junction diode to produce particular electron and hole current densities at a given forward-bias voltage.

Consider a silicon pn junction diode at $T = 300$ K. Design the diode such that $J_n = 20$ A/cm^2 and $J_p = 5$ A/cm^2 at $V_a = 0.65$ V. Assume the remaining semiconductor parameters are as given in Example 9.2.

■ **Solution**

The electron diffusion current density is given by Equation (9.24) as

$$J_n = \frac{eD_n n_{p0}}{L_n} \left[\exp\left(\frac{eV_a}{kT}\right) - 1 \right] = e\sqrt{\frac{D_n}{\tau_{n0}}} \cdot \frac{n_i^2}{N_a} \left[\exp\left(\frac{eV_a}{kT}\right) - 1 \right]$$

Substituting the numbers, we have

$$20 = (1.6 \times 10^{-19})\sqrt{\frac{25}{5 \times 10^{-7}}} \cdot \frac{(1.5 \times 10^{10})^2}{N_a} \left[\exp\left(\frac{0.65}{0.0259}\right) - 1 \right]$$

which yields

$$N_a = 1.01 \times 10^{15} \text{ cm}^{-3}$$

The hole diffusion current density is given by Equation (9.22) as

$$J_p = \frac{eD_p p_{n0}}{L_p} \left[\exp\left(\frac{eV_a}{kT}\right) - 1 \right] = e\sqrt{\frac{D_p}{\tau_{p0}}} \cdot \frac{n_i^2}{N_d} \left[\exp\left(\frac{eV_a}{kT}\right) - 1 \right]$$

Substituting the numbers, we have

$$5 = (1.6 \times 10^{-19})\sqrt{\frac{10}{5 \times 10^{-7}}} \cdot \frac{(1.5 \times 10^{10})^2}{N_d} \left[\exp\left(\frac{0.65}{0.0259}\right) - 1 \right]$$

which yields

$$N_d = 2.55 \times 10^{15} \text{ cm}^{-3}$$

■ **Comment**

The relative magnitude of the electron and hole current densities through a diode can be varied by changing the doping concentrations in the device.

Exercise Problem

EX9.4   A silicon pn junction at $T = 300$ K has the following parameters: $N_a = 5 \times 10^{16}$ cm^{-3}, $N_d = 1 \times 10^{16}$ cm^{-3}, $D_n = 25$ cm^2/s, $D_p = 10$ cm^2/s, $\tau_{n0} = 5 \times 10^{-7}$ s, and $\tau_{p0} = 1 \times 10^{-7}$ s. The cross-sectional area is $A = 10^{-3}$ cm^2 and the forward-bias voltage is $V_a = 0.625$ V. Calculate the (a) minority electron diffusion current at the space charge edge, (b) minority hole diffusion current at the space charge edge, and (c) total current in the pn junction diode.
[Ans. (a) 0.154 mA, (b) 1.09 mA, (c) 1.24 mA]

9.2.4   Summary of Physics

We have been considering the case of a forward-bias voltage being applied to a pn junction. The forward-bias voltage lowers the potential barrier so that electrons and holes are injected across the space charge region. The injected carriers become minority carriers, which then diffuse from the junction and recombine with majority carriers.

We calculated the minority-carrier diffusion current densities at the edge of the space charge region. We can reconsider Equations (9.18) and (9.19) and determine the minority-carrier diffusion current densities as a function of distance through the p and n regions. These results are

$$J_p(x) = \frac{e D_p p_{n0}}{L_p} \left[\exp\left(\frac{e V_a}{kT}\right) - 1 \right] \exp\left(\frac{x_n - x}{L_p}\right) \qquad (x \geq x_n) \qquad (9.28)$$

and

$$J_n(x) = \frac{e D_n n_{p0}}{L_n} \left[\exp\left(\frac{e V_a}{kT}\right) - 1 \right] \exp\left(\frac{x_p + x}{L_n}\right) \qquad (x \leq -x_p) \qquad (9.29)$$

The minority-carrier diffusion current densities decay exponentially in each region. However, the total current through the pn junction is constant. The difference between total current and minority-carrier diffusion current is a majority-carrier current. Figure 9.14 shows the various current components through the pn structure. The drift of majority-carrier holes in the p region far from the junction, for example, is to supply holes that are being injected across the space charge region into the n region and also to supply holes that are lost by recombination with excess minority-carrier electrons. The same discussion applies to the drift of electrons in the n region.

We have seen that excess carriers are created in a forward-biased pn junction. From the results of the ambipolar transport theory derived in Chapter 8, the behavior of the excess carriers is determined by the minority carrier parameters for low injection. In determining the current–voltage relationship of the pn junction, we consider the flow of minority carriers since we know the behavior and characteristics of these particles. It may seem strange, at times, that we concern ourselves so much with minority carriers rather than with the vast number of majority carriers, but the reason for this can be found in the results derived from the ambipolar transport theory.

The fact that we now have drift current densities in the p and n regions implies that the electric field in these regions is not zero as we had originally assumed. We

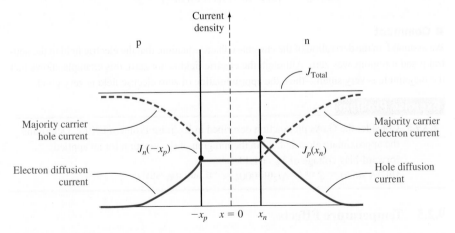

Figure 9.14 | Ideal electron and hole current components through a pn junction under forward bias.

can calculate the electric field in the neutral regions and determine the validity of our zero-field approximation.

EXAMPLE 9.5

OBJECTIVE

To calculate the electric field required to produce a given majority-carrier drift current.

Consider a silicon pn junction at $T = 300$ K with the parameters given in Example 9.2 and with an applied forward-bias voltage $V_a = 0.65$ V.

■ **Solution**

The total forward-bias current density is given by

$$J = J_s \left[\exp \left(\frac{eV}{kT} \right) - 1 \right]$$

We determined the reverse saturation current density in Example 9.2, so we can write

$$J = (4.15 \times 10^{-11}) \left[\exp \left(\frac{0.65}{0.0259} \right) - 1 \right] = 3.29 \text{ A/cm}^2$$

The total current far from the junction in the n region will be majority-carrier electron drift current, so we can write

$$J = J_n \approx e\mu_n N_d \mathcal{E}$$

The doping concentration is $N_d = 10^{16}$ cm^{-3}, and, if we assume $\mu_n = 1350$ cm^2/V-s, then the electric field must be

$$\mathcal{E} = \frac{J_n}{e\mu_n N_d} = \frac{3.29}{(1.6 \times 10^{-19})(1350)(10^{16})} = 1.52 \text{ V/cm}$$

■ **Comment**

We assumed, in the derivation of the current–voltage equation, that the electric field in the neutral p and n regions was zero. Although the electric field is not zero, this example shows that the magnitude is very small—thus, the approximation of zero electric field is very good.

Exercise Problem

EX9.5 Consider the GaAs pn junction described in Exercise Problem EX9.2. Determine the approximate electric field in the n region of the junction for an applied forward-bias voltage of $V_a = 1.1$ V.

(Ans. We find $\mu_n \approx 7000$ cm^2/V-s, so $\mathcal{E} = 0.308$ V/cm)

9.2.5 Temperature Effects

The ideal reverse saturation current density J_s, given by Equation (9.26), is a function of the thermal-equilibrium minority-carrier concentrations n_{p0} and p_{n0}. These minority-carrier concentrations are proportional to n_i^2, which is a strong function of

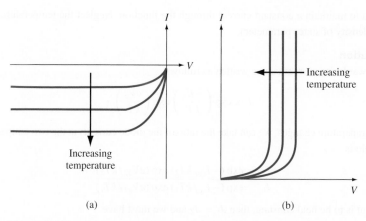

Figure 9.15 | Schematic of temperature effects in a pn junction diode under (a) reverse bias and (b) forward bias.

temperature. Neglecting the temperature effects of the diffusion coefficients, we have that

$$J_s \propto n_i^2 \propto (T)^3 \exp\left(\frac{-E_g}{kT}\right)$$

If we consider a 10°C increase in temperature about room temperature, we find

$$\frac{J_s(310\,\text{K})}{J_s(300\,\text{K})} = \left(\frac{310}{300}\right)^3 \frac{\exp\left[-1.12/(8.62 \times 10^{-5})(310)\right]}{\exp\left[-1.12/(8.62 \times 10^{-5})(300)\right]}$$

or

$$\frac{J_s(310\,\text{K})}{J_s(300\,\text{K})} = 4.46$$

For every 10°C increase in temperature around room temperature, the reverse saturation current increases by a factor of 4.46.

The forward-bias current–voltage relation was given by Equation (9.27). This relation includes J_s as well as the $\exp(eV_a/kT)$ factor, making the forward-bias current–voltage relation a function of temperature also. As temperature increases, less forward-bias voltage is required to obtain the same diode current. If the voltage is held constant, the diode current will increase as temperature increases. The change in forward-bias current with temperature is less sensitive than the reverse saturation current.

The effects of temperature on the diode current–voltage characteristics are schematically shown in Figure 9.15.

EXAMPLE 9.6

OBJECTIVE

To determine the change in the forward-bias voltage of a pn junction with a change in temperature.

Consider a silicon pn junction initially forward biased at 0.60 V at $T = 300$ K. Assume the temperature increases to $T = 310$ K. Calculate the change in forward-bias voltage required to maintain a constant current through the junction. Neglect the temperature effects on the density of states parameters.

■ **Solution**

The forward-bias current can be written as follows:

$$J \propto \exp\left(\frac{-E_g}{kT}\right) \exp\left(\frac{eV_a}{kT}\right)$$

If the temperature changes, we can take the ratio of the diode currents at the two temperatures. This ratio is

$$\frac{J_2}{J_1} = \frac{\exp\left(-E_g/kT_2\right)\exp\left(eV_{a2}/kT_2\right)}{\exp\left(-E_g/kT_1\right)\exp\left(eV_{a1}/kT_1\right)}$$

If current is to be held constant, then $J_1 = J_2$ and we must have

$$\frac{E_g - eV_{a2}}{kT_2} = \frac{E_g - eV_{a1}}{kT_1}$$

Let $T_1 = 300$ K, $T_2 = 310$ K, $E_g = 1.12$ eV, and $V_{a1} = 0.60$ V. Then, solving for V_{a2}, we obtain $V_{a2} = 0.5827$ V.

■ **Comment**

The change in the forward-bias voltage is -17.3 mV for a $10°C$ temperature change.

Exercise Problem

EX9.6   Repeat Example 9.6 for a GaAs pn junction ($E_g = 1.42$ eV) initially biased at $V_a = 1.10$ V at $T = 300$ K. (Ans. $\Delta V_a = -0.011$ V.)

9.2.6   The "Short" Diode

We assumed in the previous analysis that both p and n regions were long compared with the minority-carrier diffusion lengths. In many pn junction structures, one region may, in fact, be short compared with the minority-carrier diffusion length. Figure 9.16 shows one such example: the length W_n is assumed to be much smaller than the minority-carrier hole diffusion length, L_p.

The steady-state excess minority-carrier hole concentration in the n region is determined from Equation (9.13), which was given as

$$\frac{d^2(\delta p_n)}{dx^2} - \frac{\delta p_n}{L_p^2} = 0$$

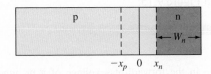

Figure 9.16 | Geometry of a "short" diode.

The original boundary condition at $x = x_n$ still applies, given by Equation (9.15a) as

$$p_n(x_n) = p_{n0} \exp\left(\frac{eV_a}{kT}\right)$$

A second boundary condition needs to be determined. In many cases, we will assume that an ohmic contact exists at $x = (x_n + W_n)$, implying an infinite surface-recombination velocity and therefore an excess minority-carrier concentration of zero. The second boundary condition is then written as

$$p_n(x = x_n + W_n) = p_{n0} \tag{9.30}$$

The general solution to Equation (9.13) is again given by Equation (9.16), which was

$$\delta p_n(x) = p_n(x) - p_{n0} = Ae^{x/L_p} + Be^{-x/L_p} \qquad (x \geq x_n)$$

In this case, because of the finite length of the n region, both terms of the general solution must be retained. Applying the boundary conditions of Equations (9.15b) and (9.30), the excess minority-carrier concentration is given by

$$\delta p_n(x) = p_{n0}\left[\exp\left(\frac{eV_a}{kT}\right) - 1\right]\frac{\sinh\left[(x_n + W_n - x)/L_p\right]}{\sinh\left[W_n/L_p\right]} \tag{9.31}$$

Equation (9.31) is the general solution for the excess minority-carrier hole concentration in the n region of a forward-biased pn junction. If $W_n \gg L_p$, the assumption for the long diode, Equation (9.31) reduces to the previous result given by Equation (9.18). If $W_n \ll L_p$, we can approximate the hyperbolic sine terms by

$$\sinh\left(\frac{x_n + W_n - x}{L_p}\right) \approx \left(\frac{x_n + W_n - x}{L_p}\right) \tag{9.32a}$$

and

$$\sinh\left(\frac{W_n}{L_p}\right) \approx \left(\frac{W_n}{L_p}\right) \tag{9.32b}$$

Then Equation (9.31) becomes

$$\delta p_n(x) = p_{n0}\left[\exp\left(\frac{eV_a}{kT}\right) - 1\right]\left(\frac{x_n + W_n - x}{W_n}\right) \tag{9.33}$$

The minority-carrier concentration becomes a linear function of distance.

The minority-carrier hole diffusion current density is given by

$$J_p = -eD_p\frac{d(\delta p_n(x))}{dx}$$

so that in the short n region, we have

$$J_p(x) = \frac{eD_p p_{n0}}{W_n}\left[\exp\left(\frac{eV_a}{kT}\right) - 1\right] \tag{9.34}$$

The "short" diode

Table 9.2 | Summary of hole current density expressions for particular n-region lengths
(Geometry shown in Figure 9.16)

Condition	Hole Current Density
"Long" diode ($W_n \gg L_p$)	$J_p(x) = \dfrac{e D_p p_{n0}}{L_p} \left[\exp\left(\dfrac{eV_a}{kT}\right) - 1 \right] \exp\left(\dfrac{x_n - x}{L_p}\right)$
"Medium" diode ($W_n \approx L_p$)	$J_p(x) = \dfrac{e D_p p_{n0}}{L_p} \left[\exp\left(\dfrac{eV_a}{kT}\right) - 1 \right]$ $\times \dfrac{\cosh\left[(x_n + W_n - x)/L_p\right]}{\sinh\left(W_n/L_p\right)}$
"Short" diode ($W_n \ll L_p$)	$J_p(x) = \dfrac{e D_p p_{n0}}{W_n} \left[\exp\left(\dfrac{eV_a}{kT}\right) - 1 \right]$

The minority-carrier hole diffusion current density now contains the length W_n in the denominator, rather than the diffusion length L_p. The diffusion current density is larger for a short diode than for a long diode since $W_n \ll L_p$. In addition, since the minority-carrier concentration is approximately a linear function of distance through the n region, the minority-carrier diffusion current density is a constant. This constant current implies that there is no recombination of minority carriers in the short region.

9.2.7 Summary of Results

We have considered the "long" diode and the "short" diode. There is a possibility that the neutral n-region width, W_n, shown in Figure 9.16 may be some arbitrary length. Table 9.2 summarizes the hole current density for the three possible conditions. These results can be determined by using the excess minority-carrier distribution given by Equation (9.31). The same general results can be applied to the electron current density in the neutral p region.

TEST YOUR UNDERSTANDING

TYU9.1   The impurity doping concentrations in a silicon pn junction at $T = 300$ K are $N_d = 5 \times 10^{15}$ cm^{-3} and $N_a = 5 \times 10^{16}$ cm^{-3}. The minority-carrier concentration at either space charge edge is to be no larger than 10 percent of the respective majority-carrier concentration. Calculate the maximum forward bias voltage that can be applied to this junction and still meet the required specifications. [Ans. V_a(max) $= 0.599$ V]

TYU9.2   Repeat TYU9.1 for a GaAs pn junction with the same doping concentrations. [Ans. V_a(max) $= 1.067$ V]

TYU9.3   Repeat EX9.4 for a GaAs pn junction diode biased at $V_a = 1.10$ V. Let $D_n = 200$ cm^2/s and $D_p = 8$ cm^2/s. [Ans. (a) 0.578 mA, (b) 1.29 mA, (c) 1.87 mA]

TYU9.4 Consider the silicon pn junction diode described in EX9.4. Calculate the electron and hole currents at (a) $x = x_n$, (b) $x = x_n + L_p$, and (c) $x = x_n + 10L_p$ (see Figure 9.14).

[Ans. (a) $I_n = 0.154$ mA, $I_p = 1.09$ mA; (b) $I_n = 0.843$ mA, $I_p = 0.401$ mA; (c) $I_n = 1.244$ mA, $I_p \approx 0$]

TYU9.5 Consider the silicon pn junction diode described in EX9.4. The p region is long and the n region is short with $W_n = 2\ \mu$m. (a) Calculate the electron and hole currents in the depletion region. (b) Why has the hole current increased compared to that found in EX9.4?

[Ans. (a) $I_n = 0.154$ mA, $I_p = 5.44$ mA; (b) the hole density gradient has increased]

9.3 | THE SCHOTTKY BARRIER JUNCTION—IDEAL CURRENT–VOLTAGE RELATIONSHIP

Objective: Develop the ideal current–voltage relationship of the Schottky barrier diode.

As mentioned previously, it has long been known that a rectifying contact can be achieved by pressing a sharp wire against selenium. A more reliable diode can be formed by depositing a metal, such as aluminum, onto the surface of a semiconductor. This type of diode is commonly known as a Schottky barrier diode, or just a Schottky diode. The Schottky barrier junction and metal–semiconductor ohmic contacts were introduced in Chapter 5.

9.3.1 The Schottky Diode

In this section, we will consider the Schottky barrier diode and develop the ideal current–voltage relationship. In most cases, the rectifying contacts are made on n-type semiconductors; for this reason, we will concentrate on this type of diode.

The current transport in a metal–semiconductor junction is due mainly to majority carriers as opposed to minority carriers in a pn junction. The basic process in the rectifying contact with an n-type semiconductor is by transport of electrons over the potential barrier, which can be described by the thermionic emission theory.

The thermionic emission characteristics are derived by using the assumptions that the barrier height is much larger than kT, so that the Maxwell–Boltzmann approximation applies and that thermal equilibrium is not affected by this process. Figure 9.17 shows the one-dimensional barrier with an applied forward-bias voltage V_a and shows two electron current density components. The current $J_{s \to m}$ is the electron current density due to the flow of electrons from the semiconductor into the metal, and the current $J_{m \to s}$ is the electron current density due to the flow of electrons from the metal into the semiconductor. The subscripts of the currents indicate the direction of electron flow. The conventional current direction is opposite to electron flow.

Thermionic emission

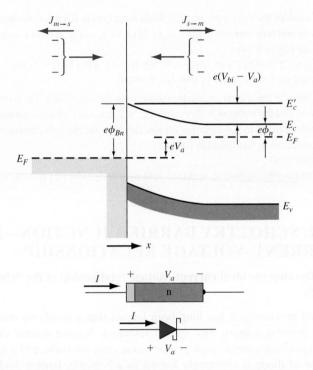

Figure 9.17 | Energy-band diagram of a forward-biased metal–semiconductor junction.

The current density $J_{s \to m}$ is a function of the concentration of electrons that have x-directed velocities sufficient to overcome the barrier. We can write

$$J_{s \to m} = e \int_{E_c'}^{\infty} v_x \, dn \tag{9.35}$$

where E_c' is the minimum energy required for thermionic emission into the metal, v_x is the carrier velocity in the direction of transport, and e is the magnitude of the electronic charge. The incremental electron concentration is given by

$$dn = g_c(E) f_F(E) \, dE \tag{9.36}$$

where $g_c(E)$ is the density of states in the conduction band and $f_F(E)$ is the Fermi–Dirac probability function. Assuming that the Maxwell–Boltzmann approximation applies, we can write

$$dn = \frac{4\pi (2m_n^*)^{3/2}}{h^3} \sqrt{E - E_c} \, \exp\left[\frac{-(E - E_F)}{kT}\right] dE \tag{9.37}$$

If all of the electron energy above E_c is assumed to be kinetic energy, then we have

$$\frac{1}{2} m_n^* v^2 = E - E_c \tag{9.38}$$

The net current density in the metal-to-semiconductor junction can be written as

$$J = J_{s \to m} - J_{m \to s} \tag{9.39}$$

which is defined to be positive in the direction from the metal to the semiconductor. We find that

$$J = \left[A^* T^2 \exp\left(\frac{-e\phi_{Bn}}{kT} \right) \right] \left[\exp\left(\frac{eV_a}{kT} \right) - 1 \right] \tag{9.40}$$

where

$$A^* \equiv \frac{4\pi e m_n^* k^2}{h^3} \tag{9.41}$$

The parameter A^* is called the effective Richardson constant for thermionic emission.

Richardson constant

Equation (9.40) can be written in the usual diode form as

$$J = J_{sT} \left[\exp\left(\frac{eV_a}{kT} \right) - 1 \right] \tag{9.42}$$

Ideal current–voltage relation

where J_{sT} is the reverse-saturation current density and is given by

Reverse-saturation current

$$J_{sT} = A^* T^2 \exp\left(\frac{-e\phi_{Bn}}{kT} \right) \tag{9.43}$$

We will assume, in this text, that the barrier height, ϕ_{Bn}, is the same as the ideal barrier height, ϕ_{B0}. We will neglect any nonideal effects. Typically, the Richardson constant for silicon is $A^* = 120$ A/cm^2/K^2 and that for GaAs is $A^* = 1.12$ A/cm^2/K^2. The difference is due to the effective mass of the electron.

EXAMPLE 9.7

OBJECTIVE

Calculate the reverse-saturation current density in a silicon Schottky diode.

Assume the barrier height is $\phi_{Bn} = 0.67$ V and the temperature is $T = 300$ K.

■ **Solution**

We have

$$J_{sT} = A^* T^2 \exp\left(\frac{-e\phi_{Bn}}{kT} \right) = (120)(300)^2 \exp\left(\frac{-0.67}{0.0259} \right)$$

or

$$J_{sT} = 6.29 \times 10^{-5} \text{ A/cm}^2$$

■ **Comment**

In general, the reverse-saturation current density in a Schottky barrier diode is several orders of magnitude larger than the reverse-saturation current density in a pn junction diode. This result is actually an advantage in several applications of Schottky diodes.

Exercise Problem

EX9.7   Calculate the reverse-saturation current density in a GaAs Schottky diode at
$T = 300$ K. Assume a Schottky barrier height of $\phi_{Bn} = 0.86$ V.
(Ans. 3.83×10^{-10} A/cm^2)

9.3.2   Comparison of the Schottky Diode and the pn Junction Diode

Although the ideal current–voltage relationship of the Schottky barrier diode given by Equation (9.42) is of the same form as that of the pn junction diode, there are two important differences between a Schottky diode and a pn junction diode: The first is in the magnitudes of the reverse-saturation current densities, and the second is in the switching characteristics.

We noted the relatively large reverse-saturation current density in a Schottky diode in Example 9.7. The reverse-bias current in a silicon pn junction diode is dominated by the generation current. Even so, the reverse-bias current density in a silicon pn junction is 2 to 3 orders of magnitude less than the reverse-bias current density in a Schottky diode.

Since $J_{sT} \gg J_s$, the forward-bias characteristics of the two types of diodes will also be different. Figure 9.18 shows typical I–V characteristics of a Schottky diode and a pn junction diode. The effective turn-on voltage of a Schottky diode is less than that of a pn junction diode. It requires less forward-bias voltage on a Schottky diode compared to the pn junction diode to obtain the same forward-bias current.

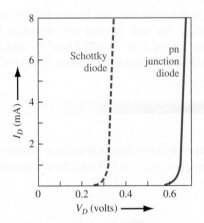

Figure 9.18 | Comparison of forward-bias I–V characteristics between a Schottky diode and a pn junction diode.

EXAMPLE 9.8

OBJECTIVE

Calculate the forward-bias voltage required to generate a forward-bias current density of 25 A/cm^2 in a Schottky diode and a pn junction diode.

Assume reverse-saturation current densities of $J_{sT} = 5 \times 10^{-5}$ A/cm^2 and $J_s = 10^{-11}$ A/cm^2 for the Schottky diode and pn junction diode, respectively. Let $T = 300$ K.

■ Solution

For the Schottky diode, we have

$$J = J_{sT}\left[\exp\left(\frac{eV_a}{kT}\right) - 1\right]$$

Neglecting the (-1) term, we can solve for the forward-bias voltage. We find

$$V_a = \left(\frac{kT}{e}\right)\ln\left(\frac{J}{J_{sT}}\right) = V_t \ln\left(\frac{J}{J_{sT}}\right) = (0.0259)\ln\left(\frac{20}{5 \times 10^{-5}}\right) = 0.334 \text{ V}$$

For the pn junction diode, we have

$$V_a = V_t \ln\left(\frac{J}{J_s}\right) = (0.0259)\ln\left(\frac{20}{10^{-11}}\right) = 0.734 \text{ V}$$

■ Comment

A comparison of the two forward-bias voltages shows that the Schottky barrier diode has a turn-on voltage that, in this case, is approximately 0.4 V smaller than the turn-on voltage of the pn junction diode.

Exercise Problem

EX9.8 (*a*) The reverse-saturation currents of a pn junction and a Schottky diode are 10^{-14} A and 10^{-9} A, respectively. Determine the required forward-bias voltages in the pn junction diode and Schottky diode to produce a current of $100 \ \mu$A in each diode. (*b*) Repeat part (*a*) for forward bias currents of 1 mA.
[Ans. (*a*) 0.596 V, 0.298 V (*b*) 0.656 V, 0.358 V]

The actual difference between the turn-on voltages will be a function of the barrier height of the metal–semiconductor contact and the doping concentrations in the pn junction, but the relatively large difference will always be realized.

The second major difference between a Schottky barrier diode and a pn junction diode is in the frequency response, or switching characteristics. In our discussion, we have considered the current in a Schottky diode as being due to the injection of majority carriers over a potential barrier. The energy-band diagram of Figure 9.17, for example, showed that there can be electrons in the metal directly adjacent to empty states in the semiconductor. If an electron from the valence band of the semiconductor were to flow into the metal, this effect would be equivalent to holes being injected into the semiconductor. This injection of holes would create excess minority-carrier holes in the n region. However, calculations as well as measurements have shown that the ratio of the minority-carrier hole current to the total current is extremely low in most cases.

Majority-carrier device

The Schottky barrier diode, then, is a majority-carrier device. This fact means that there is no diffusion capacitance associated with a forward-biased Schottky diode. The elimination of the diffusion capacitance makes the Schottky diode a higher-frequency device than the pn junction diode. Also, when switching a Schottky diode from forward to reverse bias, there is no minority-carrier stored charge to remove, as was the case in the pn junction diode. Since there is no minority-carrier storage time, the Schottky diodes can be used in fast-switching applications. A typical switching time for a Schottky diode is in the picosecond range, while for a pn junction it is normally in the nanosecond range.

TEST YOUR UNDERSTANDING

TYU9.6   A pn junction diode and a Schottky diode have equal cross-sectional areas and have forward-biased currents of 0.5 mA. The reverse-saturation current of the Schottky diode is 5×10^{-7} A. The difference in forward-bias voltage between the two diodes is 0.30 V. Determine the reverse-saturation current of the pn junction diode. (Ans. 4.66×10^{-12} A)

9.4 | SMALL-SIGNAL MODEL OF THE pn JUNCTION

Objective: Develop the small-signal equivalent circuit of the pn junction diode.

We have been considering the dc characteristics of the pn junction diode. When semiconductor devices with pn junctions are used in linear amplifier circuits, for example, sinusoidal signals are superimposed on the dc currents and voltages, so that the small-signal characteristics of the pn junction become important.

9.4.1   Diffusion Resistance

The ideal current–voltage relationship of the pn junction diode was given by Equation (9.27), where J and J_s are current densities. If we multiply both sides of the equation by the junction cross-sectional area, we have

$$I_D = I_s \left[\exp\left(\frac{eV_a}{kT}\right) - 1 \right] \tag{9.44}$$

where I_D is the diode current and I_s is the diode reverse saturation current.

Assume that the diode is forward-biased with a dc voltage V_0 producing a dc diode current I_{DQ}. If we now superimpose a small, low-frequency sinusoidal voltage as shown in Figure 9.19, then a small sinusoidal current will be produced, superimposed on the dc current. The ratio of sinusoidal current to sinusoidal voltage is called the incremental conductance. In the limit of a very small sinusoidal current and

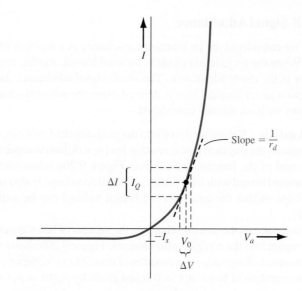

Figure 9.19 | Curve showing the concept of the small-signal diffusion resistance.

voltage, the small-signal incremental conductance is just the slope of the dc current–voltage curve, or

$$g_d = \frac{dI_D}{dV_a}\bigg|_{V_a=V_0} \tag{9.45}$$

The reciprocal of the incremental conductance is the incremental resistance, defined as

$$r_d = \frac{dV_a}{dI_D}\bigg|_{I_D=I_{DQ}} \tag{9.46}$$

where I_{DQ} is the dc quiescent diode current.

If we assume that the diode is biased sufficiently far in the forward-bias region, then the (-1) term can be neglected and the incremental conductance becomes

$$g_d = \frac{dI_D}{dV_a}\bigg|_{V_a=V_0} = \left(\frac{e}{kT}\right)I_s\,\exp\left(\frac{eV_0}{kT}\right) \approx \frac{I_{DQ}}{V_t} \tag{9.47}$$

Diffusion conductance

The small-signal incremental resistance is then the reciprocal function, or

$$\boxed{r_d = \frac{V_t}{I_{DQ}}} \tag{9.48}$$

The incremental resistance decreases as the bias current increases, and is inversely proportional to the slope of the *I–V* characteristic as shown in Figure 9.19. The incremental resistance is also known as the *diffusion resistance*.

Diffusion resistance

9.4.2 Small-Signal Admittance

In Chapter 8, we considered the pn junction capacitance as a function of the reverse-bias voltage. When the pn junction diode is forward biased, another capacitance becomes a factor in the diode admittance. The small-signal admittance, or impedance, of the pn junction under forward bias is derived using the minority-carrier diffusion current relations we have already considered.

Qualitative Analysis   Before we delve into the mathematical analysis, we can qualitatively understand the physical processes that lead to a diffusion capacitance, which is one component of the junction admittance. Figure 9.20a schematically shows a pn junction forward biased with a dc voltage. A small ac voltage is also superimposed on the dc voltage so that the total forward-biased voltage can be written as $V_a = V_{dc} + \hat{v} \sin \omega t$.

As the voltage across the junction changes, the number of holes injected across the space charge region into the n region also changes. Figure 9.20b shows the hole concentration at the space charge edge as a function of time. At $t = t_0$, the ac voltage is zero so that the concentration of holes at $x = 0$ is just given by $p_n(0) = p_{n0} \exp(V_{dc}/V_t)$, which is what we have seen previously.

Now, as the ac voltage increases during its positive half cycle, the concentration of holes at $x = 0$ will increase and reach a peak value at $t = t_1$, which corresponds to the peak value of the ac voltage. When the ac voltage is on its negative half cycle, the total voltage across the junction decreases so that the concentration of holes at $x = 0$ decreases. The concentration reaches a minimum value at $t = t_2$, which

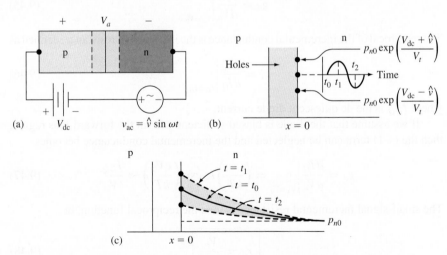

Figure 9.20 | (a) A pn junction with an ac voltage superimposed on a forward-biased dc value; (b) the hole concentration at the space charge edge versus time; and (c) the hole concentration versus distance in the n region at three different times (for relatively low ac voltage frequency).

corresponds to the time that the ac voltage reaches its maximum negative value. The minority-carrier hole concentration at $x = 0$, then, has an ac component superimposed on the dc value as indicated in Figure 9.20b.

As previously discussed, the holes at the space charge edge ($x = 0$) diffuse into the n region where they recombine with the majority-carrier electrons. We will assume that the period of the ac voltage is large compared to the time it takes carriers to diffuse into the n region. The hole concentration as a function of distance into the n region can then be treated as a steady-state distribution. Figure 9.20c shows the steady-state hole concentrations at three different times. At $t = t_0$, the ac voltage is zero, so the $t = t_0$ curve corresponds to the hole distribution established by the dc voltage. The $t = t_1$ curve corresponds to the distribution established when the ac voltage has reached its peak positive value, and the $t = t_2$ curve corresponds to the distribution established when the ac voltage has reached its maximum negative value. The shaded areas represents the charge ΔQ that is alternately charged and discharged during the ac voltage cycle.

Exactly the same process is occurring in the p region with the electron concentration. The mechanism of charging and discharging of holes in the n region and electrons in the p region leads to a capacitance. This capacitance is called *diffusion capacitance*. The physical mechanism of this diffusion capacitance is different from that of the junction capacitance discussed in Chapter 5. We will show that the magnitude of the diffusion capacitance in a forward-biased pn junction is usually substantially larger than the junction capacitance.

When the small-signal junction admittance Y is determined using the ambipolar transport equation containing both the spatial- and time-dependent terms, the result is

$$Y = \left(\frac{1}{V_t}\right)(I_{p0} + I_{n0}) + j\omega\left[\left(\frac{1}{2V_t}\right)(I_{p0}\tau_{p0} + I_{n0}\tau_{n0})\right] \qquad (9.49)$$

where I_{p0} and I_{n0} are the hole and electron components of the diode current, and τ_{p0} and τ_{n0} are the excess minority-carrier lifetimes.

Equation (9.49) can be written in the form

$$Y = g_d + j\omega C_d \qquad (9.50)$$

The parameter g_d is called the *diffusion conductance* and is given by

$$g_d = \left(\frac{1}{V_t}\right)(I_{p0} + I_{n0}) = \frac{I_{DQ}}{V_t} \qquad (9.51)$$

where I_{DQ} is the dc bias current. Equation (9.51) is exactly the same conductance as we obtained previously in Equation (9.47). The parameter C_d is called the *diffusion capacitance* and is given by

Diffusion capacitance

$$\boxed{C_d = \left(\frac{1}{2V_t}\right)(I_{p0}\tau_{p0} + I_{n0}\tau_{n0})} \qquad (9.52)$$

EXAMPLE 9.9

OBJECTIVE

To calculate the small-signal admittance of a pn junction diode.

This example is intended to give an indication of the magnitude of the diffusion capacitance as compared with the junction capacitance considered in Chapter 5. The diffusion resistance will also be calculated. Assume that $N_a \gg N_d$ so that $p_{n0} \gg n_{p0}$. This assumption implies that $I_{p0} \gg I_{n0}$. Let $T = 300$ K, $\tau_{p0} = 10^{-7}$ s, and $I_{p0} = I_{DQ} = 1$ mA.

■ Solution

The diffusion capacitance, with these assumptions, is given by

$$C_d \approx \left(\frac{1}{2V_t} \right) (I_{p0} \tau_{p0}) = \frac{1}{(2)(0.0259)} (10^{-3})(10^{-7}) = 1.93 \times 10^{-9} \text{ F}$$

The diffusion resistance is

$$r_d = \frac{V_t}{I_{DQ}} = \frac{0.0259 \text{ V}}{1 \text{ mA}} = 25.9 \; \Omega$$

■ Comment

The value of 1.93 nF for the diffusion capacitance of a forward-biased pn junction is 3 to 4 orders of magnitude larger than the junction or depletion capacitance of the reverse-biased pn junction that we found in Chapter 5. Typically, we found junction capacitances on the order of a few tenths of a pF. The forward-bias diffusion capacitance will also become important in bipolar transistors covered in Chapter 10.

Exercise Problem

EX9.9   A silicon pn junction diode at $T = 300$ K has the following parameters:
$N_d = 8 \times 10^{16}$ cm^{-3}, $N_a = 2 \times 10^{15}$ cm^{-3}, $D_n = 25$ cm^2/s, $D_p = 10$ cm^2/s,
$\tau_{n0} = 5 \times 10^{-7}$ s, and $\tau_{p0} = 10^{-7}$ s. The cross-sectional area is $A = 10^{-3}$ cm^2.
Determine the diffusion resistance and diffusion capacitance if the diode is
forward biased at (a) $V_a = 0.550$ V and (b) $V_a = 0.610$ V.
[Ans. (a) $r_d = 118 \; \Omega$, $C_d = 2.06$ nF; (b) $r_d = 11.6 \; \Omega$, $C_d = 20.9$ nF]

The diffusion capacitance tends to dominate the capacitance terms in a forward-biased pn junction. The small-signal diffusion resistance can be fairly small if the diode current is a fairly large value. As the diode current decreases, the diffusion resistance increases. We will consider the impedance of forward-biased pn junctions again when we discuss bipolar transistors.

9.4.3   Equivalent Circuit

The small-signal equivalent circuit of the forward-biased pn junction is derived from Equation (9.50). This circuit is shown in Figure 9.21a. We need to add the junction capacitance, which will be in parallel with the diffusion resistance and diffusion capacitance. The last element we add, to complete the equivalent circuit, is a series

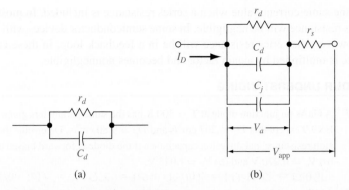

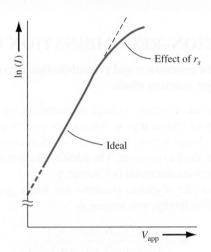

Figure 9.21 | (a) Small-signal equivalent circuit of ideal forward-biased pn junction diode; (b) complete small-signal equivalent circuit of pn junction.

Figure 9.22 | Forward-biased I–V characteristics of a pn junction diode showing the effect of series resistance.

resistance. The neutral n and p regions have finite resistances so the actual pn junction will include a series resistance. The complete equivalent circuit is given in Figure 9.21b.

The voltage across the actual junction is V_a and the total voltage applied to the pn diode is given by V_{app}. The junction voltage V_a is the voltage in the ideal current–voltage expression. We can write the expression

$$V_{\text{app}} = V_a + Ir_s \qquad (9.53)$$

Figure 9.22 is a plot of the current–voltage characteristic from Equation (9.53), showing the effect of the series resistance. A larger applied voltage is required to achieve the same current value when a series resistance is included. In most diodes, the series resistance will be negligible. In some semiconductor devices with pn junctions, however, the series resistance will be in a feedback loop; in these cases, the resistance is multiplied by a gain factor and becomes nonnegligible.

TEST YOUR UNDERSTANDING

TYU9.7 A GaAs pn junction diode at $T = 300$ K has the same parameters given in EX9.9 except that $D_n = 207$ cm^2/s and $D_p = 9.80$ cm^2/s. Determine the diffusion resistance and diffusion capacitance if the diode is forward biased at (a) $V_a = 0.970$ V and (b) $V_a = 1.045$ V.

[Ans. (a) $r_d = 263$ Ω, $C_d = 0.940$ nF; (b) $r_d = 14.6$ Ω, $C_d = 17.0$ nF]

TYU9.8 A silicon pn junction diode at $T = 300$ K has the same parameters as those described in EX9.9. The neutral n-region and neutral p-region lengths are 0.01 cm. Estimate the series resistance of the diode (neglect ohmic contacts).

(Ans. $R = 66$ Ω)

9.5 | GENERATION–RECOMBINATION CURRENTS

Objective: Analyze the generation and recombination currents in the space charge region of the pn junction diode.

In the derivation of the ideal current–voltage relationship, we neglected any effects occurring within the space charge region. Since other current components are generated within the space charge region, the actual *I–V* characteristics of a pn junction diode deviate from the ideal expression. The additional currents are generated from the recombination processes discussed in Chapter 5.

The recombination rate of excess electrons and holes, given by the Shockley–Read–Hall recombination theory, was written as

$$R = \frac{C_n C_p N_t \left(np - n_i^2\right)}{C_n(n + n') + C_p(p + p')} \tag{9.54}$$

The parameters n and p are, as usual, the concentrations of electrons and holes, respectively.

9.5.1 Reverse-Bias Generation Current

For a pn junction under reverse bias, we have argued that the mobile electrons and holes have essentially been swept out of the space charge region. Accordingly, within the space charge region, $n \approx p \approx 0$. The recombination rate from Equation (9.54) becomes

$$R = \frac{-C_n C_p N_t n_i^2}{C_n n' + C_p p'} \tag{9.55}$$

The negative sign implies a negative recombination rate; hence, we are really generating electron–hole pairs within the reverse-biased space charge region. The

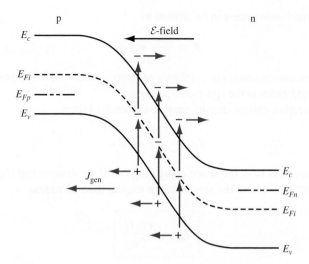

Figure 9.23 | Generation process in a reverse-biased pn junction.

recombination of excess electrons and holes is the process whereby we are trying to reestablish thermal equilibrium. Since the concentration of electrons and holes is essentially zero within the reverse-biased space charge region, electrons and holes are being generated via the trap level to also try to reestablish thermal equilibrium. This generation process is schematically shown in Figure 9.23. As the electrons and holes are generated, they are swept out of the space charge region by the electric field. The flow of charge is in the direction of a reverse-bias current. This *reverse-bias generation current,* caused by the generation of electrons and holes in the space charge region, is in addition to the ideal reverse-bias saturation current.

We can calculate the density of the reverse-bias generation current by considering Equation (9.55). If we make a simplifying assumption and let the trap level be at the intrinsic Fermi level, then, we have that $n' = n_i$ and $p' = n_i$. Equation (9.55) now becomes

$$R = \frac{-n_i}{\dfrac{1}{N_t C_p} + \dfrac{1}{N_t C_n}} \tag{9.56}$$

Using the definitions of lifetimes from Chapter 8, we can write Equation (9.56) as

$$R = \frac{-n_i}{\tau_{p0} + \tau_{n0}} \tag{9.57}$$

If we define a new lifetime as the average of τ_{p0} and τ_{n0}, or

$$\tau_0 = \frac{\tau_{p0} + \tau_{n0}}{2} \tag{9.58}$$

then the recombination rate can be written as

$$R = \frac{-n_i}{2\tau_0} \equiv -G \tag{9.59}$$

The negative recombination rate implies a generation rate, so G is the generation rate of electrons and holes in the space charge region.

Generation current   The generation current density may be determined from

$$J_{\text{gen}} = \int_0^W eG \, dx \tag{9.60}$$

where the integral is over the space charge region. If we assume that the generation rate is constant throughout the space charge region, then we obtain

$$\boxed{J_{\text{gen}} = \frac{en_i W}{2\tau_0}} \tag{9.61}$$

The total reverse-bias current density is the sum of the ideal reverse saturation current density and the generation current density, or

$$J_R = J_s + J_{\text{gen}} \tag{9.62}$$

The ideal reverse saturation current density J_s is independent of the reverse-bias voltage. However, J_{gen} is a function of the depletion width W, which in turn is a function of the reverse-bias voltage. The actual reverse-bias current density, then, is no longer independent of the reverse-bias voltage.

EXAMPLE 9.10

OBJECTIVE

Determine the relative magnitudes of the ideal reverse-saturation current density and the generation current density in a silicon pn junction at $T = 300$ K.

Consider the silicon pn junction described in Example 9.2 and let $\tau_0 = \tau_{p0} = \tau_{n0} = 5 \times 10^{-7}$ s.

■ **Solution**

The ideal reverse saturation current density was calculated in Example 9.2 and was found to be $J_s = 4.15 \times 10^{-11}$ A/cm^2. The generation current density is again given by Equation (9.61) as

$$J_{\text{gen}} = \frac{en_i W}{2\tau_0}$$

and the depletion width is given by

$$W = \left[\frac{2\epsilon_s}{e} \left(\frac{N_a + N_d}{N_a N_d} \right) (V_{bi} + V_R) \right]^{1/2}$$

If we assume, for example, that $V_{bi} + V_R = 5$ V, then using the parameters given in Example 9.2 we find that $W = 1.14 \times 10^{-4}$ cm, and then calculate the generation current density to be

$$J_{\text{gen}} = 2.74 \times 10^{-7} \text{ A/cm}^2$$

■ Comment

Comparing the solutions for the two current densities, it is obvious that, for the silicon pn junction diode at room temperature, the generation current density is approximately four orders of magnitude larger than the ideal saturation current density. The generation current is the dominant reverse-bias current in a silicon pn junction diode.

Exercise Problem

EX9.10 A GaAs pn junction diode at $T = 300$ K has the following parameters:
$N_d = 8 \times 10^{16}$ cm^{-3}, $N_a = 2 \times 10^{15}$ cm^{-3}, $D_n = 207$ cm^2/s, $D_p = 9.80$ cm^2/s, $\tau_{n0} = 5 \times 10^{-7}$ s, and $\tau_{p0} = 10^{-7}$ s. The cross-sectional area is $A = 10^{-3}$ cm^2.
(*a*) Calculate the reverse-bias generation current if the diode is reverse biased at $V_R = 5$ V. (*b*) Determine the ratio of I_{gen} calculated in part (*a*) to the ideal reverse-saturation current I_S. (Ans. (*a*) $I_{\text{gen}} = 1.03 \times 10^{-13}$ A. (*b*) 1.93×10^{7}.)

9.5.2 Forward-Bias Recombination Current

For the reverse-biased pn junction, electrons and holes are essentially completely swept out of the space charge region so that $n \approx p \approx 0$. Under forward bias, however, electrons and holes are injected across the space charge region, so we do, in fact, have some excess carriers in the space charge region. The possibility exists that some of these electrons and holes will recombine within the space charge region and not become part of the minority carrier distribution.

The recombination rate of electrons and holes is again given from Equation (9.54) as

$$R = \frac{C_n C_p N_t \left(np - n_i^2\right)}{C_n(n + n') + C_p(p + p')}$$

Dividing both numerator and denominator by $C_n C_p N_t$ and using the definitions of τ_{n0} and τ_{p0}, we can write the recombination rate as

$$R = \frac{np - n_i^2}{\tau_{p0}(n + n') + \tau_{n0}(p + p')} \tag{9.63}$$

Figure 9.24 shows the energy-band diagram of the forward-biased pn junction. Shown in the figure are the intrinsic Fermi level and the quasi-Fermi levels for electrons and holes. From the results of Chapter 8, we can write the electron concentration as

$$n = n_i \exp\left(\frac{E_{Fn} - E_{Fi}}{kT}\right) \tag{9.64}$$

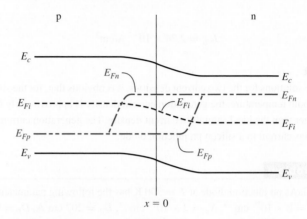

Figure 9.24 | Energy-band diagram of a forward-biased pn junction including quasi-Fermi levels.

and the hole concentration as

$$p = n_i \exp\left(\frac{E_{Fi} - E_{Fp}}{kT}\right) \tag{9.65}$$

where E_{Fn} and E_{Fp} are the quasi-Fermi levels for electrons and holes, respectively.

Since $(E_{Fn} - E_{Fi})$ and $(E_{Fi} - E_{Fp})$ vary through the space charge region. The calculation of the recombination rate is beyond the scope of this text.

Recombination current

By applying some approximations, we can write the recombination current density as

$$\boxed{J_{\text{rec}} = \frac{eWn_i}{2\tau_0}\exp\left(\frac{eV_a}{2kT}\right) = J_{r0}\exp\left(\frac{eV_a}{2kT}\right)} \tag{9.66}$$

where W is the space charge width.

EXAMPLE 9.11

OBJECTIVE

Determine the recombination current density.

Consider a silicon pn junction with the same parameters as considered in Example 9.10. (*a*) Determine the recombination current density for $V_a = 0.3$ V. (*b*) Determine the ratio of J_{rec} calculated in part (*a*) to the ideal diffusion current density at $V_a = 0.3$ V.

■ **Solution**

(*a*) We find that

$$V_{bi} = V_t \ln\left(\frac{N_a N_d}{n_i^2}\right) = (0.0259)\ln\left[\frac{(10^{16})(10^{16})}{(1.5 \times 10^{10})^2}\right] = 0.695 \text{ V}$$

and

$$W = \left[\frac{2\epsilon_s}{e} \left(\frac{N_a + N_d}{N_a N_d} \right) (V_{bi} - V_a) \right]^{1/2}$$

$$= \left\{ \frac{2(11.7)(8.85 \times 10^{-14})}{1.6 \times 10^{-19}} \left[\frac{10^{16} + 10^{16}}{(10^{16})(10^{16})} \right] (0.695 - 0.30) \right\}^{1/2}$$

or

$$W = 0.320 \ \mu\text{m}$$

Then

$$J_{\text{rec}} = \frac{eWn_i}{2\tau_0} \exp\left(\frac{V_a}{2V_t} \right)$$

$$= \frac{(1.6 \times 10^{-19})(0.32 \times 10^{-4})(1.5 \times 10^{10})}{2(5 \times 10^{-7})} \exp\left[\frac{0.30}{2\,(0.0259)} \right]$$

or

$$J_{\text{rec}} = 2.52 \times 10^{-5} \ \text{A/cm}^2$$

(b) From Example 9.2, we found that $J_S = 4.15 \times 10^{-11}$ A/cm^2. So

$$J_D \approx J_S \exp\left(\frac{V_a}{V_t} \right) = (4.15 \times 10^{-11}) \exp\left(\frac{0.30}{0.0259} \right)$$

or

$$J_D = 4.45 \times 10^{-6} \ \text{A/cm}^2$$

Then

$$\frac{J_{\text{rec}}}{J_D} = \frac{2.52 \times 10^{-5}}{4.45 \times 10^{-6}} = 5.66$$

■ **Comment**

For a low value of forward-bias voltage, the recombination current dominates the total forward-bias current.

Exercise Problem

EX9.11 Repeat Example 9.11 for a forward-bias voltage of $V_a = 0.5$ V. Compare the result to that of Example 9.11. (Ans. $J_{\text{rec}}/J_D = 0.804$.)

9.5.3 Total Forward-Bias Current

The total forward-bias current density in the pn junction is the sum of the recombination and the ideal diffusion current densities. Figure 9.25 shows a plot of the minority-carrier hole concentration in the neutral n region. This distribution yields the ideal hole diffusion current density and is a function of the minority-carrier hole diffusion length and the applied junction voltage. The distribution is established as a result of holes being injected across the space charge region. If, now, some of the injected holes in the space charge region are lost due to recombination, then additional

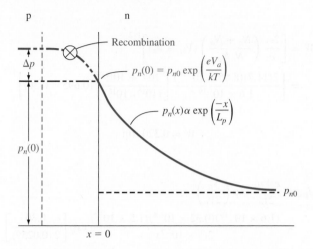

Figure 9.25 | Because of recombination, additional holes from the p region must be injected into the space charge region to establish the minority carrier hole concentration in the n region.

holes must be injected from the p region to make up for this loss. The flow of these additional injected carriers, per unit time, results in the recombination current. This added component is schematically shown in the figure.

The total forward-bias current density is the sum of the recombination and the ideal diffusion current densities, so we can write

$$J = J_{\text{rec}} + J_D \tag{9.67}$$

where J_{rec} is given by Equation (9.66) and J_D is given by

$$J_D = J_s \exp\left(\frac{eV_a}{kT}\right) \tag{9.68}$$

The (-1) term in Equation (9.27) has been neglected. The parameter J_s is the ideal reverse saturation current density, and from previous discussion, the value of J_{r0} from the recombination current is larger than the value of J_s.

If we take the natural log of Equations (9.66) and (9.68), we obtain

$$\ln J_{\text{rec}} = \ln J_{r0} + \frac{eV_a}{2kT} = \ln J_{r0} + \frac{V_a}{2V_t} \tag{9.69a}$$

and

$$\ln J_D = \ln J_s + \frac{eV_a}{kT} = \ln J_s + \frac{V_a}{V_t} \tag{9.69b}$$

Figure 9.26 shows the recombination and diffusion current components plotted on a log current scale as a function of V_a/V_t. The slopes of the two curves are not the

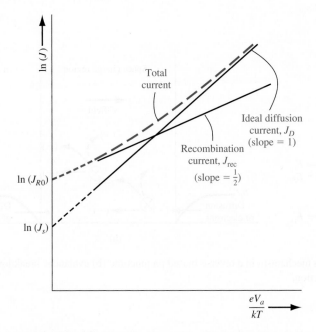

Figure 9.26 | Ideal diffusion, recombination, and total current in a forward-biased pn junction.

same. Also shown in the figure is the total current density—the sum of the two current components. We can notice that, at a low current density, the recombination current dominates, and at a higher current density, the ideal diffusion current dominates.

In general, the diode current–voltage relationship can be written as

$$I = I_s \left[\exp\left(\frac{eV_a}{nkT}\right) - 1 \right] \qquad (9.70)$$

where the parameter n is called the *ideality factor*. For a large forward-bias voltage, $n \approx 1$ when diffusion dominates, and for low forward-bias voltage, $n \approx 2$ when recombination dominates. There is a transition region where $1 < n < 2$.

Ideality factor

9.6 | JUNCTION BREAKDOWN

Objective: Discuss the breakdown voltage in the diode.

In the ideal pn junction, a reverse-bias voltage will result in a small reverse-bias current through the device. However, the reverse-bias voltage may not increase without limit; at some particular voltage, the reverse-bias current will increase rapidly. The applied voltage at this point is called the *breakdown voltage*.

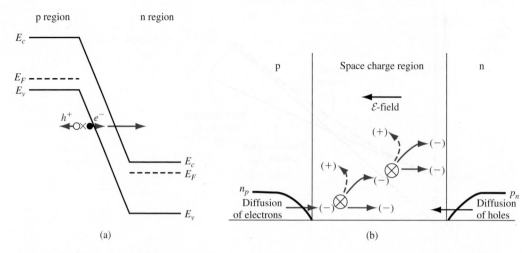

Figure 9.27 | (a) Zener breakdown mechanism in a reverse-biased pn junction; (b) avalanche breakdown process in a reverse-biased pn junction.

Zener breakdown

Two physical mechanisms give rise to the reverse-bias breakdown in a pn junction: the *Zener effect* and the *avalanche effect.* Zener breakdown occurs in highly doped pn junctions through a tunneling mechanism. In a highly doped junction, the conduction and valence bands on opposite sides of the junction are sufficiently close during reverse bias that electrons may tunnel directly from the valence band on the p side into the conduction band on the n side. This tunneling process is schematically shown in Figure 9.27a.

Avalanche breakdown

The avalanche breakdown process occurs when electrons and/or holes, moving across the space charge region, acquire sufficient energy from the electric field to create electron–hole pairs by colliding with atomic electrons within the depletion region. The avalanche process is schematically shown in Figure 9.27b. The newly created electrons and holes move in opposite directions due to the electric field and thereby add to the existing reverse-bias current. In addition, the newly generated electrons and/or holes may acquire sufficient energy to ionize other atoms, leading to the avalanche process. For most pn junctions, the predominant breakdown mechanism will be the avalanche effect.

If we assume that a reverse-bias electron current I_{n0} enters the depletion region at $x = 0$ as shown in Figure 9.28, the electron current I_n will increase with distance through the depletion region due to the avalanche process. At $x = W$, the electron current can be written as

$$I_n(W) = M_n I_{n0} \tag{9.71}$$

where M_n is a multiplication factor. The hole current is increasing through the depletion region from the n to p region and reaches a maximum value at $x = 0$. The total current is constant through the pn junction in steady state.

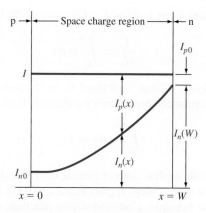

Figure 9.28 | Electron and hole current components through the space charge region during avalanche multiplication.

We can write an expression for the incremental electron current at some point x as

$$dI_n(x) = I_n(x)\alpha_n\,dx + I_p(x)\alpha_p\,dx \qquad (9.72)$$

where α_n and α_p are the electron and hole ionization rates, respectively. The ionization rates are the number of electron–hole pairs generated per unit length by an electron (α_n) or by a hole (α_p). Equation (9.72) can be written as

$$\frac{dI_n(x)}{dx} = I_n(x)\alpha_n + I_p(x)\alpha_p \qquad (9.73)$$

The total current I is given by

$$I = I_n(x) + I_p(x) \qquad (9.74)$$

which is a constant. Solving for $I_p(x)$ from Equation (9.74) and substituting into Equation (9.73), we obtain

$$\frac{dI_n(x)}{dx} + (\alpha_p - \alpha_n)I_n(x) = \alpha_p I \qquad (9.75)$$

If we make the assumption that the electron and hole ionization rates are equal so

$$\alpha_n = \alpha_p \equiv \alpha \qquad (9.76)$$

then Equation (9.75) can be simplified and integrated through the space charge region. We will obtain

$$I_n(W) - I_n(0) = I\int_0^W \alpha\,dx \qquad (9.77)$$

Using Equation (9.71), Equation (9.77) can be written as

$$\frac{M_n I_{n0} - I_n(0)}{I} = \int_0^W \alpha\,dx \qquad (9.78)$$

Since $M_n I_{n0} \approx I$ and since $I_n(0) = I_{n0}$, Equation (9.78) becomes

$$1 - \frac{1}{M_n} = \int_0^W \alpha \, dx \tag{9.79}$$

The avalanche breakdown voltage is defined to be the voltage at which M_n approaches infinity. The avalanche breakdown condition is then given by

$$\int_0^W \alpha \, dx = 1 \tag{9.80}$$

The ionization rates are strong functions of electric field and, since the electric field is not constant through the space charge region, Equation (9.80) is not easy to evaluate.

If we consider, for example, a one-sided p^+n junction, the maximum electric field is given by

$$\mathcal{E}_{max} = \frac{e N_d x_n}{\epsilon_s} \tag{9.81}$$

The depletion width x_n is given approximately as

$$x_n \approx \left(\frac{2\epsilon_s V_R}{e} \frac{1}{N_d} \right)^{1/2} \tag{9.82}$$

where V_R is the magnitude of the applied reverse-bias voltage. We have neglected the built-in potential V_{bi}.

If we now define V_R to be the breakdown voltage V_B, the maximum electric field, $\mathcal{E}_{max}$, will be defined as a critical electric field, $\mathcal{E}_{crit}$, at breakdown. Combining Equations (9.81) and (9.82), we can write

$$\boxed{V_B = \frac{\epsilon_s \mathcal{E}_{crit}^2}{2e N_B}} \tag{9.83}$$

Critical electric field

where N_B is the semiconductor doping in the low-doped region of the one-sided junction. The critical electric field, plotted in Figure 9.29, is a slight function of doping.

We have been considering a uniformly doped planar junction. The breakdown voltage will decrease for a linearly graded junction. Figure 9.30 shows a plot of the breakdown voltage for a one-sided abrupt junction and a linearly graded junction. If we take into account the curvature of a diffused junction as well, the breakdown voltage will be further degraded.

EXAMPLE 9.12

OBJECTIVE

Design an ideal one-sided n^+p junction diode to meet a breakdown voltage specification.

Consider a silicon pn junction diode at $T = 300$ K. Assume that $N_d = 3 \times 10^{18}$ cm^{-3}. Design the diode such that the breakdown voltage is $V_B = 100$ V.

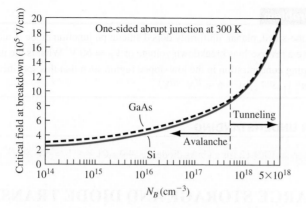

Figure 9.29 | Critical electric field at breakdown in a one-sided junction as a function of impurity doping concentrations.
(From Sze [13].)

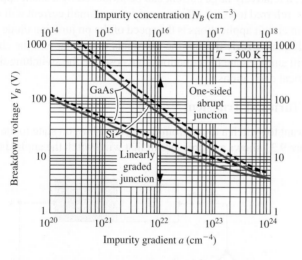

Figure 9.30 | Breakdown voltage versus impurity concentration in uniformly doped and linearly graded junctions.
(From Sze [13].)

■ Solution

From Figure 9.30, we find that the doping concentration in the low-doped side of a one-sided abrupt junction should be approximately 4×10^{15} cm^{-3} for a breakdown voltage of 100 V.

For a doping concentration of 4×10^{15} cm^{-3}, the critical electric field, from Figure 9.29, is approximately 3.7×10^5 V/cm. Then from Equation (9.83), the breakdown voltage is 110 V, which correlates quite well with the results from Figure 9.30.

■ Conclusion

As Figure 9.30 shows, the breakdown voltage increases as the doping concentration decreases in the low-doped region.

Exercise Problem

EX9.12 A one-sided, planar, uniformly doped silicon pn junction diode is required to have a reverse-bias breakdown voltage of $V_B = 60$ V. What is the maximum doping concentration in the low-doped region such that this specification is met? (Ans. $N_B \approx 9 \times 10^{15}$ cm^{-3})

TEST YOUR UNDERSTANDING

TYU9.9   Repeat EX9.12 for a GaAs diode. (Ans. $N_B \approx 1.5 \times 10^{16}$ cm^{-3})

9.7 | CHARGE STORAGE AND DIODE TRANSIENTS

Objective: Consider the switching characteristics of the diode.

The pn junction is typically used as an electrical switch. In forward bias, referred to as the *on* state, a relatively large current can be produced by a small applied voltage; in reverse bias, referred to as the *off* state, only a very small current will exist. Of primary interest in circuit applications is the speed of the pn junction diode in switching states. We will qualitatively discuss the transients that occur and the charge storage effects. We will simply state the equations that describe the switching times without any mathematical derivations.

9.7.1   The Turn-Off Transient

Suppose we want to switch a diode from the forward bias on state to the reverse-bias off state. Figure 9.31 shows a simple circuit that will switch the applied bias at $t = 0$.

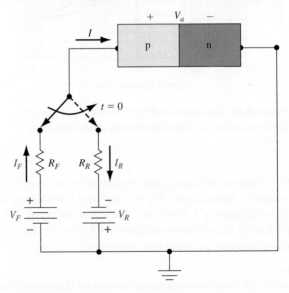

Figure 9.31 | Simple circuit for switching a diode from forward to reverse bias.

For $t < 0$, the forward-bias current is

$$I = I_F = \frac{V_F - V_a}{R_F} \qquad (9.84)$$

The minority-carrier concentrations in the device, for the applied forward voltage V_F, are shown in Figure 9.32a. There is excess minority-carrier charge stored in both the p and n regions of the diode. The excess minority-carrier concentrations at the space charge edges are supported by the forward-bias junction voltage V_a. When the voltage is switched from the forward- to the reverse-bias state, the excess minority-carrier concentrations at the space charge edges can no longer be supported and they start to decrease, as shown in Figure 9.32b.

The collapse of the minority-carrier concentrations at the edges of the space charge region leads to large concentration gradients and diffusion currents in the reverse-bias direction. If we assume, for the moment, that the voltage across the

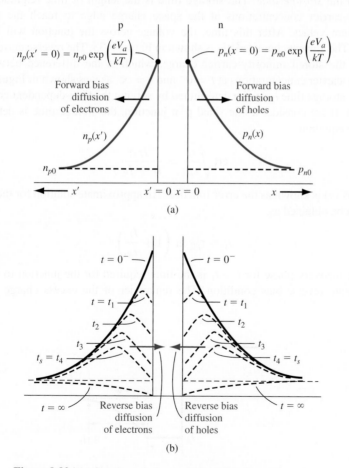

(a)

(b)

Figure 9.32 | (a) Steady-state forward-bias minority-carrier concentrations; (b) minority-carrier concentrations at various times during switching.

diode junction is small compared with V_R, then the reverse-bias current is limited to approximately

$$I = -I_R \approx \frac{-V_R}{R_R} \tag{9.85}$$

The junction capacitances do not allow the junction voltage to change instantaneously. If the current I_R were larger than this value, there would be a forward-bias voltage across the junction, which would violate our assumption of a reverse-bias current. If the current I_R were smaller than this value, there would be a reverse-bias voltage across the junction, which means that the junction voltage would have changed instantaneously. Since the reverse current is limited to the value given by Equation (9.85), the reverse-bias density gradient is constant; thus, the minority-carrier concentrations at the space charge edge decrease with time as shown in Figure 9.32b .

Storage time

This reverse current I_R will be approximately constant for $0^+ \leq t \leq t_s$, where t_s is called the *storage time*. The storage time is the length of time required for the minority-carrier concentrations at the space charge edge to reach the thermal-equilibrium values. After this time, the voltage across the junction will begin to change. The current characteristic is shown in Figure 9.33. The reverse current is the flow of the stored minority-carrier charge, which is the difference between the minority-carrier concentrations at $t = 0^-$ and $t = \infty$, as was shown in Figure 9.32b.

The storage time t_s can be determined by solving the time-dependent continuity equation. If we consider a one-sided p^+n junction, the storage time is determined from the equation

$$\text{erf}\sqrt{\frac{t_s}{\tau_{p0}}} = \frac{I_F}{I_F + I_R} \tag{9.86}$$

where erf (x) is known as the error function. An approximate solution for the storage time can be obtained as

$$t_s \approx \tau_{p0} \ln\left(1 + \frac{I_F}{I_R}\right) \tag{9.87}$$

The recovery phase for $t > t_s$ is the time required for the junction to reach its steady-state reverse-bias condition. The remainder of the excess charge is being

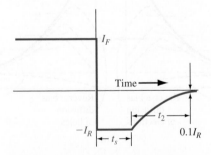

Figure 9.33 | Current characteristic versus time during diode switching.

removed and the space charge width is increasing to the reverse-bias value. The decay time t_2 is determined from

$$\text{erf}\sqrt{\frac{t_2}{\tau_{p0}}} + \frac{\exp(-t_2/\tau_{p0})}{\sqrt{\pi t_2/\tau_{p0}}} = 1 + 0.1\left(\frac{I_R}{I_F}\right) \tag{9.88}$$

The total turn-off time is the sum of t_s and t_2.

To switch the diode quickly, we need to be able to produce a large reverse current as well as have a small minority-carrier lifetime. In the design of diode circuits, then, the designer must provide a path for the transient reverse-bias current pulse in order to be able to switch the diode quickly. These same effects will be considered when we discuss the switching of bipolar transistors.

9.7.2 The Turn-On Transient

The turn-on transient occurs when the diode is switched from its "off" state into the forward-bias "on" state. The turn-on can be accomplished by applying a forward-bias current pulse. The first stage of turn-on occurs very quickly and is the length of time required to narrow the space charge width from the reverse-bias value to its thermal-equilibrium value when $V_a = 0$. During this time, ionized donors and acceptors are neutralized as the space charge width narrows.

The second stage of the turn-on process is the time required to establish the minority-carrier distributions. During this time the voltage across the junction is increasing toward its steady-state value. A small turn-on time is achieved if the minority-carrier lifetime is small and if the forward-bias current is small.

TEST YOUR UNDERSTANDING

TYU9.10   A one-sided p^+n silicon diode, that has a forward-bias current of $I_F = 1.75$ mA, is switched to reverse bias with an effective reverse-bias voltage of $V_R = 2$ V and an effective series resistance of $R_R = 4$ kΩ. The minority-carrier hole lifetime is 10^{-7} s. (a) Determine the storage time t_s. (b) Calculate the decay time t_2. (c) What is the turn-off time of the diode?

[Ans. (a) 0.746×10^{-7} s, (b) 1.25×10^{-7} s, (c) $\approx 2 \times 10^{-7}$ s]

9.8 | SUMMARY

1. The structures of the pn junction and Schottky junction and the associated energy-band diagrams at zero bias and reverse bias were reviewed.

2. A. When a forward-bias voltage is applied across a pn junction (p region positive with respect to the n region), the potential barrier is lowered so that holes from the p region and electrons from the n region can flow across the junction.

   B. The boundary conditions relating the minority-carrier hole concentration in the n region at the space charge edge and the minority-carrier electron concentration in the p region at the space charge edge as a function of forward-bias voltage were derived.

   C.   The steady-state excess carrier concentrations in the n region and p region as a function of forward-bias voltage were derived using the ambipolar transport equation. Diffusion and recombination processes occur in each region.

   D.   Gradients exist in the minority-carrier concentrations so that minority-carrier diffusion currents exist in the pn junction. These diffusion currents yield the ideal current–voltage relationship of the pn junction diode.

3. A.   When a forward-bias voltage is applied across a Schottky barrier junction (metal positive with respect to the n-type semiconductor), the potential barrier between the semiconductor and metal is lowered.

   B.   Current in a Schottky diode is due to the thermionic emission of majority-carrier electrons over the barrier. The ideal current–voltage relationship was developed.

   C.   A comparison between a Schottky diode and pn junction diode shows that the reverse-saturation current in a Schottky diode is larger than that in a pn junction diode resulting in a smaller turn-on voltage for the Schottky diode.

4. The small-signal equivalent circuit of the pn junction was developed. Two parameters of interest are the diffusion resistance and the diffusion capacitance.

5. A.   Excess carriers are generated in the space-charge region of a reverse-biased pn junction. These carriers are swept out by the electric field and create the reverse-bias generation current that is another component of the reverse bias current.

   B.   Some of the carriers injected into the space charge region from the n and p regions under forward bias may recombine. This recombination process creates the forward-bias recombination current that is another component of the forward-bias diode current.

6. Avalanche breakdown occurs when a sufficiently large reverse-bias voltage is applied to the pn junction. A large reverse-bias current may then be induced in the pn junction. The breakdown voltage as a function of the doping levels was derived. In a one-sided pn junction, the breakdown voltage is a function of the doping concentration in the low-doped region.

7. When a pn junction is switched from forward bias to reverse bias, the stored excess minority-carrier charge must be removed from the junction. The time required to remove this charge is called the storage time and is a limiting factor in the switching speed of a diode.

CHECKPOINT

After studying this chapter, the reader should have the ability to

1. Describe the structure of a uniformly doped pn junction, and sketch the energy-band diagrams of a zero- and reverse-biased pn junction.

2. A.   Describe the mechanism of charge flow across the space charge region of a pn junction when a forward-bias voltage is applied.

   B.   State the boundary conditions for the minority-carrier concentration at the edge of the space charge region.

   C.   Describe the derivation of the steady-state minority-carrier concentrations in the pn junction.

   D.   Describe the derivation of the ideal current–voltage relationship in a pn junction.

   E.   Describe the physics of charge flow through a forward-biased pn junction.

   F.   Describe the characteristics of a "short" diode.

3. A. Describe the current mechanism in a forward-biased Schottky diode.

   B. Discuss why the switching speed of a Schottky diode is faster than that of a pn junction diode.

4. Describe what is meant by diffusion resistance and diffusion capacitance.

5. A. Describe the generation current process in a reverse-biased pn junction.

   B. Describe the recombination current process in a forward-biased pn junction.

6. Describe the avalanche breakdown mechanism in a pn junction.

7. Describe the turn-off transient response in a pn junction.

REVIEW QUESTIONS

1. Sketch the energy bands of a zero- and reverse-biased pn junction and Schottky barrier junction. Define the built-in potential barriers.

2. A. Sketch the energy-band diagram of a forward-biased pn junction

   B. Why can carriers diffuse across the space charge region of a forward-biased pn junction?

   C. Write the expressions for the boundary conditions for the minority-carrier concentrations at the edge of the space charge region under forward bias and reverse bias for the pn junction.

   D. Sketch the steady-state minority-carrier concentrations in a forward-biased pn junction.

   E. Explain the procedure that is used to derive the current–voltage relationship for an ideal pn junction diode.

   F. Sketch the electron and hole currents through a forward-biased pn junction diode.

   G. What is meant by a "short" diode?

3. A. What is the current mechanism in a forward-biased Schottky diode?

   B. Why is the effective turn-on voltage for a Schottky diode smaller than that of a pn junction diode?

   C. Why is the switching speed of a Schottky diode faster than that of a pn junction diode?

4. A. Explain the physical mechanism of diffusion resistance.

   B. Explain the physical mechanism of diffusion capacitance.

5. A. Explain the physical mechanism of the generation current in a reverse-biased pn junction.

   B. Explain the physical mechanism of the recombination current in a forward-biased pn junction.

6. Why does the breakdown voltage of a pn junction decrease as the doping concentration increases?

7. Explain what is meant by storage time.

PROBLEMS

Section 9.2   The pn Junction—Ideal Current–Voltage Relationship

9.1 (*a*) Consider an ideal pn junction diode at $T = 300$ K operating in the forward-bias region. Calculate the change in diode voltage that will cause a factor of 10 increase in current. (*b*) Repeat part (*a*) for a factor of 100 increase in current.

9.2 Calculate the applied reverse-bias voltage at which the ideal reverse current in a pn junction diode at $T = 300$ K reaches 90 percent of its reverse saturation current value.

9.3 An ideal silicon pn junction at $T = 300$ K is under forward bias. The minority-carrier lifetimes are $\tau_{n0} = 10^{-6}$ s and $\tau_{p0} = 10^{-7}$ s. The doping concentration in the n region is $N_d = 10^{16}$ cm^{-3}. Plot the ratio of hole current to the total current crossing the space charge region as the p-region doping concentration varies over the range $10^{15} \le N_a \le 10^{18}$ cm^{-3}. (Use a log scale for the doping concentrations.)

9.4 A silicon pn junction diode is to be designed to operate at $T = 300$ K such that the diode current is $I = 10$ mA at a diode voltage of $V_D = 0.65$ V. The ratio of electron current to total current is to be 0.10 and the maximum current density is to be no more than 20 A/cm^2. Use the semiconductor parameters given in Example 9.2.

9.5 For a silicon pn junction at $T = 300$ K, assume $\tau_{p0} = 0.1\tau_{n0}$ and $\mu_n = 2.4\,\mu_p$. The ratio of electron current crossing the depletion region to the total current is defined as the electron injection efficiency. Determine the expression for the electron injection efficiency as a function of (a) N_d/N_a and (b) the ratio of n-type conductivity to p-type conductivity.

9.6 Consider a p$^+$n silicon diode at $T = 300$ K with doping concentrations of $N_a = 10^{18}$ cm^{-3} and $N_d = 10^{16}$ cm^{-3}. The minority-carrier hole diffusion coefficient is $D_p = 12$ cm^2/s and the minority-carrier hole lifetime is $\tau_{p0} = 10^{-7}$ s. The cross-sectional area is $A = 10^{-4}$ cm^2. Calculate the reverse saturation current and the diode current at a forward-bias voltage of 0.50 V.

9.7 Consider an ideal silicon pn junction diode with the following parameters: $\tau_{n0} = \tau_{p0} = 0.1 \times 10^{-6}$ s, $D_n = 25$ cm^2/s, $D_p = 10$ cm^2/s. What must be the ratio of N_a/N_d so that 95 percent of the current in the depletion region is carried by electrons?

9.8 A silicon pn junction with a cross-sectional area of 10^{-4} cm^2 has the following properties at $T = 300$ K:

n Region	p Region
$N_d = 10^{17}$ cm^{-3}	$N_a = 5 \times 10^{15}$ cm^{-3}
$\tau_{p0} = 10^{-7}$ s	$\tau_{n0} = 10^{-6}$ s
$\mu_n = 850$ cm^2/V-s	$\mu_n = 1250$ cm^2/V-s
$\mu_p = 320$ cm^2/V-s	$\mu_p = 420$ cm^2/V-s

(a) Sketch the thermal-equilibrium energy-band diagram of the pn junction, including the values of the Fermi level with respect to the intrinsic level on each side of the junction. (b) Calculate the reverse-saturation current I_s and determine the forward-bias current I at a forward-bias voltage of 0.5 V. (c) Determine the ratio of hole current to total current at the space charge edge x_n.

9.9 A germanium p$^+$n diode at $T = 300$ K has the following parameters: $N_a = 10^{18}$ cm^{-3}, $N_d = 10^{16}$ cm^{-3}, $D_p = 49$ cm^2/s, $D_n = 100$ cm^2/s, $\tau_{p0} = \tau_{n0} = 5\,\mu$s, and $A = 10^{-4}$ cm^2. Determine the diode current for (a) a forward-bias voltage of 0.2 V and (b) a reverse-bias voltage of 0.2 V.

9.10 An n$^+$p silicon diode at $T = 300$ K has the following parameters: $N_d = 10^{18}$ cm^{-3}, $N_a = 10^{16}$ cm^{-3}, $D_n = 25$ cm^2/s, $D_p = 10$ cm^2/s, $\tau_{n0} = \tau_{p0} = 1\,\mu$s, and $A = 10^{-4}$ cm^2. Determine the diode current for (a) a forward-bias voltage of 0.5 V and (b) a reverse-bias voltage of 0.5 V.

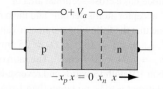

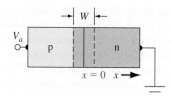

Figure P9.11 | Figure for
Problem 9.11.

Figure P9.12 | Figure for
Problem 9.12.

9.11 A silicon step junction has uniform impurity doping concentrations of $N_a = 5 \times 10^{15}$ cm^{-3} and $N_d = 1 \times 10^{15}$ cm^{-3}, and a cross-sectional area of $A = 10^{-4}$ cm^2. Let $\tau_{n0} = 0.4$ μs and $\tau_{p0} = 0.1$ μs. Consider the geometry in Figure P9.11. Calculate (a) the ideal reverse saturation current due to holes, (b) the ideal reverse saturation current due to electrons, (c) the hole concentration at x_n if $V_a = \frac{1}{2}V_{bi}$, and (d) the electron current at $x = x_n + \frac{1}{2}L_p$ for $V_a = \frac{1}{2}V_{bi}$.

9.12 Consider the ideal long silicon pn junction shown in Figure P9.12. $T = 300$ K. The n region is doped with 10^{16} donor atoms per cm^3 and the p region is doped with 5×10^{16} acceptor atoms per cm^3. The minority-carrier lifetimes are $\tau_{n0} = 0.05$ μs and $\tau_{p0} = 0.01$ μs. The minority-carrier diffusion coefficients are $D_n = 23$ cm^2/s and $D_p = 8$ cm^2/s. The forward-bias voltage is $V_a = 0.610$ V. Calculate (a) the excess hole concentration as a function of x for $x \geq 0$, (b) the hole diffusion current density at $x = 3 \times 10^{-4}$ cm, and (c) the electron current density at $x = 3 \times 10^{-4}$ cm.

9.13 The limit of low injection is normally defined to be when the minority-carrier concentration at the edge of the space charge region in the low-doped region becomes equal to one-tenth the majority-carrier concentration in this region. Determine the value of the forward-bias voltage at which the limit of low injection is reached for the diode described in (a) Problem 9.9 and (b) Problem 9.10.

9.14 The cross-sectional area of a silicon pn junction is 10^{-3} cm^2. The temperature of the diode is $T = 300$ K, and the doping concentrations are $N_d = 10^{16}$ cm^{-3} and $N_a = 8 \times 10^{15}$ cm^{-3}. Assume minority-carrier lifetimes of $\tau_{n0} = 10^{-6}$ s and $\tau_{p0} = 10^{-7}$ s. Calculate the total number of excess electrons in the p region and the total number of excess holes in the n region for (a) $V_a = 0.3$ V, (b) $V_a = 0.4$ V, and (c) $V_a = 0.5$ V.

9.15 Consider two ideal pn junctions at $T = 300$ K, having exactly the same electrical and physical parameters except for the bandgap energy of the semiconductor materials. The first pn junction has a bandgap energy of 0.525 eV and a forward-bias current of 10 mA with $V_a = 0.255$ V. For the second pn junction, "design" the bandgap energy so that a forward-bias voltage of $V_a = 0.32$ V will produce a current of 10 μA.

9.16 The reverse-bias saturation current is a function of temperature. (a) Assuming that I_s varies with temperature only from the intrinsic carrier concentration, show that we can write $I_s = CT^3 \exp(-E_g/kT)$, where C is a constant and a function only of the diode parameters. (b) Determine the increase in I_s as the temperature increases from $T = 300$ K to $T = 400$ K for a (i) germanium diode and (ii) silicon diode.

9.17 Assume that the mobilities, diffusion coefficients, and minority-carrier lifetime parameters are independent of temperature (use the $T = 300$ K values). Assume that $\tau_{n0} = 10^{-6}$ s, $\tau_{p0} = 10^{-7}$ s, $N_d = 5 \times 10^{15}$ cm^{-3}, and $N_a = 5 \times 10^{16}$ cm^{-3}. Plot the ideal reverse-saturation current density from $T = 200$ K to $T = 500$ K for (a) silicon, (b) germanium, and (c) gallium arsenide ideal pn junctions. (Use a log scale for the current density.)

9.18   An ideal uniformly doped silicon pn junction diode has a cross-sectional area of 10^{-4} cm^2. The p region is doped with 5×10^{18} acceptor atoms per cm^3 and the n region is doped with 10^{15} donor atoms per cm^3. Assume that the following parameter values are independent of temperature: $E_g = 1.10$ eV, $\tau_{n0} = \tau_{p0} = 10^{-7}$ s, $D_n = 25$ cm^2/s, $D_p = 10$ cm^2/s, $N_c = 2.8 \times 10^{19}$ cm^{-3}, and $N_v = 1.04 \times 10^{19}$ cm^{-3}. The ratio of the forward to reverse-current is to be no less than 10^4 with forward- and reverse-bias voltages of 0.50 V. Also, the reverse-saturation current is to be no larger than 1 μA. What is the maximum temperature at which the diode will meet these specifications?

*__9.19__   A p$^+$n silicon diode is fabricated with a narrow n region as shown in Figure 9.16, in which $W_n < L_p$. Assume the boundary condition of $p_n = p_{n0}$ at $x = x_n + W_n$. (a) Derive the expression for the excess hole concentration $\delta p_n(x)$ as given by Equation (9.31). (b) Using the results of part (a), show that the current density in the diode is given by

$$ J = \frac{e D_p p_{n0}}{L_p} \coth\left(\frac{W_n}{L_p}\right)\left[\exp\left(\frac{eV}{kT}\right) - 1\right] $$

9.20   A silicon diode can be used to measure temperature by operating the diode at a fixed forward-bias current. The forward-bias voltage is then a function of temperature. At $T = 300$ K, the diode voltage is found to be 0.60 V. Determine the diode voltage at (a) $T = 310$ K and (b) $T = 320$ K.

9.21   A forward-biased silicon diode is to be used as a temperature sensor. The diode is forward biased with a constant current source and V_a is measured as a function of temperature. (a) Derive an expression for $V_a(T)$ assuming that D/L for electrons and holes, and E_g are independent of temperature. (b) If the diode is biased at $I_D = 0.1$ mA and if $I_s = 10^{-15}$ A at $T = 300$ K, plot V_a versus T for $20°$C $< T < 200°$C. (c) Repeat part (b) if $I_D = 1$ mA. (d) Determine any changes in the results of parts (a) through (c) if the change in bandgap energy with temperature is taken into account.

Section 9.3   The Schottky Barrier Junction–Ideal Current–Voltage Relationship

9.22   A PtSi Schottky diode at $T = 300$ K is fabricated on n-type silicon with a doping of $N_d = 10^{16}$ cm^{-3}. The barrier height is 0.89 V. Determine (a) ϕ_n, (b) V_{bi}, (c) J_{sT}, and (d) V_a so that $J_n = 2$ A/cm^2.

9.23   (a) Consider a Schottky diode at $T = 300$ K formed with tungsten on n-type silicon. Let $N_d = 5 \times 10^{15}$ cm^{-3} and assume a cross-sectional area of $A = 5 \times 10^{-4}$ cm^2. Let $\phi_{Bn} = 0.68$ V. Determine the forward-bias voltage required to obtain a current of 1 mA, 10 mA, and 100 mA. (b) Repeat part (a) if the temperature is increased to $T = 400$ K.

9.24   A Schottky diode is formed by depositing Au on n-type GaAs doped at $N_d = 5 \times 10^{16}$ cm^{-3}. $T = 300$ K. Let $\phi_{Bn} = 0.86$ V . (a) Determine the forward-bias voltage required to obtain $J_n = 5$ A/cm^2. (b) What is the change in forward-bias voltage necessary to double the current?

9.25   (a) Consider an Au n-type GaAs Schottky diode with a cross-sectional area of 10^{-4} cm^2. Let $\phi_{Bn} = 0.86$ V. Plot the forward-bias current–voltage characteristics over a voltage range of $0 \leq V_D \leq 0.5$ V. Plot the current on a log scale. (b) Repeat part (*a*) for an Au n-type silicon Schottky diode. Let $\phi_{Bn} = 0.65$ V. (*c*) What conclusions can be drawn from these results?

9.26   A Schottky diode and a pn junction diode have cross-sectional areas of $A = 5 \times 10^{-4}$ cm^2. The reverse-saturation current density of the Schottky diode is 3×10^{-8} A/cm^2 and the reverse-saturation current density of the pn junction diode is 3×10^{-12} A/cm^2. The temperature is 300 K. Determine the forward-bias voltage in each diode required to yield diode currents of 1 mA.

9.27   The reverse-saturation current densities in a pn junction diode and a Schottky diode are 5×10^{-12} A/cm^2 and 7×10^{-8} A/cm^2, respectively, at $T = 300$ K. The cross-sectional area of the pn junction diode is $A = 8 \times 10^{-4}$ cm^2. Determine the cross-sectional area of the Schottky diode so that the difference in forward-bias voltages to achieve 1.2 mA is 0.265 V.

9.28   (*a*) The reverse-saturation currents of a Schottky diode and a pn junction diode at $T = 300$ K are 5×10^{-8} A and 10^{-12} A, respectively. The diodes are connected in parallel and are driven by a constant current of 0.5 mA. (*i*) Determine the current in each diode. (*ii*) Determine the voltage across each diode. (*b*) Repeat part (*a*) if the diodes are connected in series.

*9.29   A Schottky diode and a pn junction diode have cross-sectional areas of $A = 7 \times 10^{-4}$ cm^2. The reverse-saturation current densities at $T = 300$ K of the Schottky diode and pn junction are 4×10^{-8} A/cm^2 and 3×10^{-12} A/cm^2, respectively. A forward-bias current of 0.8 mA is required in each diode. (*a*) Determine the forward-bias voltage required across each diode. (*b*) If the voltage from part (*a*) is maintained across each diode, determine the current in each diode if the temperature is increased to 400 K. (Take into account the temperature dependence of the reverse-saturation currents. Assume $E_g = 1.12$ eV for the pn junction diode and $\phi_{B0} = 0.82$ V. for the Schottky diode.)

Section 9.4   Small-Signal Model of the pn Junction

9.30   Calculate the small-signal ac admittance of a pn junction biased at $V_a = 0.72$ V and $I_{DQ} = 2.0$ mA. Assume the minority-carrier lifetime is 1 μs in both the n and p regions. $T = 300$ K.

9.31   Consider a p$^+$n silicon diode at $T = 300$ K. The diode is forward biased at a current of 1 mA. The hole lifetime in the n region is 10^{-7} s. Neglecting the depletion capacitance, calculate the diode impedance at frequencies of 10 kHz, 100 kHz, 1 MHz, and 10 MHz.

9.32   Consider a silicon pn junction with parameters as described in Problem 9.8. (*a*) Calculate and plot the depletion capacitance and diffusion capacitance over the voltage range $-10 \leq V_a \leq 0.75$ V. (*b*) Determine the voltage at which the two capacitances are equal.

9.33   Consider a p$^+$n silicon diode at $T = 300$ K. The slope of the diffusion capacitance versus forward-bias current is 2.5×10^{-6} F/A. Determine the hole lifetime and the diffusion capacitance at a forward-bias current of 1 mA.

9.34   A one-sided n$^+$p silicon diode at $T = 300$ K with a cross-sectional area of 10^{-3} cm^2 is operated under forward bias. The doping levels are $N_d = 10^{18}$ cm^{-3} and $N_a = 10^{16}$ cm^{-3}, and the minority-carrier parameters are $\tau_{p0} = 10^{-8}$ s, $\tau_{n0} = 10^{-7}$ s, $D_p = 10$ cm^2/s, and $D_n = 25$ cm^2/s. The maximum diffusion capacitance is to be 1 nF. Determine (*a*) the maximum current through the diode, (*b*) the maximum forward-bias voltage, and (*c*) the diffusion resistance.

9.35   A silicon pn junction diode at $T = 300$ K has a cross-sectional area of 10^{-2} cm^2. The length of the p region is 0.2 cm and the length of the n region is 0.1 cm. The doping concentrations are $N_d = 10^{15}$ cm^{-3} and $N_a = 10^{16}$ cm^{-3}. Determine (a) approximately the series resistance of the diode and (b) the current through the diode that will produce a 0.1 V drop across this series resistance.

9.36   We want to consider the effect of a series resistance on the forward-bias voltage required to achieve a particular diode current. (a) Assume the reverse-saturation current in a diode is $I_s = 10^{-10}$ A at $T = 300$ K. The resistivity of the n region is 0.2 Ω-cm and the resistivity of the p region is 0.1 Ω-cm. Assume the length of each neutral region is 10^{-2} cm and the cross-sectional area is 2×10^{-5} cm^2. Determine the required applied voltage to achieve a current of (i) 1 mA and (ii) 10 mA. (b) Repeat part (a) neglecting the series resistance.

9.37   The minimum small-signal diffusion resistance of an ideal forward-biased silicon pn junction diode at $T = 300$ K is to be $r_d = 48$ Ω. The reverse-saturation current is $I_s = 2 \times 10^{-11}$ A. Calculate the maximum applied forward-bias voltage that can be applied to meet this specification.

9.38   (a) An ideal silicon pn junction diode at $T = 300$ K is forward biased at $V_a = +20$ mV. The reverse-saturation current is $I_s = 10^{-13}$ A. Calculate the small-signal diffusion resistance. (b) Repeat part (a) for an applied reverse-bias voltage of $V_a = -20$ mV.

Section 9.5   Generation-Recombination Currents

9.39   Consider a reverse-biased gallium arsenide pn junction at $T = 300$ K. Assume that a reverse-bias voltage, $V_R = 5$ V, is applied. Assume parameter values of: $N_a = N_d = 10^{16}$ cm^{-3}, $D_p = 6$ cm^2/s, $D_n = 200$ cm^2/s, and $\tau_{p0} = \tau_{n0} = \tau_0 = 10^{-8}$ s. Calculate the ideal reverse-saturation current density and the reverse-biased generation current density. How does the relative value of these two currents compare to those of the silicon pn junction?

*9.40   (a) Consider Example 9.10. Assume that all parameters except n_i are independent of temperature. Determine the temperature at which J_s and J_{gen} will be equal. What are the values of J_s and J_{gen} at this temperature? (b) Using the results of Example 9.10, calculate the forward-bias voltage at which the ideal diffusion current is equal to the recombination current.

9.41   Consider a GaAs pn diode at $T = 300$ K with $N_a = N_d = 10^{17}$ cm^{-3} and with a cross-sectional area of 10^{-3} cm^2. The minority carrier mobilities are $\mu_n = 3000$ cm^2/V-s and $\mu_p = 200$ cm^2/V-s. The lifetimes are $\tau_{p0} = \tau_{n0} = \tau_0 = 10^{-8}$ s. As a first approximation, assume the electron-hole generation and recombination rates are constant across the space charge region. (a) Calculate the total diode current at a reverse-bias voltage of 5 V and at forward-bias voltages of 0.3 V and 0.5 V. (b) Compare the results of part (a) to an ideal diode at the same applied voltages.

9.42   Consider the pn junction diode described in Problem 9.41. Plot the diode recombination current and the ideal diode current (on a log scale) versus forward-bias voltage over the range $0.1 \le V_a \le 1.0$ V.

9.43   A silicon pn junction diode at $T = 300$ K has the following parameters: $N_a = N_d = 10^{16}$ cm^{-3}, $\tau_{p0} = \tau_{n0} = \tau_0 = 5 \times 10^{-7}$ s, $D_p = 10$ cm^2/s, $D_n = 25$ cm^2/s, and a cross-sectional area of 10^{-4} cm^2. Plot the diode recombination current and the ideal

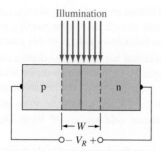

Illumination

p   n

$\leftarrow W \rightarrow$

$-\ V_R\ +$

Figure P9.45 | Figure for
Problems 9.45 and 9.46.

diode current (on a log scale) versus forward-bias voltage over the range $0.1 \leq V_a \leq 0.6$ V.

9.44 Consider a GaAs pn diode at $T = 300$ K with $N_a = N_d = 10^{17}$ cm^{-3} and with a cross-sectional area of 5×10^{-3} cm^2. The minority-carrier mobilities are $\mu_n = 3500$ cm^2/V-s and $\mu_p = 220$ cm^2/V-s. The electron-hole lifetimes are $\tau_{n0} = \tau_{p0} = \tau_0 = 10^{-8}$ s. Plot the diode forward-bias current including recombination current between diode voltages of $0.1 \leq V_D \leq 1.0$ V. Compare this plot to that for an ideal diode.

9.45 Consider, as shown in Figure P9.45, a uniformly doped silicon pn junction at $T = 300$ K with impurity doping concentrations of $N_a = N_d = 5 \times 10^{15}$ cm^{-3} and minority-carrier lifetimes of $\tau_{n0} = \tau_{p0} = \tau_0 = 10^{-7}$ s. A reverse-bias voltage of $V_R = 10$ V is applied. A light source is incident only on the space charge region, producing an excess carrier generation rate of $g' = 4 \times 10^{19}$ cm^{-3} s^{-1}. Calculate the generation current density.

9.46 A long silicon pn junction diode has the following parameters: $N_d = 10^{18}$ cm^{-3}, $N_a = 3 \times 10^{16}$ cm^{-3}, $\tau_{n0} = \tau_{p0} = \tau_0 = 10^{-7}$ s, $D_n = 18$ cm^2/s, and $D_p = 6$ cm^2/s. A light source is incident on the space charge region such as shown in Figure P9.45, producing a generation current density of $J_G = 25$ mA/cm^2. The diode is open circuited. The generation current density forward biases the junction, inducing a forward-bias current in the opposite direction to the generation current. A steady-state condition is reached when the generation current density and forward-bias current density are equal in magnitude. What is the induced forward-bias voltage at this steady-state condition?

Section 9.6 Junction Breakdown

9.47 The critical electric field for breakdown in silicon is approximately $\mathcal{E}_{crit} = 4 \times 10^5$ V/cm. Determine the maximum n-type doping concentration in an abrupt p$^+$n junction such that the breakdown voltage is 30 V.

9.48 Design an abrupt silicon p$^+$n junction diode that has a reverse breakdown voltage of 120 V and has a forward-bias current of 2 mA at $V = 0.65$ V. Assume that $\tau_{p0} = 10^{-7}$ s, and find μ_p from Figure 4.3.

9.49 Consider an abrupt n$^+$p GaAs junction with a p-type doping concentration of $N_a = 10^{16}$ cm^{-3}. Determine the breakdown voltage.

9.50   A symmetrically doped silicon pn junction has doping concentrations of $N_a = N_d = 5 \times 10^{16}$ cm^{-3}. If the peak electric field in the junction at breakdown is $\mathcal{E} = 4 \times 10^5$ V/cm, determine the breakdown voltage of this junction.

9.51   An abrupt silicon p$^+$n junction has an n-region doping concentration of $N_d = 5 \times 10^{15}$ cm^{-3}. What must be the minimum n-region width such that avalanche breakdown occurs before the depletion region reaches an ohmic contact (punchthrough)?

9.52   A silicon pn junction diode is doped with $N_a = N_d = 10^{18}$ cm^{-3}. Zener breakdown occurs when the peak electric field reaches 10^6 V/cm. Determine the reverse-bias breakdown voltage.

9.53   A diode will very often have the doping profile shown in Figure P5.28, which is known as an n$^+$pp$^+$ diode. Under reverse bias, the depletion region must remain within the p region to avoid premature breakdown. Assume the p region doping is 10^{15} cm^{-3}. Determine the reverse-bias voltage such that the depletion region remains within the p region and does not reach breakdown if the p region width is (*a*) 75 μm and (*b*) 150 μm. For each case, state whether the maximum depletion width or the breakdown voltage is reached first.

9.54   Consider a silicon pn junction at $T = 300$ K whose doping profile varies linearly from $N_a = 10^{18}$ cm^{-3} to $N_d = 10^{18}$ cm^{-3} over a distance of 2 μm. Estimate the breakdown voltage.

Section 9.7   Charge Storage and Diode Transients

9.55   (*a*) In switching a pn junction from forward to reverse bias, assume that the ratio of reverse current, I_R, to forward current, I_F, is 0.2. Determine the ratio of storage time to minority-carrier lifetime, t_s/τ_{p0}. (*b*) Repeat part (*a*) if the ratio of I_R to I_F is 1.0.

9.56   A pn junction is switched from forward to reverse bias. We want to specify that $t_s = 0.2\tau_{p0}$. Determine the required ratio of I_R to I_F to achieve this requirement. In this case, determine t_2/τ_{p0}.

*9.57   Consider a diode with a junction capacitance of 18 pF at zero bias and 4.2 pF at a reverse bias voltage of $V_R = 10$ V. The minority-carrier lifetimes are 10^{-7} s. The diode is switched from a forward bias with a current of 2 mA to a reverse-bias voltage of 10 V applied through a 10 kΩ resistor. Estimate the turn-off time.

Summary and Review

9.58   (*a*) Explain physically why the diffusion capacitance is not important in a reverse-biased pn junction. (*b*) Consider a silicon, a germanium, and gallium arsenide pn junction. If the total current density is the same in each diode under forward bias, discuss the expected relative values of electron and hole current densities.

*9.59   A silicon pn junction diode at $T = 300$ K is to be designed to have a reverse-bias breakdown voltage of at least 50 V and to handle a forward-bias current of $I_D = 100$ mA while still operating under low injection. The minority-carrier diffusion coefficients and lifetimes are $D_n = 25$ cm^2/s, $D_p = 10$ cm^2/s, and $\tau_{n0} = \tau_{p0} = 5 \times 10^{-7}$ s. The diode is to be designed for minimum cross-sectional area.

*9.60   The donor and acceptor concentrations on either side of a silicon step junction are equal. (*a*) Derive an expression for the breakdown voltage in terms of the critical electric field and doping concentration. (*b*) If the breakdown voltage is to be $V_B = 50$ V, specify the range of allowed doping concentrations.

READING LIST

1. Dimitrijev, S. *Understanding Semiconductor Devices*. New York: Oxford University Press, 2000.

2. Kano, K. *Semiconductor Devices*. Upper Saddle River, NJ: Prentice-Hall, 1998.

3. Muller, R. S., T. I. Kamins, and W. Chan. *Device Electronics for Integrated Circuits,* 3rd ed. New York: John Wiley and Sons, 2003.

4. Neamen, D. A. *Semiconductor Physics and Devices: Basic Principles,* 3rd ed. New York: McGraw-Hill, 2003.

5. Neudeck, G. W. *The PN Junction Diode.* Vol. 2 of the *Modular Series on Solid State Devices.* 2nd ed. Reading, MA: Addison-Wesley, 1989.

*6. Ng, K. K. *Complete Guide to Semiconductor Devices.* New York: McGraw-Hill, 1995.

7. Pierret, R. F. *Semiconductor Device Fundamentals.* Reading, MA: Addison-Wesley Publishing Co., 1996.

8. Roulston, D. J. *An Introduction to the Physics of Semiconductor Devices.* New York: Oxford University Press, 1999.

9. Shur, M. *Introduction to Electronic Devices.* New York: John Wiley and Sons, Inc., 1996.

*10. Shur, M. *Physics of Semiconductor Devices.* Englewood Cliffs, NJ: Prentice-Hall, 1990.

11. Streetman, B. G., and S. Banerjee. *Solid State Electronic Devices.* 5th ed. Upper Saddle River, NJ: Prentice-Hall, 2000.

12. Sze, S. M. *Physics of Semiconductor Devices.* 2nd ed. New York: John Wiley & Sons, 1981.

13. Sze, S. M. *Semiconductor Devices: Physics and Technology.* 2nd ed. New York: John Wiley and Sons, 2002.

*14. Wang, S. *Fundamentals of Semiconductor Theory and Device Physics.* Englewood Cliffs, NJ: Prentice-Hall, 1989.

15. Yang, E. S. *Microelectronic Devices.* New York: McGraw-Hill, 1988.

CHAPTER

10

The Bipolar Transistor

The bipolar junction transistor (BJT), or just the bipolar transistor, is the second transistor device to be considered. (The MOSFET was considered in Chapters 6 and 7). As with the MOSFET, the bipolar transistor, in conjunction with other circuit elements, is capable of current gain, voltage gain, and signal-power gain. For this reason, the bipolar transistor is also referred to as an active device.

The bipolar transistor has three separately doped regions and two pn junctions, sufficiently close together so that interactions occur between the two junctions. The basic transistor action is the control of current at one terminal by a voltage applied across two other terminals of the device. We will use much of the theory developed for the pn junction in the analysis of the bipolar transistor. It is called a *bipolar* transistor because the flows of both electrons and holes are involved in this device. ■

10.0 | PREVIEW

In this chapter, we will

1. Discuss the principle of operation of the bipolar transistor and develop the transistor current relations.

2. Develop the minority-carrier distributions through the device.

3. Determine the contributing factors and develop the mathematical expressions for the common-base current gain factors.

4. Consider several nonideal effects in the transistor.

5. Develop a small-signal equivalent circuit for the transistor.

6. Analyze the frequency limitations in the device.

7. Discuss the large-signal switching characteristics of the bipolar transistor.

8. Consider some special device fabrication techniques for bipolar transistors.

Historical Insight

In December 1947, the bipolar transistor was demonstrated in the amplification of voice signals at Bell Laboratories. The inventors of the bipolar transistor, William Shockley, John Bardeen, and Walter Brattain, were honored with the 1956 Nobel Prize in physics. This first transistor was fabricated in germanium, and its emitter and collector terminals were point contacts. Greater reliability was realized in 1950 when the junction transistor was demonstrated. Work at Texas Instruments led to the first silicon bipolar transistor and later to the first integrated circuit. The bipolar transistor led to a new era in electronics.

Present-Day Insight

Silicon bipolar devices continue to play a key role in microelectronics, especially in analog electronics. Integrated circuit fabrication techniques have led to small, high-speed devices. Directional, reactive ion etching is used to etch a trench with nearly vertical sides through the entire epitaxial layer. An oxide is then grown on the sides of the trench. This technique is used to isolate devices from each other. Heterojunction bipolar transistors can also be fabricated to produce special characteristics.

10.1 | THE BIPOLAR TRANSISTOR ACTION

Objective: Discuss the principle of operation of the bipolar transistor and develop the transistor current relations.

The bipolar transistor has three separately doped regions and two pn junctions. In one case, two n regions are separated by a thin p region forming an npn bipolar transistor. In the complementary case, two p regions are separated by a thin n region forming a pnp bipolar transistor. Figure 10.1 shows the basic structures of the npn and pnp transistors along with the circuit symbols. The three terminal connections are called the emitter, base, and collector. The reason for this terminology will become clearer as we go through the analysis.

The (++) and (+) notation indicates the relative magnitudes of the impurity doping concentrations normally used in the bipolar transistor, with (++) meaning very heavily doped and (+) meaning moderately doped. The emitter region has the largest doping concentration; the collector region has the smallest. The reasons for

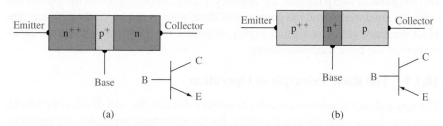

Figure 10.1 | Simplified block diagrams and circuit symbols of (a) npn and (b) pnp bipolar transistors.

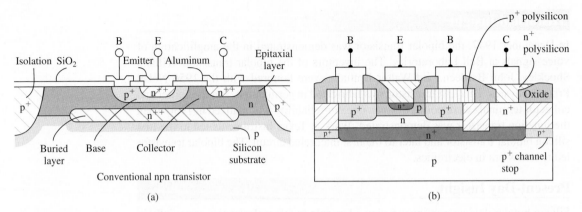

Figure 10.2 | Cross section of (a) a conventional integrated circuit npn bipolar transistor and (b) a double-polysilicon npn bipolar transistor.

using these relative impurity concentrations, and for the narrow base width, will become clear as we develop the theory of the bipolar transistor. The concepts developed for the pn junction apply directly to the bipolar transistor.

The block diagrams of Figure 10.1 show the basic structure of the transistor, but in very simplified sketches. Figure 10.2a shows a cross section of a classic npn bipolar transistor fabricated in an integrated circuit configuration, and Figure 10.2b shows the cross section of an npn bipolar transistor fabricated by a more modern technology. One can immediately observe that the actual structure of the bipolar transistor is not nearly as simple as the block diagrams of Figure 10.1 might suggest. A reason for the complexity is that terminal connections are made at the surface; to minimize semiconductor resistances, heavily doped n^+ buried layers must be included. Another reason for complexity arises out of the desire to fabricate more than one bipolar transistor on a single piece of semiconductor material. Individual transistors must be isolated from each other since all collectors, for example, will not be at the same potential. This isolation is accomplished by adding p^+ regions so that devices are separated by reverse-biased pn junctions, as shown in Figure 10.2a, or they are isolated by large oxide regions, as shown in Figure 10.2b.

An important point to note from the devices shown in Figure 10.2 is that the bipolar transistor is not a symmetrical device. Although the transistor may contain two n regions or two p regions, the impurity doping concentrations in the emitter and collector are different and the geometry of these regions can be vastly different. The block diagrams of Figure 10.1 are highly simplified, but useful, concepts in the development of the basic transistor theory.

10.1.1   The Basic Principle of Operation

The npn and pnp transistors are complementary devices. We will develop the bipolar transistor theory using the npn transistor, but the same basic principles and equations also apply to the pnp device. Figure 10.3 shows an idealized impurity doping profile in an npn bipolar transistor for the case when each region is uniformly doped. Typical

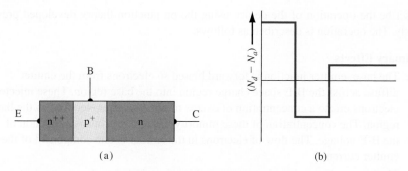

Figure 10.3 | Idealized doping profile of a uniformly doped npn bipolar transistor.

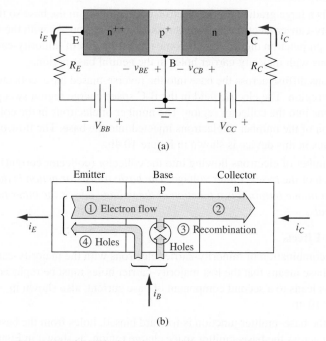

Figure 10.4 | (a) Biasing of an npn bipolar transistor in the forward-active mode (B-E junction forward biased, B-C junction reverse biased) and (b) summary of charge flow in a forward-active biased npn transistor: (1) electrons diffusing from emitter into base, (2) electrons reaching collector, (3) recombination of minority electrons and majority holes in base, and (4) holes diffusing from base into emitter.

impurity doping concentrations in the emitter, base, and collector may be on the order of 10^{19}, 10^{17}, and 10^{15} cm^{-3}, respectively.

The base–emitter (B-E) pn junction is forward biased, and the base–collector (B-C) junction is reverse biased in the normal bias configuration as shown in Figure 10.4a. This configuration is called the *forward-active* operating mode. We can

Forward-active mode

describe the operation of the device using the pn junction theory developed previously. The operation is described as follows:

Primary Effects

1. The base–emitter junction is forward biased so electrons from the emitter diffuse across the B-E space charge region into the base region. These injected electrons create a concentration of excess minority-carrier electrons in the base region. The concentration of these minority-carrier electrons is a function of the B-E voltage. The flow of electrons in the emitter is one component of the emitter current.

2. The base–collector junction is reverse biased so the minority-carrier electron concentration at the edge of the B-C junction is ideally zero.

3. There is a large gradient in the electron concentration in the base so the minority-carrier electrons diffuse across the base region. As with the forward-biased pn junction diode, there is some recombination of minority-carrier electrons with majority-carrier holes in the neutral base region.

4. Electrons diffuse across the base into the reverse-biased base–collector space charge region. The electric field in the B-C space charge region sweeps the electrons into the collector region. The number of electrons in the collector is a function of the number of electrons injected into the base. The flow of electrons in this device is shown in Figure 10.4b.

Basic transistor action

5. The number of electrons flowing into the collector (collector current) is a function of the base–emitter voltage. *The basic transistor action is that the current at one terminal is a function of the voltage across the other two terminals.*

Secondary Effects

6. The recombination of minority-carrier electrons with the majority-carrier holes in the base means that the lost majority-carrier holes must be replaced. This process leads to a second component of base current, also shown in Figure 10.4b.

7. Since the base–emitter junction is forward biased, holes from the base diffuse across the base–emitter space charge region, as shown in Figure 10.4b. Since the base region has a smaller doping concentration than the emitter, the number of holes diffusing from the base into the emitter is less than the number of electrons diffusing from the emitter into the base. The flow of these holes is also a component of base current and a second component of emitter current.

8. A reverse-biased base–collector junction current also exists. This current is normally small but will be considered in detail later in the analysis.

One primary objective in the operation of the device is to maximize the number of electrons reaching the collector compared to the number injected from the emitter. For this reason, the recombination between the minority-carrier electrons and majority-carrier holes in the base region needs to be held to a minimum. The width

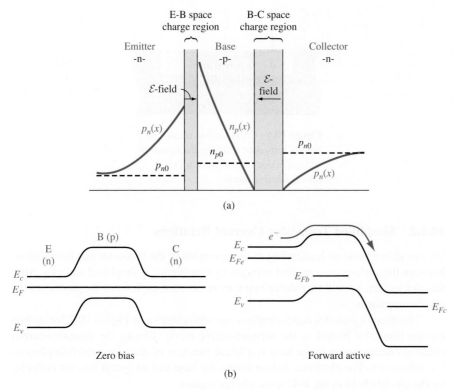

Figure 10.5 | (a) Minority-carrier distribution in an npn bipolar transistor operating in the forward-active mode, and (b) energy-band diagram of the npn bipolar transistor under zero bias and under a forward-active mode bias.

of the base region, then, needs to be small compared to the minority-carrier diffusion length. (See the "short" diode in Chapter 9.) The two pn junctions are close enough to be called *interacting pn junctions*.

The expected minority-carrier concentrations through the npn transistor is shown in Figure 10.5a. The actual distributions will be derived in Section 10.2. The energy-band diagram of the npn transistor biased in the forward-active mode is shown in Figure 10.5b. The potential barrier between the emitter and base is reduced so electrons from the emitter diffuse across the B-E space charge region. The majority of these electrons reach the collector and creates the major component of the collector current.

Figure 10.6 shows a cross section of an npn transistor with the injection of electrons from the n-type emitter (hence the name emitter) and the collection of the electrons in the collector (hence the name collector). The first transistor developed in 1947 was a point contact transistor. Two sharp metal wires (cat's whiskers) were pressed against a piece of germanium. The metal wires formed the emitter and collector, and the germanium formed the *base* or mechanical support for the transistor (hence the name base).

Emitter

Collector

Base

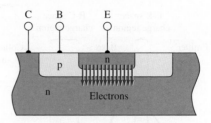

Figure 10.6 | Cross section of an npn bipolar transistor showing the injection and collection of electrons in the forward-active mode.

10.1.2   Simplified Transistor Current Relations

We can gain a basic understanding of the operation of the transistor and the relations between the various currents and voltages by considering a simplified analysis. After this discussion, we will then delve into a more detailed analysis of the physics of the bipolar transistor.

The minority-carrier concentrations are again shown in Figure 10.7 for an npn bipolar transistor biased in the forward-active mode. Ideally, the minority-carrier electron concentration in the base is a linear function of distance, which implies no recombination. The electrons diffuse across the base and are swept into the collector by the electric field in the B-C space charge region.

Collector Current   Assuming the ideal linear electron distribution in the base, the collector current can be written as a diffusion current given by

$$i_C = eD_n A_{BE} \frac{dn(x)}{dx} = eD_n A_{BE} \left[\frac{n_B(0) - 0}{0 - x_B} \right] = \frac{-eD_n A_{BE}}{x_B} \cdot n_{B0} \exp\left(\frac{v_{BE}}{V_t} \right)$$

$$(10.1)$$

where A_{BE} is the cross-sectional area of the B-E junction, n_{B0} is the thermal equilibrium electron concentration in the base, and V_t is the thermal voltage. The diffusion of electrons is in the $+x$ direction so that the conventional current is in the $-x$ direction. Considering magnitudes only, Equation (10.1) can be written as

$$i_C = I_S \exp\left(\frac{v_{BE}}{V_t} \right) \qquad (10.2)$$

Collector current   The collector current is controlled by the base–emitter voltage; that is, the current at one terminal of the device is controlled by the voltage applied to the other two terminals of the device. As we have mentioned, this is the basic transistor action.

Emitter Current   One component of emitter current, i_{E1}, shown in Figure 10.7 is due to the flow of electrons injected from the emitter into the base. This current, then, is ideally equal to the collector current given by Equation (10.1).

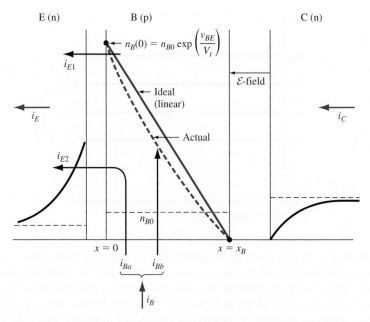

Figure 10.7 | Minority carrier distributions and basic currents in a forward-biased npn bipolar transistor.

Since the base–emitter junction is forward biased, majority-carrier holes in the base are injected across the B-E junction into the emitter. These injected holes produce a pn junction current i_{E2}, as indicated in Figure 10.7. This current is only a B-E junction current so this component of emitter current is not part of the collector current. Since i_{E2} is a forward-biased pn junction current, we can write (considering magnitude only)

$$i_{E2} = I_{S2} \exp\left(\frac{v_{BE}}{V_t}\right) \tag{10.3}$$

where I_{S2} involves the minority-carrier hole parameters in the emitter. The total emitter current is the sum of the two components, or

Emitter current

$$i_E = i_{E1} + i_{E2} = i_C + i_{E2} = I_{SE} \exp\left(\frac{v_{BE}}{V_t}\right) \tag{10.4}$$

Since all current components in Equation (10.4) are functions of $\exp(v_{BE}/V_t)$, the ratio of collector current to emitter current is a constant. We can write

$$\frac{i_C}{i_E} \equiv \alpha \tag{10.5}$$

where α is called the *common-base current gain*. By considering Equation (10.4), we see that $i_C < i_E$ or $\alpha < 1$. Since i_{E2} is not part of the basic transistor action, we would like this component of current to be as small as possible. We would then like the common-base current gain to be as close to unity as possible.

Common-base current gain

Figure 10.8 | Ideal bipolar transistor common-base current–voltage characteristics.

Referring to Figure 10.4a and Equation (10.4), note that the emitter current is an exponential function of the base–emitter voltage and the collector current is $i_C = \alpha i_E$. To a first approximation, the collector current is independent of the base–collector voltage as long as the B-C junction is reverse biased. We can sketch the ideal common-base transistor characteristics as shown in Figure 10.8. The bipolar transistor acts like a constant current source.

Base Current   As shown in Figure 10.7, the component of emitter current i_{E2} is a B-E junction current so that this current is also a component of base current shown as i_{Ba}. This component of base current is proportional to $\exp(v_{BE}/V_t)$.

There is also a second component of base current. We have considered the ideal case in which there is no recombination of minority-carrier electrons with majority-carrier holes in the base. However, in reality, there will be some recombination. Since majority-carrier holes in the base are disappearing, they must be resupplied by a flow of positive charge into the base terminal. This flow of charge is indicated as a current i_{Bb} in Figure 10.7. The number of holes per unit time recombining in the base is directly related to the number of minority-carrier electrons in the base. Therefore, the current i_{Bb} is also proportional to $\exp(v_{BE}/V_t)$. The total base current is the sum of i_{Ba} and i_{Bb}, and is proportional to $\exp(v_{BE}/V_t)$.

The ratio of collector current to base current is a constant since both currents are directly proportional to $\exp(v_{BE}/V_t)$. We can then write

$$\frac{i_C}{i_B} \equiv \beta \tag{10.6}$$

Common-emitter current gain

where β is called the *common-emitter current gain*. Normally, the base current will be relatively small so that, in general, the common-emitter current gain is much larger than unity (on the order of 100 or larger).

10.1.3   The Modes of Operation

Figure 10.9 shows the npn transistor in a simple circuit. In this configuration, the transistor may be biased in one of three modes of operation. If the B-E voltage is

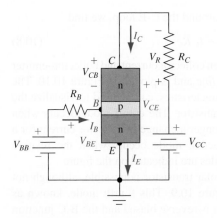

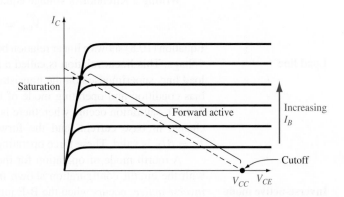

Figure 10.9 | An npn bipolar transistor in a common-emitter circuit configuration.

Figure 10.10 | Bipolar transistor common-emitter current–voltage characteristics with load line superimposed.

zero or reverse biased ($V_{BE} \leq 0$), then majority carrier electrons from the emitter will not be injected into the base. The B-C junction is also reverse biased; thus, the emitter and collector currents will be zero for this case. This condition is referred to as *cutoff*—all currents in the transistor are zero.

Cutoff mode

When the B-E junction becomes forward biased, an emitter current will be generated as we have discussed, and the injection of electrons into the base results in a collector current. We can write the Kirchhoff voltage law (KVL) equation around the collector–emitter loop as

$$V_{CC} = I_C R_C + V_{CB} + V_{BE} = V_R + V_{CE} \qquad (10.7)$$

If V_{CC} is large enough and if V_R is small enough, then $V_{CB} > 0$, which means that the B-C junction is reverse biased for this npn transistor. Again, this condition is the forward-active region of operation.

Forward-active mode

As the forward-biased B-E voltage increases, the collector current and hence V_R will also increase. The increase in V_R means that the reverse-biased C-B voltage decreases, or $|V_{CB}|$ decreases. At some point, the collector current may become large enough that the combination of V_R and V_{CC} produces zero voltage across the B-C junction. A slight increase in I_C beyond this point will cause a slight increase in V_R and the B-C junction will become forward biased ($V_{CB} < 0$). This condition is called *saturation*. In the saturation mode of operation, both B-E and B-C junctions are forward biased and the collector current is no longer controlled by the B-E voltage.

Saturation mode

Figure 10.10 shows the transistor current characteristics, I_C versus V_{CE}, for constant base currents when the transistor is connected in the common-emitter configuration (Figure 10.9). When the collector–emitter voltage is large enough so that the base–collector junction is reverse biased, the collector current is a constant in this first-order theory. For small values of C-E voltage, the base–collector junction becomes forward biased and the collector current decreases to zero for a constant base current.

Writing a Kirchhoff's voltage equation around the C-E loop, we find

$$V_{CE} = V_{CC} - I_C R_C \tag{10.8}$$

Load line

Equation (10.8) shows a linear relation between collector current and collector–emitter voltage. This linear relation is called a *load line* and is plotted in Figure 10.10. The load line, superimposed on the transistor characteristics, can be used to visualize the bias condition and operating mode of the transistor. The cutoff mode occurs when $I_C = 0$, saturation occurs when there is no longer a change in collector current for a change in base current, and the forward-active mode occurs when the relation $I_C = \beta I_B$ is valid. These three operating modes are indicated on the figure.

Inverse-active mode

A fourth mode of operation for the bipolar transistor is possible, although not with the circuit configuration shown in Figure 10.9. This fourth mode, known as *inverse active,* occurs when the B-E junction is reverse biased and the B-C junction is forward biased. In this case, the transistor is operating "upside down," and the roles of the emitter and collector are reversed. We have argued that the transistor is not a symmetrical device; therefore, the inverse-active characteristics will not be the same as the forward-active characteristics.

The junction voltage conditions for the four operating modes are shown in Figure 10.11. The minority-carrier distributions through the device and the energy-band diagrams for the four operating modes will be discussed in Section 10.2.2.

10.1.4   Amplification with Bipolar Transistors

Voltages and currents can be amplified by bipolar transistors in conjunction with other elements. We will demonstrate this amplification qualitatively in the following discussion. Figure 10.12 shows an npn bipolar transistor in a common-emitter configuration. The dc voltage sources, V_{BB} and V_{CC}, are used to bias the transistor in the

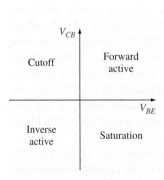

Figure 10.11 | Junction voltage conditions for the four operating modes of a bipolar transistor.

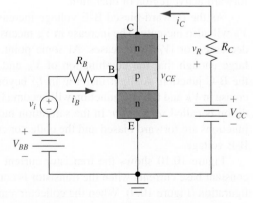

Figure 10.12 | Common-emitter npn bipolar circuit configuration with a time-varying signal voltage v_i included in the base–emitter loop.

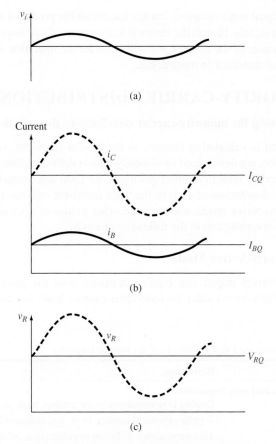

Figure 10.13 | Currents and voltages existing in the circuit shown in Figure 10.12. (a) Input sinusoidal signal voltage. (b) Sinusoidal base and collector currents superimposed on the quiescent dc values. (c) Sinusoidal voltage across the R_C resistor superimposed on the quiescent dc value.

forward-active mode. The voltage source v_i represents a time-varying input voltage (such as a signal from a satellite) that needs to be amplified.

Figure 10.13 shows the various voltages and currents that are generated in the circuit assuming that v_i is a sinusoidal voltage. The sinusoidal voltage v_i induces a sinusoidal component of base current superimposed on a dc quiescent value. Since $i_C = \beta i_B$, a relatively large sinusoidal collector current is superimposed on a dc value of collector current. The time-varying collector current induces a time-varying voltage across the R_C resistor which, by Kirchhoff's voltage law, means that a sinusoidal voltage, superimposed on a dc value, exists between the collector and emitter of the bipolar transistor. The sinusoidal voltages in the collector–emitter portion of the circuit are larger than the signal input voltage v_i, so that the circuit has produced a *voltage gain* in the time-varying signals. Hence, the circuit is known as a *voltage amplifier.*

In the remainder of the chapter, we will consider the operation and characteristics of the bipolar transistor in more detail.

10.2 | MINORITY-CARRIER DISTRIBUTION

Objective: Develop the minority-carrier distributions through the device.

We are interested in calculating currents in the bipolar transistor, which, as in the simple pn junction, are determined by minority-carrier diffusion. Since diffusion currents are produced by minority-carrier gradients, we must determine the steady-state minority-carrier distribution in each of the three transistor regions. Let us first consider the forward-active mode, and then the other modes of operation. Table 10.1 summarizes the notation used in the following analysis.

10.2.1   Forward-Active Mode

Consider a uniformly doped npn bipolar transistor with the geometry shown in Figure 10.14. When we consider the individual emitter, base, and collector regions,

Table 10.1 | Notation used in the analysis of the bipolar transistor

Notation	Definition
For both the npn and pnp transistors	
N_E, N_B, N_C	Doping concentrations in the emitter, base, and collector
x_E, x_B, x_C	Widths of neutral emitter, base, and collector regions
D_E, D_B, D_C	*Minority-carrier* diffusion coefficients in emitter, base, and collector regions
L_E, L_B, L_C	*Minority-carrier* diffusion lengths in emitter, base, and collector regions
$\tau_{E0}, \tau_{B0}, \tau_{C0}$	*Minority-carrier* lifetimes in emitter, base, and collector regions
For the npn	
p_{E0}, n_{B0}, p_{C0}	Thermal equilibrium *minority-carrier* hole, electron, and hole concentrations in the emitter, base, and collector
$p_E(x'), n_B(x), p_C(x'')$	Total *minority-carrier* hole, electron, and hole concentrations in the emitter base, and collector
$\delta p_E(x'), \delta n_B(x), \delta p_C(x'')$	Excess *minority-carrier* hole, electron, and hole concentrations in the emitter, base, and collector
For the pnp	
n_{E0}, p_{B0}, n_{C0}	Thermal equilibrium *minority-carrier* electron, hole, and electron concentrations in the emitter, base, and collector
$n_E(x'), p_B(x), n_C(x'')$	Total *minority-carrier* electron, hole, and electron concentrations in the emitter, base, and collector
$\delta n_E(x'), \delta p_B(x), \delta n_C(x'')$	Excess *minority-carrier* electron, hole, and electron concentrations in the emitter, base, and collector

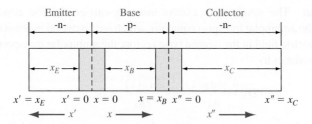

Figure 10.14 | Geometry of the npn bipolar transistor used to calculate the minority-carrier distribution.

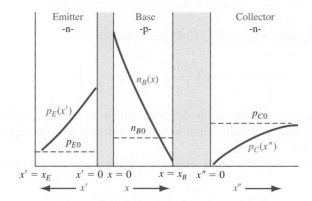

Figure 10.15 | Minority-carrier distribution in an npn bipolar transistor operating in the forward-active mode.

we will shift the origin to the edge of the space charge region and consider a positive x, x', or x'' coordinate, as shown in the figure.

In the forward-active mode, the B-E junction is forward biased and the B-C is reverse biased. We expect the minority carrier distributions to look like those shown in Figure 10.15. As there are two n regions, we will have minority-carrier holes in both emitter and collector. To distinguish between these two minority-carrier hole distributions, we will use the notation shown in the figure. Keep in mind that we will be dealing only with minority carriers. The parameters p_{E0}, n_{B0}, and p_{C0} denote the thermal-equilibrium minority-carrier concentrations in the emitter, base, and collector, respectively. The functions $p_E(x')$, $n_B(x)$, and $p_C(x'')$ denote the steady-state minority-carrier concentrations in the emitter, base, and collector, respectively. We will assume that the neutral collector length x_C is long compared to the minority-carrier diffusion length L_C in the collector, but we will take into account a finite emitter length x_E. If we assume that the surface recombination velocity at $x' = x_E$ is infinite, then the excess minority-carrier concentration at $x' = x_E$ is zero, or $p_E(x' = x_E) = p_{E0}$. An infinite surface recombination velocity is a good approximation when an ohmic contact is fabricated at $x' = x_E$.

Base Region   The steady-state excess minority-carrier electron concentration is found from the ambipolar transport equation, which we discussed in detail in Chapter 8. For a zero electric field in the neutral base region, the ambipolar transport equation in steady state reduces to

$$D_B \frac{\partial^2 [\delta n_B(x)]}{\partial x^2} - \frac{\delta n_B(x)}{\tau_{B0}} = 0 \tag{10.9}$$

where δn_B is the excess minority-carrier electron concentration, and D_B and τ_{B0} are the minority-carrier diffusion coefficient and lifetime in the base region, respectively. The excess electron concentration is defined as

$$\delta n_B(x) = n_B(x) - n_{B0} \tag{10.10}$$

The general solution to Equation (10.9) can be written as

$$\delta n_B(x) = A \exp\left(\frac{+x}{L_B}\right) + B \exp\left(\frac{-x}{L_B}\right) \tag{10.11}$$

where L_B is the minority-carrier diffusion length in the base, given by $L_B = \sqrt{D_B \tau_{B0}}$. The base is of finite width so both exponential terms in Equation (10.11) must be retained.

The excess minority-carrier electron concentrations at the two boundaries become

$$\delta n_B(x = 0) \equiv \delta n_B(0) = A + B \tag{10.12a}$$

and

$$\delta n_B(x = x_B) \equiv \delta n_B(x_B) = A \exp\left(\frac{+x_B}{L_B}\right) + B \exp\left(\frac{-x_B}{L_B}\right) \tag{10.12b}$$

The B-E junction is forward biased, so the boundary condition at $x = 0$ is

$$\delta n_B(0) = n_B(x = 0) - n_{B0} = n_{B0}\left[\exp\left(\frac{eV_{BE}}{kT}\right) - 1\right] \tag{10.13a}$$

The B-C junction is reverse biased, so the second boundary condition at $x = x_B$ is

$$\delta n_B(x_B) = n_B(x = x_B) - n_{B0} = 0 - n_{B0} = -n_{B0} \tag{10.13b}$$

From the boundary conditions given by Equation (10.13a) and (10.13b), the coefficients A and B from Equation (10.12a) and (10.12b) can be determined. The results are

$$A = \frac{-n_{B0} - n_{B0}\left[\exp\left(\frac{eV_{BE}}{kT}\right) - 1\right]\exp\left(\frac{-x_B}{L_B}\right)}{2 \sinh\left(\frac{x_B}{L_B}\right)} \tag{10.14a}$$

and

$$B = \frac{n_{B0}\left[\exp\left(\frac{eV_{BE}}{kT}\right) - 1\right]\exp\left(\frac{x_B}{L_B}\right) + n_{B0}}{2\sinh\left(\frac{x_B}{L_B}\right)} \tag{10.14b}$$

Then, substituting Equation (10.14a) and (10.14b) into Equation (10.9), we can write the excess minority carrier electron concentration in the base region as

$$\delta n_B(x) = \frac{n_{B0}\left\{\left[\exp\left(\frac{eV_{BE}}{kT}\right) - 1\right]\sinh\left(\frac{x_B - x}{L_B}\right) - \sinh\left(\frac{x}{L_B}\right)\right\}}{\sinh\left(\frac{x_B}{L_B}\right)}$$

$$(10.15a)$$

Equation (10.15a) may look formidable with the sinh functions. We have stressed that we want the base width x_B to be small compared to the minority-carrier diffusion length L_B. This condition may seem somewhat arbitrary at this point, but the reason will become clear as we proceed through all of the calculations. Since we want $x_B < L_B$, the argument in the sinh functions is always less than unity and in most cases will be much less than unity. Figure 10.16 shows a plot of sinh (y) for

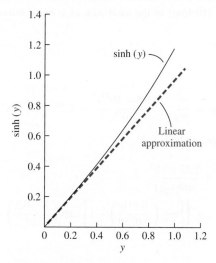

Figure 10.16 | Hyperbolic sine function and its linear approximation.

$0 \leq y \leq 1$ and also shows the linear approximation for small values of y. If $y < 0.4$, the sinh (y) function differs from its linear approximation by less than 3 percent. All of this leads to the *conclusion that the excess electron concentration δn_B in Equation (10.15a) is approximately a linear function of x through the neutral base region.* Using the approximation that sinh $(x) \approx x$ for $x \ll 1$, the excess electron concentration in the base is given by

$$\delta n_B(x) \approx \frac{n_{B0}}{x_B} \left\{ \left[\exp\left(\frac{eV_{BE}}{kT}\right) - 1 \right] (x_B - x) - x \right\} \qquad (10.15b)$$

We will use this linear approximation later in some of the example calculations. The difference in the excess carrier concentrations determined from Equations (10.15a) and (10.15b) is demonstrated in Example 10.1 and Exercise Problem 10.1. However, when we determine the common-base current gain later, we will need to use the actual expression for the excess carriers in the base and emitter.

EXAMPLE 10.1

OBJECTIVE

To determine the excess minority-carrier electron concentration in the base of an npn bipolar transistor.

Consider a uniformly doped silicon bipolar transistor at $T = 300$ K with impurity doping concentrations of $N_E = 10^{18}$ cm^{-3} and $N_B = 10^{16}$ cm^{-3}. A forward-bias B-E voltage of $V_{BE} = 0.610$ V is applied. Assume a neutral base width of $x_B = 1$ μm and a minority-carrier diffusion length of $L_B = 10$ μm. Determine the ratio of actual minority-carrier concentration at $x = x_B/2$ [Equation (10.15a)] to the ideal case of a linear minority-carrier distribution [Equation (10.15b)].

■ Solution

We find

$$n_{B0} = \frac{n_i^2}{N_B} = \frac{(1.5 \times 10^{10})^2}{10^{16}} = 2.25 \times 10^4 \text{ cm}^{-3}$$

For the actual distribution, we have

$$\delta n_B\left(x = \frac{x_B}{2}\right) = \frac{2.25 \times 10^4}{\sinh\left(\frac{1}{10}\right)}$$

$$\times \left\{ \left[\exp\left(\frac{0.610}{0.0259}\right) - 1 \right] \sinh\left(\frac{1 - 0.5}{10}\right) - \sinh\left(\frac{0.5}{10}\right) \right\}$$

or

$$\delta n_B\left(x = \frac{x_B}{2}\right) = 1.9018 \times 10^{14} \text{ cm}^{-3}$$

For the linear approximation, we find

$$\delta n_B \left(x = \frac{x_B}{2} \right) = \frac{2.25 \times 10^4}{10^{-4}}$$
$$\times \left\{ \left[\exp \left(\frac{0.610}{0.0259} \right) - 1 \right] (0.5 \times 10^{-4}) - (0.5 \times 10^{-4}) \right\}$$

or

$$\delta n_B \left(x = \frac{x_B}{2} \right) = 1.9042 \times 10^{14} \ \text{cm}^{-3}$$

Taking the ratio of the actual to the linear approximation, we obtain

$$\text{Ratio} = \frac{1.9018 \times 10^{14}}{1.9042 \times 10^{14}} = 0.9987$$

■ Comment
We see that for the case when $x_B = 1$ μm and $L_B = 10$ μm, the excess minority-carrier concentration is very nearly a linear function of distance through the base region.

Exercise Problem

EX10.1 Repeat Example 10.1 for the case when (*a*) $x_B = 2$ μm and (*b*) $x_B = 4$ μm. All other parameters are the same. [Ans. (*a*) 0.9950, (*b*) 0.980]

Table 10.2 shows the Taylor expansions of some of the hyperbolic functions that will be encountered in this section of the chapter. In most cases, we will consider only the linear terms when expanding these functions.

Emitter Region Consider, now, the minority-carrier hole concentration in the emitter. The steady-state excess hole concentration is determined from the equation

$$D_E \frac{\partial^2 (\delta p_E(x'))}{\partial x'^2} - \frac{\delta p_E(x')}{\tau_{E0}} = 0 \tag{10.16}$$

Table 10.2 | Taylor expansions of hyperbolic functions

Function	Taylor Expansion
$\sinh(x)$	$x + \dfrac{x^3}{3!} + \dfrac{x^5}{5!} + \cdots$
$\cosh(x)$	$1 + \dfrac{x^2}{2!} + \dfrac{x^4}{4!} + \cdots$
$\tanh(x)$	$x - \dfrac{x^3}{3} + \dfrac{2x^5}{15} + \cdots$

where D_E and τ_{E0} are the minority-carrier diffusion coefficient and minority-carrier lifetime, respectively, in the emitter. The excess hole concentration is given by

$$\delta p_E(x') = p_E(x') - p_{E0} \tag{10.17}$$

The general solution to Equation (10.16) can be written as

$$\delta p_E(x') = C \exp\left(\frac{+x'}{L_E}\right) + D \exp\left(\frac{-x'}{L_E}\right) \tag{10.18}$$

where $L_E = \sqrt{D_E \tau_{E0}}$. If we assume the neutral emitter length x_E is not necessarily long compared to L_E, then both exponential terms in Equation (10.18) must be retained.

The excess minority-carrier hole concentrations at the two boundaries are

$$\delta p_E(x' \geq 0) \equiv \delta p_E(0) = C + D \tag{10.19a}$$

and

$$\delta p_E(x' = x_E) \equiv \delta p_E(x_E) = C \exp\left(\frac{x_E}{L_E}\right) + D \exp\left(\frac{-x_E}{L_E}\right) \tag{10.19b}$$

Again, the B-E junction is forward biased, so

$$\delta p_E(0) = p_E(x' = 0) - p_{E0} = p_{E0}\left[\exp\left(\frac{eV_{BE}}{kT}\right) - 1\right] \tag{10.20a}$$

An infinite surface recombination velocity at $x' = x_E$ implies that

$$\delta p_E(x_E) = 0 \tag{10.20b}$$

Solving for C and D using Equations (10.19) and (10.20) yields the excess minority-carrier hole concentration in Equation (10.18):

$$\delta p_E(x') = \frac{p_{E0}\left[\exp\left(\frac{eV_{BE}}{kT}\right) - 1\right]\sinh\left(\frac{x_E - x'}{L_E}\right)}{\sinh\left(\frac{x_E}{L_E}\right)} \tag{10.21a}$$

This excess concentration will also vary approximately linearly with distance if x_E is small. We find

$$\delta p_E(x') \approx \frac{p_{E0}}{x_E}\left[\exp\left(\frac{eV_{BE}}{kT}\right) - 1\right](x_E - x') \tag{10.21b}$$

If x_E is comparable to L_E, then $\delta p_E(x')$ shows an exponential dependence on x_E.

EXAMPLE 10.2

OBJECTIVE

To determine the excess minority-carrier concentration in the emitter compared to that in the base of a bipolar transistor.

Consider a silicon bipolar transistor with the same parameters as given in Example 10.1. Determine the ratio $\delta p_E(x' = 0)/\delta n_B(x = 0)$.

■ **Solution**

We find from Equation (10.20a)

$$\delta p_E(0) = p_{E0}\left[\exp\left(\frac{eV_{BE}}{kT}\right) - 1\right]$$

and we find from Equation (10.13a)

$$\delta n_B(0) = n_{B0}\left[\exp\left(\frac{eV_{BE}}{kT}\right) - 1\right]$$

so

$$\frac{\delta p_E(0)}{\delta n_B(0)} = \frac{p_{E0}}{n_{B0}} = \frac{n_i^2/N_E}{n_i^2/N_B} = \frac{N_B}{N_C} = \frac{10^{16}}{10^{18}}$$

Then

$$\frac{\delta p_E(0)}{\delta n_B(0)} = 0.01$$

■ **Comment**

As we continue our analysis of the bipolar transistor, we will see that this ratio needs to be fairly small for a "good" transistor.

Exercise Problem

EX10.2 Repeat Example 10.2 for the case when $N_E = 8 \times 10^{17}$ cm^{-3} and $N_B = 2 \times 10^{16}$ cm^{-3}. (Ans. Ratio $= 0.025$)

Collector Region The excess minority-carrier hole concentration in the collector can be determined from the equation

$$D_C\frac{\partial^2(\delta p_C(x''))}{\partial x''^2} - \frac{\delta p_C(x'')}{\tau_{C0}} = 0 \tag{10.22}$$

where D_C and τ_{C0} are the minority-carrier diffusion coefficient and minority-carrier lifetime, respectively, in the collector. We can express the excess minority-carrier hole concentration in the collector as

$$\delta p_C(x'') = p_C(x'') - p_{C0} \tag{10.23}$$

The general solution to Equation (10.22) can be written as

$$\delta p_C(x'') = G\exp\left(\frac{x''}{L_C}\right) + H\exp\left(\frac{-x''}{L_C}\right) \tag{10.24}$$

where $L_C = \sqrt{D_C \tau_{C0}}$. If we assume that the collector is long, then the coefficient G must be zero since the excess concentration must remain finite. The second boundary condition gives

$$\delta p_C(x'' = 0) \equiv \delta p_C(0) = p_C(x'' = 0) - p_{C0} = 0 - p_{C0} = -p_{C0} \quad (10.25)$$

The excess minority-carrier hole concentration in the collector is then given as

$$\delta p_C(x'') = -p_{C0} \exp\left(\frac{-x''}{L_C}\right) \quad (10.26)$$

This result is exactly what we expect from the results of a reverse-biased pn junction.

EXAMPLE 10.3

OBJECTIVE

To calculate a distance into the collector region.

Consider the collector region of an npn bipolar transistor biased in the forward-active mode. At what value of x'', compared to L_C, does the magnitude of the minority-carrier concentration reach 95 percent of the thermal equilibrium value?

■ Solution

Combining Equations (10.23) and (10.26), we find the minority-carrier concentration to be

$$p_C(x'') = \delta p_C(x'') + p_{C0} = p_{C0}\left[1 - \exp\left(\frac{-x''}{L_C}\right)\right]$$

or

$$\frac{p_C(x'')}{p_{C0}} = 1 - \exp\left(\frac{-x''}{L_C}\right)$$

For $\frac{p_C(x'')}{p_{C0}} = 0.95$, we find

$$\frac{x''}{L_C} \approx 3$$

■ Comment

In order for the excess minority-carrier concentration in the collector to reach the steady-state value as assumed in the preceding analysis, the collector region must be fairly wide. This situation may not be valid in all cases.

Exercise Problem

EX10.3 Repeat Example 10.3 for the case when $\delta p(x'')/p_{C0} = 0.50$. (Ans. 0.693)

10.2.2   Other Modes of Operation

We have been analyzing the npn bipolar transistor biased in the forward-active mode with the B-E junction forward biased and the B-C junction reverse biased. The resulting minority-carrier distribution through the device was shown in Figure 10.5a and the energy-band diagram was shown in Figure 10.5b.

The bipolar transistor can also operate in the cutoff, saturation, or inverse-active modes. We will qualitatively discuss the minority-carrier distributions for these operating modes and treat the actual calculations as problems at the end of the chapter. We will also consider the energy-band diagrams for each condition.

Figure 10.17 shows the situation for the cutoff mode. Both the B-E and B-C junctions are reverse biased (as a minimum the B-E junction is zero biased). For reverse-biased junctions, the minority-carrier concentrations are ideally zero at each space charge edge. The emitter and collector regions are assumed to be "long" in this figure, while the base is narrow compared with the minority-carrier diffusion length. Since $x_B \ll L_B$, essentially all minority carriers are swept out of the base region. The barrier heights of both the B-E and B-C junctions have increased so there is essentially no charge flow.

Figure 10.18 shows the minority-carrier distribution and energy-band diagram for the saturation mode. Both junctions are forward biased. However, for a transistor connected in the circuit configuration shown in Figure 10.9, there will be net positive collector and emitter currents, which means, for the npn transistor, there will be a net flow of electrons from the emitter to the collector. This situation implies that the B-E potential barrier is smaller than the potential barrier of the B-C junction. This condition is shown in Figure 10.18b. Since both junctions are forward biased, the

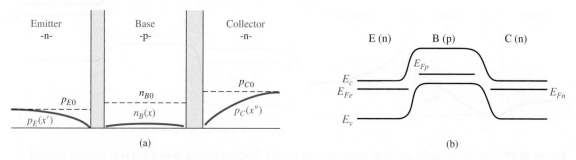

Figure 10.17 | The cutoff mode of operation with both B-E and B-C junctions reverse biased: (a) minority-carrier distribution and (b) energy-band diagram.

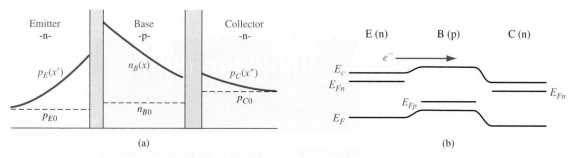

Figure 10.18 | The saturation mode of operation with both B-E and B-C junctions forward biased: (a) minority-carrier distribution and (b) energy-band diagram.

minority-carrier concentrations are greater than the thermal equilibrium values at the space charge edges, as shown in Figure 10.18a. However, there is still a gradient in the minority-carrier concentration in the base to induce the collector current.

Finally, Figure 10.19 shows the situation for the inverse-active mode. The B-E is reverse biased and the B-C junction is forward biased. The minority-carrier distribution is shown in Figure 10.19a and is essentially the "mirror image" of the forward-active mode. The energy-band diagram for the inverse-active mode is shown in Figure 10.19b. Electrons from the collector now diffuse across the B-C junction into the base and then diffuse into the emitter. We must keep in mind that the bipolar transistor is not a symmetrical device. Figure 10.20 shows the injection of electrons from the collector into the base. Since the B-C area is normally much larger than the B-E area, not all of the injected electrons will be collected by the emitter. The relative doping concentrations in the base and collector are also different compared with those of the base and emitter. We then expect the characteristics to be significantly different between the forward-active and inverse-active modes of operation.

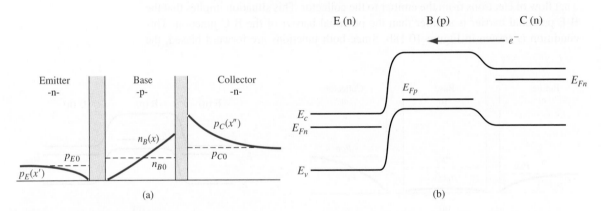

(a) (b)

Figure 10.19 | The inverse-active mode of operation with the B-E junction reverse biased and B-C junction forward biased: (a) minority-carrier distribution and (b) energy-band diagram.

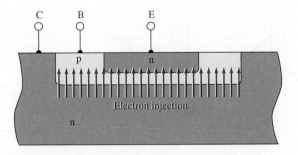

Figure 10.20 | Cross section of an npn bipolar transistor biased in the inverse-active mode showing the injection and collection of electrons.

10.3 | LOW-FREQUENCY COMMON-BASE CURRENT GAIN

Objective: Determine the contributing factors and develop the mathematical expressions for the common-base current gain factors.

The basic principle of operation of the bipolar transistor is the control of the collector current by the B-E voltage. The collector current is a function of the number of majority carriers reaching the collector after being injected from the emitter across the B-E junction. The *common-base current gain* is defined as the ratio of collector current to emitter current. The flow of various charged carriers leads to definitions of particular currents in the device. We can use these definitions to define the current gain of the transistor in terms of several factors.

10.3.1 Contributing Factors

Figure 10.21 shows the various particle flux components in the npn bipolar transistor. We will define the various flux components and then consider the resulting currents. Although there seems to be a large number of flux components, we can help clarify the situation by correlating each factor with the minority-carrier distributions shown in Figure 10.15.

The factor J_{nE}^- is the electron flux injected from the emitter into the base. As the electrons diffuse across the base, a few will recombine with majority-carrier holes. The majority-carrier holes that are lost by recombination must be replenished from the base terminal. This replacement hole flux is denoted by J_{RB}^+. The electron flux that reaches the collector is J_{nC}^-. The majority-carrier holes from the base that are injected back into the emitter result in a hole flux denoted by J_{pE}^+. Some electrons and holes that are injected into the forward-biased B-E space charge region will recombine in this region. This recombination leads to the electron flux J_R^-. Generation of electrons and holes occurs in the reverse-biased B-C junction. This generation yields a hole flux J_G^+. Finally, the ideal reverse-saturation current in the B-C junction is denoted by the hole flux J_{pc0}^+.

The corresponding electric current density components in the npn transistor are shown in Figure 10.22 along with the minority-carrier distributions for the

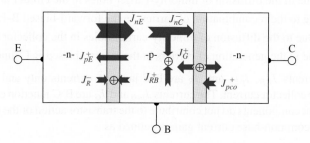

Figure 10.21 | Particle current density or flux components in an npn bipolar transistor operating in the forward-active mode.

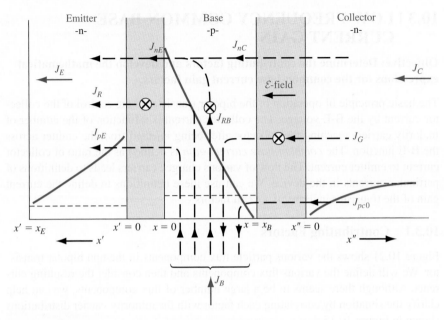

Figure 10.22 | Current density components in an npn bipolar transistor operating in the forward-active mode.

forward-active mode. The curves are the same as in Figure 10.15. As in the pn junction, the currents in the bipolar transistor are defined in terms of minority-carrier diffusion currents. The current densities are defined as follows:

J_{nE}: Due to the diffusion of minority-carrier electrons in the base at $x = 0$.

J_{nC}: Due to the diffusion of minority-carrier electrons in the base at $x = x_B$.

J_{RB}: The difference between J_{nE} and J_{nC}, which is due to the recombination of excess minority-carrier electrons with majority-carrier holes in the base. The J_{RB} current is the flow of holes into the base to replace the holes lost by recombination.

J_{pE}: Due to the diffusion of minority-carrier holes in the emitter at $x' = 0$.

J_R: Due to the recombination of carriers in the forward-biased B-E junction.

J_{pc0}: Due to the diffusion of minority-carrier holes in the collector at $x'' = 0$.

J_G: Due to the generation of carriers in the reverse-biased B-C junction.

The currents J_{RB}, J_{pE}, and J_R are B-E junction currents only and do not contribute to the collector current. The currents J_{pc0} and J_G are B-C junction currents only. These current components do not contribute to the transistor action or the current gain.

dc common-base current gain   The dc common-base current gain is defined as

$$\alpha_0 = \frac{I_C}{I_E} \tag{10.27}$$

If we assume that the active cross-sectional area is the same for the collector and emitter, then we can write the current gain in terms of the current densities, or

$$\alpha_0 = \frac{J_C}{J_E} = \frac{J_{nC} + J_G + J_{pc0}}{J_{nE} + J_R + J_{pE}} \qquad (10.28)$$

We are primarily interested in determining how the collector current will change with a change in emitter current. The small-signal, or sinusoidal, common-base current gain is defined as

ac common-base current gain

$$\alpha = \frac{\partial J_C}{\partial J_E} = \frac{J_{nC}}{J_{nE} + J_R + J_{pE}} \qquad (10.29)$$

The reverse-bias B-C currents, J_G and J_{pc0}, are not functions of the emitter current.

We can rewrite Equation (10.29) in the form

$$\alpha = \left(\frac{J_{nE}}{J_{nE} + J_{pE}}\right)\left(\frac{J_{nC}}{J_{nE}}\right)\left(\frac{J_{nE} + J_{pE}}{J_{nE} + J_R + J_{pE}}\right) \qquad (10.30a)$$

or

$$\alpha = \gamma \alpha_T \delta \qquad (10.30b)$$

The factors in Equation (10.30b) are defined as:

$$\gamma = \left(\frac{J_{nE}}{J_{nE} + J_{pE}}\right) \qquad \equiv \text{emitter injection efficiency factor} \qquad (10.31a)$$

$$\alpha_T = \left(\frac{J_{nC}}{J_{nE}}\right) \qquad \equiv \text{base transport factor} \qquad (10.31b)$$

$$\delta = \frac{J_{nE} + J_{pE}}{J_{nE} + J_R + J_{pE}} \qquad \equiv \text{recombination factor} \qquad (10.31c)$$

Keep in mind that these current definitions apply to an npn transistor. Similar expressions for the current gain limitations apply to the pnp transistor: electron currents are replaced by hole currents and hole currents are replaced by electron currents.

We would like to have the change in collector current be exactly the same as the change in emitter current or, ideally, to have $\alpha = 1$. However, a consideration of Equation (10.29) shows that α will always be less than unity. The goal is to make α as close to one as possible. To achieve this goal, we must make each term in Equation (10.30b) as close to one as possible, since each factor is less than unity.

The *emitter injection efficiency factor* γ takes into account the minority-carrier hole diffusion current in the emitter. This current is part of the emitter current, but does not contribute to the transistor action in that J_{pE} is not part of the collector current. The *base transport factor* α_T takes into account any recombination of excess minority-carrier electrons in the base. Ideally, we want no recombination in the base. The *recombination factor* δ takes into account the recombination in the forward-biased B-E junction. The current J_R contributes to the emitter current, but does not contribute to collector current.

Common-base current gain limiting factors

10.3.2   Mathematical Derivation of Current Gain Factors

We now wish to determine each of the gain factors in terms of the electrical and geometrical parameters of the transistor. The results of these derivations will show how the various parameters in the transistor influence the electrical properties of the device and will point the way to the design of a "good" bipolar transistor.

Emitter Injection Efficiency Factor   Consider, initially, the emitter injection efficiency factor. We have from Equation (10.31a)

$$\gamma = \left(\frac{J_{nE}}{J_{nE} + J_{pE}} \right) = \frac{1}{\left(1 + \dfrac{J_{pE}}{J_{nE}} \right)} \tag{10.32}$$

We derived the minority-carrier distribution functions for the forward-active mode in Section 10.2.1. Noting that J_{nE}, as defined in Figure 10.22, is in the negative x direction, we can write the current densities as

$$J_{pE} = -e D_E \frac{d[\delta p_E(x')]}{dx'} \bigg|_{x'=0} \tag{10.33a}$$

and

$$J_{nE} = (-)e D_B \frac{d[\delta n_B(x)]}{dx} \bigg|_{x=0} \tag{10.33b}$$

where $\delta p_E(x')$ and $\delta n_B(x)$ are given by Equations (10.21) and (10.15), respectively. Taking the appropriate derivatives of $\delta p_E(x')$ and $\delta n_B(x)$, we obtain

$$J_{pE} = \frac{e D_E p_{E0}}{L_E} \left[\exp\left(\frac{e V_{BE}}{kT} \right) - 1 \right] \frac{1}{\tanh (x_E / L_E)} \tag{10.34a}$$

and

$$J_{nE} = \frac{e D_B n_{B0}}{L_B} \left\{ \frac{1}{\sinh (x_B / L_B)} + \frac{[\exp (e V_{BE} / kT) - 1]}{\tanh (x_B / L_B)} \right\} \tag{10.34b}$$

Positive J_{pE} and J_{nE} values imply that the currents are in the directions shown in Figure 10.22. If we assume that the B-E junction is biased sufficiently far in the forward bias so that $V_{BE} \gg kT/e$, then

$$\exp\left(\frac{e V_{BE}}{kT} \right) \gg 1$$

and also

$$\frac{\exp (e V_{BE} / kT)}{\tanh (x_B / L_B)} \gg \frac{1}{\sinh (x_B / L_B)}$$

The emitter injection efficiency, from Equation (10.32), then becomes

$$\gamma = \cfrac{1}{1 + \cfrac{p_{E0} D_E L_B \tanh (x_B/L_B)}{n_{B0} D_B L_E \tanh (x_E/L_E)}} \qquad (10.35a)$$

If we assume that all the parameters in Equation (10.35a) except p_{E0} and n_{B0} are fixed, then in order for $\gamma \approx 1$, we must have $p_{E0} \ll n_{B0}$. We can write

$$p_{E0} = \frac{n_i^2}{N_E} \qquad \text{and} \qquad n_{B0} = \frac{n_i^2}{N_B}$$

where N_E and N_B are the impurity doping concentrations in the emitter and base, respectively. Then the condition that $p_{E0} \ll n_{B0}$ implies that $N_E \gg N_B$. For the emitter injection efficiency to be close to unity, the emitter doping must be large compared to the base doping. This condition means that many more electrons from the n-type emitter than holes from the p-type base will be injected across the B-E space charge region. If both $x_B \ll L_B$ and $x_E \ll L_E$, then the emitter injection efficiency can be written as

$$\gamma \approx \cfrac{1}{1 + \cfrac{N_B}{N_E} \cfrac{D_E}{D_B} \cfrac{x_B}{x_E}} \qquad (10.35b)$$

Base Transport Factor   The next term to consider is the base transport factor, given by Equation (10.31b) as $\alpha_T = J_{nC}/J_{nE}$. From the definitions of the current directions shown in Figure 10.19, we can write

$$J_{nC} = (-)e D_B \frac{d[\delta n_B(x)]}{dx}\bigg|_{x = x_B} \qquad (10.36a)$$

and

$$J_{nE} = (-)e D_B \frac{d[\delta n_B(x)]}{dx}\bigg|_{x = 0} \qquad (10.36b)$$

Using the expression for $\delta n_B(x)$ given in Equation (10.15), we find that

$$J_{nC} = \frac{e D_B n_{B0}}{L_B} \left\{ \frac{[\exp (e V_{BE}/kT) - 1]}{\sinh (x_B/L_B)} + \frac{1}{\tanh (x_B/L_B)} \right\} \qquad (10.37)$$

The expression for J_{nE} was given in Equation (10.34a).

If we again assume that the B-E junction is biased sufficiently far in the forward bias so that $V_{BE} \gg kT/e$, then $\exp (e V_{BE}/kT) \gg 1$. Substituting Equations (10.37) and (10.34b) into Equation (10.31b), we have

$$\alpha_T = \frac{J_{nC}}{J_{nE}} \approx \frac{\exp (e V_{BE}/kT) + \cosh (x_B/L_B)}{1 + \exp (e V_{BE}/kT) \cosh (x_B/L_B)} \qquad (10.38)$$

In order for α_T to be close to unity, the neutral base width x_B must be much smaller than the minority carrier diffusion length in the base L_B. If $x_B \ll L_B$, then $\cosh(x_B/L_B)$ will be just slightly greater than unity. In addition, if $\exp(eV_{BE}/kT) \gg 1$, then the base transport factor is approximately

Base transport factor

$$\alpha_T \approx \frac{1}{\cosh(x_B/L_B)} \tag{10.39a}$$

For $x_B \ll L_B$, we may expand the cosh function in a Taylor series, so that

$$\alpha_T = \frac{1}{\cosh(x_B/L_B)} \approx \frac{1}{1 + \frac{1}{2}(x_B/L_B)^2} \approx 1 - \frac{1}{2}(x_B/L_B)^2 \tag{10.39b}$$

The base transport factor α_T will be close to one if $x_B \ll L_B$. We can now see why we indicated earlier that the neutral base width x_B would be less than L_B.

Recombination Factor   The recombination factor was given by Equation (10.31c). We can write

$$\delta = \frac{J_{nE} + J_{pE}}{J_{nE} + J_R + J_{pE}} \approx \frac{J_{nE}}{J_{nE} + J_R} = \frac{1}{1 + J_R/J_{nE}} \tag{10.40}$$

We have assumed in Equation (10.40) that $J_{pE} \ll J_{nE}$. The recombination current density, due to carrier recombination in the forward-biased pn junction space charge region was discussed in Chapter 9 and can be written as

$$J_R = \frac{ex_{BE}n_i}{2\tau_0} \exp\left(\frac{eV_{BE}}{2kT}\right) = J_{r0} \exp\left(\frac{eV_{BE}}{2kT}\right) \tag{10.41}$$

where x_{BE} is the B-E space charge width.

The current J_{nE} from Equation (10.34b) can be approximated as

$$J_{nE} = J_{s0} \exp\left(\frac{eV_{BE}}{kT}\right) \tag{10.42}$$

where

$$J_{s0} = \frac{eD_B n_{B0}}{L_B \tanh(x_B/L_B)} \tag{10.43}$$

Recombination factor

The recombination factor, from Equation (10.40), can then be written as

$$\delta = \frac{1}{1 + \dfrac{J_{r0}}{J_{s0}} \exp\left(\dfrac{-eV_{BE}}{2kT}\right)} \tag{10.44}$$

The recombination factor is a function of the B-E voltage. As V_{BE} increases, the recombination current becomes less dominant and the recombination factor approaches unity.

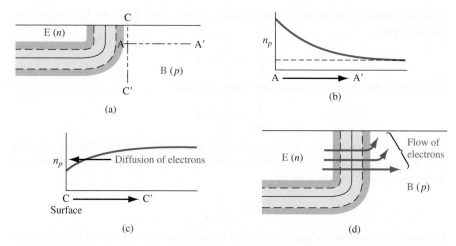

Figure 10.23 | The surface at the E-B junction showing the diffusion of carriers toward the surface.

The recombination factor must also include surface effects. The surface effects can be described by the surface recombination velocity as we discussed briefly in Chapter 8. Figure 10.23a shows the B-E junction of an npn transistor near the semiconductor surface. We will assume that the B-E junction is forward biased. Figure 10.23b shows the excess minority-carrier electron concentration in the base along the cross section A-A′. This curve is the usual forward-biased junction minority-carrier concentration. Figure 10.23c shows the excess minority-carrier electron concentration along the cross section C-C′ from the surface. We showed earlier that the excess concentration at a surface is smaller than the excess concentration in the bulk material. With this electron distribution, there is a diffusion of electrons from the bulk toward the surface where the electrons recombine with the majority carrier holes. Figure 10.23d shows the injection of electrons from the emitter into the base and the diffusion of electrons toward the surface. This diffusion generates another component of recombination current and this component of recombination current must be included in the recombination factor δ. Although the actual calculation is difficult because of the two-dimensional analysis required, the form of the recombination current is the same as that of Equation (10.41).

10.3.3 Summary and Review

Although we have considered an npn transistor in all of the derivations, exactly the same analysis applies to a pnp transistor; the same minority-carrier distributions will be obtained except that the electron concentrations will become hole concentrations and vice versa. The current directions and voltage polarities will also change.

We have been considering the common-base current gain, defined in Equation (10.27) as $\alpha_0 = I_C/I_E$. The common-emitter current gain is defined as $\beta_0 = I_C/I_B$. From Figure 10.9 we see that $I_E = I_B + I_C$. We can determine the relation between common-emitter and common-base current gains from the KCL equation. We can write

$$\frac{I_E}{I_C} = \frac{I_B}{I_C} + 1$$

Substituting the definitions of current gains, we have

$$\frac{1}{\alpha_0} = \frac{1}{\beta_0} + 1$$

Common-emitter current gain

Since this relation actually holds for both dc and small-signal conditions, we can drop the subscript. The common-emitter current gain can now be written in terms of the common-base current gain as

$$\beta = \frac{\alpha}{1 - \alpha}$$

The common-base current gain, in terms of the common-emitter current gain, is found to be

$$\alpha = \frac{\beta}{1 + \beta}$$

Table 10.3 summarizes the expressions for the limiting factors in the common base current gain assuming that $x_B \ll L_B$ and $x_E \ll L_E$. Also given are the approximate expressions for the common-base current gain and the common-emitter current gain.

10.3.4   Example Calculations of the Gain Factors

If we assume a typical value of β to be 100, then $\alpha = 0.99$. If we also assume that $\gamma = \alpha_T = \delta$, then each factor would have to be equal to 0.9967 in order that $\beta = 100$. This calculation gives an indication of how close to unity each factor must be to achieve a reasonable current gain. We will use these factors in some of the following calculations.

EXAMPLE 10.4

OBJECTIVE

To design the ratio of emitter doping to base doping to achieve an emitter injection efficiency factor equal to $\gamma = 0.9967$.

Consider an npn bipolar transistor. Assume, for simplicity, that $D_E = D_B$, $L_E = L_B$, and $x_E = x_B$.

■ **Solution**

Equation (10.35a) reduces to

$$\gamma = \frac{1}{1 + \dfrac{p_{E0}}{n_{B0}}} = \frac{1}{1 + \dfrac{n_i^2 / N_E}{n_i^2 / N_B}}$$

Table 10.3 | Summary of limiting factors

Emitter injection efficiency

$$\gamma \approx \frac{1}{1 + \dfrac{N_B}{N_E} \dfrac{D_E}{D_B} \dfrac{x_B}{x_E}} \qquad (x_B \ll L_B), (x_E \ll L_E)$$

Base transport factor

$$\alpha_T \approx \frac{1}{1 + \dfrac{1}{2}\left(\dfrac{x_B}{L_B}\right)^2} \qquad (x_B \ll L_B)$$

Recombination factor

$$\delta = \frac{1}{1 + \dfrac{J_{r0}}{J_{s0}}\exp\left(\dfrac{-eV_{BE}}{2kT}\right)}$$

Common-base current gain

$$\alpha = \gamma\alpha_T\delta \approx \frac{1}{1 + \dfrac{N_B}{N_E}\dfrac{D_E}{D_B}\dfrac{x_B}{x_E} + \dfrac{1}{2}\left(\dfrac{x_B}{L_B}\right)^2 + \dfrac{J_{r0}}{J_{s0}}\exp\left(\dfrac{-eV_{BE}}{2kT}\right)}$$

Common-emitter current gain

$$\beta = \frac{\alpha}{1 - \alpha} \approx \frac{1}{\dfrac{N_B}{N_E}\dfrac{D_E}{D_B}\dfrac{x_B}{x_E} + \dfrac{1}{2}\left(\dfrac{x_B}{L_B}\right)^2 + \dfrac{J_{r0}}{J_{s0}}\exp\left(\dfrac{-eV_{BE}}{2kT}\right)}$$

so

$$\gamma = \frac{1}{1 + \dfrac{N_B}{N_E}} = 0.9967$$

Then

$$\frac{N_B}{N_E} = 0.00331 \qquad \text{or} \qquad \frac{N_E}{N_B} = 302$$

■ **Comment**

The emitter doping concentration must be much larger than the base doping concentration to achieve a high emitter injection efficiency.

Exercise Problem

EX10.4 If the emitter doping concentration is $N_E = 5 \times 10^{18}$ cm^{-3}, find the base doping concentration such that the emitter injection efficiency is $\gamma = 0.9950$. Assume the following parameters: $x_E = 2x_B = 2$ μm, $D_E = 8$ cm^2/s, $D_B = 20$ cm^2/s, $\tau_{E0} = 10^{-8}$ s, and $\tau_{B0} = 10^{-7}$ s. (Ans. $N_B = 1.03 \times 10^{16}$ cm^{-3})

EXAMPLE 10.5

OBJECTIVE

To design the base width required to achieve a base transport factor equal to $\alpha_T = 0.9967$.

Consider a pnp bipolar transistor. Assume that $D_B = 10 \text{ cm}^2/\text{s}$ and $\tau_{B0} = 10^{-7}$ s.

■ Solution

The base transport factor applies to both pnp and npn transistors and is given by

$$\alpha_T = \frac{1}{\cosh{(x_B/L_B)}} = 0.9967$$

Then

$$\frac{x_B}{L_B} = 0.0814$$

We have

$$L_B = \sqrt{D_B \tau_{B0}} = \sqrt{(10)(10^{-7})} = 10^{-3} \text{ cm}$$

so that the base width must then be

$$x_B = 0.814 \times 10^{-4} \text{ cm} = 0.814 \; \mu\text{m}$$

■ Comment

If the base width is less than approximately $0.8 \; \mu$m, then the required base transport factor will be achieved. In most cases, the base transport factor will not be the limiting factor in the bipolar transistor current gain.

Exercise Problem

EX10.5 Determine the minimum neutral base width x_B such that the base transport factor is $\alpha_T = 0.9980$. Assume parameters of $D_E = 8 \text{ cm}^2/\text{s}$, $D_B = 20 \text{ cm}^2/\text{s}$, $\tau_{E0} = 10^{-8}$ s, and $\tau_{B0} = 10^{-7}$ s. (Ans. $x_B = 0.895 \; \mu$m.)

EXAMPLE 10.6

OBJECTIVE

To calculate the forward-bias B-E voltage required to achieve a recombination factor equal to $\delta = 0.9967$.

Consider an npn bipolar transistor at $T = 300$ K. Assume that $J_{r0} = 10^{-8} \text{ A/cm}^2$ and that $J_{s0} = 10^{-11} \text{ A/cm}^2$.

■ Solution

The recombination factor, from Equation (10.44), is

$$\delta = \frac{1}{1 + \dfrac{J_{r0}}{J_{s0}} \exp{\left(\dfrac{-eV_{BE}}{2kT}\right)}}$$

We then have

$$0.9967 = \cfrac{1}{1 + \cfrac{10^{-8}}{10^{-11}} \exp\left(\cfrac{-eV_{BE}}{2kT}\right)}$$

We can rearrange this equation and write

$$\exp\left(\frac{+eV_{BE}}{2kT}\right) = \frac{0.9967 \times 10^3}{1 - 0.9967} = 3.02 \times 10^5$$

Then

$$V_{BE} = 2(0.0259)\ln(3.02 \times 10^5) = 0.654 \text{ V}$$

■ **Comment**

This example demonstrates that the recombination factor may be an important limiting factor in the bipolar current gain. In this example, if V_{BE} is smaller than 0.654 V, then the recombination factor δ will fall below the desired 0.9967 value.

Exercise Problem

EX10.6 If $J_{r0} = 10^{-8}$ A/cm² and $J_{s0} = 10^{-11}$ A/cm², find the value of V_{BE} such that $\delta = 0.9960$. Assume parameters of $D_E = 8$ cm²/s, $D_B = 20$ cm²/s, $\tau_{E0} = 10^{-8}$ s, and $\tau_{B0} = 10^{-7}$ s. (Ans. $V_{BE} = 0.6436$ V)

EXAMPLE 10.7

OBJECTIVE

To calculate the common-emitter current gain of a silicon npn bipolar transistor at $T = 300$ K given a set of parameters.

Assume the following parameters:

$$D_E = 10 \text{ cm}^2/\text{s} \qquad\qquad x_B = 0.70 \text{ } \mu\text{m}$$
$$D_B = 25 \text{ cm}^2/\text{s} \qquad\qquad x_E = 0.50 \text{ } \mu\text{m}$$
$$\tau_{E0} = 1 \times 10^{-7} \text{ s} \qquad\quad N_E = 1 \times 10^{18} \text{ cm}^{-3}$$
$$\tau_{B0} = 5 \times 10^{-7} \text{ s} \qquad\quad N_B = 1 \times 10^{16} \text{ cm}^{-3}$$
$$J_{r0} = 5 \times 10^{-8} \text{ A/cm}^2 \qquad V_{BE} = 0.65 \text{ V}$$

The following parameters are calculated:

$$p_{E0} = \frac{(1.5 \times 10^{10})^2}{1 \times 10^{18}} = 2.25 \times 10^2 \text{ cm}^{-3}$$

$$n_{B0} = \frac{(1.5 \times 10^{10})^2}{1 \times 10^{16}} = 2.25 \times 10^4 \text{ cm}^{-3}$$

$$L_E = \sqrt{D_E \tau_{E0}} = 10^{-3} \text{ cm}$$

$$L_B = \sqrt{D_B \tau_{B0}} = 3.54 \times 10^{-3} \text{ cm}$$

■ Solution

The emitter injection efficiency factor, from Equation (10.35a), is

$$\gamma = \frac{1}{1 + \dfrac{(2.25 \times 10^2)(10)(3.54 \times 10^{-3})}{(2.25 \times 10^4)(25)(10^{-3})} \cdot \dfrac{\tanh(0.0198)}{\tanh(0.050)}} = 0.9944$$

The base transport factor, from Equation (10.39a) is

$$\alpha_T = \frac{1}{\cosh\left(\dfrac{0.70 \times 10^{-4}}{3.54 \times 10^{-3}}\right)} = 0.9998$$

The recombination factor, from Equation (10.44), is

$$\delta = \frac{1}{1 + \dfrac{5 \times 10^{-8}}{J_{s0}} \exp\left(\dfrac{-0.65}{2(0.0259)}\right)}$$

where

$$J_{s0} = \frac{e D_B n_{B0}}{L_B \tanh\left(\dfrac{x_B}{L_B}\right)} = \frac{(1.6 \times 10^{-19})(25)(2.25 \times 10^4)}{3.54 \times 10^{-3} \tanh(1.977 \times 10^{-2})} = 1.29 \times 10^{-9} \ \text{A/cm}^2$$

We can now calculate $\delta = 0.99986$. The common-base current gain is then

$$\alpha = \gamma \alpha_T \delta = (0.9944)(0.9998)(0.99986) = 0.99406$$

which gives a common-emitter current gain of

$$\beta = \frac{\alpha}{1 - a} = \frac{0.99406}{1 - 0.99406} = 167$$

■ Comment

In this example, the emitter injection efficiency is the limiting factor in the current gain.

Exercise Problem

EX10.7 Determine the common-emitter current gain of a pnp bipolar transistor with the parameters $D_E = 15 \ \text{cm}^2/\text{s}$, $D_B = 8 \ \text{cm}^2/\text{s}$, $\tau_{E0} = 2 \times 10^{-7}$ s, and $\tau_{B0} = 3 \times 10^{-7}$ s. All other parameters are the same as described in Example 10.7.

(Ans. We have $\gamma = 0.9744$, $\alpha_T = 0.9990$, and $\delta = 0.9996$, so $\beta = 36$)

TEST YOUR UNDERSTANDING

In the following exercises, assume a silicon npn bipolar transistor at $T = 300$ K has the following parameters: $D_E = 15 \ \text{cm}^2/\text{s}$, $D_B = 8 \ \text{cm}^2/\text{s}$, $D_C = 12 \ \text{cm}^2/\text{s}$, $\tau_{E0} = 2 \times 10^{-7}$ s, $\tau_{B0} = 3 \times 10^{-7}$ s, and $\tau_{C0} = 10^{-6}$ s.

TYU10.1   Assume that $\alpha_T = \delta = 0.9967$, $x_B = x_E = 1 \ \mu$m, $N_B = 5 \times 10^{16}$ cm^{-3}, and
$N_E = 5 \times 10^{18}$ cm^{-3}. Determine the common emitter current gain β.
(Ans. $\beta = 92.5$)

TYU10.2   Assume that $\gamma = \delta = 0.9967$ and $x_B = 0.80 \ \mu$m. Determine the common-
emitter current gain β. (Ans. $\beta = 121$)

TYU10.3   Assume that $\gamma = \alpha_T = 0.9967$, $J_{r0} = 5 \times 10^{-9}$ A/cm^2, $J_{s0} = 10^{-11}$ A/cm^2,
and $V_{BE} = 0.585$ V. Determine the common-emitter current gain β.
(Ans. $\beta = 77.4$)

TYU10.4   (a) If, because of fabrication tolerances, the neutral base width for a set of
transistors varies over the range of $0.800 \le x_B \le 1.00 \ \mu$m, determine the
variation in the base transport factor α_T. Assume $L_B = 1.414 \times 10^{-3}$ cm.
(b) Using the results of part (a) and assuming $\gamma = \delta = 0.9967$, what is the
variation in common emitter current gain.
[Ans. (a) $0.9975 \le \alpha_T \le 0.9984$, (b) $109 \le \beta \le 121$]

10.4 | NONIDEAL EFFECTS

Objective: Consider several nonideal effects in the transistor.

In all previous discussions, we have considered a transistor with uniformly doped regions, low injection, constant emitter and base widths, an ideal constant energy
bandgap, uniform current densities, and junctions that are not in breakdown. If any
of these ideal conditions are not present, then the transistor properties will deviate
from the ideal characteristics we have derived.

10.4.1   Base Width Modulation

We have implicitly assumed that the neutral base width x_B was constant. This base
width, however, is a function of the B-C voltage, since the width of the space
charge region extending into the base region varies with B-C voltage. As the B-C
reverse-bias voltage increases, the B-C space charge region width increases, which
reduces x_B. A change in the neutral base width will change the collector current as
can be observed in Figure 10.24. A reduction in base width will cause the gradient in
the minority-carrier concentration to increase, which in turn causes an increase in the
diffusion current. This effect is known as *base width modulation;* it is also called the
Early effect.   **Early effect**

The Early effect can be seen in the current–voltage characteristics shown in Figure 10.25. In most cases, a constant base current is equivalent to a constant B-E voltage. Ideally the collector current is independent of the B-C voltage so that the slope
of the curves would be zero; thus the output conductance of the transistor would be
zero. However, the base width modulation, or Early effect, produces a nonzero slope
and gives rise to a finite output conductance. If the collector current characteristics
are extrapolated to zero collector current, the curves intersect the voltage axis at a point
that is defined as the Early voltage. The Early voltage is considered to be a positive   **Early voltage**
value. It is a common parameter given in transistor specifications; typical values of
Early voltage are in the 100- to 300-V range.

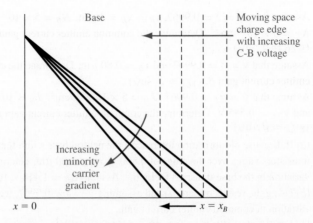

Figure 10.24 | The change in the base width and the change in the minority-carrier gradient as the B-C space charge width changes.

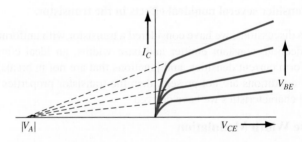

Figure 10.25 | The collector current versus collector–emitter voltage showing the Early effect and Early voltage.

From Figure 10.25, we can write that

$$\frac{dI_C}{dV_{CE}} = g_0 = \frac{I_C}{V_{CE} + V_A} \tag{10.45a}$$

Output conductance   where V_A and V_{CE} are defined as positive quantities and g_0 is defined as the output conductance. Equation (10.45a) can be rewritten in the form

$$I_C = g_0(V_{CE} + V_A) \tag{10.45b}$$

showing explicitly that the collector current is now a function of the C-E voltage or the C-B voltage.

EXAMPLE 10.8

OBJECTIVE

To calculate the change in the neutral base width with a change in C-B voltage.

Consider a uniformly doped silicon bipolar transistor at $T = 300$ K with a base doping of $N_B = 5 \times 10^{16}$ cm^{-3} and a collector doping of $N_C = 2 \times 10^{15}$ cm^{-3}. Assume the metallurgical base width is 0.70 μm. Calculate the change in the neutral base width as the C-B voltage changes from 2 to 10 V.

■ **Solution**

The space charge width extending into the base region can be written as

$$x_{dB} = \left\{ \frac{2\epsilon_s (V_{bi} + V_{CB})}{e} \left[\frac{N_C}{N_B} \frac{1}{(N_B + N_C)} \right] \right\}^{1/2}$$

or

$$x_{dB} = \left\{ \frac{2(11.7)(8.85 \times 10^{-14})(V_{bi} + V_{CB})}{1.6 \times 10^{-19}} \times \left[\frac{2 \times 10^{15}}{5 \times 10^{16}} \frac{1}{(5 \times 10^{16} + 2 \times 10^{15})} \right] \right\}^{1/2}$$

which becomes

$$x_{dB} = [(9.96 \times 10^{-12})(V_{bi} + V_{CB})]^{1/2}$$

The built-in potential is

$$V_{bi} = \frac{kT}{e} \ln \left(\frac{N_B N_C}{n_i^2} \right) = 0.718 \text{ V}$$

For $V_{CB} = 2$ V, we find $x_{dB} = 0.052$ μm, and for $V_{CB} = 10$ V, we find $x_{dB} = 0.103$ μm. If we neglect the B-E space charge region, which will be small because of the forward-biased junction, then we can calculate the neutral base width. For $V_{CB} = 2$ V.

$$x_B = 0.70 - 0.052 = 0.648 \text{ } \mu\text{m}$$

and for $V_{CB} = 10$ V,

$$x_B = 0.70 - 0.103 = 0.597 \text{ } \mu\text{m}$$

■ **Comment**

This example shows that the neutral base width can easily change by approximately 8 percent as the C-B voltage changes from 2 to 10 V.

Exercise Problem

EX10.8 Repeat Example 10.8 for the case when the base doping is $N_B = 3 \times 10^{16}$ cm^{-3} and the collector doping is $N_C = 10^{15}$ cm^{-3}.

(Ans. For $V_{CB} = 2$ V, $x_B = 0.639$ μm; for $V_{CB} = 10$ V, $x_B = 0.578$ μm)

EXAMPLE 10.9

OBJECTIVE

To calculate the change in collector current with a change in neutral base width, and to estimate the Early voltage.

Consider a uniformly doped silicon npn bipolar transistor with parameters described in Example 10.8. Assume $D_B = 25$ cm^2/s, and $V_{BE} = 0.60$ V, and also assume that $x_B \ll L_B$.

■ Solution

The excess minority-carrier electron concentration in the base is given by Equation (10.15) as

$$\delta n_B(x) = \frac{n_{B0}\left\{\left[\exp\left(\dfrac{eV_{BE}}{kT}\right) - 1\right]\sinh\left(\dfrac{x_B - x}{L_B}\right) - \sinh\left(\dfrac{x}{L_B}\right)\right\}}{\sinh\left(\dfrac{x_B}{L_B}\right)}$$

If $x_B \ll L_B$, then $(x_B - x) \ll L_B$ so we can write the approximations

$$\sinh\left(\frac{x_B}{L_B}\right) \approx \left(\frac{x_B}{L_B}\right) \quad \text{and} \quad \sinh\left(\frac{x_B - x}{L_B}\right) \approx \left(\frac{x_B - x}{L_B}\right)$$

The expression for $\delta n_B(x)$ can then be approximated as

$$\delta n_B(x) \approx \frac{n_{B0}}{x_B}\left\{\left[\exp\left(\frac{eV_{BE}}{kT}\right) - 1\right](x_B - x) - x\right\}$$

The collector current is now

$$|J_C| = eD_B\frac{d[\delta n_B(x)]}{dx} \approx \frac{eD_B n_{B0}}{x_B}\exp\left(\frac{eV_{BE}}{kT}\right)$$

The value of n_{B0} is calculated as

$$n_{B0} = \frac{n_i^2}{N_B} = \frac{(1.5 \times 10^{10})^2}{5 \times 10^{16}} = 4.5 \times 10^3 \text{ cm}^{-3}$$

If we let $x_B = 0.648 \ \mu m$ when $V_{CB} = 2$ V ($V_{CE} = 2.6$ V), then

$$|J_C| = \frac{(1.6 \times 10^{-19})(25)(4.5 \times 10^3)}{0.648 \times 10^{-4}}\exp\left(\frac{0.60}{0.0259}\right) = 3.20 \text{ A/cm}^2$$

Now let $x_B = 0.597 \ \mu m$ when $V_{CB} = 10$ V ($V_{CE} = 10.6$ V). In this case we have $|J_C| = 3.47$ A/cm^2. From Equation (10.45a), we can write

$$\frac{dJ_C}{dV_{CE}} = \frac{J_C}{V_{CE} + V_A} = \frac{\Delta J_C}{\Delta V_{CE}}$$

Using the calculated values of current and voltage, we have

$$\frac{\Delta J_C}{\Delta V_{CE}} = \frac{3.47 - 3.20}{10.6 - 2.6} = \frac{J_C}{V_{CE} + V_A} \approx \frac{3.20}{2.6 + V_A}$$

The Early voltage is then determined to be

$$V_A \approx 92 \text{ V}$$

■ Comment

This example indicates how much the collector current can change as the neutral base width changes with a change in the B-C space charge width, and it also indicates the magnitude of the Early voltage.

EX10.9 A particular transistor has an output resistance of 200 kΩ and an Early voltage of $V_A = 125$ V. Determine the change in collector current when V_{CE} increases from 2 V to 8 V. (Ans. $\Delta I_C = 30 \ \mu A$.)

Example 10.9 also demonstrates that we can expect variations in transistor properties due to tolerances in transistor-fabrication processes. There will be variations, in particular, in the base width of narrow-base transistors that will cause variations in the collector current characteristics simply due to the tolerances in processing.

10.4.2 High Injection

The ambipolar transport equation that we have used to determine the minority-carrier distributions assumed low injection. As V_{BE} increases, the injected minority-carrier concentration may approach, or even become larger than, the majority-carrier concentration. If we assume quasi–charge neutrality, then the majority-carrier hole concentration in the p-type base at $x = 0$ will increase as shown in Figure 10.26 because of the excess holes.

Two effects occur in the transistor at high injection. The first effect is a reduction in emitter injection efficiency. Since the majority-carrier hole concentration at $x = 0$ increases above the N_B doping level with high injection, more holes are injected back into the emitter because of the forward-biased B-E voltage. A large increase in the hole injection causes an increase in the J_{pE} current, and an increase in J_{pE} reduces the emitter injection efficiency. The common-emitter current gain decreases, then, with high injection. Figure 10.27 shows a typical common-emitter current gain versus collector current curve. The low gain at low currents is due to the small recombination factor and the drop-off at the high current is due to the high-injection effect.

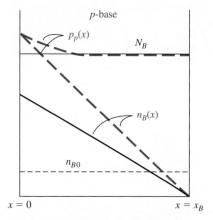

Figure 10.26 | Minority- and majority-carrier concentrations in the base under low and high injection (solid line: low injection; dashed line: high injection).

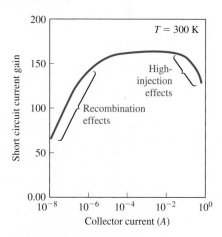

Figure 10.27 | Common-emitter current gain versus collector current.
(From Shur [15].)

We will now consider the second high-injection effect. At low injection, the majority carrier hole concentration at $x = 0$ for the npn transistor is

$$p_p(0) = p_{p0} = N_a \tag{10.46a}$$

and the minority carrier electron concentration is

$$n_p(0) = n_{p0} \exp\left(\frac{eV_{BE}}{kT}\right) \tag{10.46b}$$

The pn product is

$$p_p(0)n_p(0) = p_{p0}n_{p0} \exp\left(\frac{eV_{BE}}{kT}\right) \tag{10.46c}$$

At high injection, Equation (10.46c) still applies. However, $p_p(0)$ will also increase, and for very high injection it will increase at nearly the same rate as $n_p(0)$. The increase in $n_p(0)$ will asymptotically approach the function

$$n_p(0) \approx n_{p0} \exp\left(\frac{eV_{BE}}{2kT}\right) \tag{10.47}$$

The excess minority carrier concentration in the base, and hence the collector current, will increase at a slower rate with B-E voltage in high injection than low injection. This effect is shown in Figure 10.28. The high-injection effect is very similar to the effect of a series resistance in a pn junction diode.

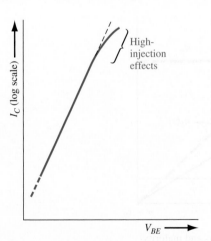

Figure 10.28 | Collector current versus base–emitter voltage showing high-injection effects.

10.4.3 Emitter Bandgap Narrowing

Another phenomenon affecting the emitter injection efficiency is bandgap narrowing. We implied from our previous discussion that the emitter injection efficiency factor would continue to increase and approach unity as the ratio of emitter doping to base doping continued to increase. As silicon becomes heavily doped, the discrete donor energy level in an n-type emitter splits into a band of energies. The distance between donor atoms decreases as the concentration of impurity donor atoms increases and the splitting of the donor level is caused by the interaction of donor atoms with each other. As the doping continues to increase, the donor band widens, becomes skewed, and moves up toward the conduction band, eventually merging with it. At this point, the effective bandgap energy has decreased. Figure 10.29 shows a plot of the change in the bandgap energy with impurity doping concentration.

A reduction in the bandgap energy increases the intrinsic carrier concentration. The intrinsic carrier concentration is given by

$$n_i^2 = N_c N_v \exp\left(\frac{-E_g}{kT}\right) \tag{10.48}$$

In a heavily doped emitter, the intrinsic carrier concentration can be written as

$$n_{iE}^2 = N_c N_v \exp\left[\frac{-(E_{g0} - \Delta E_g)}{kT}\right] = n_i^2 \exp\left(\frac{\Delta E_g}{kT}\right) \tag{10.49}$$

where E_{g0} is the bandgap energy at a low doping concentration and ΔE_g is the bandgap narrowing factor.

The emitter injection efficiency factor was given by Equation (10.35) as

$$\gamma = \frac{1}{1 + \dfrac{p_{E0} D_E L_B}{n_{B0} D_B L_E} \dfrac{\tanh(x_B/L_B)}{\tanh(x_E/L_E)}}$$

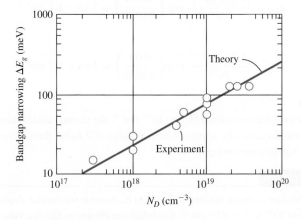

Figure 10.29 | Bandgap-narrowing factor versus donor impurity concentration in silicon.
(From Sze [20].)

The term p_{E0} is the thermal-equilibrium minority carrier concentration in the emitter and must be written as

$$p_{E0} = \frac{n_{iE}^2}{N_E} = \frac{n_i^2}{N_E} \exp\left(\frac{\Delta E_g}{kT}\right) \tag{10.50}$$

As the emitter doping increases, ΔE_g increases; thus, p_{E0} does not continue to decrease with increased emitter doping. If p_{E0} starts to increase because of the bandgap narrowing, the emitter injection efficiency begins to fall off instead of continuing to increase with increased emitter doping.

EXAMPLE 10.10

OBJECTIVE

To determine the increase in p_{E0} in the emitter due to bandgap narrowing.

Consider a silicon emitter at $T = 300$ K. Assume the emitter doping increases from 10^{18} cm^{-3} to 10^{19} cm^{-3}. Calculate the change in the p_{E0} value.

■ Solution

For emitter dopings of $N_E = 10^{18}$ cm^{-3} and 10^{19} cm^{-3}, we have, neglecting bandgap narrowing,

$$p_{E0} = \frac{n_i^2}{N_E} = \frac{(1.5 \times 10^{10})^2}{10^{18}} = 2.25 \times 10^2 \text{ cm}^{-3}$$

and

$$p_{E0} = \frac{(1.5 \times 10^{10})^2}{10^{19}} = 2.25 \times 10^1 \text{ cm}^{-3}$$

Taking into account the bandgap narrowing, we obtain, respectively, for $N_E = 10^{18}$ cm^{-3} and $N_E = 10^{19}$ cm^{-3}

$$p_{E0} = \frac{(1.5 \times 10^{10})^2}{10^{18}} \exp\left(\frac{0.030}{0.0259}\right) = 7.16 \times 10^2 \text{ cm}^{-3}$$

and

$$p_{E0} = \frac{(1.5 \times 10^{10})^2}{10^{19}} \exp\left(\frac{0.08}{0.0259}\right) = 4.94 \times 10^2 \text{ cm}^{-3}$$

■ Comment

If the emitter doping increases from 10^{18} to 10^{19} cm^{-3}, the thermal equilibrium minority carrier concentration decreases by approximately a factor of 2 rather than a factor of 10. This effect is due to bandgap narrowing.

Exercise Problem

EX10.10   Consider a silicon emitter at $T = 300$ K. Assume the emitter doping increases from 10^{18} to 7×10^{18} cm^{-3}. Calculate the change in the p_{E0} value.

(Ans. For 10^{18} cm^{-3}, $p_{E0} \approx 7.16 \times 10^2$ cm^{-3}; for 7×10^{18} cm^{-3}, $p_{E0} \approx 4.8 \times 10^2$ cm^{-3}.)

As the emitter doping increases, the bandgap narrowing factor, ΔE_g, will increase; this can actually cause p_{E0} to increase. As p_{E0} increases, the emitter injection efficiency decreases; this then causes the transistor gain to decrease, as in Figure 10.27. A very high emitter doping may result in a smaller current gain than we anticipate because of the bandgap-narrowing effect.

10.4.4 Current Crowding

It is tempting to minimize the effects of base current in a transistor since the base current is usually much smaller than either the collector or emitter currents. Figure 10.30a is a cross section of an npn transistor showing the lateral distribution of base current in the base region. The base region is typically less than a micrometer thick, so there can be a sizable base resistance under the emitter, as shown in Figure 10.30b. A lateral voltage drop ΔV is developed across this resistance due to the base current. For the npn transistor, the potential decreases from the edge of the emitter toward the center. The emitter is highly doped, so as a first approximation, the emitter can be considered an equipotential region.

The number of electrons from the emitter injected into the base is exponentially dependent on the B-E voltage. With the lateral voltage drop in the base between the edge and center of the emitter, more electrons will be injected near the emitter edges than in the center, causing the emitter current to be crowded toward the edges. This current-crowding effect is schematically shown in Figure 10.31. The larger current density near the emitter edge may cause localized heating effects as well as localized high-injection effects. The nonuniform emitter current also results in a nonuniform lateral base current under the emitter. A two-dimensional analysis would be required to calculate the actual potential drop versus distance because of the nonuniform base current. Another approach is to slice the transistor into a number of smaller parallel transistors and to lump the resistance of each base section into an equivalent external resistance.

Emitter current crowding

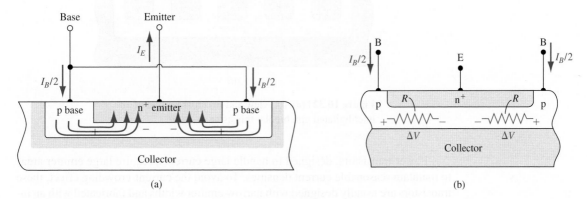

Figure 10.30 | Cross section of an npn bipolar transistor showing the (a) base current distribution and (b) base region resistance and resulting lateral potential drop in the base region.

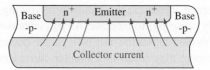

Figure 10.31 | Cross section of an npn bipolar transistor showing the emitter current-crowding effect. The emitter current density is greater at the edge of the emitter.

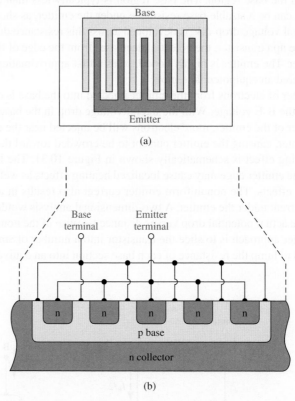

(a)

(b)

Figure 10.32 | (a) Top view and (b) cross section of an interdigitated npn bipolar transistor structure.

Power transistors, designed to handle large currents, require large emitter areas to maintain reasonable current densities. To avoid the current-crowding effect, these transistors are usually designed with narrow emitter widths and fabricated with an interdigitated design. Figure 10.32 shows the basic geometry. In effect, many narrow emitters are connected in parallel to achieve the required emitter area.

EXAMPLE 10.11

OBJECTIVE

To determine the effect of emitter current crowding.

Consider the geometry shown in Figure 10.33. The base doping concentration is $N_B = 10^{16}$ cm^{-3}, the neutral base width is $x_B = 0.80$ μm, the emitter width is $S = 10$ μm, and the emitter length is $L = 10$ μm. (a) Determine the resistance of the base between $x = 0$ and $x = S/2$. Assume a hole mobility of $\mu_p = 400$ cm^2/V-s. (b) If the base current in this region is uniform and given by $I_B/2 = 5$ μA, determine the potential difference between $x = 0$ and $x = S/2$. (c) Using the results of part (b), what is the ratio of emitter current density at $x = 0$ and $x = S/2$?

■ **Solution**

(a) The resistance is found from

$$R = \frac{\rho l}{A} = \left(\frac{1}{e\mu_p N_B}\right) \frac{(S/2)}{(x_B L)}$$

$$= \frac{1}{(1.6 \times 10^{-19})(400)(10^{16})} \frac{5 \times 10^{-4}}{(0.8 \times 10^{-4})(10 \times 10^{-4})}$$

or

$$R = 9.77 \times 10^3 \ \Omega = 9.77 \ \text{k}\Omega$$

(b) The potential difference is

$$\Delta V = \left(\frac{I_B}{2}\right) R = (5 \times 10^{-6})(9.77 \times 10^3)$$

or

$$\Delta V = 4.885 \times 10^{-2} \ \text{V} = 48.85 \ \text{mV}$$

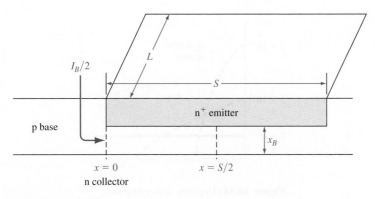

Figure 10.33 | Geometry used for Example 10.11 and Exercise Problem EX 10.11.

(*c*) The ratio of emitter current at $x = 0$ to that at $x = S/2$ is found to be

$$\frac{I_E(x = 0)}{I_E(x = S/2)} = \exp\left(\frac{\Delta V}{V_t}\right) = \exp\left(\frac{0.04885}{0.0259}\right)$$

or

$$\frac{I_E(x = 0)}{I_E(x = S/2)} = 6.59$$

■ **Comment**
Because the B-E voltage at the emitter edge ($x = 0$) is larger than that in the center of the emitter ($x = S/2$), the current at the edge is larger than that in the center of the emitter.

Exercise Problem

EX10.11   Repeat Example 10.11 for the case when the emitter width is reduced to $S = 2\ \mu m$. Comment on the results of Example 10.11 and this exercise problem.   [Ans. (*a*) $R = 1.95\ k\Omega$, (*b*) $\Delta V = 9.75$ mV, (*c*) Ratio $= 1.46$]

Σ   **10.4.5   Nonuniform Base Doping**

In the analysis of the bipolar transistor, we assumed uniformly doped regions. However, uniform doping rarely occurs. Figure 10.34 shows a doping profile in a doubly diffused npn transistor. We can start with a uniformly doped n-type substrate, diffuse acceptor atoms from the surface to form a compensated p-type base, and then diffuse donor atoms from the surface to form a doubly compensated n-type emitter. The diffusion process results in a nonuniform doping profile.

We determined in Chapter 4 that a graded impurity concentration leads to an induced electric field. For the p-type base region in thermal equilibrium, we can write

$$J_p = e\mu_p N_a \mathcal{E} - eD_p \frac{dN_a}{dx} = 0 \tag{10.51}$$

Then

$$\mathcal{E} = +\left(\frac{kT}{e}\right) \frac{1}{N_a} \frac{dN_a}{dx} \tag{10.52}$$

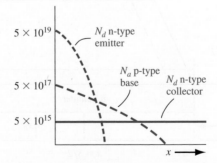

Figure 10.34 | Impurity concentration profiles of a double-diffused npn bipolar transistor.

According to the example of Figure 10.34, dN_a/dx is negative; hence, the induced electric field is in the negative x direction.

Electrons are injected from the n-type emitter into the base and the minority-carrier base electrons begin diffusing toward the collector region. The induced electric field in the base, because of the nonuniform doping, produces a force on the electrons in the direction toward the collector. The induced electric field, then, aids the flow of minority carriers across the base region. This electric field is called an *accelerating field.*

The accelerating field will produce a drift component of current that is in addition to the existing diffusion current. Since the minority-carrier electron concentration varies across the base, the drift current density will not be constant. The total current across the base, however, is nearly constant. The induced electric field in the base due to nonuniform base doping will alter the minority-carrier distribution through the base so that the sum of drift current and diffusion current will be a constant. Calculations have shown that the uniformly doped base theory is very useful for estimating the base characteristics.

10.4.6 Breakdown Voltage

There are two breakdown mechanisms to consider in a bipolar transistor. The first is called punch-through. As the reverse-bias B-C voltage increases, the B-C space charge region widens and extends farther into the neutral base. It is possible for the B-C depletion region to penetrate completely through the base and reach the B-E space charge region, the effect called *punch-through.* Figure 10.35a shows the energy-band diagram of an npn bipolar transistor in thermal equilibrium and Figure 10.35b shows the energy-band diagram for two values of reverse-bias B-C

Punch-through

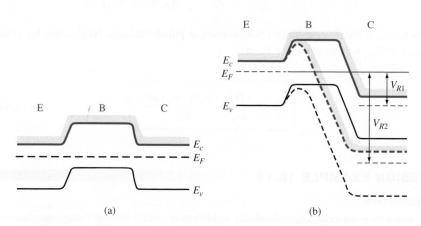

Figure 10.35 | Energy-band diagram of an npn bipolar transistor (a) in thermal equilibrium and (b) with a reverse-bias B-C voltage before punch-through, V_{R1}, and after punch-through, V_{R2}.

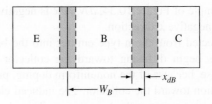

Figure 10.36 | Geometry of a bipolar transistor to calculate the punch-through voltage.

junction voltage. When a small C-B voltage, V_{R1}, is applied, the B-E potential barrier is not affected; thus, the transistor current is still essentially zero. When a large reverse-bias voltage, V_{R2}, is applied, the depletion region extends through the base region and the B-E potential barrier is lowered because of the C-B voltage. The lowering of the potential barrier at the B-E junction produces a large increase in current with a very small increase in C-B voltage. This effect is the punch-through breakdown phenomenon.

Figure 10.36 shows the geometry for calculating the punch-through voltage. Assume that N_B and N_C are the uniform impurity doping concentrations in the base and collector, respectively. Let W_B be the metallurgical width of the base and let x_{dB} be the space charge width extending into the base from the B-C junction. If we neglect the narrow space charge width of a zero-biased or forward-biased B-E junction, then punch-through, assuming the abrupt junction approximation, occurs when $x_{dB} = W_B$. We can write that

$$x_{dB} = W_B = \left[\frac{2\epsilon_s (V_{bi} + V_{pt})}{e} \frac{N_C}{N_B} \frac{1}{N_C + N_B} \right]^{1/2} \tag{10.53}$$

where V_{pt} is the reverse-biased B-C voltage at punch-through. Neglecting V_{bi} compared to V_{pt}, we can solve for V_{pt} as

$$\boxed{V_{pt} = \frac{e W_B^2}{2\epsilon_s} \frac{N_B (N_C + N_B)}{N_C}} \tag{10.54}$$

DESIGN EXAMPLE 10.12

OBJECTIVE

To design the collector doping and collector width to meet a punch-through voltage specification.

Consider a uniformly doped silicon bipolar transistor with a metallurgical base width of 0.5 μm and a base doping of $N_B = 10^{16}$ cm^{-3}. The punch-through voltage is to be $V_{pt} = 25$ V.

■ Solution

The maximum collector doping concentration can be determined from Equation (10.54) as

$$25 = \frac{(1.6 \times 10^{-19})(0.5 \times 10^{-4})^2(10^{16})(N_C + 10^{16})}{2(11.7)(8.85 \times 10^{-14})N_C}$$

or

$$12.94 = 1 + \frac{10^{16}}{N_C}$$

which yields

$$N_C = 8.38 \times 10^{14} \text{ cm}^{-3}$$

This n-type doping concentration in the collector must extend at least as far as the depletion width extends into the collector to avoid breakdown in the collector region. We have, using results from Chapter 5.

$$x_n = \left[\frac{2\epsilon_s(V_{bi} + V_R)}{e} \left(\frac{N_B}{N_C} \cdot \frac{1}{N_B + N_C} \right) \right]^{1/2}$$

Neglecting V_{bi} compared to $V_R = V_{pt}$, we obtain

$$x_n = \left[\frac{2(11.7)(8.85 \times 10^{-14})(25)}{1.6 \times 10^{-19}} \left(\frac{10^{16}}{8.38 \times 10^{14}} \right) \left(\frac{1}{10^{16} + 8.38 \times 10^{14}} \right) \right]^{1/2}$$

or

$$x_n = 5.97 \ \mu\text{m}$$

■ Comment

From Figure 9.30, the expected avalanche breakdown voltage for this junction is greater than 300 V. Obviously punch-through will occur before the normal breakdown voltage in this case. For a larger punch-through voltage, a larger metallurgical base width will be required, since a lower collector doping concentration is becoming impractical. A larger punch-through voltage will also require a larger collector width in order to avoid premature breakdown in this region.

Exercise Problem

EX10.12 The metallurgical base width of a silicon npn bipolar transistor is $W_B = 0.80 \ \mu\text{m}$. The base and collector doping concentrations are $N_B = 2 \times 10^{16} \text{ cm}^{-3}$ and $N_C = 10^{15} \text{ cm}^{-3}$. Find the punch-through breakdown voltage. (Ans. 208 V)

The second breakdown mechanism to consider is avalanche breakdown, but taking into account the gain of the transistor.[1] Figure 10.37a is an npn transistor with a reverse-bias voltage applied to the B-C junction and with the emitter left open. The current I_{CBO} is the reverse-biased junction current. Figure 10.37b shows the transistor with an applied C-E voltage and with the base terminal left open. This bias condition also makes the B-C junction reverse biased. The current in the transistor for this bias configuration is denoted as I_{CEO}.

Avalanche breakdown

---

[1] We assume that the doping concentrations in the base and collector of the transistor are small enough that Zener breakdown is not a factor to be considered.

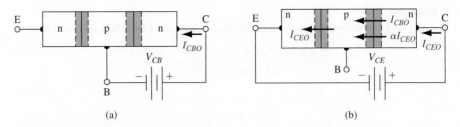

Figure 10.37 | (a) Open-emitter configuration with saturation current I_{CBO}. (b) Open-base configuration with saturation current I_{CEO}.

The current I_{CBO} shown in Figure 10.37b is the normal reverse-biased B-C junction current. Part of this current is due to the flow of minority-carrier holes from the collector across the B-C space charge region into the base. The flow of holes into the base makes the base positive with respect to the emitter, and the B-E junction becomes forward biased. The forward-biased B-E junction produces the current I_{CEO}, due primarily to the injection of electrons from the emitter into the base. The injected electrons diffuse across the base toward the B-C junction. These electrons are subject to all of the recombination processes in the bipolar transistor. When the electrons reach the B-C junction, this current component is αI_{CEO}, where α is the common-base current gain. We therefore have

$$I_{CEO} = \alpha I_{CEO} + I_{CBO} \tag{10.55a}$$

or

$$I_{CEO} = \frac{I_{CBO}}{1 - \alpha} \approx \beta I_{CBO} \tag{10.55b}$$

where β is the common-emitter current gain. The reverse-biased junction current I_{CBO} is multiplied by the current gain β when the transistor is biased in the open-base configuration.

When the transistor is biased in the open-emitter configuration as in Figure 10.37a, the current I_{CBO} at breakdown becomes $I_{CBO} \rightarrow M I_{CBO}$, where M is the multiplication factor. An empirical approximation for the multiplication factor is usually written as

$$M = \frac{1}{1 - (V_{CB}/BV_{CBO})^n} \tag{10.56}$$

where n is an empirical constant, usually between 3 and 6, and BV_{CBO} is the B-C breakdown voltage with the emitter left open.

When the transistor is biased with the base open circuited, as shown in Figure 10.37b, the currents in the B-C junction at breakdown are multiplied, so that

$$I_{CEO} = M(\alpha I_{CEO} + I_{CBO}) \tag{10.57}$$

Solving for I_{CEO}, we obtain

$$I_{CEO} = \frac{M I_{CBO}}{1 - \alpha M} \tag{10.58}$$

The condition for breakdown corresponds to

$$\alpha M = 1 \qquad (10.59)$$

Using Equation (10.56) and assuming that $V_{CB} \approx V_{CE}$, Equation (10.59) becomes

$$\frac{\alpha}{1 - (BV_{CEO}/BV_{CBO})^n} = 1 \qquad (10.60)$$

where BV_{CEO} is the C-E voltage at breakdown in the open-base configuration. Solving for BV_{CEO}, we find

$$BV_{CEO} = BV_{CBO}\sqrt[n]{1 - \alpha} \qquad (10.61)$$

where, again, α is the common-base current gain. The common-emitter and common-base current gains are related by

$$\beta = \frac{\alpha}{1 - \alpha} \qquad (10.62a)$$

Normally $\alpha \approx 1$, so that

$$1 - \alpha \approx \frac{1}{\beta} \qquad (10.62b)$$

Then Equation (10.61) can be written as

$$\boxed{BV_{CEO} = \frac{BV_{CBO}}{\sqrt[n]{\beta}}} \qquad (10.63)$$

The breakdown voltage in the open-base configuration is smaller, by the factor $\sqrt[n]{\beta}$, than the actual avalanche junction breakdown voltage. This characteristic is shown in Figure 10.38.

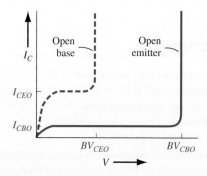

Figure 10.38 | Relative breakdown voltages and saturation currents of the open-base and open-emitter configurations.

DESIGN EXAMPLE 10.13

OBJECTIVE

To design a bipolar transistor to meet a breakdown voltage specification.

Consider a silicon bipolar transistor with a common-emitter current gain of $\beta = 100$ and a base doping concentration of $N_B = 10^{17}$ cm^{-3}. The minimum open-base breakdown voltage is to be 15 V.

■ Solution

From Equation (10.63), the minimum open-emitter junction breakdown voltage must be

$$BV_{CBO} = \sqrt[n]{\beta}\, BV_{CEO}$$

Assuming the empirical constant n is 3, we find

$$BV_{CBO} = \sqrt[3]{100}(15) = 69.6 \text{ V}$$

From Figure 9.30, the maximum collector doping concentration should be approximately 7×10^{15} cm^{-3} to achieve this breakdown voltage.

■ Comment

In a transistor circuit, the transistor must be designed to operate under a worst-case situation. In this example, the transistor must be able to operate in an open-base configuration without going into breakdown. As we determined previously, an increase in breakdown voltage can be achieved by decreasing the collector doping concentration.

Exercise Problem

EX10.13 A uniformly doped silicon transistor has base and collector doping concentrations of 5×10^{16} cm^{-3} and 5×10^{15} cm^{-3}, respectively. The common-emitter current gain is $\beta = 85$. Assuming an empirical constant value of $n = 3$, determine BV_{CEO}. (Ans. 21.6 V)

TEST YOUR UNDERSTANDING

TYU10.5 The base impurity doping concentration is $N_B = 3 \times 10^{16}$ cm^{-3} and the metallurgical base width is $W_B = 0.70 \ \mu$m. The minimum required punch-through breakdown voltage is specified to be $V_{pt} = 70$ V. What is the maximum allowed collector doping concentration?
(Ans. $N_C = 5.81 \times 10^{15}$ cm^{-3})

TYU10.6 The minimum required breakdown voltage of a uniformly doped silicon npn bipolar transistor is to be $BV_{CEO} = 70$ V. The base impurity doping concentration is $N_B = 3 \times 10^{16}$ cm^{-3}, the common-emitter current gain is $\beta = 85$, and the empirical constant value is $n = 3$. Determine the maximum collector impurity doping concentration. (Ans. $N_C \approx 1 \times 10^{15}$ cm^{-3})

10.5 | HYBRID-PI EQUIVALENT CIRCUIT MODEL

Objective: Develop a small-signal equivalent circuit for the transistor.

To analyze a transistor circuit either by hand calculations or using computer codes, one needs a mathematical model, or equivalent circuit, of the transistor. There are several possible models, each one having certain advantages and disadvantages. A detailed study of all possible models is beyond the scope of this text.

It is useful to divide bipolar transistors into two categories—switching and amplification—defined by their use in electronic circuits. Switching usually involves turning a transistor from its "off" state, or cutoff, to its "on" state, either forward-active or saturation, and then back to its "off" state. Amplification usually involves superimposing sinusoidal signals on dc values so that bias voltages and currents are only perturbed. The *Ebers–Moll model* is used in switching applications. The *Gummel–Poon model* of the BJT considers more physics of the transistor than the Ebers–Moll model. Each of these models can be found in more advanced texts. The *hybrid-pi model*, which we will consider, is used in linear amplifier applications.

Bipolar transistors are commonly used in circuits that amplify time-varying or sinusoidal signals. In these linear amplifier circuits, the transistor is biased in the forward-active region and small sinusoidal voltages and currents are superimposed on dc voltages and currents. In these applications, the sinusoidal parameters are of interest, so it is convenient to develop a small-signal equivalent circuit of the bipolar transistor using the small-signal admittance parameters of the pn junction developed in Chapter 9.

Figure 10.39a shows an npn bipolar transistor in a common-emitter configuration with the small-signal terminal voltages and currents. Figure 10.39b shows the

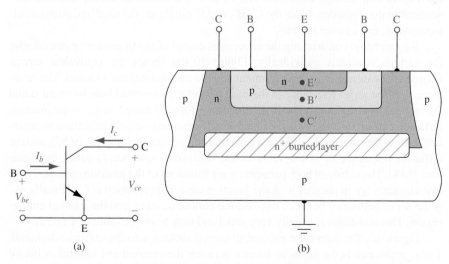

(a)   (b)

Figure 10.39 | (a) Common-emitter npn bipolar transistor with small-signal current and voltages. (b) Cross section of an npn bipolar transistor for the hybrid-pi model.

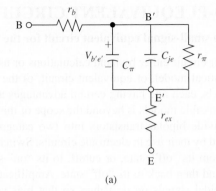

(a)

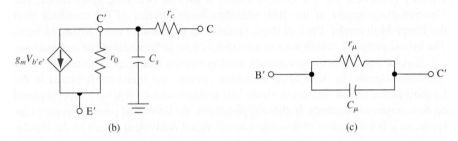

(b)

(c)

Figure 10.40 | Components of the hybrid-pi equivalent circuit between (a) the base and emitter, (b) the collector and emitter, and (c) the base and collector.

cross section of the npn transistor. The C, B, and E terminals are the external connections to the transistor, while the C′, B′, and E′ points are the idealized internal collector, base, and emitter regions.

We can begin constructing the equivalent circuit of the transistor by considering the various terminals individually. Figure 10.40a shows the equivalent circuit between the external input base terminal and the external emitter terminal. The resistance r_b is the series resistance in the base between the external base terminal B and the internal base region B′. The B′-E′ junction is forward biased, so C_π is the junction diffusion capacitance and r_π is the junction diffusion resistance. The diffusion capacitance C_π is the same as the diffusion capacitance C_d given by Equation (9.52), and the diffusion resistance r_π is the same as the diffusion resistance r_d given by Equation (9.48). The values of both parameters are functions of the junction current. These two elements are in parallel with the junction capacitance, which is C_{je}. Finally, r_{ex} is the series resistance between the external emitter terminal and the internal emitter region. This resistance is usually very small and may be on the order of 1 to 2 Ω.

Figure 10.40b shows the equivalent circuit looking into the collector terminal. The r_c resistance is the series resistance between the external and internal collector connections and the capacitance C_s is the junction capacitance of the reverse-biased collector-substrate junction. The dependent current source, $g_m V_{b'e'}$, is the collector

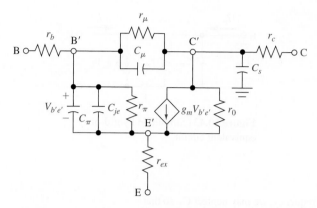

Figure 10.41 | Hybrid-pi equivalent circuit.

current in the transistor, which is controlled by the internal base-emitter voltage. The resistance r_0 is the inverse of the output conductance g_0 and is primarily due to the Early effect.

Finally, Figure 10.40c shows the equivalent circuit of the reverse-biased B'-C' junction. The C_μ parameter is the reverse-biased junction capacitance and r_μ is the reverse-biased diffusion resistance. Normally, r_μ is on the order of megohms and can be neglected. The value of C_μ is usually much smaller than C_π but, because of the feedback effect, which leads to the Miller effect and Miller capacitance, C_μ cannot be ignored in most cases. The Miller capacitance is the equivalent capacitance between B' and E' due to C_μ and the feedback effect, which includes the gain of the transistor. The Miller effect also reflects C_μ between the C' and E' terminals at the output. However, the effect on the output characteristics can usually be ignored.

Figure 10.41 shows the complete hybrid-pi equivalent circuit. A computer simulation is usually required for this complete model because of the large number of elements. However, some simplifications can be made to gain an appreciation for the frequency effects of the bipolar transistor. The capacitances lead to frequency effects in the transistor, which means that the gain, for example, is a function of the input signal frequency.

Hybrid-pi equivalent circuit

EXAMPLE 10.14

OBJECTIVE

To determine, to a first approximation, the frequency at which the small-signal current gain decreases to $1/\sqrt{2}$ of its low frequency value.

Consider the simplified hybrid-pi circuit shown in Figure 10.42. We are ignoring C_μ, C_s, r_μ, C_{je}, r_0, and the series resistances. We must emphasize that this is a first-order calculation and that C_μ normally cannot be neglected.

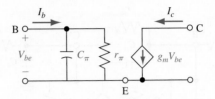

Figure 10.42 | Simplified hybrid-pi equivalent circuit.

■ Solution

At very low frequency, we may neglect C_π so that

$$V_{be} = I_b r_\pi \quad \text{and} \quad I_c = g_m V_{be} = g_m r_\pi I_b$$

We can then write

$$h_{fe0} = \frac{I_c}{I_b} = g_m r_\pi$$

where h_{fe0} is the low-frequency, small-signal common-emitter current gain.

Taking into account C_π, we have

$$V_{be} = I_b \left(\frac{r_\pi}{1 + j\omega r_\pi C_\pi} \right)$$

Then

$$I_c = g_m V_{be} = I_b \left(\frac{h_{fe0}}{1 + j\omega r_\pi C_\pi} \right)$$

or the small-signal current gain can be written as

$$A_i = \frac{I_c}{I_b} = \left(\frac{h_{fe0}}{1 + j\omega r_\pi C_\pi} \right)$$

The magnitude of the current gain drops to $1/\sqrt{2}$ of its low-frequency value at $f = 1/2\pi r_\pi C_\pi$.

If, for example, $r_\pi = 2.6 \text{ k}\Omega$ and $C_\pi = 4 \text{ pF}$, then

$$f = 15.3 \text{ MHz}$$

■ Comment

**Beta cutoff
frequency**

The frequency calculated in this example is called the *beta cutoff frequency*. High-frequency transistors must have small diffusion capacitances, implying the use of small devices.

Exercise Problem

EX10.14 Consider a bipolar transistor whose input resistance is $r_\pi = 1.2 \text{ k}\Omega$. It is found that the current gain drops to $1/\sqrt{2}$ of its low-frequency value at $f_\beta = 150 \text{ MHz}$. What is the value of C_π? (Ans. $C_x = 0.884 \text{ pF}$)

10.6 | FREQUENCY LIMITATIONS

Objective: Analyze the frequency limitations in the device.

The hybrid-pi equivalent circuit, developed in Section 10.5, introduces frequency effects through the capacitor–resistor circuits. We will now discuss the various physical factors in the bipolar transistor affecting the frequency limitations of the device, and then define the transistor cutoff frequency, which is a figure of merit for a transistor.

10.6.1 Time-Delay Factors

The bipolar transistor is a transit-time device. When the voltage across the B-E junction increases, for example, additional carriers from the emitter are injected into the base, diffuse across the base, and are collected in the collector region. As the frequency increases, this transit time can become comparable to the period of the input signal. At this point, the output response will no longer be in phase with the input and the magnitude of the current gain will decrease.

The total emitter-to-collector time constant or delay time is composed of four separate time constants. We can write

$$\tau_{ec} = \tau_e + \tau_b + \tau_d + \tau_c \tag{10.64}$$

where

τ_{ec} = emitter-to-collector time delay

τ_e = emitter–base junction capacitance charging time

τ_b = base transit time

τ_d = collector depletion region transit time

τ_c = collector capacitance charging time

We will apply these time delays to the small-signal response since we will be assuming constant capacitance values.

The equivalent circuit of the forward-biased B-E junction was given in Figure 10.40a. The capacitance C_{je} is the junction capacitance. If we ignore the series resistance, then the emitter–base junction capacitance charging time is

$$\boxed{\tau_e = r_e'(C_{je} + C_p)} \tag{10.65}$$

Emitter–base junction capacitance charging time

where r_e' is the emitter junction or diffusion resistance. The capacitance C_p includes any parasitic capacitance between the base and emitter. The resistance r_e' is found as the inverse of the slope of the I_E versus V_{BE} curve. We obtain

$$r_e' = \frac{kT}{e} \frac{1}{I_E} \tag{10.66}$$

where I_E is the dc emitter current.

The second term, τ_b, is the base transit time, the time required for the minority carriers to diffuse across the neutral base region. The base transit time is related to the diffusion capacitance C_π of the B-E junction. For the npn transistor, the electron current density in the base can be written as

$$J_n = -en_B(x)v(x) \tag{10.67}$$

where $v(x)$ is an average velocity. We can write

$$v(x) = dx/dt \qquad \text{or} \qquad dt = dx/v(x) \tag{10.68}$$

The transit time can then be found by integrating, or

$$\tau_b = \int_0^{x_B} dt = \int_0^{x_B} \frac{dx}{v(x)} = \int_0^{x_B} \frac{en_B(x)\,dx}{(-J_n)} \tag{10.69}$$

The electron concentration in the base is approximately linear (see Example 10.1) so we can write

$$n_B(x) \approx n_{B0}\left[\exp\left(\frac{eV_{BE}}{kT}\right)\right]\left(1 - \frac{x}{x_B}\right) \tag{10.70}$$

and the electron current density is given by

$$J_n = eD_n\frac{dn_B(x)}{dx} \tag{10.71}$$

Base transit time   The base transit time is then found by combining Equations (10.70) and (10.71) with Equation (10.69). We find that

$$\boxed{\tau_b = \frac{x_B^2}{2D_n}} \tag{10.72}$$

Collector depletion region transit time   The third time-delay factor is τ_d, the collector depletion region transit time. Assuming that the electrons in the npn device travel across the B-C space charge region at their saturation velocity, we have

$$\boxed{\tau_d = \frac{x_{dc}}{v_s}} \tag{10.73}$$

where x_{dc} is the B-C space charge width and v_s is the electron saturation velocity.

Collector capacitance charging time   The fourth time-delay factor, τ_c, is the collector capacitance charging time. The B-C is reverse biased so that the diffusion resistance in parallel with the junction capacitance is very large. The charging time constant is then a function of the collector series resistance r_c. We can write

$$\boxed{\tau_c = r_c(C_\mu + C_s)} \tag{10.74}$$

where C_μ is the B-C junction capacitance and C_s is the collector-to-substrate capacitance. The series resistance in small epitaxial transistors is usually small; thus, the time delay τ_c may be neglected in some cases.

Example calculations of the various time-delay factors will be given in Section 10.6.2 as part of the cutoff frequency discussion.

10.6.2 Transistor Cutoff Frequency

The current gain as a function of frequency was developed in Example 10.14 so that we can also write the common base current gain as

$$\alpha = \frac{\alpha_0}{1 + j\dfrac{f}{f_\alpha}} \tag{10.75}$$

where α_0 is the low-frequency common base current gain and f_α is defined as the *alpha cutoff frequency*. The frequency f_α is related to the emitter-to-collector time delay τ_{ec} as

$$f_\alpha = \frac{1}{2\pi\tau_{ec}} \tag{10.76}$$

When the frequency is equal to the alpha cutoff frequency, the magnitude of the common base current gain is $1/\sqrt{2}$ of its low-frequency value.

We can relate the alpha cutoff frequency to the common emitter current gain by considering

$$\beta = \frac{\alpha}{1 - \alpha} \tag{10.77}$$

We can replace α in Equation (10.77) with the expression given by Equation (10.75). When the frequency f is of the same order of magnitude as f_α, then

$$|\beta| = \left|\frac{\alpha}{1 - \alpha}\right| \approx \frac{f_\alpha}{f} \tag{10.78}$$

where we have assumed that $\alpha_0 \approx 1$. When the signal frequency is equal to the alpha cutoff frequency, the magnitude of the common-emitter current gain is equal to unity. The usual notation is to define this *cutoff frequency* as f_T, so we have   **Cutoff frequency**

$$\boxed{f_T = \frac{1}{2\pi\tau_{ec}}} \tag{10.79}$$

From the analysis in Example 10.14, we can also write the common-emitter current gain as

$$\beta = \frac{\beta_0}{1 + j(f/f_\beta)} \tag{10.80}$$

where f_β is called the *beta cutoff frequency* and is the frequency at which the magnitude of the common-emitter current gain β drops to $1/\sqrt{2}$ of its low-frequency value.

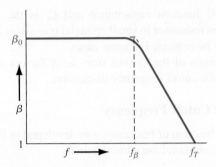

Figure 10.43 | Bode plot of common-emitter current gain versus frequency.

Combining Equations (10.77) and (10.75), we can write

$$\beta = \frac{\alpha}{1-\alpha} = \frac{\dfrac{\alpha_0}{1+j(f/f_T)}}{1 - \dfrac{\alpha_0}{1+j(f/f_T)}} = \frac{\alpha_0}{1-\alpha_0+j(f/f_T)} \qquad (10.81)$$

or

$$\beta = \frac{\alpha_0}{(1-\alpha_0)\left[1 + j\dfrac{f}{(1-\alpha_0)f_T}\right]} \approx \frac{\beta_0}{1 + j\dfrac{\beta_0 f}{f_T}} \qquad (10.82)$$

where

$$\beta_0 = \frac{\alpha_0}{1-\alpha_0} \approx \frac{1}{1-\alpha_0}$$

Comparing Equations (10.82) and (10.80), the beta cutoff frequency is related to the cutoff frequency by

$$\boxed{f_\beta \approx \frac{f_T}{\beta_0}} \qquad (10.83)$$

Figure 10.43 shows a Bode plot of the common emitter current gain as a function of frequency and shows the relative values of the beta and cutoff frequencies. Keep in mind that the frequency is plotted on a log scale, so f_β and f_T usually have significantly different values.

EXAMPLE 10.15

OBJECTIVE

To calculate the emitter-to-collector transit time and the cutoff frequency of a bipolar transistor, given the transistor parameters.

Consider a silicon npn transistor at $T = 300$ K. Assume the following parameters:

$$I_E = 1 \text{ mA} \qquad C_{je} = 1 \text{ pF}$$
$$x_B = 0.5 \ \mu m \qquad D_n = 25 \text{ cm}^2/\text{s}$$
$$x_{dc} = 2.4 \ \mu m \qquad r_c = 20 \ \Omega$$
$$C_\mu = 0.1 \text{ pF} \qquad C_s = 0.1 \text{ pF}$$

■ **Solution**

We will initially calculate the various time-delay factors. If we neglect the parasitic capacitance, the emitter–base junction charging time is

$$\tau_e = r_e' C_{je}$$

where

$$r_e' = \frac{kT}{e} \cdot \frac{1}{I_E} = \frac{0.0259}{1 \times 10^{-3}} = 25.9 \ \Omega$$

Then

$$\tau_e = (25.9)(10^{-12}) = 25.9 \text{ ps}$$

The base transit time is

$$\tau_b = \frac{x_B^2}{2D_n} = \frac{(0.5 \times 10^{-4})^2}{2(25)} = 50 \text{ ps}$$

The collector depletion region transit time is

$$\tau_b = \frac{x_{dc}}{v_s} = \frac{2.4 \times 10^{-4}}{10^7} = 24 \text{ ps}$$

The collector capacitance charging time is

$$\tau_c = r_c(C_\mu + C_s) = (20)(0.2 \times 10^{-12}) = 4 \text{ ps}$$

The total emitter-to-collector time delay is then

$$\tau_{ec} = 25.9 + 50 + 24 + 4 = 103.9 \text{ ps}$$

so that the cutoff frequency is calculated as

$$f_T = \frac{1}{2\pi \tau_{ec}} = \frac{1}{2\pi(103.9 \times 10^{-12})} = 1.53 \text{ GHz}$$

If we assume a low-frequency common-emitter current gain of $\beta = 100$, then the beta cutoff frequency is

$$f_\beta = \frac{f_T}{\beta_0} = \frac{1.53 \times 10^9}{100} = 15.3 \text{ MHz}$$

■ **Comment**

The design of high-frequency transistors requires small device geometries to reduce capacitances and narrow base widths to reduce the base transit time.

EX10.15 A silicon npn bipolar transistor is biased at $I_E = 0.5$ mA and has a junction
capacitance of $C_{je} = 2$ pF. All other parameters are the same as listed in
Example 10.15. Find the emitter-to-collector transit time, the cutoff frequency,
and the beta cutoff frequency.
(Ans. $\tau_{ec} = 181.6$ ps, $f_T = 1.14$ GHz, $f_\beta = 11.4$ MHz)

Σ 10.7 | LARGE-SIGNAL SWITCHING

**Objective: Discuss the large-signal switching characteristics of the bipolar
transistor.**

Switching a transistor from one state to another is strongly related to the frequency
characteristics just discussed. However, switching is considered to be a large-signal
change, whereas the frequency effects assumed only small changes in the magnitude
of the signal.

   Consider an npn transistor in the circuit shown in Figure 10.44a switching from
cutoff to saturation, and then switching back from saturation to cutoff. We will describe the physical processes taking place in the transistor during the switching cycle.

   Consider, initially, the case of switching from cutoff to saturation. Assume that
in cutoff $V_{BE} \approx V_{BB} < 0$, thus the B-E junction is reverse biased. At $t = 0$, assume

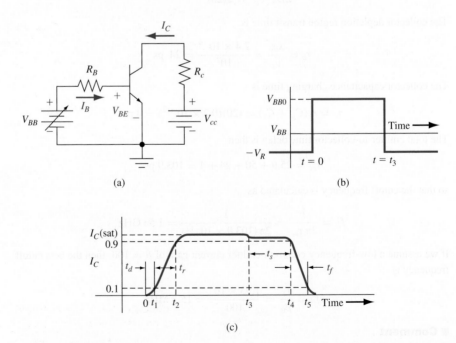

(a)

(b)

(c)

Figure 10.44 | (a) Circuit used for transistor switching. (b) Input base drive for transistor
switching. (c) Collector current versus time during transistor switching.

that V_{BB} switches to a value of V_{BB0} as shown in Figure 10.44b. We will assume that V_{BB0} is sufficiently positive to eventually drive the transistor into saturation. For $0 \leq t \leq t_1$, the base current supplies charge to bring the B-E junction from reverse bias to a slight forward bias. The space charge width of the B-E junction is narrowing, and ionized donors and acceptors are being neutralized. A small amount of charge is also injected into the base during this time. The collector current increases from zero to 10 percent of its final value during this time period, referred to as the delay time.

During the next time period, $t_1 \leq t \leq t_2$, the base current is supplying charge, which increases the B-E junction voltage from near cutoff to near saturation. During this time, additional carriers are being injected into the base so that the gradient of the minority carrier electron concentration in the base increases, causing the collector current to increase. We refer to this time period as the rise time, during which the collector current increases from 10 percent to 90 percent of the final value. For $t > t_2$, the base drive continues to supply base current, driving the transistor into saturation and establishing the final minority carrier distribution in the device.

The switching of the transistor from saturation to cutoff involves removing all of the excess minority carriers stored in the emitter, base, and collector regions. Figure 10.45 shows the charge storage in the base and collector when the transistor is in saturation. The charge Q_B is the excess charge stored in a forward-active transistor, and Q_{BX} and Q_C are the extra charges stored when the transistor is biased in saturation. At $t = t_3$, the base voltage V_{BB} switches to a negative value of $(-V_R)$. The base current in the transistor reverses direction, as was the case in switching a pn junction diode from forward to reverse bias. The reverse base current pulls the excess stored carriers from the emitter and base regions. Initially, the collector current does not change significantly, since the gradient of the minority-carrier concentration in the base does not change instantaneously. Recall that when the transistor is biased in saturation, both the B-E and B-C junctions are forward biased. The charge Q_{BX} in the base must be removed to reduce the forward-biased B-C voltage to zero volts before

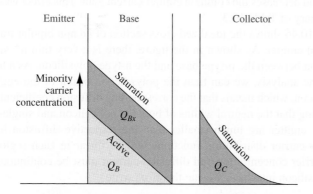

Figure 10.45 | Charge storage in the base and collector at saturation and in the active mode.

the collector current can change. This time delay is called the *storage time* and is denoted by t_s. The storage time is the time between the point at which V_{BB} switches to the time when the collector current is reduced to 90 percent of its maximum saturation value. The storage time is usually the most important parameter in the switching speed of the bipolar transistor.

The final switching delay time is the fall time t_f, during which the collector current decreases from the 90 percent to the 10 percent value. During this time, the B-C junction is reverse biased but excess carriers in the base are still being removed, and the B-E junction voltage is decreasing.

The switching-time response of the transistor can be determined by using the Ebers–Moll model. The frequency-dependent gain parameters must be used, and normally the Laplace transform technique is used to obtain the time response. The details of this analysis are long and complex and will not be presented here.

Σ 10.8 | DEVICE FABRICATION TECHNIQUES

Objective: Consider some special device fabrication techniques for bipolar transistors.

This section is intended to briefly introduce a few specialized bipolar transistor structures and also to briefly introduce a basic fabrication procedure. We will consider a polysilicon emitter BJT and its fabrication techniques, a SiGe-base transistor, and a power bipolar transistor.

10.8.1 Polysilicon Emitter BJT

The emitter injection efficiency is degraded by the carriers injected from the base back into the emitter. The emitter width, in general, is thin, which increases speed and reduces parasitic resistance. However, a thin emitter increases the gradient in the minority carrier concentration, as indicated in Figure 10.22. The increase in the gradient increases the B-E junction current, which in turn decreases the emitter injection efficiency and decreases the common emitter current gain. This effect was also shown in the summary of Table 10.3.

Figure 10.46 shows the idealized cross section of an npn bipolar transistor with a polysilicon emitter. As shown in the figure, there is a very thin n^+ single crystal silicon region between the p-type base and the n-type polysilicon. As a first approximation to the analysis, we can treat the polysilicon portion of the emitter as low-mobility silicon, which means that the corresponding diffusion coefficient is small.

Assuming that the neutral widths of both the polysilicon and single-crystal portions of the emitter are much smaller than the respective diffusion lengths, then the minority-carrier distribution functions will be linear in each region. Both the minority-carrier concentration and diffusion current must be continuous across the polysilicon/silicon interface. We can therefore write

$$e D_{E(\text{poly})} \frac{d\left(\delta p_{E(\text{poly})}\right)}{dx} = e D_{E(\text{n}^+)} \frac{d\left(\delta p_{E(\text{n}^+)}\right)}{dx} \qquad (10.84a)$$

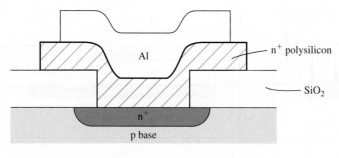

Figure 10.46 | Simplified cross section of an npn polysilicon emitter BJT.

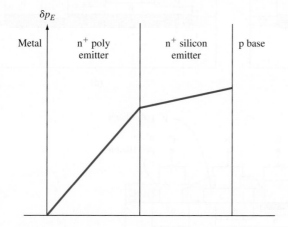

Figure 10.47 | Excess minority-carrier hole concentrations in n^+ polysilicon and n^+ silicon emitter.

or

$$\frac{d\left(\delta p_{E(n^+)}\right)}{dx} = \frac{D_{E(\text{poly})}}{D_{E(n^+)}} \frac{d\left(\delta p_{E(\text{poly})}\right)}{dx} \tag{10.84b}$$

Since $D_{E(\text{poly})} < D_{E(n^+)}$, the gradient of the minority carrier concentration at the emitter edge of the B-E depletion region in the n^+ region is reduced as Figure 10.47 shows. This implies that the current back-injected from the base into the emitter is reduced so that the common-emitter current gain is increased.

10.8.2 Fabrication of Double-Polysilicon npn Transistor

We will briefly consider the fabrication of a double-polysilicon self-aligned npn silicon bipolar transistor. The process steps are shown in Figure 10.48. Since junctions

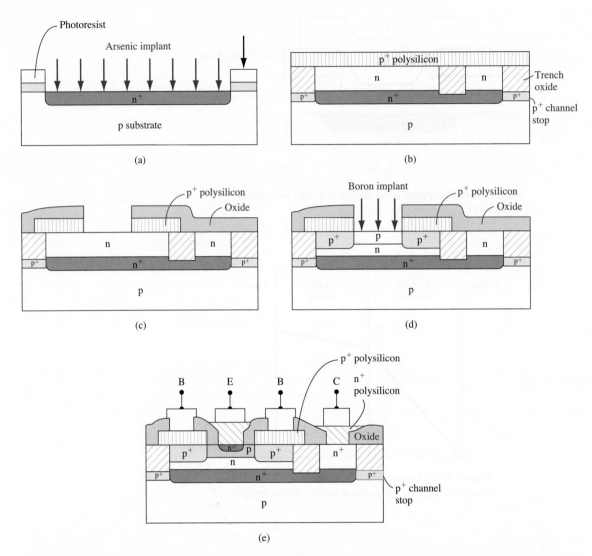

Figure 10.48 | Basic fabrication steps for a double-polysilicon self-aligned npn silicon bipolar transistor: (a) n^+ buried layer, (b) n-epitaxial layer followed by trench isolation and p^+ polysilicon surface layer, (c) base–emitter window, (d) boron implant for base and formation of p^+ extrinsic base region, and (e) final cross section showing n^+ emitter and collector contacts.

are formed within the semiconductor, the orientation of the starting material is not important. Initially, a p-type substrate is oxidized and windows are etched in the oxide using photolithography. Donor ions are implanted into the p-type substrate to form a heavily doped n-type region that is called an n^+ buried layer. This step is shown in Figure 10.48a. This heavily doped region will minimize the resistance in the collector. The oxide is then removed and an n-type epitaxial layer is deposited.

During this high-temperature process step, the implanted donor ions are activated in the buried layer.

In fabricating integrated circuits, individual transistors must be isolated since all collectors are not necessarily at the same potential. One such technique is to create a trench with straight sidewalls in the silicon by reactive ion etching. Oxide is then formed in the trench. Figure 10.48b shows a simplified sketch after this step. Also shown are p$^+$ channel stops. A heavily doped p$^+$ polysilicon layer (poly 1) is deposited on the surface.

An oxide layer is deposited and windows are opened using photolithography techniques. These windows will form the base and emitter regions. This structure is shown in Figure 10.48c. An oxide is formed over this structure. During this time, boron from the polysilicon diffuses into the n region to form an extrinsic base region. Boron is implanted to form the intrinsic base region, as shown in Figure 10.48d. The extrinsic base region reduces the base resistance.

Another oxide is deposited and then etched to open up a space for the emitter and collector contacts. Heavily doped n$^+$ polysilicon (poly 2) is deposited on the existing silicon forming the polysilicon emitter and the collector contact. Photolithography is again used to form contacts to the collector, base, and emitter. The final structure is shown in Figure 10.48e.

10.8.3 Silicon-Germanium Base Transistor

The bandgap energy of Ge ($\sim$0.67 eV) is significantly smaller than the bandgap energy of Si ($\sim$1.12 eV). By incorporating Ge into Si, the bandgap energy will decrease compared to pure Si. If Ge is incorporated into the base region of a Si bipolar transistor, the decrease in bandgap energy will influence the device characteristics. The desired Ge concentration profile is to have the largest amount of Ge near the base–collector junction and the least amount of Ge near the base–emitter junction. Figure 10.49a shows an ideal uniform boron doping concentration in the p-type base and a linear Ge concentration profile.

The energy bands of a SiGe-base npn transistor compared to a Si-base npn transistor, assuming the boron and Ge concentrations given in Figure 10.49a, are shown in Figure 10.49b. The emitter–base junctions of the two transistors are essentially identical, since the Ge concentration is very small in this region. However, the bandgap energy of the SiGe-base transistor near the base–collector junction is smaller than that of the Si-base transistor. The base current is determined by the base–emitter junction parameters and hence will be essentially the same in the two transistors. This change in bandgap energy will influence the collector current.

Collector Current and Current Gain Effects Figure 10.50 shows the thermal equilibrium minority carrier electron concentration through the base region of the SiGe and Si transistors. This concentration is given by

$$n_{B0} = \frac{n_i^2}{N_B} \qquad (10.85)$$

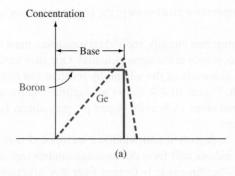

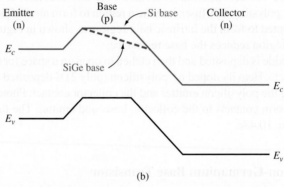

Figure 10.49 | (a) Assumed boron and germanium concentrations in the base of the SiGe-base transistor. (b) Energy band diagram of the Si- and SiGe-base transistors.

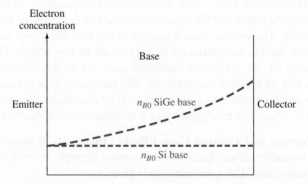

Figure 10.50 | Thermal equilibrium minority carrier electron concentration through the base of the Si- and SiGe-base transistors.

where N_B is assumed to be constant. The intrinsic concentration, however, is a function of the bandgap energy. We can write

$$\frac{n_i^2(\text{SiGe})}{n_i^2(\text{Si})} = \exp\left(\frac{\Delta E_g}{kT}\right) \tag{10.86}$$

where $n_i(\text{SiGe})$ is the intrinsic carrier concentration in the SiGe material, $n_i(\text{Si})$ is the intrinsic carrier concentration in the Si material, and ΔE_g is the change in the bandgap energy of the SiGe material compared to that of Si.

The collector current in a SiGe-base transistor will increase. As a first approximation, we can see this from the previous analysis. The collector current was found from Equation (10.36a), in which the derivative was evaluated at the base–collector junction. This means that the value of n_{B_0} in the collector current expression in Equation (10.37) is the value at the base–collector junction. Since this value is larger for the SiGe-base transistor (Figure 10.50), the collector current will be larger compared to the Si-base transistor. Since the base currents are the same in the two transistors, the increase in collector current then implies that the current gain in the SiGe-base transistor is larger. If the bandgap narrowing is 100 meV, then the increase in the collector current and current gain will be approximately a factor of four.

Early Voltage Effects   The Early voltage in a SiGe-base transistor is larger than that of the Si-base transistor. The explanation for this effect is less obvious than the explanation for the increase in collector current and current gain. For a bandgap narrowing of 100 meV, the Early voltage is increased by approximately a factor of 12. Incorporating Ge into the base region can increase the Early voltage by a large factor.

Base Transit Time and Emitter–Base Charging Time Effects   The decrease in bandgap energy from the base–emitter junction to the base–collector junction induces an electric field in the base that helps accelerate electrons across the p-type base region. For a bandgap narrowing of 100 meV, the induced electric field can be on the order of 10^3 to 10^4 V/cm. This electric field reduces the base-transit time by approximately a factor of 2.5.

The emitter–base junction charging time constant, given by Equation (10.65), is directly proportional to the emitter diffusion resistance r_e'. This parameter is inversely proportional to the emitter current, as seen in Equation (10.66). For a given base current, the emitter current in the SiGe-base transistor is larger, since the current gain is larger. The emitter–base junction charging time is then smaller in a SiGe-base transistor than that in a Si-base transistor.

The reduction in both the base transit time and the emitter–base charging time increases the cutoff frequency of the SiGe-base transistor. The cutoff frequency of these devices can be substantially higher than that of the Si-base device.

10.8.4   The Power BJT

In our previous discussions, we have ignored any physical transistor limitations in terms of maximum current, voltage, and power. We implicitly assumed that the

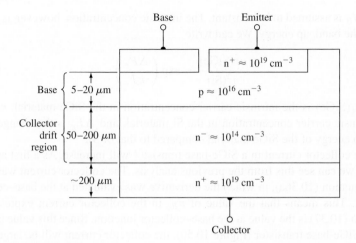

Figure 10.51 | Cross section of a typical vertical npn power BJT.

transistors were capable of handling the current and voltage, and could handle the power dissipated within the device without suffering any damage.

However, with power transistors, we must be concerned with various transistor limitations. The limitations involve maximum rated current (on the order of amperes), maximum rated voltage (on the order of 100 V), and maximum rated power (on the order of watts or tens of watts).[2]

Figure 10.51 shows the structure of a vertical npn power transistor. We have considered vertical npn bipolar transistors previously. However, with small switching devices, the collector terminal is still formed at the surface. In the vertical configuration for the power bipolar transistor, the collector terminal is at the "bottom" of the device. This configuration is preferred since it maximizes the cross-sectional area through which current is flowing in the device. In addition, the doping concentrations and dimensions are not the same as we have encountered in small switching transistors. The primary collector region has a low-doped impurity concentration so that a large base–collector voltage can be applied without initiating breakdown. Another n region, with a higher doping concentration, reduces collector resistance and makes contact with the external collector terminal. The base region is also much wider than normally encountered in small devices. A large base–collector voltage implies a relatively large space charge width being induced in both the collector and base regions. A relatively large base width is required to prevent punch-through breakdown.

Power transistors must also be large-area devices to handle large currents. We have previously considered the interdigitated structure that is repeated in Figure 10.52. Relatively small emitter widths are required to prevent the emitter current crowding effects that were discussed in Section 10.4.4.

---

[2]We must note that, in general, the maximum rated current and maximum rated voltage cannot occur at the same time.

Table 10.4 | Comparison of the characteristics and maximum ratings of small-signal and power BJTs

Parameter	Small-Signal BJT (2N2222A)	Power BJT (2N3055)	Power BJT (2N6078)
V_{CE}(max) (V)	40	60	250
I_C(max) (A)	0.8	15	7
P_D(max) (W) (at $T = 25°C$)	1.2	115	45
β	35–100	5–20	12–70
f_T (MHz)	300	0.8	1

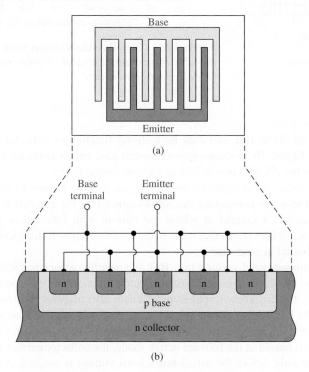

Figure 10.52 | An interdigitated bipolar transistor structure showing the top view and cross-sectional view.

Power Transistor Characteristics The relatively wide base width implies a much smaller current gain β for power transistors compared to small switching transistors, and large-area device implies a larger junction capacitance and hence lower cutoff frequency for a power transistor compared to a small switching transistor. Table 10.4 compares the parameters of a general-purpose small-signal BJT to those of two power BJTs. The current gain is generally smaller in the power transistors, typically

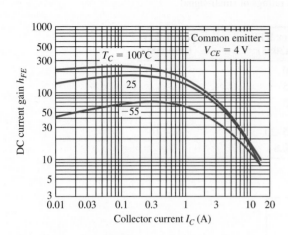

Figure 10.53 | Typical dc beta characteristics (h_{FE} versus I_C) for 2N3055.

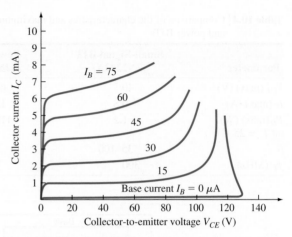

Figure 10.54 | Typical collector current versus collector–emitter voltage characteristics of a bipolar transistor, showing breakdown effects.

in the range of 20 to 100, and may be a strong function of collector current and temperature. Figure 10.53 shows typical current gain versus collector current characteristics for the 2N3055 power BJT at various temperatures.

The *maximum rated collector current* $I_{C,\text{max}}$ may be related to the maximum current that the wires connecting the semiconductor to the external terminals can handle, the collector current at which the current gain falls below a minimum specified value, or the current that leads to the maximum power dissipation when the transistor is biased in saturation.

The *maximum rated voltage* in a BJT is generally associated with avalanche breakdown in the reverse-biased base–collector junction. In the common-emitter configuration, the breakdown voltage mechanism also involves the transistor gain, as well as the breakdown phenomenon in the pn junction. This was discussed in Section 10.4.6. Typical I_C versus V_{CE} characteristics are shown in Figure 10.54. When the transistor is biased in the forward-active mode, the collector current begins to increase significantly before the actual breakdown voltage is reached. All the curves tend to merge to the same collector–emitter voltage once breakdown has occurred. This voltage, $V_{CE,sus}$, is the minimum voltage necessary to sustain the transistor in breakdown.

Another breakdown effect is called *second breakdown,* which occurs in a BJT operating at high voltage and high current. Slight nonuniformities in current density produce local regions of increased heating that increase the minority-carrier concentrations in the semiconductor material, which in turn increases the current in these regions. This effect results in positive feedback, and the current continues to increase, producing a further increase in temperature, until the semiconductor material can actually melt, creating a short circuit between the collector and emitter.

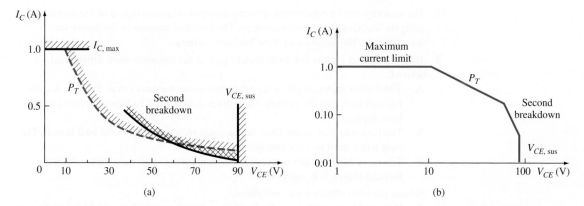

Figure 10.55 | The safe operating area of a bipolar transistor plotted on (a) linear scales and (b) logarithmic scales.

The average power dissipated in a BJT must be kept below a specified maximum value, to ensure that the temperature of the device remains below a maximum value. If we assume the collector current and collector–emitter voltage are dc values, then at the *maximum rated power* P_T for the transistor, we can write

$$P_T = V_{CE}I_C \qquad (10.87)$$

Equation (10.87) neglects the $V_{BE}I_B$ component of power dissipation in the transistor.

The maximum current, voltage, and power limitations can be illustrated on the I_C versus V_{CE} characteristics, as shown in Figure 10.55. The average power limitation, P_T, is a hyperbola described by Equation (10.87). The region where the transistor can be operated safely is known as the safe operating area (SOA) and is bounded by $I_{C,\max}$, $V_{CE,sus}$, P_T, and the transistor's second breakdown characteristic curve. Figure 10.55a shows the safe operating area using linear current and voltage scales. Figure 10.55b shows the same characteristics using log scales.

10.9 | SUMMARY

1. A. There are two complementary bipolar transistors—npn and pnp. Each transistor has three separately doped regions and two pn junctions. Since the center region (base) is very narrow, the two pn junctions are interacting junctions.

   B. In the forward-active mode, the B-E junction is forward biased and the B-C junction is reverse biased. Majority carriers from the emitter are injected into the base, where they become minority carriers. These minority carriers diffuse across the base into the B-C space charge region where they are swept into the collector.

   C. When a transistor is biased in the forward-active mode of operation, the current at one terminal of the transistor (collector current) is controlled by the voltage applied across the other two terminals of the transistor (base–emitter voltage). This is the basic transistor action.

2. The minority-carrier concentrations were determined in each region of the transistor using the ambipolar transport equations. The principal currents in the device are determined by the diffusion of these minority carriers.

3. The contributing factors that limit current gain of the transistor were defined and derived.

    A. The emitter injection efficiency takes into account carriers from the base that are injected back into the emitter. The emitter doping must be large compared to the base doping.

    B. The base transport factor takes into account recombination in the base region. The base width must be very narrow.

    C. The recombination factor takes into account carriers that recombine within the forward-biased B-E junction.

4. Several nonideal effects were considered.

    A. Base width modulation, or Early effect, is the change in the neutral base width with a change in the B-C voltage, producing a change in collector current with a change in B-C voltage.

    B. High-injection effects cause the collector current to increase at a slower rate with base–emitter voltage.

    C. Emitter bandgap narrowing occurs at large emitter doping concentrations and results in a lower emitter injection efficiency.

    D. A nonuniform base doping concentration induces an electric field in the base region that aids the flow of minority carriers across the base.

    E. Two breakdown mechanisms—punch-through and avalanche—were considered.

5. The small-signal hybrid-pi equivalent circuit of the bipolar transistor biased in the forward-active mode was developed. This equivalent circuit is used for linear amplifiers.

6. The time-delay factors in the bipolar transistor were defined and derived. These time-delay factors limit the frequency response of the transistor. The cutoff frequency, a figure of merit for the transistor, is the frequency at which the magnitude of the common-emitter current gain becomes equal to unity.

7. The large-signal switching characteristics were discussed. An important parameter in switching is the charge storage time, which applies to a transistor switching from saturation to cutoff.

8. Several special bipolar structures were considered and the basic fabrication process of the bipolar transistor was presented.

CHECKPOINT

After studying this chapter, the reader should have the ability to

1. A. Describe the basic operation of the bipolar transistor biased in the forward-active mode.

    B. Describe the four operating modes of the transistor.

    C. Describe the basic relations between base, collector, and emitter currents.

    D. Describe the basic transistor action.

2. A. Sketch the minority-carrier concentrations through the bipolar transistor biased in the forward-active mode.

    B.   Sketch the minority-carrier concentrations through the bipolar transistor biased in cutoff and in saturation.

3. A.   Define the various currents in the transistor biased in the forward-active mode.
    B.   Define the common-base current gain in the bipolar transistor.
    C.   Define the physical mechanism of the contributing factors that limit the current gain in the bipolar transistor.

4. A.   Describe the physical mechanism of the base-width modulation and its effect on the current–voltage characteristics.
    B.   Describe the physical mechanism of the current crowding effect.
    C.   Describe the punch-through and avalanche breakdown effects in the bipolar transistor.

5. Describe the hybrid-pi equivalent circuit of the bipolar transistor.

6. Define the transistor cutoff frequency.

7. Describe the characteristics of switching a bipolar transistor from saturation to cutoff.

8. Describe the characteristics of a polysilicon emitter bipolar transistor.

REVIEW QUESTIONS

1. A.   Define the basic transistor action in a bipolar transistor.
    B.   Describe the four operating modes of the bipolar transistor.
    C.   Describe the basic operation of a pnp bipolar transistor biased in the forward-active mode.

2. A.   Sketch the minority-carrier concentrations through a pnp bipolar transistor biased in the forward-active mode. Repeat for the case when the transistor is biased in the saturation mode.
    B.   Define the boundary conditions for the minority-carrier concentrations when the transistor is biased in the forward-active mode.

3. A.   Define emitter injection efficiency, base transport factor, and recombination factor.
    B.   Define the ac common-base current gain in terms of the limiting factors.
    C.   Relate the common-emitter current gain and common-base current gain.

4. A.   Define the Early voltage and relate this parameter to base-width modulation.
    B.   Describe emitter current crowding and describe a solution to this problem.
    C.   Describe the avalanche breakdown effect in a bipolar transistor with an open base terminal.

5. Sketch the simplified hybrid-pi model of the bipolar transistor and define the circuit parameters.

6. Define the four time-delay factors in a bipolar transistor and relate these parameters to the cutoff frequency.

7. Define the storage time parameter.

8. Describe the advantages of polysilicon emitter bipolar transistors.

PROBLEMS

(Note: In the following problems, use the transistor geometry shown in Figure 10.14. Assume $T = 300$ K unless otherwise stated.)

Section 10.1   The Bipolar Transistor Action

10.1   For a uniformly doped $n^{++}p^+n$ bipolar transistor in thermal equilibrium, (*a*) sketch the energy-band diagram, (*b*) sketch the electric field through the device, and (*c*) repeat parts (*a*) and (*b*) for the transistor biased in the forward-active region.

10.2   Consider a $p^{++}n^+p$ bipolar transistor, uniformly doped in each region. Sketch the energy-band diagram for the case when the transistor is (*a*) in thermal equilibrium, (*b*) biased in the forward-active mode, (*c*) biased in the inverse-active region, and (*d*) biased in cutoff with both the B-E and B-C junctions reverse biased.

10.3   The parameters in the base region of an npn bipolar transistor are $D_n = 20\,\text{cm}^2/\text{s}$, $n_{B0} = 10^4$ cm^{-3}, $x_B = 1$ μm, and $A_{BE} = 10^{-4}$ cm^2. (*a*) Comparing Equations (10.1) and (10.2), calculate the magnitude of I_S. (*b*) Determine the collector current for (*i*) $v_{BE} = 0.5$ V, (*ii*) $v_{BE} = 0.6$ V, and (*iii*) $v_{BE} = 0.7$ V.

10.4   Assume the common-base current gain for the transistor described in Problem 10.3 is $\alpha = 0.9920$. (*a*) What is the common-emitter current gain β? [Note that $\beta = \alpha/(1 - \alpha)$.] (*b*) Determine the emitter and base currents corresponding to the collector currents determined in Problem 10.3, part (*b*).

10.5   (*a*) In a bipolar transistor biased in the forward-active region, the base current is $i_B = 6.0$ μA and the collector current is $i_C = 510$ μA. Determine β, α, and i_E. (Note that $i_E = i_C + i_B$.) (*b*) Repeat part (*a*) if $i_B = 50$ μA and $i_C = 2.65$ mA.

10.6   Assume that an npn bipolar transistor has a common-emitter current gain of $\beta = 100$. (*a*) Sketch the ideal current–voltage characteristics (i_C versus v_{CE}), like those in Figure 10.10, as i_B varies from zero to 0.1 mA in 0.01-mA increments. Let v_{CE} vary over the range $0 \le v_{CE} \le 10$ V. (*b*) Assuming $V_{CC} = 10$ V and $R_C = 1$ kΩ in the circuit in Figure 10.9, superimpose the load line on the transistor characteristics in part (*a*). (*c*) Plot, on the resulting graph, the value of i_C and v_{CE} corresponding to $i_B = 0.05$ mA.

10.7   Consider Equation (10.7). Assume $V_{CC} = 10$ V, $R_C = 2$ kΩ, and $V_{BE} = 0.6$ V. (*a*) Plot V_{CB} versus I_C over the range $0 \le I_C \le 5$ mA. (*b*) At what value of I_C does $V_{CB} = 0$?

Section 10.2   Minority-Carrier Distribution

10.8   A uniformly doped silicon npn bipolar transistor is to be biased in the forward-active mode with the B-C junction reverse biased by 3 V. The metallurgical base width is 1.10 μm. The transistor dopings are $N_E = 10^{17}$ cm^{-3}, $N_B = 10^{16}$ cm^{-3}, and $N_C = 10^{15}$ cm^{-3}. (*a*) For $T = 300$ K, calculate the B-E voltage at which the minority-carrier electron concentration at $x = 0$ is 10 percent of the majority-carrier hole concentration. (*b*) At this bias, determine the minority-carrier hole concentration at $x' = 0$. (*c*) Determine the neutral base width for this bias.

10.9   A silicon npn bipolar transistor is uniformly doped and biased in the forward-active region. The neutral base width is $x_B = 0.8$ μm. The transistor doping concentrations are $N_E = 5 \times 10^{17}$ cm^{-3}, $N_B = 10^{16}$ cm^{-3}, and $N_C = 10^{15}$ cm^{-3}. (*a*) Calculate the values of p_{E0}, n_{B0}, and p_{C0}. (*b*) For $V_{BE} = 0.625$ V, determine n_B at $x = 0$ and p_E at $x' = 0$. (*c*) Sketch the minority-carrier concentrations through the device and label each curve.

10.10 A uniformly doped silicon pnp transistor is biased in the forward-active mode. The doping concentrations are $N_E = 10^{18}$ cm^{-3}, $N_B = 5 \times 10^{16}$ cm^{-3}, and $N_C = 10^{15}$ cm^{-3}. (a) Calculate the values of n_{E0}, p_{B0}, and n_{C0}. (b) For $V_{EB} = 0.650$ V, determine p_B at $x = 0$ and n_E at $x' = 0$. (c) Sketch the minority-carrier concentrations through the device and label each curve.

10.11 Consider the minority-carrier electron concentration in the base of an npn bipolar transistor as given by Equation (10.15a). In this problem, we want to compare the gradient of the electron concentration evaluated at the B-C junction to that evaluated at the B-E junction. In particular, calculate the ratio of $d(\delta n_B)/dx$ at $x = x_B$ to $d(\delta n_B)/dx$ at $x = 0$ for (a) $x_B/L_B = 0.1$, (b) $x_B/L_B = 1.0$, and (c) $x_B/L_B = 10$.

10.12 Derive the expressions for the coefficients given by Equation (10.14a) and (10.14b).

*10.13 Derive the expression for the excess minority-carrier hole concentration in the base region of a uniformly doped pnp bipolar transistor operating in the forward-active region.

10.14 The excess electron concentration in the base of an npn bipolar transistor is given by Equation (10.15a). The linear approximation is given by Equation (10.15b). If $\delta n_{B0}(x)$ is the linear approximation given by Equation (10.15b) and $\delta n_B(x)$ is the actual distribution given by Equation (10.15a), determine

$$\frac{\delta n_{B0}(x) - \delta n_B(x)}{\delta n_{B0}(x)} \times 100\%$$

at $x = x_B/2$ for (a) $x_B/L_B = 0.1$ and (b) $x_B/L_B = 1.0$. Assume $V_{BE} \gg kT/e$.

10.15 Consider a pnp bipolar transistor. Assume that the excess minority carrier hole concentrations at the edges of the B-E and B-C space charge regions are $\delta p_B(0) = 8 \times 10^{14}$ cm^{-3} and $\delta p_B(x_B) = -2.25 \times 10^4$ cm^{-3}, respectively. Plot, on the same graph, $\delta p_B(x)$ for (a) the ideal case when no recombination occurs in the base, and (b) the case when $x_B = L_B = 10$ μm. (c) Assuming $D_B = 10$ cm^2/s, calculate the diffusion current density at $x = 0$ and $x = x_B$ for the conditions in parts (a) and (b). Determine the ratio $J(x = x_B)/J(x = 0)$ for the two cases.

*10.16 (a) A uniformly doped npn bipolar transistor at $T = 300$ K is biased in saturation. Starting with the continuity equation for minority carriers, show that the excess electron concentration in the base region can be expressed as

$$\delta n_B(x) = n_{B0} \left\{ \left[\exp\left(\frac{eV_{BE}}{kT} \right) - 1 \right] \left[1 - \frac{x}{x_B} \right] + \left[\exp\left(\frac{eV_{BC}}{kT} \right) - 1 \right] \left[\frac{x}{x_B} \right] \right\}$$

for $x_B/L_B \ll 1$ where x_B is the neutral base width. (b) Show that the minority carrier diffusion current in the base is then given by

$$J_n = -\frac{eD_B n_{B0}}{x_B} \left[\exp\left(\frac{eV_{BE}}{kT} \right) - \exp\left(\frac{eV_{BC}}{kT} \right) \right]$$

(c) Show that the total excess minority-carrier charge (C/cm^2) in the base region is given by

$$\delta Q_{nB} = \frac{-e n_{B0} x_B}{2} \left\{ \left[\exp\left(\frac{eV_{BE}}{kT} \right) - 1 \right] + \left[\exp\left(\frac{eV_{BC}}{kT} \right) - 1 \right] \right\}$$

*10.17 Consider a silicon pnp bipolar transistor at $T = 300$ K with uniform dopings of $N_E = 5 \times 10^{18}$ cm^{-3}, $N_B = 10^{17}$ cm^{-3}, and $N_C = 5 \times 10^{15}$ cm^{-3}. Let $D_B = 10$ cm^2/s, $x_B = 0.7$ μm, and assume $x_B \ll L_B$. The transistor is operating in saturation with $J_p = 165$ A/cm^2 and $V_{EB} = 0.75$ V. Determine (a) V_{CB}, (b) V_{EC}(sat), (c) the #/cm^2 of excess minority-carrier holes in the base, and (d) the #/cm^2 of excess minority-carrier electrons in the long collector. Let $L_C = 35$ μm.

10.18 An npn silicon bipolar transistor at $T = 300$ K has uniform dopings of $N_E = 10^{19}$ cm^{-3}, $N_B = 10^{17}$ cm^{-3}, and $N_C = 7 \times 10^{15}$ cm^{-3}. The transistor is operating in the inverse-active mode with $V_{BE} = -2$ V and $V_{BC} = 0.565$ V. (a) Sketch the minority-carrier distribution through the device. (b) Determine the minority-carrier concentrations at $x = x_B$ and $x'' = 0$. (c) If the metallurgical base width is 1.2 μm, determine the neutral base width.

10.19 A uniformly doped silicon pnp bipolar transistor at $T = 300$ K with dopings of $N_E = 5 \times 10^{17}$ cm^{-3}, $N_B = 10^{16}$ cm^{-3}, and $N_C = 5 \times 10^{14}$ cm^{-3} is biased in the inverse-active mode. What is the maximum B-C voltage so that the low-injection condition applies?

Section 10.3   Low-Frequency Common-Base Current Gain

10.20 The following currents are measured in a uniformly doped npn bipolar transistor:

$$I_{nE} = 1.20 \text{ mA} \qquad I_{pE} = 0.10 \text{ mA}$$
$$I_{nC} = 1.18 \text{ mA} \qquad I_R = 0.20 \text{ mA}$$
$$I_G = 0.001 \text{ mA} \qquad I_{pc0} = 0.001 \text{ mA}$$

Determine (a) α, (b) γ, (c) α_T, (d) δ, and (e) β.

10.21 A silicon npn transistor at $T = 300$ K has an area of 10^{-3} cm^2, neutral base width of 1 μm, and doping concentrations of $N_E = 10^{18}$ cm^{-3}, $N_B = 10^{17}$ cm^{-3}, $N_C = 10^{16}$ cm^{-3}. Other semiconductor parameters are $D_B = 20$ cm^2/s, $\tau_{E0} = \tau_{B0} = 10^{-7}$ s, and $\tau_{C0} = 10^{-6}$ s. Assuming the transistor is biased in the active region and the recombination factor is unity, calculate the collector current for (a) $V_{BE} = 0.5$ V, (b) $I_E = 1.5$ mA, and (c) $I_B = 2$ μA.

10.22 Consider a uniformly doped npn bipolar transistor at $T = 300$ K with the following parameters:

$N_E = 10^{18}$ cm^{-3}	$N_B = 5 \times 10^{16}$ cm^{-3}	$N_C = 10^{15}$ cm^{-3}
$D_E = 8$ cm^2/s	$D_B = 15$ cm^2/s	$D_C = 12$ cm^2/s
$\tau_{E0} = 10^{-8}$ s	$\tau_{B0} = 5 \times 10^{-8}$ s	$\tau_{C0} = 10^{-7}$ s
$x_E = 0.8$ μm	$x_B = 0.7$ μm	$J_{r0} = 3 \times 10^{-8}$ A/cm^2

For $V_{BE} = 0.60$ V and $V_{CE} = 5$ V, calculate (a) the currents J_{nE}, J_{pE}, J_{nC}, and J_R and (b) the current gain factors γ, α_T, δ, α, and β.

10.23 Three npn bipolar transistors have identical parameters except for the base doping concentrations and neutral base widths. The base parameters for the three devices are as follows:

Device	Base Doping	Base Width
A	$N_B = N_{B0}$	$x_B = x_{B0}$
B	$N_B = 2N_{B0}$	$x_B = x_{B0}$
C	$N_B = N_{B0}$	$x_B = x_{B0}/2$

(The base doping concentration for the B device is twice that of A and C, and the neutral base width for the C device is half that of A and B.)
(a) Determine the ratio of the emitter injection efficiency of (i) device B to device A and (ii) device C to device A.
(b) Repeat part (a) for the base transport factor.
(c) Repeat part (a) for the recombination factor.
(d) Which device has the largest common-emitter current gain β?

10.24 Repeat Problem 10.23 for three devices in which the emitter parameters vary. The emitter parameters for the three devices are as follows:

Device	Emitter Doping	Emitter Width
A	$N_E = N_{E0}$	$x_E = x_{E0}$
B	$N_E = 2N_{E0}$	$x_E = x_{E0}$
C	$N_E = N_{E0}$	$x_E = x_{E0}/2$

10.25 An npn silicon transistor is biased in the inverse active mode with $V_{BE} = -3$ V and $V_{BC} = 0.6$ V. The doping concentrations are $N_E = 10^{18}$ cm^{-3}, $N_B = 10^{17}$ cm^{-3}, and $N_C = 10^{16}$ cm^{-3}. Other parameters are $x_B = 1 \ \mu$m, $\tau_{E0} = \tau_{B0} = \tau_{C0} = 2 \times 10^{-7}$ s, $D_E = 10$ cm^2/s, $D_B = 20$ cm^2/s, $D_C = 15$ cm^2/s, and $A = 10^{-3}$ cm^2. (a) Calculate and plot the minority-carrier distribution in the device. (b) Calculate the collector and emitter currents. (Neglect geometry factors and assume the recombination factor is unity.)

10.26 (a) Calculate the base transport factor, α_T, for $x_B/L_B = 0.01, 0.10, 1.0,$ and 10. Assuming that γ and δ are unity, determine β for each case. (b) Calculate the emitter injection efficiency, γ, for $N_B/N_E = 0.01, 0.10, 1.0,$ and 10. Assuming that α_T and δ are unity, determine β for each case. (c) Considering the results of parts (a) and (b), what conclusions can be made concerning when the base transport factor or when the emitter injection efficiency are the limiting factors for the common-emitter current gain?

10.27 (a) Calculate the recombination factor for $V_{BE} = 0.2, 0.4,$ and 0.6 V. Assume the following parameters:

$$D_B = 25 \text{ cm}^2\text{/s} \qquad D_E = 10 \text{ cm}^2\text{/s}$$
$$N_E = 5 \times 10^{18} \text{ cm}^{-3} \qquad N_B = 1 \times 10^{17} \text{ cm}^{-3}$$
$$N_C = 5 \times 10^{15} \text{ cm}^{-3} \qquad x_B = 0.7 \ \mu\text{m}$$
$$\tau_{B0} = \tau_{E0} = 10^{-7} \text{ s} \qquad J_{r0} = 2 \times 10^{-9} \text{ A/cm}^2$$
$$n_i = 1.5 \times 10^{10} \text{ cm}^{-3}$$

(b) Assuming the base transport and emitter injection efficiency factors are unity, calculate the common-emitter current gain for the conditions in part (a).
(c) Considering the results of part (b), what can be said about the recombination factor being the limiting factor in the common-emitter current gain?

10.28 Consider an npn silicon bipolar transistor at $T = 300$ K with the following parameters:

$$D_B = 25 \text{ cm}^2/\text{s} \qquad D_E = 10 \text{ cm}^2/\text{s}$$
$$\tau_{B0} = 10^{-7} \text{ s} \qquad \tau_{E0} = 5 \times 10^{-8} \text{ s}$$
$$N_B = 10^{16} \text{ cm}^{-3} \qquad x_E = 0.5 \ \mu\text{m}$$

The recombination factor, δ, has been determined to be $\delta = 0.998$. We need a common-emitter current gain of $\beta = 120$. Assuming that $\alpha_T = \gamma$, determine the maximum base width, x_B, and the minimum emitter doping, N_E, to achieve this specification.

*10.29 (a) The recombination current density, J_{r0}, in an npn silicon bipolar transistor at $T = 300$ K is $J_{r0} = 5 \times 10^{-8}$ A/cm^2. The uniform dopings are $N_E = 10^{18}$ cm^{-3}, $N_B = 5 \times 10^{16}$ cm^{-3}, and $N_C = 10^{15}$ cm^{-3}. Other parameters are $D_E = 10$ cm^2/s, $D_B = 25$ cm^2/s, $\tau_{E0} = 10^{-8}$ s, and $\tau_{B0} = 10^{-7}$ s. Determine the neutral base width so that the recombination factor is $\delta = 0.995$ when $V_{BE} = 0.55$ V (b) If J_{r0} remains constant with temperature, what is the value of δ when $V_{BE} = 0.55$ V for the case when the temperature is $T = 400$ K? Use the value of x_B determined in part (a).

10.30 (a) Plot, for a bipolar transistor, the base transport factor, α_T, as a function of (x_B/L_B) over the range $0.01 \le (x_B/L_B) \le 10$. (Use a log scale on the horizontal axis.)
(b) Assuming that the emitter injection efficiency and recombination factors are unity, plot the common-emitter gain for the conditions in part (a). (c) Considering the results of part (b), what can be said about the base transport factor being the limiting factor in the common-emitter current gain?

10.31 (a) Plot the emitter injection efficiency as a function of the doping ratio, N_B/N_E, over the range $0.01 \le N_B/N_E \le 10$. Assume that $D_E = D_B$, $L_B = L_E$, and $x_B = x_E$. (Use a log scale on the horizontal axis.) Neglect bandgap narrowing effects.
(b) Assuming that the base transport factor and recombination factors are unity, plot the common-emitter current gain for the conditions in part (a). (c) Considering the results of part (b), what can be said about the emitter injection efficiency being the limiting factor in the common-emitter current gain?

10.32 (a) Plot the recombination factor as a function of the forward-bias B-E voltage for $0.1 \le V_{BE} \le 0.6$. Assume the following parameters:

$$D_B = 25 \text{ cm}^2/\text{s} \qquad\qquad D_E = 10 \text{ cm}^2/\text{s}$$
$$N_E = 5 \times 10^{18} \text{ cm}^{-3} \qquad N_B = 1 \times 10^{17} \text{ cm}^{-3}$$
$$N_C = 5 \times 10^{15} \text{ cm}^{-3} \qquad x_B = 0.7 \ \mu\text{m}$$
$$\tau_{B0} = \tau_{E0} = 10^{-7} \text{ s} \qquad J_{r0} = 2 \times 10^{-9} \text{ A/cm}^2$$
$$n_i = 1.5 \times 10^{10} \text{ cm}^{-3}$$

(b) Assuming the base transport and emitter injection efficiency factors are unity, plot the common-emitter current gain for the conditions in part (a). (c) Considering the results of part (b), what can be said about the recombination factor being the limiting factor in the common-emitter current gain?

10.33 The emitter in a BJT is often made very thin to achieve high operating speed. In this problem, we investigate the effect of emitter width on current gain. Consider the emitter injection efficiency given by Equation (10.35a). Assume that $N_E = 100N_B$, $D_E = D_B$, and $L_E = L_B$. Also let $x_B = 0.1L_B$. Plot the emitter injection efficiency for $0.01L_E \leq x_E \leq 10L_E$. From these results, discuss the effect of emitter width on the current gain.

Section 10.4 Nonideal Effects

10.34 A silicon pnp bipolar transistor at $T = 300$ K has uniform dopings of $N_E = 10^{18}$ cm^{-3}, $N_B = 10^{16}$ cm^{-3}, and $N_C = 10^{15}$ cm^{-3}. The metallurgical base width is 1.2 μm. Let $D_B = 10$ cm^2/s and $\tau_{B0} = 5 \times 10^{-7}$ s. Assume that the minority-carrier hole concentration in the base can be approximated by a linear distribution. Let $V_{EB} = 0.625$ V. (a) Determine the hole diffusion current density in the base for $V_{BC} = 5$ V, $V_{BC} = 10$ V, and $V_{BC} = 15$ V. (b) Estimate the Early voltage.

*10.35 The base width of a bipolar transistor is normally small to provide a large current gain and increased speed. The base width also affects the Early voltage. In a silicon npn bipolar transistor at $T = 300$ K, the doping concentrations are $N_E = 10^{18}$ cm^{-3}, $N_B = 3 \times 10^{16}$ cm^{-3}, and $N_C = 5 \times 10^{15}$ cm^{-3}. Assume $D_B = 20$ cm^2/s and $\tau_{B0} = 5 \times 10^{-7}$ s, and let $V_{BE} = 0.70$ V. Using voltages $V_{CB} = 5$ V and $V_{CB} = 10$ V as two data points, estimate the Early voltage for metallurgical base widths of (a) 1.0 μm, (b) 0.80 μm, and (c) 0.60 μm.

10.36 An npn silicon bipolar transistor has a base doping concentration of $N_B = 10^{17}$ cm^{-3}, a collector doping concentration of $N_C = 10^{16}$ cm^{-3}, a metallurgical base width of 1.1 μm, and a base minority-carrier diffusion coefficient of $D_B = 20$ cm^2/s. The transistor is biased in the forward-active region with $V_{BE} = 0.60$ V. Determine (a) the change in the neutral base width as V_{CB} changes from 1 V to 5 V, and (b) the corresponding change in the collector current.

10.37 Consider a uniformly doped silicon npn bipolar transistor in which $x_E = x_B$, $L_E = L_B$, and $D_E = D_B$. Assume that $\alpha_T = \delta = 0.995$ and let $N_B = 10^{17}$ cm^{-3}. Calculate and plot the common-emitter current gain β for $N_E = 10^{17}, 10^{18}, 10^{19}$, and 10^{20} cm^{-3}, and for the case (a) when the bandgap narrowing effect is neglected, and (b) when the bandgap narrowing effect is taken into account.

10.38 A silicon pnp bipolar transistor at $T = 300$ K is to be designed so that the emitter injection efficiency is $\gamma = 0.996$. Assume that $x_E = x_B$, $L_E = L_B$, $D_E = D_B$, and let $N_E = 10^{19}$ cm^{-3}. (a) Determine the maximum base doping, taking into account bandgap narrowing. (b) If bandgap narrowing were neglected, what would be the maximum base doping required?

10.39 A first-approximation type calculation of the current crowding effect can be made using the geometry shown in Figure P10.39. Assume that one-half of the base current enters from each side of the emitter strip and flows uniformly to the center of the emitter. Assume the base is p type with the following parameters:

$$N_B = 10^{16} \text{ cm}^{-3} \qquad x_B = 0.70 \text{ } \mu\text{m}$$
$$\mu_p = 400 \text{ cm}^2\text{/V-s} \qquad S = 8 \text{ } \mu\text{m}$$
$$\text{Emitter length} \qquad L = 100 \text{ } \mu\text{m}$$

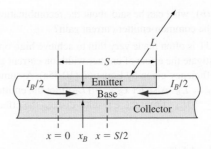

Figure P10.39 | Figure for
Problems 10.39 and 10.40.

(a) Calculate the resistance between $x = 0$ and $x = S/2$. (b) If $\frac{1}{2} I_B = 10 \ \mu A$,
calculate the voltage drop between $x = 0$ and $x = S/2$. (c) If $V_{BE} = 0.6$ V at $x = 0$,
estimate in percent the number of electrons being injected into the base at
$x = S/2$ compared to $x = 0$.

10.40   Consider the geometry shown in Figure P10.39 and the device parameters in
Problem 10.39 except the emitter width S. The emitter width S is to be changed so
that the number of electrons injected into the base at $x = S/2$ is no more than
10 percent less than the number of electrons injected into the base at $x = 0$.
Calculate S.

*10.41   The base doping in a diffused n^+pn bipolar transistor can be approximated by an
exponential as

$$N_B = N_B(0) \exp\left(\frac{-ax}{x_B}\right)$$

where a is a constant and is given by

$$a = \ln\left(\frac{N_B(0)}{N_B(x_B)}\right)$$

(a) Show that, in thermal equilibrium, the electric field in the neutral base region is a
constant. (b) Indicate the direction of the electric field. Does this electric field aid or
retard the flow of minority-carrier electrons across the base? (c) Derive an expression for the steady-state minority-carrier electron concentration in the base under
forward bias. Assume no recombination occurs in the base. (Express the electron
concentration in terms of the electron current density.)

10.42   Consider a silicon npn bipolar transistor with uniform dopings of $N_E = 5 \times 10^{18} \ \text{cm}^{-3}$,
$N_B = 10^{17} \ \text{cm}^{-3}$, and $N_C = 5 \times 10^{15} \ \text{cm}^{-3}$. Assume the common-base current gain is
$\alpha = 0.9920$. Determine (a) BV_{CBO}, (b) BV_{CEO}, and (c) the base–emitter breakdown
voltage. (Assume $n = 3$ for the empirical constant.)

10.43   A high-voltage silicon npn bipolar transistor is to be designed such that the uniform
base doping is $N_B = 10^{16} \ \text{cm}^{-3}$ and the common-emitter current grain is $\beta = 50$. The
breakdown voltage BV_{CEO} is to be at least 60 V. Determine the maximum collector
doping and the minimum collector length to support this voltage. (Assume $n = 3$.)

10.44 A uniformly doped silicon epitaxial npn bipolar transistor is fabricated with a base doping of $N_B = 3 \times 10^{16}$ cm^{-3} and a heavily doped collector region with $N_C = 5 \times 10^{17}$ cm^{-3}. The neutral base width is $x_B = 0.70$ μm when $V_{BE} = V_{BC} = 0$. Determine V_{BC} at which punch-through occurs. Compare this value to the expected avalanche breakdown voltage of the junction.

10.45 A silicon npn bipolar transistor has a base doping concentration of $N_B = 10^{17}$ cm^{-3}, a collector doping concentration of $N_C = 7 \times 10^{15}$ cm^{-3}, and a metallurgical base width of 0.50 μm. Let $V_{BE} = 0.60$ V. (*a*) Determine V_{CE} at punch-through. (*b*) Determine the peak electric field in the B-C space charge region at punch-through.

10.46 A uniformly doped silicon pnp bipolar transistor is to be designed with $N_E = 10^{19}$ cm^{-3} and $N_C = 10^{16}$ cm^{-3}. The metallurgical base width is 0.75 μm. Determine the minimum base doping so that the punch-through voltage is no less than $V_{pt} = 25$ V.

Section 10.6   Frequency Limitations

10.47 Consider a silicon npn transistor at $T = 300$ K. Assume the following parameters:

$$I_E = 0.5 \text{ mA} \qquad C_{je} = 0.8 \text{ pF}$$
$$x_B = 0.7 \ \mu\text{m} \qquad D_n = 25 \text{ cm}^2/\text{s}$$
$$x_{dc} = 2.0 \ \mu\text{m} \qquad r_c = 30 \ \Omega$$
$$C_s = C_\mu = 0.08 \text{ pF} \qquad \beta = 50$$

(*a*) Calculate the transit time factors. (*b*) Calculate the cutoff and beta cutoff frequencies, f_T and f_β, respectively.

10.48 In a particular bipolar transistor, the base transit time is 20 percent of the total delay time. The base width is 0.5 μm and the base diffusion coefficient is $D_B = 20$ cm^2/s. Determine the cutoff frequency.

10.49 Assume the base transit time of a BJT is 100 ps and carriers cross the 1.2 μm B-C space charge region at a speed of 10^7 cm/s. The emitter–base junction charging time is 25 ps and the collector capacitance and resistance are 0.10 pF and 10 Ω, respectively. Determine the cutoff frequency.

Summary and Review

*10.50 (*a*) A silicon npn bipolar transistor at $T = 300$ K is to be designed with an Early voltage of at least 200 V and a current gain of at least $\beta = 80$. (*b*) Repeat part (*a*) for a pnp bipolar transistor.

*10.51 Design a uniformly doped silicon npn bipolar transistor so that $\beta = 100$ at $T = 300$ K. The maximum CE voltage is to be 15 V and any breakdown voltage is to be at least three times this value. Assume the recombination factor is constant at $\delta = 0.995$. The transistor is to be operated in low injection with a maximum collector current of $I_C = 5$ mA. Bandgap narrowing effects and base width modulation effects are to be minimized. Let $D_E = 6$ cm^2/s, $D_B = 25$ cm^2/s, $\tau_{E0} = 10^{-8}$ s, and $\tau_{B0} = 10^{-7}$ s. Determine doping concentrations, the metallurgical base width, the active area, and the maximum allowable V_{BE}.

*10.52 Design a pair of complementary npn and pnp bipolar transistors. The transistors are to have the same metallurgical base and emitter widths of $W_B = 0.75$ μm and $x_E = 0.5$ μm. Assume that the following minority-carrier parameters apply to each device.

$$D_n = 23 \text{ cm}^2/\text{s} \qquad \tau_{n0} = 10^{-7} \text{ s}$$
$$D_p = 8 \text{ cm}^2/\text{s} \qquad \tau_{p0} = 5 \times 10^{-8} \text{ s}$$

The collector doping concentration in each device is 5×10^{15} cm^{-3} and the recombination factor in each device is constant at $\delta = 0.9950$. (*a*) Design, if possible, the devices so that $\beta = 100$ in each device. If this is not possible, how close a match can be obtained? (*b*) With equal forward-bias base–emitter voltages applied, the collector currents are to be $I_C = 5$ mA with each device operating in low injection. Determine the active cross-sectional areas.

READING LIST

1.   'Dimitrijev, S. *Understanding Semiconductor Devices*. New York: Oxford University Press, 2000.

2.   Kano, K. *Semiconductor Devices*. Upper Saddle River, NJ: Prentice-Hall, 1998.

3.   Muller, R. S., T. I. Kamins, and W. Chan. *Device Electronics for Integrated Circuits,* 3rd ed. New York: John Wiley and Sons, 2003.

4.   Navon, D. H. *Semiconductor Microdevices and Materials*. New York: Holt, Rinehart, & Winston, 1986.

5.   Neamen, D. A. *Semiconductor Physics and Devices: Basic Principles,* 3rd ed. New York: McGraw-Hill, 2003.

6.   Neudeck, G. W. *The Bipolar Junction Transistor*. Vol. 3 of the *Modular Series on Solid State Devices*. 2nd ed. Reading, MA: Addison-Wesley, 1989.

7.   Ng, K. K. *Complete Guide to Semiconductor Devices*. New York: McGraw-Hill, 1995.

8.   Ning, T. H., and R. D. lsaac. "Effect of Emitter Contact on Current Gain of Silicon Bipolar Devices." *Polysilicon Emitter Bipolar Transistors*. eds. A. K. Kapoor and D. J. Roulston. New York: IEEE Press, 1989.

9.   Pierret, R. F. *Semiconductor Device Fundamentals*. Reading, MA: Addison-Wesley, 1996.

10.   Roulston, D. J. *Bipolar Semiconductor Devices*. New York: McGraw-Hill, 1990.

11.   Roulston, D. J. *An Introduction to the Physics of Semiconductor Devices*. New York: Oxford University Press, 1999.

12.   Runyan, W. R., and K. E. Bean. *Semiconductor Integrated Circuit Processing Technology*. Reading, MA: Addison-Wesley Publishing Co, 1990.

*13.   Shur, M. *GaAs Devices and Circuits*. New York: Plenum Press, 1987.

14.   Shur, M. *Introduction to Electronic Devices*. New York: John Wiley & Sons, Inc., 1996.

*15.   Shur, M. *Physics of Semiconductor Devices*. Englewood Cliffs, NJ: Prentice-Hall, 1990.

16.   Singh, J. *Semiconductor Devices: An Introduction*. New York: McGraw-Hill, 1994.

17.   Singh, J. *Semiconductor Devices: Basic Principles*. New York: John Wiley & Sons, Inc., 2001.

18. Streetman, B. G., and S. Banerjee. *Solid State Electronic Devices,* 5th ed. Upper Saddle River, NJ: Prentice-Hall, 2000.

19. Sze, S. M. *High-Speed Semiconductor Devices.* New York: Wiley, 1990.

20. Sze, S. M. *Physics of Semiconductor Devices.* 2nd ed. New York: Wiley, 1981.

21. Sze, S. M. *Semiconductor Devices: Physics and Technology,* 2nd ed. New York: John Wiley and Sons, 2002.

*22. Taur, Y., and T. H. Ning. *Fundamentals of Modern VLSI Devices.* New York: Cambridge University Press, 1998.

*23. Wang, S. *Fundamentals of Semiconductor Theory and Device Physics.* Englewood Cliffs, NJ: Prentice-Hall, 1989.

*24. Warner, R. M., Jr., and B. L. Grung. *Transistors: Fundamentals for the Integrated-Circuit Engineer.* New York: Wiley, 1983.

25. Wolf, S. *Silicon Processing for the VLSI Era: Volume 3—The Submicron MOSFET.* Sunset Beach, CA: Lattice Press, 1995.

26. Yang, E. S. *Microelectronic Devices.* New York: McGraw-Hill, 1988.

*27. Yuan, J. S. *SiGe, GaAs, and InP Heterojunction Bipolar Transistors.* New York: John Wiley & Sons, Inc., 1999.

11

CHAPTER 11

Additional Semiconductor Devices and Device Concepts

We have considered the pn junction diode and the two major types of transistors—the MOSFET and BJT. There are many other semiconductor devices. However, we will not be able to consider all such devices. In this chapter, we will consider a third transistor structure—the junction field-effect transistor. Another semiconductor device to be considered is the thyristor. This device is a four-layered structure that is primarily used in switching applications. We will also consider additional MOSFET concepts that involve parasitic bipolar transistor structures and parasitic four-layer structures. Finally in this chapter, we will briefly discuss a few MEMS devices.

11.0 | PREVIEW

In this chapter, we will

1. Analyze the junction field-effect transistor.
2. Analyze the heterojunction and heterojunction devices.
3. Analyze the thyristor—a four-layer semiconductor structure.
4. Analyze additional MOSFET concepts, based on parasitic bipolar and four-layered structures.
5. Briefly discuss a few microelectromechanical systems (MEMS).

Historical Insight

In 1926, Julius Lilienfeld patented his idea for a field-effect transistor. However, the technology was not available at that time to fabricate the device. In 1966, the MESFET was invented by C. Mead. This is a fundamental device for microwave integrated circuits.

In 1952, the Thyristor, which is a very versatile switching device, was invented by J. Ebers. In 1957, the heterojunction bipolar transistor was demonstrated by H. Kroemer and in 1980, the heterojunction field-effect transistor (MODFET) was demonstrated.

Present-Day Insight

Junction field-effect transistors with Schottky barrier gates (MESFETS) are used in specialized applications where very high speed (high-frequency) devices are required. Thyristors continue to be used in power switching applications.

11.1 | THE JUNCTION FIELD-EFFECT TRANSISTOR

Objective: Analyze the junction field-effect transistor.

We have considered two types of transistors—the MOS and bipolar junction transistors. The third type of transistor is the junction field-effect transistor.

There are two general categories of junction field-effect transistors. The first is the pn junction FET, or pn JFET, and the second is the **me**tal–**s**emiconductor **f**ield–**e**ffect **t**ransistor (MESFET). The pn JFET is fabricated with a pn junction, and the MESFET with a Schottky barrier rectifying junction.

The current in a junction field-effect transistor is through a semiconductor region known as the channel, with ohmic contacts at each end. The basic transistor action is the modulation of the channel conductance by an electric field that is perpendicular to the channel. The modulating electric field is induced in the space charge region of a reverse-biased pn junction or a reverse-biased Schottky barrier junction and is, therefore, a function of a gate voltage. The modulation of the channel conductance by the gate voltage modulates the channel current.

11.1.1 The pn JFET

The first type of field-effect transistor is the pn junction field-effect transistor, or pn JFET. A simplified cross section of a symmetrical device is shown in Figure 11.1. The n region between the two p regions is known as the channel and, in this n-channel device, majority-carrier electrons flow between the source and drain terminals. The source is the terminal from which carriers enter the channel from the external circuit, the drain is the terminal where carriers leave, or are drained from, the device, and the gate is the control terminal. The two gate terminals shown in Figure 11.1 are tied together to form a single gate connection. Since majority-carrier electrons are

n-channel pn JFET

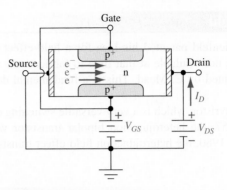

Figure 11.1 | Cross section of a symmetrical n-channel pn junction FET showing voltage polarities and electron flow through the channel.

primarily involved in the conduction in this n-channel transistor, the JFET is a majority-carrier device.

p-channel pn JFET

A complementary p-channel JFET can also be fabricated in which the p and n regions are reversed from those of the n-channel device. Holes will flow in the p-type channel between source and drain and the source terminal will now be the source of the holes. The current direction and voltage polarities in the p-channel JFET are the reverse of those in the n-channel device. The p-channel JFET is generally a lower-frequency device than the n-channel JFET due to the lower hole mobility.

Figure 11.2a shows an n-channel pn JFET with zero volts applied to the gate. If the source is at ground potential, and if a small positive drain voltage is applied, a drain current I_D is produced between the source and drain terminals. The n channel is essentially a resistance, so the I_D versus V_{DS} characteristic, for small V_{DS} values, is approximately linear, as shown in the figure.

When we apply a voltage to the gate of a pn JFET with respect to the source and drain, we alter the channel conductance. If a negative voltage is applied to the gate of the n-channel pn JFET shown in Figure 11.2, the gate-to-channel pn junction becomes reverse biased. The space charge region now widens so the channel region becomes narrower and the resistance of the n channel increases. The slope of the I_D versus V_{DS} curve, for small V_{DS}, decreases. These effects are shown in Figure 11.2b. If a larger negative gate voltage is applied, the condition shown in Figure 11.2c can be achieved. The reverse-biased gate-to-channel space charge region has completely

Pinchoff

filled the channel region. This condition is known as *pinchoff*. The drain current at pinchoff is essentially zero, since the depletion region isolates the source and drain terminals. Figure 11.2c shows the I_D versus V_{DS} curve for this case, as well as the other two cases.

The current in the channel is controlled by the gate voltage. The control of the current in one part of the device by a voltage in another part of the device is the basic

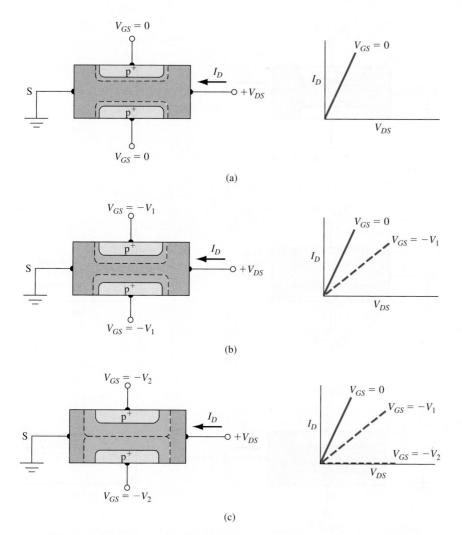

Figure 11.2 | Gate-to-channel space charge regions and I–V characteristics for small V_{DS} values and for (a) zero gate voltage, (b) a small reverse-biased gate voltage, and (c) a gate voltage to achieve pinchoff.

transistor action. This device is a normally on or *depletion mode* device, which means that a voltage must be applied to the gate terminal to turn the device off.

Now consider the situation in which the gate voltage is held at 0 V, $V_{GS} = 0$, and the drain voltage changes. Figure 11.3a is a replica of Figure 11.2a for zero gate voltage and a small drain voltage. As the drain voltage increases (positive), the gate-to-channel pn junction becomes reverse biased near the drain terminal so that the space charge region extends farther into the channel. The channel is essentially a resistor, and the effective channel resistance increases as the space charge region widens;

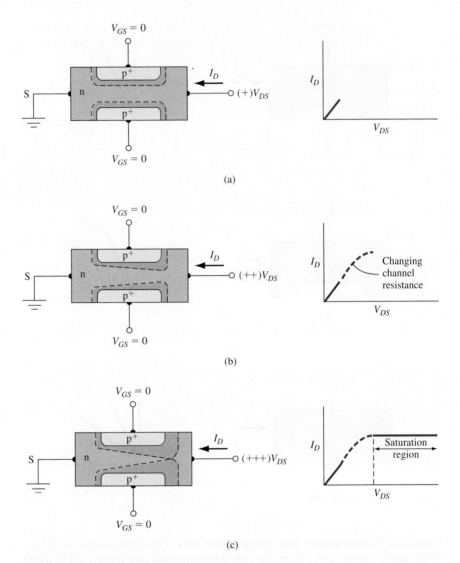

Figure 11.3 | Gate-to-channel space charge regions and I–V characteristics for zero gate voltage and for (a) a small drain voltage, (b) a larger drain voltage, and (c) a drain voltage to achieve pinchoff at the drain terminal.

therefore, the slope of the I_D versus V_{DS} characteristic decreases, as shown in Figure 11.3b. The effective channel resistance now varies along the channel length and, since the channel current must be constant, the voltage drop through the channel becomes dependent on position.

If the drain voltage increases further, the condition shown in Figure 11.3c can result. The channel has been pinched off at the drain terminal. Any further increase in drain voltage will not cause an increase in drain current. The I–V characteristic for this condition is also shown in this figure. The drain voltage at pinchoff is referred to as V_{DS}(sat). For $V_{DS} > V_{DS}$(sat), the transistor is said to be in the saturation region and the drain current, for this ideal case, is independent of V_{DS}. At first glance, we might expect the drain current to go to zero when the channel becomes pinched off at the drain terminal, but we will show why this does not happen.

Figure 11.4 shows an expanded view of the pinchoff region in the channel. The n channel and drain terminal are now separated by a space charge region that has a length ΔL. The electrons move through the n channel from the source and are injected into the space charge region where, subjected to the $\mathcal{E}$-field force, they are swept through into the drain contact area. If we assume that $\Delta L \ll L$, then the electric field in the n-channel region remains unchanged from the V_{DS}(sat) case; the drain current will remain constant as V_{DS} changes. Once the carriers are in the drain region, the drain current will be independent of V_{DS}; thus, the device looks like a constant current source.

11.1.2 The MESFET

The second type of junction field-effect transistor is the MESFET. The gate junction in the pn junction FET is replaced by a Schottky barrier rectifying contact. Although MESFETs can be fabricated in silicon, they are usually associated with gallium arsenide or other compound semiconductor materials. A simplified cross section of a GaAs MESFET is shown in Figure 11.5. A thin epitaxial layer of GaAs is used for the active region; the substrate is a very high resistivity GaAs material referred to as a semi-insulating substrate. GaAs is intentionally doped with chromium, which behaves as a single acceptor close to the center of the energy bandgap, to make it semi-insulating with a resistivity as high as 10^9 Ω-cm. The advantages of these devices include higher electron mobility, hence smaller transit time and faster response; and decreased parasitic capacitance and a simplified fabrication process, resulting from the semi-insulating GaAs substrate.

Semi-insulating substrate

In the MESFET shown in Figure 11.5, a reverse-bias gate-to-source voltage induces a space charge region under the metal gate, which modulates the channel

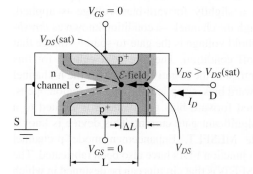

Figure 11.4 I Expanded view of the space charge region in the channel for $V_{DS} > V_{DS}$(sat).

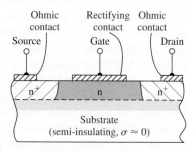

Figure 11.5 I Cross section of an n-channel MESFET with a semi-insulating substrate.

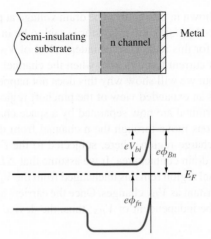

Figure 11.6 | Idealized energy-band diagram of the substrate-channel-metal in the n-channel MESFET.

conductance as in the case of the pn junction FET. The space charge region will eventually reach the substrate if the applied negative gate voltage is sufficiently large. This condition, again, is known as pinchoff. The device shown in this figure is also a depletion-mode device, since a gate voltage must be applied to pinch off the channel.

If we treat the semi-insulating substrate as an intrinsic material, then the energy-band diagram of the substrate-channel-metal structure is as shown in Figure 11.6 for the case of zero bias applied to the gate. Because there is a potential barrier between the channel and substrate and between the channel and metal, the majority-carrier electrons are confined to the channel region.

Consider, now, another type of MESFET in which the channel is pinched off even at $V_{GS} = 0$. Figure 11.7a shows this condition, in which the channel thickness is smaller than the zero-biased space charge width. To open a channel, the depletion region must be reduced: A forward-bias voltage must be applied to the gate–semiconductor junction. When a slightly forward-bias voltage is applied, the depletion region just extends through the channel—a condition known as *threshold,* shown in Figure 11.7b. The threshold voltage is the gate-to-source voltage that must be applied to create the pinchoff condition. The threshold voltage for this n-channel MESFET is positive, in contrast to the negative voltage for the n-channel depletion-mode device. If a larger forward bias is applied, the channel region opens, as shown in Figure 11.7c. The applied forward-bias gate voltage is limited to a few tenths of a volt before there is significant gate current. This device is known as an n-channel enhancement-mode MESFET. Enhancement-mode p-channel MESFETs and enhancement-mode pn junction FETs have also been fabricated. The advantage of enhancement-mode MESFETs is that circuits can be designed in which the voltage polarity on the gate and drain is the same. However, the output voltage swing will be quite small with these devices.

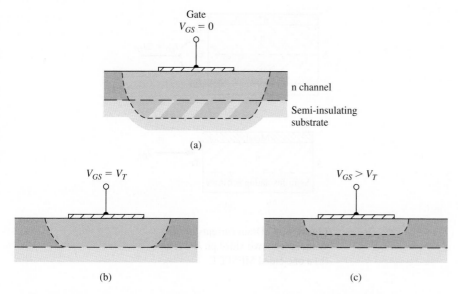

(a)

(b)   (c)

Figure 11.7 | Channel space charge region of an enhancement-mode MESFET for (a) $V_{GS} = 0$, (b) $V_{GS} = V_T$, and (c) $V_{GS} > V_T$.

11.1.3 Electrical Characteristics

To describe the basic electrical characteristics of the JFET, we will initially consider a uniformly doped depletion-mode pn JFET and then later discuss the enhancement-mode device. The pinchoff voltage and drain-to-source saturation voltage will be defined and expressions for these parameters are derived in terms of geometry and electrical properties. The ideal current–voltage relationship will be developed, and then the transconductance, or transistor gain.

Figure 11.8a shows a symmetrical, two-sided pn JFET and Figure 11.8b shows a MESFET with the semi-insulating substrate. One can derive the ideal dc current–voltage relationship for both devices by simply considering the two-sided device to be two JFETs in parallel. We will derive the I–V characteristics in terms of I_{D1} so that the drain current in the two-sided device will then be $I_{D2} = 2I_{D1}$. We will ignore any depletion region at the substrate of the one-sided device in the ideal case.

Internal Pinchoff Voltage, Pinchoff Voltage, and Saturation Voltage   Figure 11.9a shows a simplified one-sided n-channel pn JFET. The metallurgical channel thickness between the p^+ gate region and the substrate is a, and the induced depletion region width for the one-sided p^+n junction is h. Assume the drain-to-source voltage is zero. If we assume the abrupt depletion approximation, then the space charge width is given by

$$h = \left[\frac{2\epsilon_s (V_{bi} - V_{GS})}{e N_d} \right]^{1/2} \qquad (11.1)$$

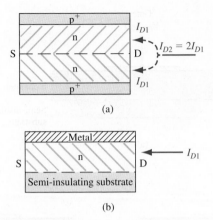

Figure 11.8 | Drain currents of (a) a symmetrical, two-sided pn JFET, and (b) a one-sided MESFET.

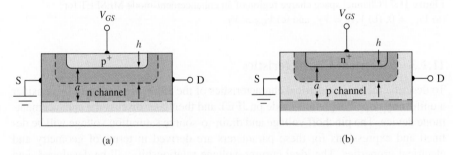

Figure 11.9 | Geometries of simplified (a) n-channel and (b) p-channel pn JFETs.

where V_{GS} is the gate-to-source voltage and V_{bi} is the built-in potential barrier. For a reverse-biased p^+n junction, V_{GS} must be a negative voltage.

At pinchoff, $h = a$ and the total potential across the p^+n junction is called the *internal pinchoff voltage*, denoted by V_{p0}. We now have

Internal pinchoff voltage

$$a = \left(\frac{2\epsilon_s V_{p0}}{eN_d} \right)^{1/2} \tag{11.2}$$

or

$$V_{p0} = \frac{ea^2 N_d}{2\epsilon_s} \tag{11.3}$$

Note that the internal pinchoff voltage is defined as a positive quantity.

The internal pinchoff voltage V_{p0} is not the gate-to-source voltage to achieve pinchoff. The gate-to-source voltage that must be applied to achieve pinchoff is described as the *pinchoff voltage* and is also variously called the *turn-off voltage* or *threshold voltage*. The pinchoff voltage is denoted by V_p and is defined from Equations (11.1) and (11.2) as

Pinchoff voltage

$$V_{bi} - V_p = V_{p0} \quad \text{or} \quad \boxed{V_p = V_{bi} - V_{p0}} \tag{11.4}$$

The gate-to-source voltage to achieve pinchoff in an n-channel depletion mode JFET is negative; thus, $V_{p0} > V_{bi}$.

EXAMPLE 11.1

OBJECTIVE

To calculate the internal pinchoff voltage and pinchoff voltage of an n-channel JFET.

Assume that the p^+n junction of a uniformly doped silicon n-channel JFET at $T = 300$ K has doping concentrations of $N_a = 10^{18}$ cm^{-3} and $N_d = 10^{16}$ cm^{-3}. Assume that the metallurgical channel thickness, a, is 0.75 μm $= 0.75 \times 10^{-4}$ cm.

■ **Solution**

The internal pinchoff voltage is given by Equation (11.3), so we have

$$V_{p0} = \frac{ea^2 N_d}{2\epsilon_s} = \frac{(1.6 \times 10^{-19})(0.75 \times 10^{-4})^2(10^{16})}{2(11.7)(8.85 \times 10^{-14})} = 4.35 \text{ V}$$

The built-in potential barrier is

$$V_{bi} = V_t \ln\left(\frac{N_a N_d}{n_i^2}\right) = (0.0259) \ln\left[\frac{(10^{18})(10^{16})}{(1.5 \times 10^{10})^2}\right] = 0.814 \text{ V}$$

The pinchoff voltage, from Equation (11.4), is then found as

$$V_p = V_{bi} - V_{p0} = 0.814 - 4.35 = -3.54 \text{ V}$$

■ **Comment**

The pinchoff voltage, or gate-to-source voltage, to achieve pinchoff for the n-channel depletion-mode device is a negative quantity, as we have said.

Exercise Problem

EX11.1 Repeat Example 11.1 for the case when the channel doping is $N_d = 2 \times 10^{16}$ cm^{-3} and the metallurgical channel thickness is $a = 0.50\,\mu$m. (Ans. $V_{p0} = 3.86$ V, $V_p = -3.03$ V)

The pinchoff voltage is the gate-to-source voltage that must be applied to turn the JFET off and so must be within the voltage range of the circuit design. The magnitude of the pinchoff voltage must also be less than the breakdown voltage of the junction.

Figure 11.9b shows a p-channel JFET with the same basic geometry as the n-channel JFET we considered. The induced depletion region for the one-sided n^+p junction is again denoted by h and is given by

$$h = \left[\frac{2\epsilon_s (V_{bi} + V_{GS})}{eN_a} \right]^{1/2} \tag{11.5}$$

For a reverse-biased n^+p junction, V_{GS} must be positive. The internal pinchoff voltage is again defined to be the total pn junction voltage to achieve pinchoff, so that when $h = a$, we have

$$a = \left(\frac{2\epsilon_s V_{p0}}{eN_a} \right)^{1/2} \tag{11.6}$$

or

$$\boxed{V_{p0} = \frac{ea^2 N_a}{2\epsilon_s}} \tag{11.7}$$

The internal pinchoff voltage for the p-channel device is also defined to be a positive quantity.

The pinchoff voltage is again defined as the gate-to-source voltage to achieve the pinchoff condition. For the p-channel depletion-mode device, we have, from Equation (11.5), at pinchoff

$$V_{bi} + V_p = V_{p0} \quad \text{or} \quad \boxed{V_p = V_{p0} - V_{bi}} \tag{11.8}$$

The pinchoff voltage for a p-channel depletion mode JFET is a positive quantity.

EXAMPLE 11.2

OBJECTIVE

Design the channel doping concentration and metallurgical channel thickness to achieve a given pinchoff voltage.

Consider a silicon p-channel pn JFET at $T = 300$ K. Assume that the gate doping concentration is $N_d = 10^{18}$ cm^{-3}. Determine the channel doping concentration and channel thickness so that the pinchoff voltage is $V_p = 2.25$ V.

■ **Solution**

There is not a unique solution to this design problem. We will pick a channel doping concentration of $N_a = 2 \times 10^{16}$ cm^{-3} and determine the channel thickness. The built-in potential barrier is

$$V_{bi} = V_t \ln\left(\frac{N_a N_d}{n_i^2}\right) = (0.0259)\ln\left[\frac{(2\times10^{16})(10^{18})}{(1.5\times10^{10})^2}\right] = 0.832 \text{ V}$$

From Equation (11.8), the internal pinchoff voltage must be

$$V_{p0} = V_{bi} + V_p = 0.832 + 2.25 = 3.08 \text{ V}$$

and from Equation (11.6), the channel thickness can be determined as

$$a = \left(\frac{2\epsilon_s V_{p0}}{eN_a}\right)^{1/2} = \left[\frac{2(11.7)(8.85\times10^{-14})(3.08)}{(1.6\times10^{-19})(2\times10^{16})}\right]^{1/2} = 0.446 \ \mu\text{m}$$

■ Comment
If the channel doping concentration chosen were larger, the required channel thickness would decrease; a very small value of channel thickness would be difficult to fabricate within reasonable tolerance limits.

Exercise Problem

EX11.2 The n^+p junction of a uniformly doped silicon p-channel JFET at $T = 300$ K has a doping concentration of $N_d = 5\times10^{18}$ cm^{-3} and $N_a = 5\times10^{15}$ cm^{-3}. The metallurgical channel thickness is $a = 0.50 \ \mu$m. Determine the internal pinchoff voltage and the pinchoff voltage of the JFET.

(Ans. $V_{p0} = 0.966$ V, $V_p = 0.128$ V)

We have determined the pinchoff voltage for both n-channel and p-channel JFETs when the drain-to-source voltage is zero. Now consider the case when both gate and drain voltages are applied. The depletion region width will vary with distance through the channel. Figure 11.10 shows the simplified geometry for an n-channel device. The depletion width h_1 at the source end is a function of V_{bi} and V_{GS} but is not

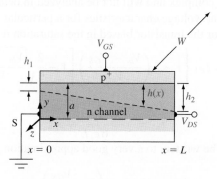

Figure 11.10 | Simplified geometry of an n-channel pn junction JFET showing various space charge widths.

a function of drain voltage. The depletion width at the drain terminal is given by

$$h_2 = \left[\frac{2\epsilon_s (V_{bi} + V_{DS} - V_{GS})}{eN_d} \right]^{1/2} \tag{11.9}$$

Again, we must keep in mind that V_{GS} is a negative quantity for the n-channel device.

Pinchoff at the drain terminal occurs when $h_2 = a$. At this point we reach what is known as the saturation condition; thus, we can write that $V_{DS} = V_{DS}(\text{sat})$. Then

$$a = \left[\frac{2\epsilon_s (V_{bi} + V_{DS}(\text{sat}) - V_{GS})}{eN_d} \right]^{1/2} \tag{11.10}$$

This can be rewritten as

$$V_{bi} + V_{DS}(\text{sat}) - V_{GS} = \frac{ea^2 N_d}{2\epsilon_s} = V_{p0} \tag{11.11}$$

or

$$\boxed{V_{DS}(\text{sat}) = V_{p0} - (V_{bi} - V_{GS})} \tag{11.12}$$

Equation (11.12) gives the drain-to-source voltage to cause pinchoff at the drain terminal. The drain-to-source saturation voltage decreases with increasing reverse-bias gate-to-source voltage. We can note that Equation (11.12) has no meaning if $|V_{GS}| > |V_p|$.

In a p-channel JFET, the voltage polarities are the reverse of those in the n-channel device. We can show that, in the p-channel JFET at saturation,

$$\boxed{V_{SD}(\text{sat}) = V_{p0} - (V_{bi} + V_{GS})} \tag{11.13}$$

where now the source is positive with respect to the drain.

Current–Voltage Relationship   The derivation of the ideal current–voltage relationship is somewhat complex and will not be analyzed in detail here. Figure 11.11 shows the ideal current–voltage characteristics for a particular device. The current–voltage relationship for the transistor biased in the saturation region is given by

$$I_{D1}(\text{sat}) = I_{P1} \left\{ 1 - 3 \left(\frac{V_{bi} - V_{GS}}{V_{p0}} \right) \left[1 - \frac{2}{3} \sqrt{\frac{V_{bi} - V_{GS}}{V_{p0}}} \right] \right\} \tag{11.14}$$

where

$$I_{p1} = \frac{\mu_n (eN_d)^2 W a^3}{6\epsilon_s L} \tag{11.15}$$

Approximate current–voltage relation   Equation (11.14) can be written, to a very good approximation, in the form

$$I_D(\text{sat}) = I_{DSS} \left(1 - \frac{V_{GS}}{V_p} \right)^2 \tag{11.16}$$

where I_{DSS} is the saturation current when $V_{GS} = 0$.

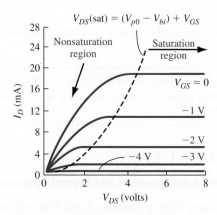

Figure 11.11 | Ideal current–voltage characteristics of a silicon n-channel JFET with $a = 1.5 \, \mu\text{m}$, $W/L = 170$, and $N_d = 2.5 \times 10^{15} \, \text{cm}^{-3}$.

Transconductance   The transconductance is the transistor gain of the JFET; it indicates the amount of control the gate voltage has on the drain current. The transconductance is defined as

$$g_m = \frac{\partial I_D}{\partial V_{GS}} \tag{11.17}$$

Using the previous equations for the current, we can write the expressions for the transconductance.

Cutoff Frequency   The cutoff frequency for the JFET, a figure of merit for the transistor, is defined to be the frequency at which the magnitude of the input gate current is equal in magnitude to the ideal output current of the intrinsic transistor. We find that

$$f_T = \frac{e \mu_n N_d a^2}{2\pi \epsilon_s L^2} \tag{11.18}$$

EXAMPLE 11.3

OBJECTIVE

To calculate the cutoff frequency of a GaAs JFET. Consider a GaAs JFET with the following parameters: $\mu_n = 8000 \, \text{cm}^2/\text{V-s}$, $N_d = 10^{16} \, \text{cm}^{-3}$, $a = 0.50 \, \mu\text{m}$, and $L = 2 \, \mu\text{m}$.

■ **Solution**

Substituting the parameters in Equation (11.18), we have

$$f_T = \frac{(1.6 \times 10^{-19})(8000)(10^{16})(0.5 \times 10^{-4})^2}{2\pi(13.1)(8.85 \times 10^{-14})(2 \times 10^{-4})^2}$$

or

$$f_T = 110 \, \text{GHz}$$

■ **Comment**

This example shows that GaAs JFETs can have large cutoff frequencies.

Exercise Problem

EX11.3 Repeat Example 11.3 for a silicon JFET with a mobility of $\mu_n = 1000$ cm^2/V-s. Assume all other parameters are the same as given in the example.

(Ans. 15.4 GHz)

11.2 | HETEROJUNCTIONS

Objective: Analyze the heterojunction and heterojunction devices.

Homojunction

Heterojunction

In the discussion of pn junctions in Chapters 5 and 9, we assumed that the semiconductor material was homogeneous throughout the entire structure. This type of junction is called a *homojunction*. When two different semiconductor materials are used to form a junction, the junction is called a *semiconductor heterojunction*.

As with many topics in this text, our goal is to provide an introduction to the basic concepts concerning the heterojunction. The complete analysis of heterojunction structures involves quantum mechanics and detailed calculations that are beyond the scope of this text.

11.2.1 The Heterojunction

Since the two materials used to form a heterojunction will have different energy bandgaps, the energy band will have a discontinuity at the junction interface. We may have an abrupt junction in which the semiconductor changes abruptly from a narrow-bandgap material to a wide-bandgap material. On the other hand, if we have a GaAs–Al$_x$Ga$_{1-x}$As system, for example, the value of x may continuously vary over a distance of several nanometers to form a graded heterojunction. Changing the value of x in the Al$_x$Ga$_{1-x}$As system enables us to engineer, or design, the bandgap energy.

To have a useful heterojunction, the lattice constants of the two materials must be well matched. The lattice match is important because any lattice mismatch can introduce dislocations resulting in interface states. For example, germanium and gallium arsenide have lattice constants matched to within approximately 0.13 percent. Germanium–gallium arsenide heterojunctions have been studied quite extensively. More recently, gallium arsenide–aluminum gallium arsenide (GaAs–AlGaAs) junctions have been investigated quite thoroughly, since the lattice constants of GaAs and the AlGaAs system vary by no more than 0.14 percent.

Energy-Band Diagrams In the formation of a heterojunction with a narrow-bandgap material and a wide-bandgap material, the alignment of the bandgap energies is important in determining the characteristics of the junction. Figure 11.12 shows three possible situations. In Figure 11.12a we see the case when the forbidden bandgap of the wide-gap material completely overlaps the bandgap of the narrow-gap material. This case, called *straddling,* applies to most heterojunctions. We will

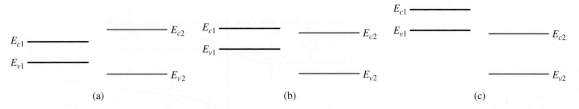

Figure 11.12 | Relation between narrow-bandgap and wide-bandgap energies: (a) straddling, (b) staggered, and (c) broken gap.

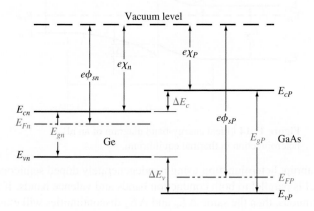

Figure 11.13 | Energy-band diagrams of a narrow-bandgap and a wide-bandgap material before contact.

consider only this case here. The other possibilities are called *staggered* and *broken gap* and are shown in Figure 11.12b and 11.12c.

There are four basic types of heterojunction. Those in which the dopant type changes at the junction are called *anisotype*. We can form nP or Np junctions, where the capital letter indicates the larger-bandgap material. Heterojunctions with the same dopant type on either side of the junction are called *isotype*. We can form nN and pP isotype heterojunctions.

Anisotype junction

Isotype junction

Figure 11.13 shows the energy-band diagrams of isolated n-type and P-type materials, with the vacuum level used as a reference. The electron affinity of the wide-bandgap material is less than that of the narrow-bandgap material. The difference between the two conduction band energies is denoted by ΔE_c, and the difference between the two valence band energies is denoted by ΔE_v. From Figure 11.13, we can see that

$$\Delta E_c = e(\chi_n - \chi_P) \tag{11.19a}$$

and

$$\Delta E_c + \Delta E_v = E_{gP} - E_{gn} = \Delta E_g \tag{11.19b}$$

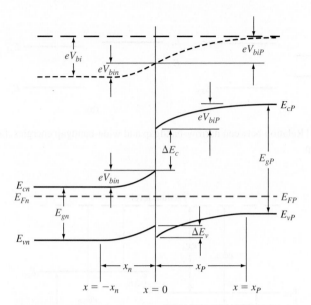

Figure 11.14 | Ideal energy-band diagram of an nP heterojunction in thermal equilibrium.

In the ideal abrupt heterojunction using nondegenerately doped semiconductors, the vacuum level is parallel to both conduction bands and valence bands. If the vacuum level is continuous, then the same ΔE_c and ΔE_v discontinuities will exist at the heterojunction interface. This ideal situation is known as the *electron affinity rule*. There is still some uncertainty about the applicability of this rule, but it provides a good starting point for the discussion of heterojunctions.

Electron affinity rule

Figure 11.14 shows a general ideal nP heterojunction in thermal equilibrium. In order for the Fermi levels in the two materials to become aligned, electrons from the narrow-gap n region and holes from the wide-gap P region must flow across the junction. As in the case of a homojunction, this flow of charge creates a space charge region in the vicinity of the metallurgical junction. The space charge width into the n-type region is denoted by x_n and the space charge width into the P-type region is denoted by x_P. The discontinuities in the conduction and valence bands and the change in the vacuum level are shown in the figure.

Two-Dimensional Electron Gas   Before we consider the electrostatics of the heterojunction, we will discuss a unique characteristic of an isotype junction. Figure 11.15 shows the energy-band diagram of an nN GaAs–AlGaAs heterojunction in thermal equilibrium. The AlGaAs can be moderately to heavily doped n type, while the GaAs can be more lightly doped or even intrinsic. As mentioned previously, to achieve thermal equilibrium, electrons from the wide-bandgap AlGaAs flow into the GaAs, forming an accumulation layer of electrons in the potential well adjacent to the interface. One basic quantum-mechanical result that we have found previously is that the energy of an electron contained in a potential well is quantized.

Two-dimensional electron gas

The phrase *two-dimensional electron gas* refers to the condition in which the

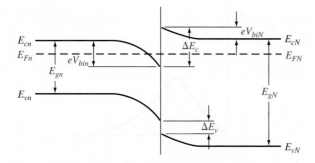

Figure 11.15 | Ideal energy-band diagram of an nN heterojunction in thermal equilibrium.

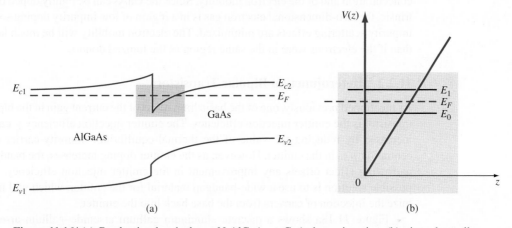

(a)   (b)

Figure 11.16 | (a) Conduction-band edge at N-AlGaAs, n-GaAs heterojunction; (b) triangular well approximation with discrete electron energies.

electrons have quantized energy levels in one spatial direction (perpendicular to the interface), but are free to move in the other two spatial directions.

The potential function near the interface can be approximated by a triangular potential well. Figure 11.16a shows the conduction band edges near the abrupt junction interface and Figure 11.16b shows the approximation of the triangular potential well. We can write

$$V(x) = e\mathcal{E}z \qquad z > 0 \qquad\qquad (11.20a)$$

$$V(z) = \infty \qquad z < 0 \qquad\qquad (11.20b)$$

Schrödinger's wave equation can be solved using this potential function. The quantized energy levels are shown in Figure 11.16b. Higher energy levels are usually not considered.

The qualitative distribution of electrons in the potential well is shown in Figure 11.17. A current parallel to the interface will be a function of this electron

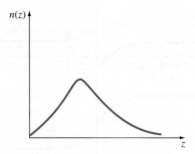

Figure 11.17 | Electron density in
triangular potential well.

concentration and of the electron mobility. Since the GaAs can be lightly doped or intrinsic, the two-dimensional electron gas is in a region of low impurity doping so that
impurity scattering effects are minimized. The electron mobility will be much larger
than if the electrons were in the same region as the ionized donors.

11.2.2   Heterojunction Bipolar Transistors

As mentioned previously, one of the basic limitations of the current gain in the bipolar
transistor is the emitter injection efficiency. The emitter injection efficiency γ can be
increased by reducing the value of the thermal-equilibrium minority-carrier concentration p_{E0} in the emitter. However, as the emitter doping increases, the bandgap-
narrowing effect offsets any improvement in the emitter injection efficiency. One
possible solution is to use a wide-bandgap material for the emitter, which will minimize the injection of carriers from the base back into the emitter.

Figure 11.18a shows a discrete aluminum gallium arsenide–gallium arsenide
heterojunction bipolar transistor, and Figure 11.18b shows the band diagram of the
n-AlGaAs emitter to p-GaAs base junction. The large potential barrier V_h limits the
number of holes that will be injected back from the base into the emitter.

The intrinsic carrier concentration is a function of bandgap energy as

$$n_i^2 \propto \exp\left(\frac{-E_g}{kT}\right)$$

For a given emitter doping, the number of minority-carrier holes injected into the
emitter is reduced by a factor of

$$\exp\left(\frac{\Delta E_g}{kT}\right)$$

in changing from a narrow- to wide-bandgap emitter. If $\Delta E_g = 0.30$ eV, for example,
n_i^2 would be reduced by approximately 10^5 at $T = 300$ K. The drastic reduction in n_i^2
for the wide-bandgap emitter means that the requirements of a very high emitter
doping can be relaxed and a high emitter injection efficiency can still be obtained. A
lower emitter doping reduces the bandgap-narrowing effect.

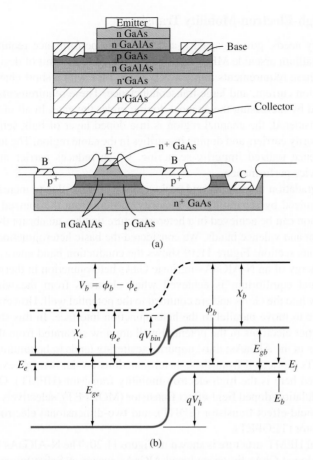

Figure 11.18 | (a) Cross section of AlGaAs–GaAs hetero-
junction bipolar transistor showing a discrete and integrated
structure. (b) Energy-band diagram of the n AlGaAs emitter
and p GaAs base junction.
(From Tiwari et al. [26].)

The heterojunction GaAs bipolar transistor has the potential of being a very high
frequency device. A lower emitter doping in the wide-bandgap emitter leads to a
smaller junction capacitance, increasing the speed of the device. Also, for the GaAs
npn device, the minority carriers in the base are electrons with a high mobility. The
electron mobility in GaAs is approximately five times that in silicon; thus, the base
transit time in the GaAs base is very short. Experimental AlGaAs–GaAs heterojunction transistors with base widths on the order of 0.1 μm have shown cutoff frequencies on the order of 40 GHz.

One disadvantage of GaAs is the low minority-carrier lifetime. The small
lifetime is not a factor in the base of a narrow-base device, but results in a larger B-E
recombination current, which decreases the recombination factor and reduces the
current gain. A current gain of 150 has been reported.

11.2.3 High-Electron-Mobility Transistor

As frequency needs, power capacity, and low noise performance requirements increase, the gallium arsenide MESFET is being pushed to its limit of design and performance. These requirements imply a very small FET with a short channel length, large saturation current, and large transconductance. These requirements are generally achieved by increasing the channel doping under the gate. In all of the devices we have considered, the channel region is in a doped layer of bulk semiconductor with the majority carriers and doping impurities in the same region. The majority carriers experience ionized impurity scattering, which reduces carrier mobility and degrades device performance.

The degradation in mobility and peak velocity in GaAs due to increased doping can be minimized by separating the majority carriers from the ionized impurities. This separation can be achieved in a heterostructure that has an abrupt discontinuity in conduction and valence bands. We considered the basic heterojunction properties in the previous section. Figure 11.19 shows the conduction-band energy relative to the Fermi energy of an N-AlGaAs-intrinsic GaAs heterojunction in thermal equilibrium. Thermal equilibrium is achieved when electrons from the wide-bandgap AlGaAs flow into the GaAs and are confined to the potential well. However, the electrons are free to move parallel to the heterojunction interface. In this structure, the majority-carrier electrons in the potential well are now separated from the impurity dopant atoms in the AlGaAs; thus, impurity scattering tends to be minimized.

The FETs fabricated from these heterojunctions are known by several names. The term used here is the **h**igh-**e**lectron-**m**obility **t**ransistor (HEMT). Other names include **mo**dulation-**d**oped **f**ield-**e**ffect **t**ransistor (MODFET), **s**electively **d**oped **h**eterojunction field-**e**ffect **t**ransistor (SDHT), and **t**wo-dimensional **e**lectron **g**as **f**ield-**e**ffect **t**ransistor (TEGFET).

HEMT

MODFET

A typical HEMT structure is shown in Figure 11.20. The N-AlGaAs is separated from the undoped GaAs by an undoped AlGaAs spacer. A Schottky contact to the N-AlGaAs forms the gate of the transistor.

The density of electrons in the two-dimensional electron gas layer in the potential well can be controlled by the gate voltage. The electric field of the Schottky gate

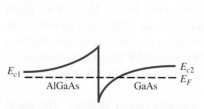

Figure 11.19 | Conduction-band edges for N AlGaAs–intrinsic GaAs abrupt heterojunction.

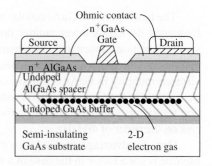

Figure 11.20 | A "normal" AlGaAs–GaAs HEMT.

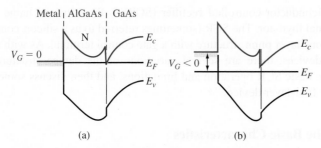

Figure 11.21 | Energy-band diagram of a normal HEMT (a) with zero gate bias and (b) with a negative gate bias.

depletes the two-dimensional electron gas layer in the potential well when a sufficiently large negative voltage is applied to the gate. Figure 11.21 shows the energy-band diagrams of the metal–AlGaAs–GaAs structure under zero bias and with a reverse bias applied to the gate. With zero bias, the conduction-band edge in the GaAs is below the Fermi level, implying a large density of the two-dimensional electron gas. With a negative voltage applied to the gate, the conduction-band edge in the GaAs is above the Fermi level, implying that the density of the two-dimensional electron gas is very small and the current in an FET would be essentially zero.

The Schottky barrier depletes the AlGaAs layer from the surface, and the heterojunction depletes the AlGaAs layer from the heterojunction interface. Ideally the device should be designed so that the two depletion regions just overlap to prevent electron conduction through the AlGaAs layer. For depletion-mode devices, the depletion layer from the Schottky gate should extend only to the heterojunction depletion layer. For enhancement-mode devices, the thickness of the doped AlGaAs layer is smaller and the Schottky gate built-in potential barrier will completely deplete the AlGaAs layer and the two-dimensional electron gas channel. A positive voltage applied to the gate of the enhancement-mode device will turn on the device.

11.3 | THE THYRISTOR

Objective: Analyze the thyristor—a four-layer semiconductor structure.

One of the important applications of electronic devices is in switching between an off or blocking state to an on or low-impedance state. Thyristor is the name given to a general class of semiconductor pnpn switching devices that exhibit bistable regenerative switching characteristics. We have considered the field-effect and bipolar transistors, which can be switched on with the application of a base drive or a gate voltage. The base drive or gate voltage must be applied as long as the transistor is to remain on. There are a number of applications in which it is useful to have a device remain in a blocking state until switched to the low-impedance state by a control signal, which then does not necessarily have to remain on. These devices are efficient in switching large currents at low frequencies, such as industrial control circuits operating at 60 Hz.

A **s**emiconductor-**c**ontrolled **r**ectifier (SCR) is the common name given to a three-terminal thyristor. The SCR (sometimes referred to as a silicon-controlled rectifier) is a four-layer pnpn structure with a gate control terminal. As with most semiconductor devices, there are several variations of the device structure. We will consider the basic SCR operation and limitations, and then discuss some variations of the basic four-layer device.

11.3.1 The Basic Characteristics

The four-layer pnpn structure is shown in Figure 11.22a. The upper p region is called the anode and the lower n region is called the cathode. If a positive voltage is applied to the anode, the device is said to be forward biased. However, the junction J_2 is reverse biased so that only a very small current exists. If a negative voltage is applied to the anode, then junctions J_1 and J_3 are reverse biased—again only a very small current will exist. Figure 11.22b shows the I–V characteristics for these conditions. The voltage V_p is the breakdown voltage of the J_2 junction. For properly designed devices, the blocking voltage can be several thousand volts.

To consider the characteristics of the device as it goes into its conducting state, we can model the structure as coupled npn and pnp bipolar transistors. Figure 11.23a shows how we can split the four-layer structure and Figure 11.23b shows the two-transistor equivalent circuit with the associated currents. Since the base of the pnp device is the same as the collector of the npn transistor, the base current I_{B1} must in fact be the same as the collector current I_{C2}. Similarly, since the collector of the pnp transistor is the same as the base of the npn device, the collector current I_{C1} must be the same as the base current I_{B2}. In this bias configuration, the B-C of the pnp and the B-C of the npn devices are reverse biased while the B-E junctions are both forward biased. The parameters α_1 and α_2 are the common-base current gains of the pnp and npn transistors, respectively.

We can write

$$I_{C1} = \alpha_1 I_A + I_{C01} = I_{B2} \tag{11.21a}$$

and

$$I_{C2} = \alpha_2 I_K + I_{C02} = I_{B1} \tag{11.21b}$$

where I_{C01} and I_{C02} are the reverse B-C junction saturation currents in the two devices. In this particular configuration, $I_A = I_K$ and $I_{C1} + I_{C2} = I_A$. If we add Equation (11.21a) and (11.21b), we obtain

$$I_{C1} + I_{C2} = I_A = (\alpha_1 + \alpha_2)I_A + I_{C01} + I_{C02} \tag{11.22}$$

The anode current I_A, from Equation (11.22), can be found as

$$I_A = \frac{I_{C01} + I_{C02}}{1 - (\alpha_1 + \alpha_2)} \tag{11.23}$$

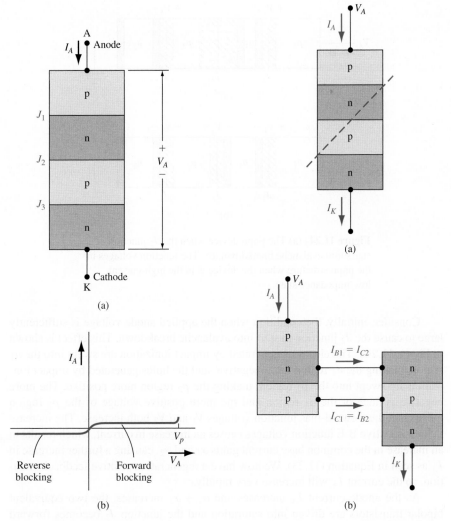

Figure 11.22 | (a) The basic four-layer pnpn structure. (b) The initial current–voltage characteristic of the pnpn device.

Figure 11.23 | (a) The splitting of the basic pnpn structure. (b) Two-transistor equivalent circuit of the four-layer pnpn device.

As long as $(\alpha_1 + \alpha_2)$ is much smaller than unity, the anode current is small, as we indicated in Figure 11.22b.

The common-base current gains, α_1 and α_2, are very strong functions of collector current, as we discussed in Chapter 10. For small values of V_A, the collector current in each device is just the reverse saturation current, which is very small. The small collector current implies that both α_1 and α_2 are much smaller than unity. The four-layer structure maintains this blocking condition until the junction J_2 starts into breakdown or until a current is induced in the J_2 junction by some external means.

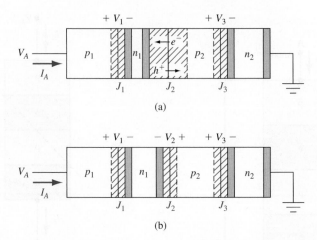

Figure 11.24 | (a) The pnpn device when the J_2 junction starts into avalanche breakdown. (b) The junction voltages in the pnpn structure when the device is in the high-current, low-impedance state.

Consider, initially, the condition when the applied anode voltage is sufficiently large to cause the J_2 junction to start into avalanche breakdown. This effect is shown in Figure 11.24a. The electrons generated by impact ionization are swept into the n_1 region, making the n_1 region more negative, and the holes generated by impact ionization are swept into the p_2 region, making the p_2 region more positive. The more negative voltage of the n_1 region and the more positive voltage of the p_2 region means that the forward-bias junction voltages V_1 and V_3 both increase. The increase in the respective B-E junction voltages causes an increase in current, which results in an increase in the common base current gains α_1 and α_2, causing a further increase in I_A as seen in Equation (11.23). We now have a regenerative positive feedback situation, so the current I_A will increase very rapidly.

As the anode current I_A increases and $\alpha_1 + \alpha_2$ increases, the two equivalent bipolar transistors are driven into saturation and the junction J_2 becomes forward biased. The total voltage across the device decreases and is approximately equal to one diode drop as shown in Figure 11.24b. The current in the device is limited by the external circuit. If the current is allowed to increase, ohmic losses may become important so that the voltage drop across the device may increase slightly with current. The I_A versus V_A characteristic is shown in Figure 11.25.

11.3.2 Triggering the SCR

In Section 11.3.1, we considered the case when the four-layer pnpn device is turned on by the avalanche breakdown process in the center junction. The turn-on condition can also be initiated by other means. Figure 11.26a shows a three-terminal SCR in which the third terminal is the gate control. We can determine the effect of the gate current by reconsidering Equation (11.21a) and (11.21b).

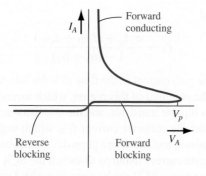

Figure 11.25 | The current–voltage characteristics of the pnpn device.

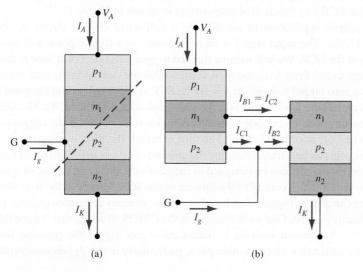

| (a) | (b) |

Figure 11.26 | (a) The three-terminal SCR. (b) The two-transistor equivalent circuit of the three-terminal SCR.

Figure 11.26b again shows the two-transistor equivalent circuit including the gate current. We can write

$$I_{C1} = \alpha_1 I_A + I_{C01} \tag{11.24a}$$

and

$$I_{C2} = \alpha_2 I_K + I_{C02} \tag{11.24b}$$

We now have $I_K = I_A + I_g$ and we can still write $I_{C1} + I_{C2} = I_A$. Adding Equation (11.24a) and (11.24b), we find that

$$I_{C1} + I_{C2} = I_A = (\alpha_1 + \alpha_2)I_A + \alpha_2 I_g + I_{C01} + I_{C02} \tag{11.25}$$

Solving for I_A, we find

$$I_A = \frac{\alpha_2 I_g + (I_{C01} + I_{C02})}{1 - (\alpha_1 + \alpha_2)} \qquad (11.26)$$

We can think of the gate current as the flow of holes into the p_2 region. The additional holes increase the potential of this region, which increases the forward-biased B-E voltage of the npn bipolar transistor, and the transistor action. The transistor action of the npn increases the collector current I_{C2}, which starts the transistor action of the pnp bipolar transistor, and the entire pnpn device can be turned on into its low-impedance state. The gate current required to switch the SCR into its on condition is typically in the milliamp range. SCR can be turned on with a small gate current, which can control hundreds of amperes of anode current. The gate current can be turned off and the SCR will remain in its conducting state. The gate loses control of the device once the SCR is triggered into its conducting state. The current–voltage characteristics of the SCR as a function of gate current is shown in Figure 11.27.

A simple application of an SCR in a half-wave control circuit is shown in Figure 11.28a. The input signal is an ac voltage and a trigger pulse will control the turn-on of the SCR. We will assume that the trigger pulse occurs at time t_1 during the ac voltage cycle. Prior to t_1, the SCR is off so that the current in the load is zero, thus there is a zero output voltage. At $t = t_1$, the SCR is triggered on and the input voltage appears across the load (neglecting the voltage drop across the SCR). The SCR turns off when the anode-to-cathode voltage becomes zero even though the trigger pulse has been turned off prior to this time. The time at which the SCR is triggered during the voltage cycle can be varied, changing the amount of power delivered to the load. Full-wave control circuits can be designed to increase efficiency and degree of control.

The gate enables control of the turn-on of the SCR. However, the four-layer pnpn structure can also be triggered on by other means. In many integrated circuits, parasitic pnpn structures exist. One such example is the CMOS structure that we considered in Chapter 6. A transient ionizing radiation pulse can trigger the parasitic four-layer device by generating electron–hole pairs, particularly in the J_2 junction, producing a

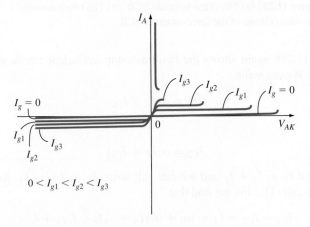

Figure 11.27 | Current–voltage characteristics of an SCR.

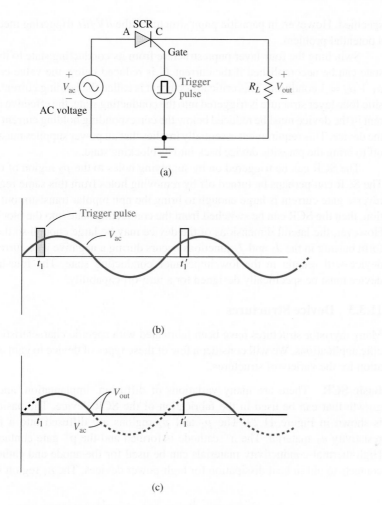

Figure 11.28 | (a) Simple SCR circuit. (b) Input ac voltage
signal and trigger pulse. (c) Output voltage versus time.

photocurrent. The photocurrent is equivalent to a gate current in an SCR so the parasitic
device can be switched into its conducting state. Again, once the device is switched on,
it will remain in its conducting state even when the radiation ceases. An optical signal
can also trigger the device in the same manner by generating electron–hole pairs.

Another triggering mechanism in the pnpn device is by dV/dt triggering. If the
forward-bias anode voltage is applied rapidly, the voltage across the J_2 junction will
also change quickly. This changing reverse-biased J_2 junction voltage means that the
space charge region width is increasing; thus, electrons are being removed from
the n_1 side of the junction and holes are being removed from the p_2 side of the junction. If dV/dt is large, the rate of removal of these carriers is rapid, which leads to a
large transient current that is equivalent to a gate current and can trigger the device
into a low impedance conducting state. In SCR devices, a dV/dt rating is usually

specified. However, in parasitic pnpn structures, the dV/dt triggering mechanism is a potential problem.

Switching the four-layer pnpn structure from its conducting state to its blocking state can be accomplished if the current I_A is reduced below the value creating the $\alpha_1 + \alpha_2 = 1$ condition. This critical I_A current is called the holding current. If a parasitic four-layer structure is triggered into the conducting state, the effective anode current in the device must be reduced below the corresponding holding current to turn off the device. This requirement essentially implies that all power supplies must be turned off to bring the parasitic device back into its blocking state.

The SCR can be triggered on by supplying holes to the p_2 region of the device. The SCR can perhaps be turned off by removing holes from this same region. If the reverse gate current is large enough to bring the npn bipolar transistor out of saturation, then the SCR can be switched from the conducting state into the blocking state. However, the lateral dimensions of the device may be large enough so that nonuniform biasing in the J_2 and J_3 junctions occurs during a negative gate current and the device will remain in the low impedance conducting state. The four-layer pnpn device must be specifically designed for a turn-off capability.

11.3.3   Device Structures

Many thyristor structures have been fabricated with specific characteristics for specific applications. We will consider a few of these types of device to gain an appreciation for the variety of structures.

Basic SCR   There are many variations of diffusion, implantation, and epitaxial growth that can be used in the fabrication of the SCR device. The basic structure is shown in Figure 11.29. The p_1 and p_2 regions are diffused into a fairly high resistivity n_1 material. The n$^+$ cathode is formed and the p$^+$ gate contact is made. High-thermal-conductivity materials can be used for the anode and cathode ohmic contacts to aid in heat dissipation for high-power devices. The n_1 region width may

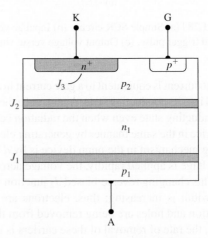

Figure 11.29 | The basic SCR device structure.

be on the order of 250 μm to support very large reverse-bias voltages across the J_2 junction. The p_1 and p_2 regions may be on the order of 75 μm wide, while the n$^+$ and p$^+$ regions are normally quite thin.

Bilateral Thyristor   Since thyristors are often used in ac power applications, it may be useful to have a device that switches symmetrically in the positive and negative cycles of the ac voltage. There are a number of such devices, but the basic concept is to connect two conventional thyristors in antiparallel as shown in Figure 11.30a. The integration of this concept into a single device is shown in Figure 11.30b. Symmetrical n regions can be diffused into a pnp structure. Figure 11.30c shows the

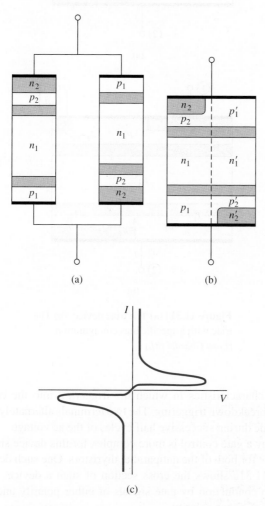

(a)   (b)

(c)

Figure 11.30 | (a) The antiparallel connection of two thyristors to form a bilateral device. (b) The bilateral thyristor as an integrated device. (c) The current–voltage characteristics of the bilateral thyristor.
(From Ghandhi [8].)

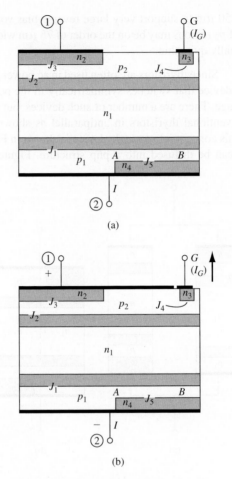

Figure 11.31 | (a) The triac device. (b) The triac with a specific bias configuration. *(From Ghandhi [8].)*

current–voltage characteristics in which the triggering into the conduction mode would be due to breakdown triggering. The two terminals alternately share the role of anode and cathode during successive half cycles of the ac voltage.

Triggering by a gate control is more complex for this device since a single gate region must serve for both of the antiparallel thyristors. One such device is known as a *triac*. Figure 11.31a shows the cross section of such a device. This device can be triggered into conduction by gate signals of either polarity and with anode-to-cathode voltages of either polarity.

One particular gate control situation is shown in Figure 11.31b. Terminal 1 is positive with respect to terminal 2, and a negative gate voltage is applied with respect to terminal 1, so the gate current is negative. This polarity arrangement induces the

Triac

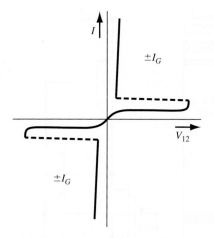

Figure 11.32 | The current–voltage characteristics of the triac.

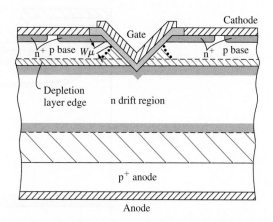

Figure 11.33 | The V groove MOS gated thyristor. *(From Baliga [2].)*

current I_1 and the junction J_4 becomes forward biased. Electrons are injected from n_3, diffuse across p_2, and are collected in the n_1 region. In this case $n_3 p_2 n_1$ behaves like a saturated transistor. The collected electrons in n_1 lower the potential of n_1 with respect to p_2. The current across the $p_2 n_1$ junction increases, which can trigger the $p_2 n_1 p_1 n_4$ thyristor into its conducting mode.

We can show that the other combinations of gate, anode, and cathode voltages will also trigger the triac into conduction. Figure 11.32 shows the terminal characteristics.

MOS-Gated Thyristor The operation of an MOS-gated thyristor is based on controlling the gain of the npn bipolar transistor. Figure 11.33 shows a V-groove MOS-gated thyristor. The MOS gate structure must extend into the n-drift region. If the gate voltage is zero, the depletion edge in the p base remains essentially flat and parallel to the junction J_2; the gain of the npn transistor is low. This effect is shown in the figure by the dashed line. When a positive gate voltage is applied, the surface of the p base becomes depleted—the depletion region in the p base adjacent to the gate is shown by the dotted line. The undepleted base width W_μ of the npn bipolar device narrows and the gain of the device increases.

At a gate voltage approximately equal to the threshold voltage, electrons from the n^+ emitter are injected through the depletion region into the n-drift region. The potential of the n-drift region is lowered, which further forward biases the p^+ anode to n-drift junction voltage, and the regenerative process is initiated. The gate voltage required to initiate turn-on is approximately the threshold voltage of the MOS device. One advantage of this device is that the input impedance to the control terminal is very high; relatively large currents can be switched with very small capacity coupled gate currents.

MOS Turn-Off Thyristor The MOS turn-off thyristor can both turn on and turn off the anode current by applying a signal to a MOS gate terminal. The basic device structure is shown in Figure 11.34. By applying a positive gate voltage, the n^+pn

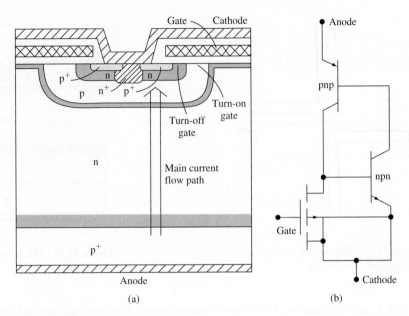

Figure 11.34 | (a) The MOS turn-off thyristor. (b) Equivalent circuit for the MOS turn-off thyristor.
(From Baliga [2].)

bipolar transistor can be turned on as just discussed. Once the thyristor is turned on, the device can be turned off by applying a negative gate voltage: the negative gate voltage turns on the p-channel MOS transistor, which effectively short circuits the B-E junction of the n^+pn bipolar transistor. Holes that now enter the p-base have an alternative path to the cathode. If the resistance of the p-channel MOSFET becomes low enough, all current will be diverted away from the n^+p emitter and the n^+pn device will effectively be turned off.

11.4 | ADDITIONAL MOSFET CONCEPTS

Objective: Analyze additional MOSFET concepts, based on parasitic bipolar and four-layered structures.

There are two additional MOSFET concepts that we need to consider. The first concept involves a four-layer parasitic structure in the basic CMOS inverter. We considered the four-layer semiconductor structure in this chapter, so we are now in a position to consider latch-up. The second concept that we need to consider is breakdown. We considered the basic avalanche breakdown process in Chapter 9. However, another breakdown mechanism involves a parasitic bipolar transistor structure in the basic MOSFET device.

11.4.1 Latch-Up

One major problem in CMOS circuits has been *latch-up*. Latch-up refers to a high-current, low-voltage condition that may occur in a four-layer pnpn structure.

Figure 11.35a shows the circuit of a CMOS inverter and Figure 11.35b shows a simplified integrated circuit layout of the inverter circuit. In the CMOS layout, the p^+ source to n substrate to p well to n^+ source forms such a four-layer structure.

The equivalent circuit of this four-layer structure is shown in Figure 11.36. The silicon-controlled rectifier action involves the interaction of the parasitic pnp and npn transistors. The npn transistor corresponds to the vertical n^+ source to p well to n substrate structure and the pnp transistor corresponds to the lateral p well to n substrate

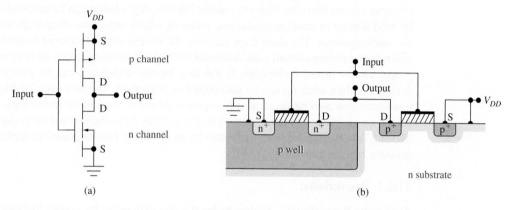

(a)   (b)

Figure 11.35 | (a) CMOS inverter circuit. (b) Simplified integrated circuit cross section of CMOS inverter.

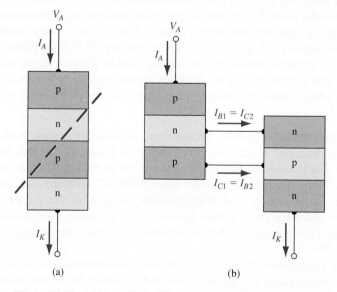

(a)   (b)

Figure 11.36 | (a) The splitting of the basic pnpn structure. (b) The two-transistor equivalent circuit of the four-layered pnpn device.

Latch-up

to p^+ source structure. Under normal CMOS operation, both parasitic bipolar transistors are cut off. However, under certain conditions, avalanche breakdown may occur in the p well to n substrate junction, driving both bipolar transistors into saturation. This high-current, low-voltage condition—latch-up—can sustain itself by positive feedback. The condition can prevent the CMOS circuit from operating and can also cause permanent damage and burn-out of the circuit.

Latch-up can be prevented if the product $\beta_n \beta_p$ is less than unity at all times, where β_n and β_p are the common-emitter current gains of the npn and pnp parasitic bipolar transistors, respectively. One method of preventing latch-up is to "kill" the minority-carrier lifetime. Minority-carrier lifetime degradation can be accomplished by gold doping or neutron irradiation, either of which introduces deep traps within the semiconductor. The deep traps increase the excess minority-carrier recombination rate and reduce current gain. A second method of preventing latch-up is by using proper circuit layout techniques. If the two bipolar transistors can be effectively decoupled, then latch-up can be minimized or prevented. The two parasitic bipolar transistors can also be decoupled by using a different fabrication technology. The silicon-on-insulator technology, for example, enables the n-channel and the p-channel MOSFETs to be isolated from each other by an insulator. This isolation decouples the parasitic bipolar transistors.

11.4.2 Breakdown

Avalanche Breakdown   Avalanche breakdown may occur by impact ionization in the space charge region near the drain terminal. We considered avalanche breakdown in pn junctions in Chapter 9. In an ideal planar one-sided pn junction, breakdown is a function primarily of the doping concentration in the low-doped region of the junction. For the MOSFET, the low-doped region corresponds to the semiconductor substrate. If a p-type substrate doping is $N_a = 3 \times 10^{16} \, \text{cm}^{-3}$, for example, the pn junction breakdown voltage would be approximately 25 V for a planar junction. However, the n^+ drain contact may be a fairly shallow diffused region with a large curvature. The electric field in the depletion region tends to be concentrated at the curvature, which lowers the breakdown voltage. This curvature effect is shown in Figure 11.37.

Near Avalanche and Snapback Breakdown   Another breakdown mechanism results in the S-shaped breakdown curve shown in Figure 11.38. This breakdown process is due to second-order effects and can be explained with the aid of Figure 11.39. The n-channel enhancement mode MOSFET geometry in Figure 11.39a shows the n-type source and drain contacts along with the p-type substrate. The source and body are at ground potential. The n(source)–p(substrate)–n(drain) structure also forms a parasitic bipolar transistor. The equivalent circuit is shown in Figure 11.39b.

Figure 11.40a shows the device when avalanche breakdown is just beginning in the space charge region near the drain. We tend to think of the avalanche breakdown suddenly occurring at a particular voltage. However, avalanche breakdown is a gradual process that starts at low current levels and for electric fields somewhat below the

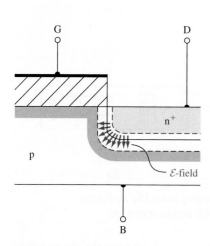

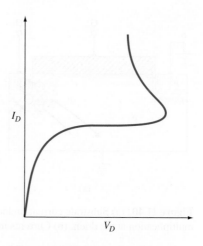

Figure 11.37 | Curvature effect on the electric field in the drain junction.

Figure 11.38 | Current–voltage characteristic showing the snapback breakdown effect.

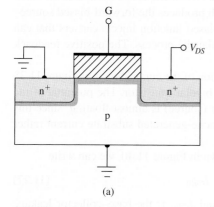

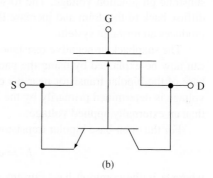

(a)

(b)

Figure 11.39 | (a) Cross section of the n-channel MOSFET. (b) Equivalent circuit including the parasitic bipolar transistor.

breakdown field. The electrons generated by the avalanche process flow into the drain and contribute to the drain current. The avalanche-generated holes generally flow through the substrate to the body terminal. Since the substrate has a nonzero resistance, a voltage drop is produced, as shown. This potential difference drives the source-to-substrate pn junction into forward bias near the source terminal. The source is heavily doped n-type; thus, a large number of electrons can be injected from the source contact into the substrate under forward bias. This process will become severe as the voltage drop in the substrate approaches 0.6 to 0.7 V. A fraction of the injected electrons will diffuse across the parasitic base region into the reverse-biased drain space charge region where they also add to the drain current.

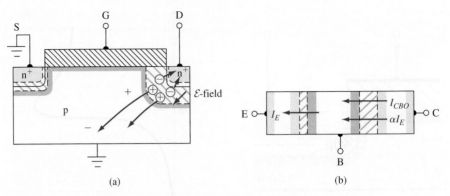

Figure 11.40 | (a) Substrate current–induced voltage drop caused by avalanche multiplication at the drain. (b) Currents in the parasitic bipolar transistor.

The avalanche breakdown process is a function of not only the electric field but the number of carriers involved. The rate of avalanche breakdown increases as the number of carriers in the drain space charge region increases. We now have a regenerative or positive feedback mechanism. Avalanche breakdown near the drain terminal produces the substrate current, which produces the forward-biased source–substrate pn junction voltage. The forward-biased junction injects carriers that can diffuse back to the drain and increase the avalanche process. The positive feedback produces an unstable system.

The snapback or negative resistance portion of the curve shown in Figure 11.38 can now be explained by using the parasitic bipolar transistor. The potential of the base of the bipolar transistor near the emitter (source) is almost floating, since this voltage is determined primarily by the avalanche-generated substrate current rather than an externally applied voltage.

For the open-base bipolar transistor shown in Figure 11.40, we can write

$$I_C = \alpha I_E + I_{CB0} \tag{11.27}$$

where α is the common base current gain and I_{CB0} is the base–collector leakage current. For an open base, $I_C = I_E$, so Equation (11.27) becomes

$$I_C = \alpha I_C + I_{CB0} \tag{11.28}$$

At breakdown, the current in the B-C junction is multiplied by the multiplication factor M, so we have

$$I_C = M(\alpha I_C + I_{CB0}) \tag{11.29}$$

Solving for I_C we obtain

$$I_C = \frac{M I_{CB0}}{1 - \alpha M} \tag{11.30}$$

Breakdown is defined as the condition that produces $I_C \to \infty$. For a single reverse-biased pn junction, $M \to \infty$ at breakdown. However, from Equation (11.30), breakdown is now defined to be the condition when $\alpha M \rightarrow 1$ or, for the open-base condition, breakdown occurs when $M \rightarrow 1/\alpha$, which is a much lower multiplication factor than for the simple pn junction.

An empirical relation for the multiplication factor is usually written as

$$M = \frac{1}{1 - (V_{CE}/V_{BD})^m} \tag{11.31}$$

where m is an empirical constant in the range of 3 to 6 and V_{BD} is the junction breakdown voltage.

The common base current gain factor α is a strong function of collector current for small values of collector current. This effect was discussed in Chapter 10 on bipolar transistors. At low currents, the recombination current in the B-E junction is a significant fraction of the total current so that the common-base current gain is small. As the collector current increases, the value of α increases. As avalanche breakdown begins and I_C is small, particular values of M and V_{CE} are required to produce the condition of $\alpha M = 1$. As the collector current increases, α increases; therefore, smaller values of M and V_{CE} are required to produce the avalanche breakdown condition. The snapback, or negative resistance, breakdown characteristic is then produced.

Only a fraction of the injected electrons from the forward-biased source–substrate junction are collected by the drain terminal. A more exact calculation of the snapback characteristic would necessarily involve taking into account this fraction; thus, the simple model would need to be modified. However, the preceding discussion qualitatively describes the snapback effect. The snapback effect can be minimized by using a heavily doped substrate that will prevent any significant voltage drop from being developed. A thin epitaxial p-type layer with the proper doping concentration to produce the required threshold voltage can be grown on a heavily doped substrate.

11.5 | MICROELECTROMECHANICAL SYSTEMS (MEMS)

Objective: Briefly discuss a few microelectromechanical systems (MEMS)

An aspect of microelectronics that is becoming more prevalent and important is the area of microelectromechanical systems. Very small mechanical devices can be fabricated using techniques similar to those used in fabricating integrated circuits. The mechanical devices are then controlled by electrical signals or produce electrical signals. Applications include pressure sensors, accelerometers, and gyros. MEMS is also being applied to medical and biochemical problems. We will briefly consider only a few applications in this section to obtain a flavor of this area of research.

11.5.1 Accelerometers

Micromachined accelerometers are being incorporated, for example, in automobiles in airbag deployment. The heart of one such device is an interdigitated structure of polysilicon fingers schematically shown in Figure 11.41. Two sets of fingers are fixed

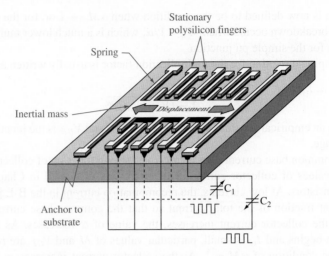

Figure 11.41 | An example of an analog accelerometer. The interdigitated center structure on the die is suspended above the substrate. *(From Madou [11])*

to the substrate while a third set of fingers is suspended approximately 1 μm above the surface. The suspended interdigitated structure in the center of the die is the sensitive element. Deceleration in the axis of sensitivity exerts a force on the substrate that displaces the interdigitated capacitor plates, causing a change in capacitance. The change in the finger movement is only a few nanometers, which means that the change in capacitance is very small. This small change in capacitance necessitates on-chip integrated electronics to minimize the effects of parasitics. A feedback control loop provides an output that is linear with respect to the input signal.

11.5.2   Inkjet Printing

Thermal inkjet technology was invented in 1979 at Hewlett-Packard (H-P) Laboratories. Inkjet printing is now used extensively. Integration of the mechanical inkjet nozzle with microelectronics has led to the advancement.

Figure 11.42 shows the sequence of bubble formation, ink injection, and refill. A tiny metallic resistor is used to rapidly heat (at a rate of 100°C per microsecond) a thin layer of liquid ink. This heated ink vaporizes a portion of the ink to form an expanding bubble that injects a drop of ink onto the paper. The bubble collapses and draws in a fresh supply of ink.

The heating resistor can be turned on by a MOSFET integrated on the same silicon surface, as schematically shown in Figure 11.43. As many as 300 inkjet orifices per inch can be fabricated. The *x-y* motion of the inkjet is computer controlled.

11.5.3   Biomedical Sensors

Medical sensors and instrumentation for *in vitro* diagnostics can be a very large opportunity for micromachining. An example of a MEMS contribution to *in vitro*

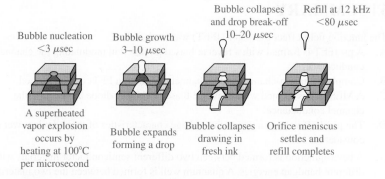

Bubble nucleation
$<3\ \mu sec$

Bubble growth
$3\text{--}10\ \mu sec$

Bubble collapses
and drop break-off
$10\text{--}20\ \mu sec$

Refill at 12 kHz
$<80\ \mu sec$

A superheated
vapor explosion
occurs by
heating at 100°C
per microsecond

Bubble expands
forming a drop

Bubble collapses
drawing in
fresh ink

Orifice meniscus
settles and
refill completes

Figure 11.42 | HP's thermal inkjet technology; bubble formation, expansion, collapse, and refill.
(From Madou [11])

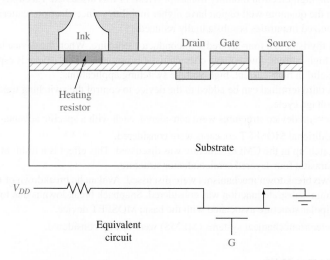

Figure 11.43 | Simplified schematic of the integration of the thermal inkjet structure and MOS switching transistor. A voltage pulse at the gate turns on the transistor producing the I^2R heating of the metallic resistor.

diagnostics would be in glucose sensors. A method that allows for painless blood testing while providing accurate and reliable results are necessary. A great amount of research has gone into trying to develop such an instrument. In 1987, an amperometric glucose sensor was introduced. The sensor is based on a traditional thick-film manufacturing process and an innovative mediator chemistry process.

In some cases, MEMS microneedles have been developed for minimally invasive sampling. This device uses capillary action to draw a small amount of blood into a chamber where it is mixed with a chemical reagent. A laser then measures the glucose and the blood's glucose level is then displayed. In systems such as this, the chemical sensor is disposable, while the electronics are contained in a handheld pack.

11.6 | SUMMARY

1. The junction field-effect transistor (JFET) was analyzed.
   A. A pn JFET is formed with a reverse-biased pn junction modulating the channel conductance.
   B. Complementary n-channel and p-channel pn junction FETs can be formed.
   C. A MESFET is formed with a reverse-biased Schottky diode modulating the channel conductance.
   D. The pinchoff voltage and current–voltage characteristics of these devices were considered.

2. A. A heterojunction is formed between two different semiconductor materials with different bandgap energies. A quantum well is formed between the two materials that may contain electrons.
   B. A heterojunction bipolar transistor was considered. A higher bandgap material as the emitter produces a higher emitter injection efficiency and higher gain transistor.
   C. The high-electron mobility transistor (HEMT) was discussed. Electrons flowing in the quantum well region have higher mobilities since electron scattering due to ionized impurities is substantially reduced.

3. A. A thyristor is a four-layered semiconductor structure. When the device turns on, a high-current, low-voltage characteristic is produced. This device is especially useful in high-current, high-voltage switching applications.
   B. A third terminal can be added to the device to control the switching time during a voltage cycle.
   C. Several device structures were considered, each with a specific advantage.

4. Two additional MOSFET concepts were considered.
   A. Latch-up in the CMOS structure was discussed. This effect is a result of the parasitic four-layered semiconductor structure.
   B. Two breakdown mechanisms were discussed. Avalanche breakdown of the drain–substrate junction was considered. Snapback breakdown is due to a parasitic bipolar structure associated with the basic MOSFET device.

5. Microelectromechanical systems (MEMS) were briefly considered.

CHECKPOINT

After studying this chapter, the reader should have the ability to

1. A. Sketch the cross section of an n-channel pn JFET. Discuss the voltage polarities applied to the device.
   B. Sketch the cross section of a GaAs MESFET fabricated on an insulating substrate.
   C. Discuss the difference between the pinchoff voltage and internal pinchoff voltage of a JFET.

2. A. Sketch the energy-band diagram of a heterojunction. Discuss the formation of a quantum well.
   B. Discuss the advantage of a heterojunction bipolar transistor.
   C. Discuss the advantage of a HEMT compared to a pn JFET.

3. A. Discuss the switching characteristics of a basic thyristor.
   B. Discuss the turn-on characteristics of an SCR.
   C. Sketch the cross section of a bilateral SCR.

4. A. Discuss latch-up in a CMOS inverter.
   B. Discuss the breakdown mechanisms in a MOSFET.

REVIEW QUESTIONS

1. A. What is the difference between the pinchoff voltage and internal pinchoff voltage of a pn JFET?
   B. Discuss the mechanism by which the drain current saturates with drain voltage in a JFET.

2. A. Sketch the energy-band diagram of a heterojunction. How is the quantum well formed?
   B. Why does the emitter injection efficiency and current gain increase in the heterojunction bipolar transistor?
   C. Why is the carrier mobility in the HEMT greater than in a pn JFET?

3. A. Sketch and explain the switching characteristics of the two terminal thyristor.
   B. Explain the turn-on characteristics of an SCR.

4. A. Discuss the latchup mechanism in a CMOS inverter.
   B. Sketch the parasitic bipolar transistor in the basic MOSFET device. Explain how this parasitic device can enhance the breakdown effect.

PROBLEMS

(*Note:* Assume $T = 300$ K for the following problems unless otherwise stated.)

Section 11.1 The Junction Field-Effect Transistor

11.1 A p-channel silicon JFET at $T = 300$ K has doping concentrations of $N_d = 5 \times 10^{18}$ cm^{-3} and $N_a = 3 \times 10^{16}$ cm^{-3}. The channel thickness dimension is $a = 0.5$ μm. (*a*) Compute the internal pinchoff voltage V_{p0} and the pinchoff voltage V_p. (*b*) Determine the minimum undepleted channel thickness, $a - h$, for $V_{GS} = 1$ V and for (*i*) $V_{DS} = 0$, (*ii*) $V_{DS} = -2.5$ V, and (*iii*) $V_{DS} = -5$ V.

11.2 Repeat Problem 11.1 for a GaAs JFET with the same electrical and geometrical parameters.

11.3 Consider an n-channel silicon JFET with the following parameters: $N_a = 3 \times 10^{18}$ cm^{-3}, $N_d = 8 \times 10^{16}$ cm^{-3}, and $a = 0.5$ μm. (*a*) Calculate the internal pinchoff voltage. (*b*) Determine the gate voltage required such that the undepleted channel is 0.20 μm.

11.4 Consider a GaAs JFET with the same parameters as those of the silicon JFET described in Problem 11.3. Repeat the calculations of parts (*a*) and (*b*).

11.5 Consider a p-channel GaAs JFET with parameters $N_d = 5 \times 10^{18}$ cm^{-3}, $N_a = 3 \times 10^{16}$ cm^{-3}, and $a = 0.30$ μm. (*a*) Calculate the internal pinchoff voltage and the pinchoff voltage. (*b*) For $V_{DS} = 0$, determine the width of the undepleted channel for (*i*) $V_{GS} = 0$ and (*ii*) $V_{GS} = 1$ V.

11.6 Consider an n-channel silicon JFET at $T = 300$ K with impurity doping concentrations of $N_d = 4 \times 10^{16}$ cm^{-3} and $N_a = 5 \times 10^{18}$ cm^{-3}. The channel thickness dimension is $a = 0.35$ μm. (*a*) Compute the internal pinchoff voltage V_{p0} and the pinchoff voltage V_p. (*b*) Determine the undepleted channel thickness, $a - h$, at the drain terminal for (*i*) $V_{GS} = 0$, $V_{DS} = 1$ V; (*ii*) $V_{GS} = -1.0$ V, $V_{DS} = 1$ V; and (*iii*) $V_{GS} = -1.0$ V, $V_{DS} = 2$ V.

11.7   Consider a GaAs JFET with the same electrical and geometrical parameters as given in Problem 11.6. Calculate the gate bias required to make the width of the undepleted channel 0.05 μm for (*a*) $V_{DS} = 0$ and (*b*) $V_{DS} = 1$ V.

11.8   An n-channel silicon JFET at $T = 300$ K has the following parameters:

$$N_a = 10^{19} \text{ cm}^{-3} \qquad N_d = 10^{16} \text{ cm}^{-3}$$
$$a = 0.50 \ \mu\text{m} \qquad L = 20 \ \mu\text{m}$$
$$W = 400 \ \mu\text{m} \qquad \mu_n = 1000 \text{ cm}^2/\text{V-s}$$

Ignoring velocity saturation effects, calculate (*a*) I_{P1}; (*b*) V_{DS}(sat) for (*i*) $V_{GS} = 0$, (*ii*) $V_{GS} = V_p/4$, (*iii*) $V_{GS} = V_p/2$, and (*iv*) $V_{GS} = 3V_p/4$; and (*c*) I_{D1}(sat) for the same V_{GS} values in part (*b*). (*d*) Using the results from parts (*b*) and (*c*), plot the *I–V* characteristics.

Section 11.2   Heterojunctions

11.9   Sketch the energy-band diagrams of an abrupt $Al_{0.3}Ga_{0.7}As$–GaAs heterojunction for (*a*) N$^+$-AlGaAs, intrinsic GaAs, (*b*) N$^+$-AlGaAs, p-GaAs, and (*c*) P$^+$-AlGaAs, n$^+$-GaAs. Assume $E_g = 1.85$ eV for $Al_{0.3}Ga_{0.7}As$ and assume $\Delta E_c = \frac{2}{3}\Delta E_g$.

11.10   Repeat Problem 11.9 assuming the ideal electron affinity rule. Determine ΔE_c and ΔE_v.

Section 11.3   The Thyristor

11.11   One condition for switching a thyristor is that $\alpha_1 + \alpha_2 = 1$. Show that this condition corresponds to $\beta_1 \beta_2 = 1$, where β_1 and β_2 are the common-emitter current gains of the pnp and npn bipolar transistors in the equivalent circuit of the thyristor.

11.12   Show that the triac can be triggered into its ON state by gate signals of either polarity and with anode-to-cathode voltages of either polarity. Consider each voltage polarity combination.

Section 11.4   Additional MOSFET Concepts

11.13   Explain how a pulse of ionizing radiation could trigger a basic CMOS structure into a high-current, low-impedance state.

READING LIST

1.   Anderson, R. L. "Experiments on Ge–GaAs Heterojunctions." *Solid-State Electronics* 5, no. 5 (September–October 1962), pp. 341–51.

2.   Baliga, B. J. *Modern Power Devices*. New York: Wiley, 1987.

3.   Baliga, B. J. *Power Semiconductor Devices*. Boston: PWS Publishing Co., 1996.

4.   Chang, C. S., and D. Y. S. Day. "Analytic Theory for Current-Voltage Characteristics and Field Distribution of GaAs MESFETs." *IEEE Transactions on Electron Devices* 36, no. 2 (February 1989), pp. 269–80.

5.   'Dimitrijev, S. *Understanding Semiconductor Devices*. New York: Oxford University Press, 2000.

6. Drummond, T. J., W. T. Masselink, and H. Morkoc. "Modulation-Doped GaAs/(Al,Ga)As Heterojunction Field-Effect Transistors: MODFETs." *Proceedings of the IEEE* 74, no. 6 (June 1986), pp. 773–812.

7. Fritzsche, D. "Heterostructures in MODFETs." *Solid-State Electronics* 30, no. 11 (November 1987), pp. 1183–95.

8. Ghandhi, S. K. *Semiconductor Power Devices: Physics of Operation and Fabrication Technology.* New York: Wiley, 1977.

9. Kano, K. *Semiconductor Devices.* Upper Saddle River, NJ: Prentice-Hall, 1998.

10. Liao, S. Y. *Microwave Solid-State Devices.* Englewood Cliffs, NJ: Prentice-Hall, 1985.

11. Madou, M. J. *Fundamentals of Microfabrication: The Science of Miniaturization,* 2nd ed. Boca Raton, FL: CRC PressLLC, 2002.

12. Muller, R. S., T. I. Kamins, and W. Chan. *Device Electronics for Integrated Circuits,* 3rd ed. New York: John Wiley and Sons, 2003.

13. Neamen, D. A. *Semiconductor Physics and Devices: Basic Principles,* 3rd ed. New York: McGraw-Hill, 2003.

14. Ng, K. K. *Complete Guide to Semiconductor Devices.* New York: McGraw-Hill, 1995.

15. Pierret, R. F. *Field Effect Devices.* Vol. 4 of the *Modular Series on Solid State Device.* 2nd ed. Reading, MA: Addison-Wesley, 1990.

16. Pierret, R. F. *Semiconductor Device Fundamentals.* Reading, MA: Addison-Wesley, 1996.

17. Roulston, D. J. *An Introduction to the Physics of Semiconductor Devices.* New York: Oxford University Press, 1999.

*18. Shur, M. *GaAs Devices and Circuits.* New York: Plenum Press, 1987.

19. Shur, M. *Introduction to Electronic Devices.* New York: John Wiley and Sons, 1996.

20. Singh, J. *Semiconductor Devices: An Introduction.* New York: McGraw-Hill, 1994.

21. Singh, J. *Semiconductor Devices: Basic Principles.* New York: John Wiley and Sons, 2001.

22. Streetman, B. G., and S. Banerjee. *Solid State Electronic Devices,* 5th ed. Upper Saddle River, NJ: Prentice-Hall, 2000.

23. Sze, S. M. *High-Speed Semiconductor Devices.* New York: Wiley, 1990.

24. Sze, S. M. *Physics of Semiconductor Devices.* 2nd ed. New York: Wiley, 1981.

25. Sze, S. M. *Semiconductor Devices: Physics and Technology,* 2nd ed. New York: John Wiley and Sons, 2002.

26. Tiwari, S., S. L. Wright, and A. W. Kleinsasser. "Transport and Related Properties of (Ga, Al)As/GaAs Double Heterojunction Bipolar Junction Transistors." IEEE *Transactions on Electron Devices,* ED-34 (February 1987), pp. 185–87.

27. Yang, E. S. *Microelectronic Devices.* New York: McGraw-Hill, 1988.

C H A P T E R

12

Optical Devices

S o far we have considered the basic physics of transistors used to amplify or switch electrical signals. Semiconductor devices can also be designed and fabricated to detect and generate optical signals. In this chapter, we discuss the basic principles of solar cells, photodetectors, light-emitting diodes, and laser diodes. Solar cells and photodetectors convert optical power into electrical power; light-emitting diodes and laser diodes convert electrical power into optical power.

The characteristics of solar cells and photodetectors are a function of optical energy that is absorbed in the semiconductor and that generates excess electron–hole pairs, producing photocurrents. The inverse mechanism of a photodetector is electroluminescence. Excess carriers are also generated in these devices, but the excess carriers then recombine and may result in the emission of photons in a forward-biased pn junction—such a device, for example, is the light-emitting diode, or LED.

12.0 | PREVIEW

In this chapter, we will

1. Analyze the optical absorption of semiconductors.
2. Analyze the solar cell.
3. Analyze semiconductor photodetectors.
4. Analyze semiconductor light-emitting diodes.
5. Analyze semiconductor laser diodes.

Historical Insight

The electroluminescence phenomenon was discovered by H. Round in 1907. He observed the generation of yellowish light from a crystal of carborundom when he applied a potential of 10 V between two points on the crystal. The interaction of light and semiconductors has been studied for a long time, including the photoelectric effect, which proved that light acted as a particle in many cases. The solar cell was invented by D. Chapin et al. in 1954. The laser action in direct bandgap semiconductors was demonstrated in 1962, and the next year the use of heterostructures was proposed.

Present-Day Insight

Solar cells have gained tremendous importance in the area of energy sources in the space program. Optoelectronic semiconductor devices have also been developed as display devices. Photodetectors continue to acquire importance due to the increasing importance of optical communications. Other optical devices such as LEDs and lasers are becoming more important because of the developments in fiber optics technology. Optical computers and computation at the speed of light continues to be desired, although this technology is probably not "just around the corner."

12.1 | OPTICAL ABSORPTION

Objective: Analyze the optical absorption of semiconductors.

In Chapter 2, we discussed the wave–particle duality principle and indicated that light waves could be treated as particles, which are referred to as photons. The energy of a photon is $E = h\nu$, where h is Planck's constant and ν is the frequency. We can also relate the wavelength and energy by

$$\lambda = \frac{c}{\nu} = \frac{hc}{E} = \frac{1.24}{E}\mu m \qquad (12.1) \qquad \textbf{Photon wavelength}$$

where E is the photon energy in eV and c is the speed of light.

There are several possible photon–semiconductor interaction mechanisms. For example, photons can interact with the semiconductor lattice whereby the photon energy is converted into heat. Photons can also interact with impurity atoms, either donors or acceptors, or they can interact with defects within the semiconductor. However, the basic photon interaction process of greatest interest is the interaction with valence electrons. When a photon collides with a valence electron, enough energy may be imparted to elevate the electron into the conduction band. Such a process generates electron–hole pairs and creates excess carrier concentrations. The behavior of excess carriers in a semiconductor was considered in Chapter 8.

12.1.1 Photon Absorption Coefficient

When a semiconductor is illuminated with light, the photons may be absorbed or they may propagate through the semiconductor, depending on the photon energy and

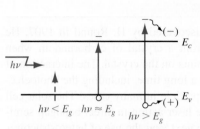

Figure 12.1 | Optically generated electron–hole pair formation in a semiconductor.

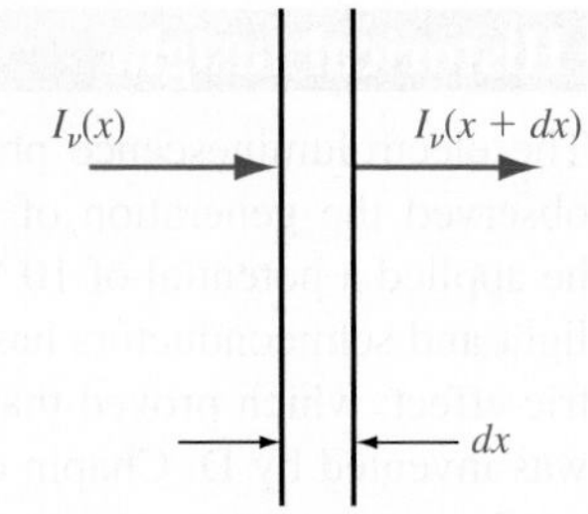

Figure 12.2 | Optical absorption in a differential length.

on the bandgap energy E_g. If the photon energy is less than E_g, the photons are not readily absorbed. In this case, the light is transmitted through the material and the semiconductor appears to be transparent.

If $E = h\nu > E_g$, the photon can interact with a valence electron and elevate the electron into the conduction band. The valence band contains many electrons and the conduction band contains many empty states, so the probability of this interaction is high when $h\nu > E_g$. This interaction creates an electron in the conduction band and a hole in the valence band—an electron–hole pair. The basic absorption processes for different values of $h\nu$ are shown in Figure 12.1. When $h\nu > E_g$, an electron–hole pair is created and the excess energy may give the electron or hole additional kinetic energy, which will be dissipated as heat in the semiconductor.

The intensity of the photon flux is denoted by $I_\nu(x)$ and is expressed in terms of energy/cm^2-s. Figure 12.2 shows an incident photon intensity at a position x and the photon flux emerging at a distance $x + dx$. The energy absorbed per unit time in the distance dx is given by

$$\alpha I_\nu(x)\,dx \tag{12.2}$$

Absorption coefficient

where α is the absorption coefficient. The absorption coefficient is the relative number of photons absorbed per unit distance, given in units of cm^{-1}.

From Figure 12.2, we can write

$$I_\nu(x + dx) - I_\nu(x) = \frac{dI_\nu(x)}{dx}\,dx = -\alpha I_\nu(x)\,dx \tag{12.3}$$

or

$$\frac{dI_\nu(x)}{dx} = -\alpha I_\nu(x) \tag{12.4}$$

If the initial condition is given as $I_\nu(0) = I_{\nu 0}$, then the solution to the differential equation, Equation (12.4), is

Photon intensity

$$I_\nu(x) = I_{\nu 0}e^{-\alpha x} \tag{12.5}$$

The intensity of the photon flux decreases exponentially with distance through the semiconductor material. The photon intensity as a function of x for two general

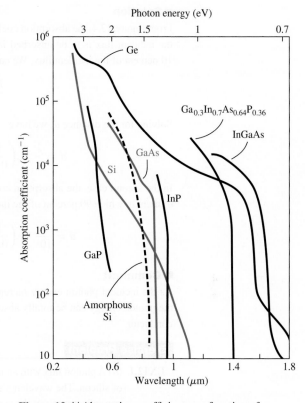

Figure 12.4 | Absorption coefficient as a function of wavelength for several semiconductors. *(From Shur [14].)*

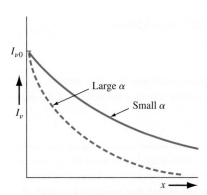

Figure 12.3 | Photon intensity versus distance for two absorption coefficients.

values of absorption coefficient is shown in Figure 12.3. If the absorption coefficient is large, the photons are absorbed over a relatively short distance.

The absorption coefficient in the semiconductor is a very strong function of photon energy and bandgap energy. Figure 12.4 shows the absorption coefficient α plotted as a function of wavelength for several semiconductor materials. The absorption coefficient increases very rapidly for $h\nu > E_g$, or for $\lambda < 1.24/E_g$. The absorption coefficients are very small for $h\nu < E_g$, so the semiconductor appears transparent to photons in this energy range.

EXAMPLE 12.1

OBJECTIVE

To calculate the thickness of a semiconductor that will absorb 90 percent of the incident photon energy.

Consider silicon and assume that in the first case the incident wavelength is $\lambda = 1.0\,\mu\text{m}$ and in the second case, the incident wavelength is $\lambda = 0.5\,\mu\text{m}$.

■ **Solution**

From Figure 12.4, the absorption coefficient is $\alpha \approx 10^2 \text{ cm}^{-1}$ for $\lambda = 1.0 \, \mu\text{m}$. If 90 percent of the incident flux is to be absorbed in a distance d, then the flux emerging at $x = d$ will be 10 percent of the incident flux. We can write

$$\frac{I_\nu(d)}{I_{\nu 0}} = 0.1 = e^{-\alpha d}$$

Solving for the distance d, we have

$$d = \frac{1}{\alpha} \ln \left(\frac{1}{0.1} \right) = \frac{1}{10^2} \ln (10) = 0.0230 \text{ cm}$$

In the second case, the absorption coefficient is $\alpha \approx 10^4 \text{ cm}^{-1}$ for $\lambda = 0.5 \, \mu\text{m}$. The distance d, then, in which 90 percent of the incident flux is absorbed, is

$$d = \frac{1}{10^4} \ln \left(\frac{1}{0.1} \right) = 2.30 \times 10^{-4} \text{ cm} = 2.30 \, \mu\text{m}$$

■ **Comment**

As the incident photon energy increases, the absorption coefficient increases rapidly, so that the photon energy can be totally absorbed in a very narrow region at the surface of the semiconductor.

Exercise Problem

EX12.1 (*a*) A photon flux with an intensity of $I_{\nu 0} = 0.10 \text{ W/cm}^2$ is incident on the surface of silicon. The wavelength of the incident photon signal is $\lambda = 1 \, \mu\text{m}$. Neglecting any reflection from the surface, determine the photon flux intensity at a depth of (*i*) $x = 5 \, \mu\text{m}$ and (*ii*) $x = 20 \, \mu\text{m}$ from the surface. (*b*) Repeat part (*a*) for a wavelength of $\lambda = 0.60 \, \mu\text{m}$.

[Ans. (*a*) (*i*) 0.0951 W/cm^2, (*ii*) 0.0819 W/cm^2, (*b*) (*i*) 0.0135 W/cm^2, (*ii*) $3.35 \times 10^{-5} \text{ W/cm}^2$]

The relation between the bandgap energies of some of the common semiconductor materials and the light spectrum is shown in Figure 12.5. We can note that silicon and gallium arsenide will absorb all of the visible spectrum, whereas gallium phosphide, for example, will be transparent to the red spectrum.

12.1.2 Electron–Hole Pair Generation Rate

We have shown that photons with energy greater than E_g can be absorbed in a semiconductor, thereby creating electron–hole pairs. The intensity $I_\nu(x)$ is in units of energy/cm²-s and $\alpha I_\nu(x)$ is the rate at which energy is absorbed per unit volume. If we assume that one absorbed photon at an energy $h\nu$ creates one electron–hole pair, then the generation rate of electron–hole pairs is

Electron–hole generation rate

$$g' = \frac{\alpha I_\nu(x)}{h\nu} \qquad (12.6)$$

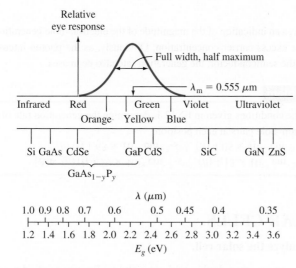

Figure 12.5 | Light spectrum versus wavelength and energy.
Figure includes relative response of the human eye.
(From Sze [18].)

which is in units of #/cm³-s. We may note that the ratio $I_\nu(x)/h\nu$ is the photon flux. If, on the average, one absorbed photon produces less than one electron–hole pair, then Equation (12.6) must be multiplied by an efficiency factor.

EXAMPLE 12.2

OBJECTIVE
To calculate the generation rate of electron–hole pairs given an incident intensity of photons.

Consider gallium arsenide at $T = 300\,\text{K}$. Assume the photon intensity at a particular point is $I_\nu(x) = 0.05$ W/cm² at a wavelength of $\lambda = 0.75\ \mu\text{m}$. This intensity is typical of sunlight, for example.

■ **Solution**
The absorption coefficient for gallium arsenide at this wavelength is $\alpha \approx 0.7 \times 10^4\ \text{cm}^{-1}$. The photon energy, using Equation (12.1), is

$$E = h\nu = \frac{1.24}{0.75} = 1.65\,\text{eV}$$

Then, from Equation (12.6) and including the conversion factor between joules and eV, we have, for a unity efficiency factor,

$$g' = \frac{\alpha I_\nu(x)}{h\nu} = \frac{(0.7 \times 10^4)(0.05)}{(1.6 \times 10^{-19})(1.65)} = 1.33 \times 10^{21}\ \text{cm}^{-3}\text{-s}^{-1}$$

If the incident photon intensity is a steady-state intensity, then, from Chapter 8, the steady-state excess carrier concentration is $\delta n = g'\tau$, where τ is the excess minority-carrier lifetime. If $\tau = 10^{-7}$ s, for example, then

$$\delta n = (1.33 \times 10^{21})(10^{-7}) = 1.33 \times 10^{14}\ \text{cm}^{-3}$$

■ **Comment**

This example gives an indication of the magnitude of the electron–hole generation rate and the magnitude of the excess carrier concentration. Obviously, as the photon intensity decreases with distance in the semiconductor, the generation rate also decreases.

Exercise Problem

EX12.2 For the conditions given in EX12.1, determine the generation rate of excess electron–hole pairs at each position.

[Ans. (a) (i) 4.79×10^{19} cm^{-3}-s^{-1}, (ii) 4.13×10^{19} cm^{-3}-s^{-1}, (b) (i) 1.63×10^{20} cm^{-3}-s^{-1}, (ii) 4.05×10^{17} cm^{-3}-s^{-1}]

12.2 | SOLAR CELLS

Objective: Analyze the solar cell.

A solar cell is a pn junction device with no voltage directly applied across the junction. The solar cell converts photon power into electrical power and delivers this power to a load. These devices have long been used for the power supply of satellites and space vehicles, and also as the power supply to some calculators. We will first consider the simple pn junction solar cell with uniform generation of excess carriers. We will also discuss briefly the heterojunction and amorphous silicon solar cells.

12.2.1 The pn Junction Solar Cell

Consider the pn junction shown in Figure 12.6 with a resistive load. Even with zero bias applied to the junction, an electric field exists in the space charge region, as shown in the figure. Incident photon illumination can create electron–hole pairs in the space charge region that will be swept out producing the photocurrent I_L in the reverse-bias direction as shown.

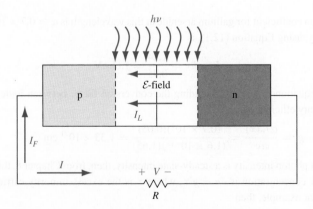

Figure 12.6 | A pn junction solar cell with resistive load.

The photocurrent I_L produces a voltage drop across the resistive load, which forward biases the pn junction. The forward-bias voltage produces a forward-bias current I_F, as indicated in the figure. The net pn junction current, in the reverse-bias direction, is

$$I = I_L - I_F = I_L - I_S \left[\exp\left(\frac{eV}{kT} \right) - 1 \right] \qquad (12.7)$$

Photocurrent

where the ideal diode equation has been used. As the diode becomes forward biased, the magnitude of the electric field in the space charge region decreases, but does not go to zero or change direction. The photocurrent is always in the reverse-bias direction and the net solar cell current is also always in the reverse-bias direction.

There are two limiting cases of interest. The short-circuit condition occurs when $R = 0$ so that $V = 0$. The current in this case is referred to as the *short-circuit current*, or

Short-circuit current

$$I = I_{sc} = I_L \qquad (12.8)$$

The second limiting case is the open-circuit condition and occurs when $R \rightarrow \infty$. The net current is zero and the voltage produced is the *open-circuit voltage*. The photocurrent is just balanced by the forward-biased junction current so we have

$$I = 0 = I_L - I_S \left[\exp\left(\frac{eV_{oc}}{kT} \right) - 1 \right] \qquad (12.9)$$

We can find the open-circuit voltage V_{oc} as

Open-circuit voltage

$$V_{oc} = V_t \ln \left(1 + \frac{I_L}{I_S} \right) \qquad (12.10)$$

A plot of the diode current I as a function of the diode voltage V from Equation (12.7) is shown in Figure 12.7. We can note the short-circuit current and open-circuit voltage points on the figure.

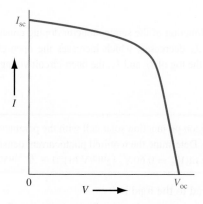

Figure 12.7 | *I–V* characteristics of a pn junction solar cell.

EXAMPLE 12.3

OBJECTIVE

To calculate the open-circuit voltage of a silicon pn junction solar cell.

Consider a silicon pn junction at $T = 300\,\text{K}$ with the following parameters:

$$N_a = 5 \times 10^{18}\,\text{cm}^{-3} \qquad N_d = 10^{16}\,\text{cm}^{-3}$$

$$D_n = 25\,\text{cm}^2/\text{s} \qquad D_p = 10\,\text{cm}^2/\text{s}$$

$$\tau_{n0} = 5 \times 10^{-7}\,\text{s} \qquad \tau_{p0} = 10^{-7}\,\text{s}$$

Let the photocurrent density be $J_L = I_L/A = 15\,\text{mA/cm}^2$.

■ **Solution**

We have that

$$J_S = \frac{I_S}{A} = \left(\frac{eD_n n_{p0}}{L_n} + \frac{eD_p p_{n0}}{L_p} \right) = en_i^2 \left(\frac{D_n}{L_n N_a} + \frac{D_p}{L_p N_d} \right)$$

We can calculate

$$L_n = \sqrt{D_n \tau_{n0}} = \sqrt{(25)(5 \times 10^{-7})} = 35.4\,\mu\text{m}$$

and

$$L_p = \sqrt{D_p \tau_{p0}} = \sqrt{(10)(10^{-7})} = 10.0\,\mu\text{m}$$

Then

$$J_S = (1.6 \times 10^{-19})(1.5 \times 10^{10})^2 \left[\frac{25}{(35.4 \times 10^{-4})(5 \times 10^{18})} + \frac{10}{(10 \times 10^{-4})(10^{16})} \right]$$

$$= 3.6 \times 10^{-11}\,\text{A/cm}^2$$

Then from Equation (12.10), we can find

$$V_{\text{oc}} = V_t \ln\left(1 + \frac{I_L}{I_S} \right) = V_t \ln\left(1 + \frac{J_L}{J_S} \right) = (0.0259) \ln\left(1 + \frac{15 \times 10^{-3}}{3.6 \times 10^{-11}} \right) = 0.514\,\text{V}$$

■ **Comment**

We can note that J_S is a function of the semiconductor doping concentrations. As the doping concentrations increase, J_S decreases, which increases the open-circuit voltage. However, since V_{oc} is a function of the log of I_L and I_S, the open-circuit voltage is not a strong function of these parameters.

Exercise Problem

EX12.3 Consider a silicon pn junction solar cell with the parameters given in Example 12.3. Determine the required photocurrent density to produce an open-circuit voltage of $V_{\text{oc}} = 0.60\,\text{V}$. (Ans. $J_L = 0.414\,\text{A/cm}^2$.)

The power delivered to the load is

$$P = IV = I_L V - I_S \left[\exp\left(\frac{eV}{kT} \right) - 1 \right] V \qquad (12.11)$$

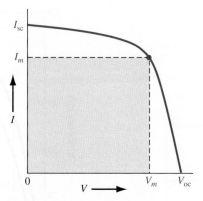

Figure 12.8 | Maximum power rectangle of the solar cell I–V characteristics.

We may find the current and voltage which will deliver the maximum power to the load by setting the derivative equal to zero, or $dP/dV = 0$. Using Equation (12.11), we find

$$\frac{dP}{dV} = 0 = I_L - I_S\left[\exp\left(\frac{eV_m}{kT}\right) - 1\right] - I_S V_m\left(\frac{e}{kT}\right)\exp\left(\frac{eV_m}{kT}\right) \qquad (12.12)$$

where V_m is the voltage which produces the maximum power. We can rewrite Equation (12.12) in the form **Maximum power**

$$\left(1 + \frac{V_m}{V_t}\right)\exp\left(\frac{eV_m}{kT}\right) = 1 + \frac{I_L}{I_S} \qquad (12.13)$$

The value of V_m can be determined by trial and error. Figure 12.8 shows the maximum power rectangle where I_m is the current when $V = V_m$.

12.2.2 Conversion Efficiency and Solar Concentration

The conversion efficiency of a solar cell is defined as the ratio of output electrical power to incident optical power. For the maximum power output, we can write   **Conversion efficiency**

$$\eta = \frac{P_m}{P_{\text{in}}} \times 100\% = \frac{I_m V_m}{P_{\text{in}}} \times 100\% \qquad (12.14)$$

The maximum possible current and the maximum possible voltage in the solar cell are I_{sc} and V_{oc}, respectively. The ratio $I_m V_m/I_{\text{sc}} V_{\text{oc}}$ is called the fill factor and is a measure of the realizable power from a solar cell. Typically, the fill factor is between 0.7 and 0.8.

The conventional pn junction solar cell has a single semiconductor bandgap energy. When the cell is exposed to the solar spectrum, a photon with energy less than E_g will have no effect on the electrical output power of the solar cell. A photon with energy greater than E_g will contribute to the solar cell output power, but the fraction of

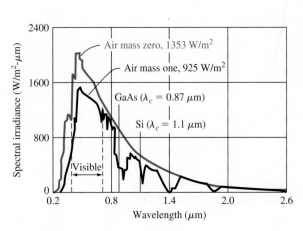

Figure 12.9 | Solar spectral irradiance.
(From Sze [18].)

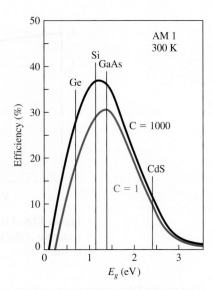

Figure 12.10 | Ideal solar cell efficiency at $T = 300$ K for $C = 1$ sun and for a $C = 1000$ sun concentration as a function of bandgap energy.
(From Sze [18].)

Maximum efficiency

photon energy that is greater than E_g will eventually only be dissipated as heat. Figure 12.9 shows the solar spectral irradiance (power per unit area per unit wavelength) where air mass zero represents the solar spectrum outside the earth's atmosphere and air mass one is the solar spectrum at the earth's surface at noon. The maximum efficiency of a silicon pn junction solar cell is approximately 28 percent. Nonideal factors, such as series resistance and reflection from the semiconductor surface, will lower the conversion efficiency typically to the range of 10 to 15 percent.

A large optical lens can be used to concentrate sunlight onto a solar cell so that the light intensity can be increased up to several hundred times. The short-circuit current increases linearly with light concentration, while the open-circuit voltage increases only slightly with concentration. Figure 12.10 shows the ideal solar cell efficiency at 300 K for two values of solar concentration. We can see that the conversion efficiency increases only slightly with optical concentration. The primary advantage of using concentration techniques is to reduce the overall system cost since an optical lens is less expensive than an equivalent area of solar cells.

EXAMPLE 12.4

OBJECTIVE

To calculate the open-circuit voltage when solar concentration is used.

Consider the silicon pn junction solar cell described in Example 12.3. Let the solar intensity increase by a factor of 10.

■ **Solution**

The photocurrent density in Example 12.3 for one sun was $J_L = 15 \, \text{mA/cm}^2$. If the intensity of sunlight increases by a factor of 10, then the photocurrent density for 10 suns is $J_L = 150 \, \text{mA/cm}^2$. The reverse-saturation current density J_S remains unchanged at $J_S = 3.6 \times 10^{-11} \, \text{A/cm}^2$ (assuming the temperature remains constant). The open-circuit voltage from Equation (12.10) is

$$V_{\text{oc}} = V_t \ln\left(1 + \frac{J_L}{J_S}\right) = (0.0259) \ln\left(1 + \frac{150 \times 10^{-3}}{3.6 \times 10^{-11}}\right) = 0.574 \, \text{V}$$

■ **Comment**

The open-circuit voltage increases slightly as the solar concentration increases, which means that the efficiency will increase slightly with solar concentration.

Exercise 12.4

EX12.4 The silicon pn junction solar cell described in EX12.3 has a cross-sectional area of 1 cm². Determine the maximum power that can be delivered to a load.
(Ans. 0.205 W)

12.2.3   The Heterojunction Solar Cell

As we have already mentioned, a heterojunction is formed between two semiconductors with different bandgap energies. A typical pN heterojunction energy-band diagram in thermal equilibrium is shown in Figure 12.11. Assume that photons are incident on the wide-bandgap material. Photons with energy less than E_{gN} will pass through the wide-bandgap material, which acts as an optical window, and photons with energies greater than E_{gp} will be absorbed in the narrow-bandgap material. On the average, excess carriers created in the depletion region and within a diffusion length of the junction will be collected and will contribute to the photocurrent. Photons with an energy greater than E_{gN} will be absorbed in the wide-bandgap material, and excess carriers generated within one diffusion length of the junction will

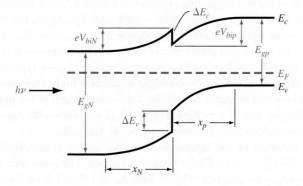

Figure 12.11 | The energy-band diagram of a pN heterojunction in thermal equilibrium.

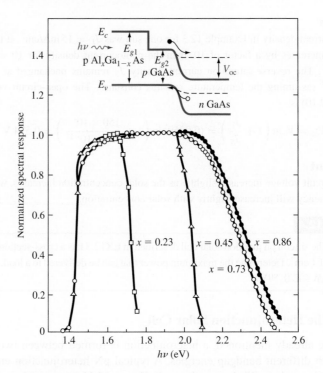

Figure 12.12 | The normalized spectral response of several AlGaAs/GaAs solar cells with different compositions. *(From Sze [17].)*

be collected. If E_{gN} is large enough, then the high-energy photons will be absorbed in the space charge region of the narrow-bandgap material. This heterojunction solar cell should have better characteristics than a homojunction cell, especially at the shorter wavelengths.

A variation of the heterojunction is shown in Figure 12.12. A pn homojunction is formed and then a wide-bandgap material is grown on top. Again, the wide-bandgap material acts as an optical window for photon energies $h\nu < E_{g1}$. Photons with energies $E_{g2} < h\nu < E_{g1}$ will create excess carriers in the homojunction and photons with energies $h\nu > E_{g1}$ will create excess carriers in the window type material. If the absorption coefficient in the narrow-bandgap material is high, then essentially all of the excess carriers will be generated within a diffusion length of the junction, so the collection efficiency will be very high. Figure 12.12 also shows the normalized spectral response for various mole fractions x in the $Al_xGa_{1-x}As$.

Another variation of the heterojunction solar cell is schematically shown in Figure 12.13. This device is called a tandem solar cell. The basic idea of this cell is that a wide-bandgap pn junction (GaInP with $E_g = 1.9$ eV) is on top of a smaller-bandgap pn junction (GaAs with $E_g = 1.42$ eV). Photons with energies greater than 1.9 eV will be absorbed in the top pn junction and photons with energies between

Tandem solar cell

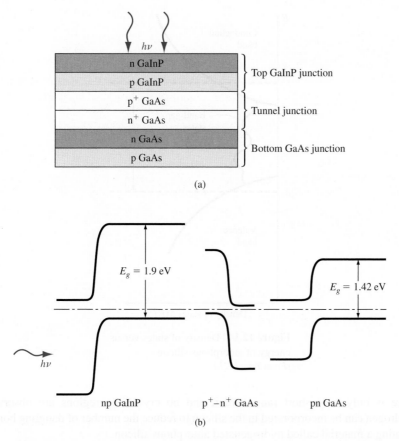

Figure 12.13 | (a) Simplified schematic of a tandem solar cell. (b) Energy-band diagram of the tandem solar cell.

$1.42 < h\nu < 1.9$ eV will pass through the top pn junction but will be absorbed in the bottom pn junction.

The energy-band diagram of this tandem solar cell is also schematically shown in Figure 12.13. A tunneling p^+–n^+ GaAs junction is placed between the top and bottom pn junctions to connect the two absorbing pn junctions.

12.2.4 Amorphous Silicon Solar Cells

Single-crystal silicon solar cells tend to be expensive and are limited to approximately 6 in. in diameter. A system powered by solar cells requires, in general, a very large area solar cell array to generate the required power. Amorphous silicon solar cells provide the possibility of fabricating large area and relatively inexpensive solar cell systems.

When silicon is deposited by CVD techniques at temperatures below 600°C, an amorphous film is formed regardless of the type of substrate. In amorphous silicon,   **Amorphous silicon**

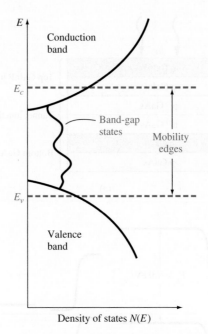

Figure 12.14 | Density of states versus
energy of amorphous silicon.
(From Yang [22].)

there is only very short range order, and no crystalline regions are observed. Hydrogen can be incorporated in the silicon to reduce the number of dangling bonds, creating a material called hydrogenated amorphous silicon.

The density of states versus energy for amorphous silicon is shown in Figure 12.14. Amorphous silicon contains large numbers of electronic energy states within the normal bandgap of single-crystal silicon. However, because of the short-range order, the effective mobility is quite small, typically in the range between 10^{-6} and 10^{-3} cm^2/V-s. The mobilities in the states above E_c and below E_v are between 1 and 10 cm^2/V-s. Consequently, conduction through the energy states between E_c and E_v is negligible because of the low mobility. Because of the difference in mobility values, E_c and E_v are referred to as the mobility edges and the energy between E_c and E_v is referred to as the mobility gap. The mobility gap can be modified by adding specific types of impurities. Typically, the mobility gap is on the order of 1.7 eV.

Amorphous silicon has a very high optical absorption coefficient, so most sunlight is absorbed within approximately 1 μm of the surface. Consequently, only a very thin layer of amorphous silicon is required for a solar cell. A typical amorphous silicon solar cell is a PIN device shown in Figure 12.15. The amorphous silicon is deposited on an optically transparent indium tin oxide–coated glass substrate. If aluminum is used as the back contact it will reflect any transmitted photons back through the PIN device. The n$^+$ and p$^+$ regions can be quite thin, while the intrinsic region can be in the range of 0.5 to 1.0 μm thick. The energy-band diagram for the

**Amorphous silicon
PIN solar cell**

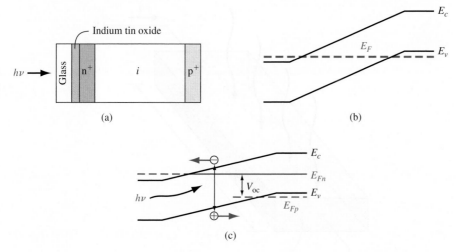

Figure 12.15 | The (a) cross section, (b) energy-band diagram at thermal equilibrium, and (c) energy-band diagram under photon illumination of an amorphous silicon PIN solar cell. *(From Yang [22].)*

thermal equilibrium case is shown in the figure. Excess carriers generated in the intrinsic region are separated by the electric field and produce the photocurrent, as we have discussed. Conversion efficiencies are smaller than in single-crystal silicon, but the reduced cost makes this technology attractive. Amorphous silicon solar cells approximately 40 cm wide and many meters long have been fabricated.

12.3 | PHOTODETECTORS

Objective: Analyze semiconductor photodetectors.

There are several semiconductor devices that can be used to detect the presence of photons. These devices are known as photodetectors; they convert optical signals into electrical signals. When excess electrons and holes are generated in a semiconductor, there is an increase in the conductivity of the material. This change in conductivity is the basis of the photoconductor, perhaps the simplest type of photodetector. If electrons and holes are generated within the space charge region of a pn junction, then they will be separated by the electric field and a current will be produced. The pn junction is the basis of several photodetector devices including the photodiode and the phototransistor.

12.3.1 Photoconductor

Figure 12.16 shows a bar of semiconductor material with ohmic contacts at each end and a voltage applied between the terminals. The initial thermal-equilibrium conductivity is

$$\sigma_0 = e(\mu_n n_0 + \mu_p p_0) \tag{12.15}$$

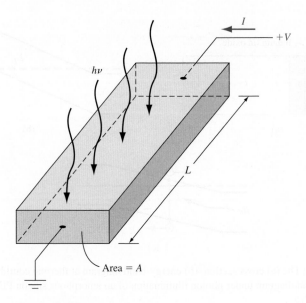

Figure 12.16 | A photoconductor.

If excess carriers are generated in the semiconductor, the conductivity becomes

$$\sigma = e[\mu_n(n_0 + \delta n) + \mu_p(p_0 + \delta p)] \qquad (12.16)$$

where δn and δp are the excess electron and hole concentrations, respectively. If we consider an n-type semiconductor, then, from charge neutrality, we can assume that $\delta n = \delta p \equiv \delta p$. We will use δp as the concentration of excess carriers. In steady state, the excess carrier concentration is given by $\delta p = G_L \tau_p$, where G_L is the generation rate of excess carriers $(\text{cm}^{-3}\text{-s}^{-1})$ and τ_p is the excess minority carrier lifetime.

The conductivity from Equation (12.16) can be rewritten as

$$\sigma = e(\mu_n n_0 + \mu_p p_0) + e(\delta p)(\mu_n + \mu_p) \qquad (12.17)$$

Photoconductivity
The change in conductivity due to the optical excitation, known as the *photoconductivity,* is then

$$\Delta\sigma = e(\delta p)(\mu_n + \mu_p) \qquad (12.18)$$

An electric field is induced in the semiconductor by the applied voltage, which produces a current. The current density can be written as

$$J = (J_0 + J_L) = (\sigma_0 + \Delta\sigma)\mathcal{E} \qquad (12.19)$$

where J_0 is the current density in the semiconductor prior to optical excitation and J_L is the photocurrent density. The photocurrent density is $J_L = \Delta\sigma\mathcal{E}$. If the excess electrons and holes are generated uniformly throughout the semiconductor, then the
Photocurrent
photocurrent is given by

$$I_L = J_L A = \Delta\sigma A\mathcal{E} = eG_L\tau_p(\mu_n + \mu_p)A\mathcal{E} \qquad (12.20)$$

where A is the cross-sectional area of the device. The photocurrent is directly proportional to the excess carrier generation rate, which in turn is proportional to the incident photon flux.

If excess electrons and holes are not generated uniformly throughout the semiconductor material, then the total photocurrent is found by integrating the photoconductivity over the cross-sectional area.

Since $\mu_n \mathcal{E}$ is the electron drift velocity, the electron transit time, that is, the time required for an electron to flow through the photoconductor, is

$$t_n = \frac{L}{\mu_n \mathcal{E}} \tag{12.21}$$

The photocurrent, from Equation (12.20), can be rewritten as

$$I_L = eG_L \left(\frac{\tau_p}{t_n} \right) \left(1 + \frac{\mu_p}{\mu_n} \right) AL \tag{12.22}$$

We may define a photoconductor gain, Γ_{ph}, as the ratio of the rate at which charge is collected by the contacts to the rate at which charge is generated within the photoconductor. We can write the gain as

Photoconductor gain

$$\Gamma_{ph} = \frac{I_L}{eG_L AL} \tag{12.23}$$

which, using Equation (12.22), can be written

$$\Gamma_{ph} = \frac{\tau_p}{t_n} \left(1 + \frac{\mu_p}{\mu_n} \right) \tag{12.24}$$

EXAMPLE 12.5

OBJECTIVE

To calculate the gain of a silicon photodetector.

Consider an n-type silicon photoconductor with a length $L = 100 \, \mu m$, cross-sectional area $A = 10^{-7} \, cm^2$, and minority carrier lifetime $\tau_p = 10^{-6} \, s$. Let the applied voltage be $V = 10$ volts.

■ **Solution**

The electron transit time is determined as

$$t_n = \frac{L}{\mu_n \mathcal{E}} = \frac{L^2}{\mu_n V} = \frac{(100 \times 10^{-4})^2}{(1350)(10)} = 7.41 \times 10^{-9} \, s$$

The photoconductor gain is then

$$\Gamma_{ph} = \frac{\tau_p}{t_n} \left(1 + \frac{\mu_p}{\mu_n} \right) = \frac{10^{-6}}{7.41 \times 10^{-9}} \left(1 + \frac{480}{1350} \right) = 1.83 \times 10^2$$

■ **Comment**

The fact that a photoconductor—a bar of semiconductor material—has a gain may be surprising.

Exercise Problem

EX12.5 Repeat Example 12.5 if the length of the photodetector is reduced to $L = 50 \ \mu m$. (Ans. $\Gamma_{ph} = 733$.)

Let's consider physically what happens to a photon-generated electron, for example. After the excess electron is generated, it drifts very quickly out of the photoconductor at the anode terminal. To maintain charge neutrality throughout the entire photoconductor, another electron immediately enters the photoconductor at the cathode and drifts toward the anode. This process will continue during a time period equal to the mean carrier lifetime. At the end of this period, on the average, the photoelectron will recombine with a hole.

The electron transit time, using the parameters from Example 12.5, is $t_n = 7.41 \times 10^{-9}$ s. In a simplistic sense, the photoelectron will circulate around the photoconductor circuit 135 times during the 10^{-6} s time duration, which is the mean carrier lifetime. If we take into account the photon-generated hole, the total number of charges collected at the photoconductor contacts for every electron generated is 183.

When the optical signal ends, the photocurrent will decay exponentially with a time constant equal to the minority carrier lifetime. The switching speed of frequency response is inversely proportional to the lifetime. From the photoconductor gain expression, we would like a large minority-carrier lifetime, but the switching speed is enhanced by a small minority-carrier lifetime. There is obviously a trade-off between gain and speed. In general, the performance of a photodiode, which we will discuss next, is superior to that of a photoconductor.

12.3.2   Photodiode

A photodiode is a pn junction diode operated with an applied reverse-bias voltage. We will initially consider a long diode in which excess carriers are generated uniformly throughout the entire semiconductor device. Figure 12.17a shows the reverse-biased diode and Figure 12.17b shows the minority-carrier distribution in the reverse-biased junction prior to photon illumination.

Let G_L be the generation rate of excess carriers. The excess carriers generated within the space charge region are swept out of the depletion region very quickly by the electric field; the electrons are swept into the n region and the holes into the p region. The photon-generated current density from the space charge region is given by

$$J_{L1} = e \int G_L \, dx \tag{12.25}$$

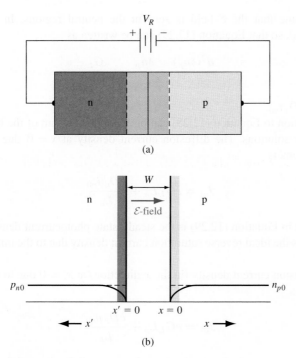

V_R

n

p

(a)

W

n

$\mathcal{E}$-field

p

p_{n0}

n_{p0}

$x' = 0$ $x = 0$

x' x

(b)

Figure 12.17 | (a) A reverse-biased pn junction. (b) Minority-carrier concentration in the reverse-biased pn junction.

where the integral is over the space charge region width. If G_L is constant throughout the space charge volume, then

$$J_{L1} = e G_L W \tag{12.26}$$

where W is the space charge width. We can note that J_{L1} is in the reverse-bias direction through the pn junction. This component of photocurrent responds very quickly to the photon illumination and is known as the prompt photocurrent.

Prompt photocurrent

Comparing Equations (12.26) and (12.23), we note that the photodiode gain is unity. The speed of the photodiode is limited by the carrier transport through the space charge region. If we assume that the saturation drift velocity is 10^7 cm/s and the depletion width is $2\,\mu$m, the transit time is $\tau_t = 20$ ps. The ideal modulating frequency has a period of $2\tau_t$, so the frequency is $f = 25$ GHz. This frequency response is substantially higher than that of photoconductors.

Excess carriers are also generated within the neutral n and p regions of the diode. The excess minority-carrier electron distribution in the p region is found from the ambipolar transport equation, which is

$$D_n \frac{\partial^2 (\delta n_p)}{\partial x^2} + G_L - \frac{\delta n_p}{\tau_{n0}} = \frac{\partial (\delta n_p)}{\partial t} \tag{12.27}$$

We will assume that the $\mathcal{E}$-field is zero in the neutral regions. In steady state, $\partial(\delta n_p)/\partial t = 0$, so that Equation (12.27) can be written as

$$\frac{d^2(\delta n_p)}{dx^2} - \frac{\delta n_p}{L_n^2} = -\frac{G_L}{D_n} \tag{12.28}$$

where $L_n^2 = D_n \tau_{n0}$.

The solution to Equation (12.28) can be found as the sum of the homogeneous and particular solutions. The diffusion current density at $x = 0$ due to minority-carrier electrons is

$$J_{n1} = eG_L L_n + \frac{eD_n n_{p0}}{L_n} \tag{12.29}$$

The first term in Equation (12.29) is the steady-state photocurrent density while the second term is the ideal reverse saturation current density due to the minority-carrier electrons.

The diffusion current density (in the x direction) at $x' = 0$ due to the minority-carrier holes is

$$J_{p1} = eG_L L_p + \frac{eD_p p_{n0}}{L_p} \tag{12.30}$$

Similarly, the first term is the steady-state photocurrent density and the second term is the ideal reverse-saturation current density.

The total steady-state diode photocurrent density for the long diode is now

Steady-state photocurrent

$$J_L = eG_L W + eG_L L_n + eG_L L_p = e(W + L_n + L_p)G_L \tag{12.31}$$

Again note that the photocurrent is in the reverse-bias direction through the diode. The photocurrent given by Equation (12.31) is the result of assuming uniform generation of excess carriers throughout the entire structure, a long diode, and steady state.

The time response of the diffusion components of the photocurrent is relatively slow, since these currents are the results of the diffusion of minority carriers toward the depletion region. The diffusion components of photocurrent are referred to as the delayed photocurrent.

EXAMPLE 12.6

OBJECTIVE

To calculate the steady-state photocurrent density in a reverse-biased, long pn diode.

Consider a silicon pn diode at $T = 300$ K with the following parameters:

$$N_a = 10^{16} \text{ cm}^{-3} \qquad N_d = 10^{16} \text{ cm}^{-3}$$

$$D_n = 25 \text{ cm}^2/\text{s} \qquad D_p = 10 \text{ cm}^2/\text{s}$$

$$\tau_{n0} = 5 \times 10^{-7} \text{ s} \qquad \tau_{p0} = 10^{-7} \text{ s}$$

Assume that a reverse-bias voltage of $V_R = 5$ volts is applied and let $G_L = 10^{21} \text{ cm}^{-3}\text{-s}^{-1}$.

■ Solution

We can calculate various parameters as follows:

$$L_n = \sqrt{D_n \tau_{n0}} = \sqrt{(25)(5 \times 10^{-7})} = 35.4\,\mu m$$

$$L_p = \sqrt{D_p \tau_{p0}} = \sqrt{(10)(10^{-7})} = 10.0\,\mu m$$

$$V_{bi} = V_t \ln\left(\frac{N_a N_d}{n_i^2}\right) = (0.0259)\ln\left[\frac{(10^{16})(10^{16})}{(1.5 \times 10^{10})^2}\right] = 0.695\ V$$

$$W = \left[\frac{2\varepsilon_s}{e}\left(\frac{N_a + N_d}{N_a N_d}\right)(V_{bi} + V_R)\right]^{1/2}$$

$$= \left[\frac{2(11.7)(8.85 \times 10^{-14})}{1.6 \times 10^{-19}} \cdot \frac{(2 \times 10^{16})}{(10^{16})(10^{16})} \cdot (0.695 + 5)\right]^{1/2} = 1.21\,\mu m$$

Finally, the steady-state photocurrent density is

$$J_L = e(W + L_n + L_p)G_L$$

$$= (1.6 \times 10^{-19})(1.21 + 35.4 + 10.0) \times 10^{-4}(10^{21}) = 0.75\ A/cm^2$$

■ Comment

Again, keep in mind that this photocurrent is in the reverse-bias direction through the diode and is many orders of magnitude larger than the reverse-bias saturation current density in the pn junction diode.

Exercise Problem

EX12.6 Consider a long silicon pn junction photodiode with the parameters given in Example 12.6. The cross-sectional area is $A = 10^{-3}\ cm^2$. Assume the photodiode is reverse biased by a 5-V battery in series with a 5-kΩ load resistor. An optical signal at a wavelength of $\lambda = 1\,\mu m$ is incident on the photodiode producing a uniform generation rate of excess carriers throughout the entire device. Determine the incident intensity such that the voltage across the load resistor is 0.5 V. (Ans. $I_\nu = 0.266\ W/cm^2$)

In the calculation of Example 12.6, $L_n \gg W$ and $L_p \gg W$. In many pn junction structures, the assumption of a long diode will not be valid so that the photocurrent expression will have to be modified. In addition, the photon energy absorption may not be uniform throughout the pn structure. The effect of nonuniform absorption will be considered in Section 12.3.3.

12.3.3 PIN Photodiode

In many photodetector applications, the speed of response is important; therefore the prompt photocurrent generated in the space charge region is the only photocurrent of interest. To increase the photodetector sensitivity, the depletion region width should be made as large as possible. This can be achieved in a PIN photodiode.

The PIN diode consists of a p region and an n region separated by an intrinsic region. A sketch of a PIN diode is shown in Figure 12.18a. The intrinsic region width W

PIN diode

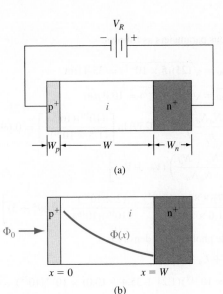

Figure 12.18 | (a) A reverse-biased PIN photodiode. (b) Geometry showing nonuniform photon absorption.

is much larger than the space charge width of a normal pn junction. If a reverse bias is applied to the PIN diode, the space charge region extends completely through the intrinsic region.

Assume that a photon flux Φ_0 is incident on the p^+ region. If we assume that the p^+ region width W_p is very thin, then the photon flux, as a function of distance, in the intrinsic region is $\Phi(x) = \Phi_0 e^{-\alpha x}$, where α is the photon absorption coefficient. This nonlinear photon absorption is shown in Figure 12.18b. The photocurrent density generated in the intrinsic region can be found as

$$J_L = e \int_0^W G_L \, dx = e \int_0^W \Phi_0 \alpha e^{-\alpha x} \, dx = e\Phi_0(1 - e^{-\alpha W}) \qquad (12.32)$$

This equation assumes that there is no electron–hole recombination within the space charge region and also that each photon absorbed creates one electron–hole pair.

EXAMPLE 12.7

OBJECTIVE

To calculate the photocurrent density in a PIN photodiode.

Consider a silicon PIN diode with an intrinsic region width of $W = 20 \, \mu m$. Assume that the photon flux is $10^{17} \, \text{cm}^{-2}\text{-s}^{-1}$ and the absorption coefficient is $\alpha = 10^3 \, \text{cm}^{-1}$.

■ **Solution**

The generation rate of electron–hole pairs at the front edge of the intrinsic region is

$$G_{L1} = \alpha\Phi_0 = (10^3)(10^{17}) = 10^{20} \, \text{cm}^{-3}\text{-s}^{-1}$$

and the generation rate at the back edge of the intrinsic region is

$$G_{L2} = \alpha \Phi_0 e^{-\alpha W} = (10^3)(10^{17}) \exp\left[-(10^3)(20 \times 10^{-4})\right]$$

$$= 0.135 \times 10^{20} \text{ cm}^{-3}\text{-s}^{-1}$$

The generation rate is obviously not uniform throughout the intrinsic region. The photocurrent density is then

$$J_L = e\Phi_0(1 - e^{-\alpha W})$$

$$= (1.6 \times 10^{-19})(10^{17})\{1 - \exp\left[-(10^3)(20 \times 10^{-4})\right]\}$$

$$= 13.8 \text{ mA/cm}^2$$

■ Comment

The prompt photocurrent density of a PIN photodiode will be larger than that of a regular photodiode since the space charge region is larger in a PIN photodiode.

Exercise Problem

EX12.7 For the PIN photodiode described in Example 12.7, determine the intrinsic width W for which 90 percent of the maximum possible photocurrent ($W = \infty$) is generated. Assume the same parameters as given in the example.
(Ans. $W = 24 \ \mu$m)

An important aspect of photodetector design is to consider an optimal material for the frequency or frequencies to be detected. For long-fiber optical communications, a wavelength of 1.55 μm is being used. The optical fiber propagation loss tends to be a minimum at this wavelength. The corresponding energy for this wavelength [Equation (12.1)] is $E = 0.8$ eV. The PIN diode schematically shown in Figure 12.19 could be used for this application. The InP has a bandgap energy of $E_g = 1.35$ eV and is used as a window. The In$_{0.53}$Ga$_{0.47}$As has a bandgap energy of $E_g = 0.75$ eV. Electrons and holes are generated in the depleted wide n$^-$ region of the InGaAs.

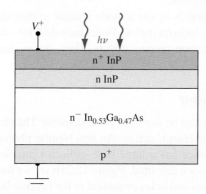

Figure 12.19 | A multilayer heterojunction PIN photodiode for detecting 1.55-μm-wavelength optical signals.

Heterojunction PIN photodiode

12.3.4 Avalanche Photodiode

The avalanche photodiode is similar to the pn or PIN photodiode except that the bias applied to the avalanche photodiode is sufficiently large to cause impact ionization. Electron–hole pairs are generated in the space charge region by photon absorption, as we have discussed previously. The photon-generated electrons and holes now generate additional electron–hole pairs through impact ionization. The avalanche photodiode now has a current gain introduced by the avalanche multiplication factor.

The electron–hole pairs generated by photon absorption and by impact ionization are swept out of the space charge region very quickly. If the saturation velocity is 10^7 cm/s in a depletion region that is $10\,\mu$m wide, then the transit time is

$$\tau_t = \frac{10^7}{10 \times 10^{-4}} = 100\ \text{ps}$$

The period of a modulation signal would be $2\tau_t$, so that the frequency would be

$$f = \frac{1}{2\tau_t} = \frac{1}{200 \times 10^{-12}} = 5\ \text{GHz}$$

If the avalanche photodiode current gain is 20, then the gain-bandwidth product is 100 GHz. The avalanche photodiode could respond to light waves modulated at microwave frequencies.

Avalanche photodiodes provide gain through the avalanche multiplication process. Unfortunately, the random fluctuations in the avalanche process introduce added noise compared to the PIN photodiode. This noise can be reduced if the avalanche process is due to only one type of carrier. In silicon, the ionization rate for electrons is larger than that for holes. Unfortunately, the bandgap energy of silicon is larger than the energy of most optical fiber communication so that silicon is transparent to these optical signals.

One possible solution is to use a diode similar to that shown in Figure 12.20. Light is absorbed in the InGaAs region. Holes then drift into the n InP region, where the avalanche multiplication process occurs. Thus, the avalanche process involves only one carrier.

12.3.5 Phototransistor

A bipolar transistor can also be used as a photodetector. The phototransistor can have high gain through the transistor action. An npn bipolar phototransistor is shown in Figure 12.21a. This device has a large base–collector junction area and is usually operated with the base open circuited. Figure 12.21b shows the block diagram of the phototransistor. Electrons and holes generated in the reverse-biased B-C junction are swept out of the space charge region, producing a photocurrent I_L. Holes are swept into the p-type base making the base positive with respect to the emitter. Since the B-E becomes forward biased, electrons will be injected from the emitter back into the base, leading to the normal transistor action.

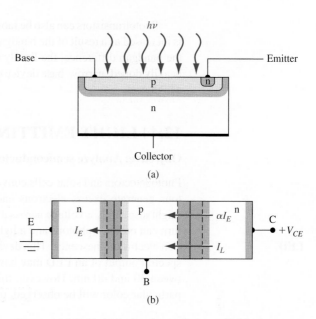

Figure 12.21 | (a) A bipolar phototransistor. (b) Block diagram of the open-base phototransistor.

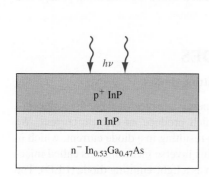

Figure 12.20 | An avalanche photodetector. Light is absorbed in the n^--$In_{0.53}Ga_{0.47}As$ region. Holes drift into the n-InP region where the avalanche multiplication process occurs.

From Figure 12.21b, we see that

$$I_E = \alpha I_E + I_L \tag{12.33}$$

where I_L is the photon-generated current and α is the common-base current gain. Since the base is an open circuit, we have $I_C = I_E$, so Equation (12.33) can be written as

$$I_C = \alpha I_C + I_L \tag{12.34}$$

Solving for I_C, we find

$$I_C = \frac{I_L}{1 - \alpha} \tag{12.35}$$

Relating α to β, the dc common-emitter current gain, Equation (12.35) becomes

$$I_C = (1 + \beta)I_L \tag{12.36}$$

Equation (12.36) shows that the basic B-C photocurrent is multiplied by the factor $(1 + \beta)$. The phototransistor, then, amplifies the basic photocurrent.

Photocurrent

With the relatively large B-C junction area, the frequency response of the phototransistor is limited by the B-C junction capacitance. Since the base is essentially the input to the device, the large B-C capacitance is multiplied by the Miller effect, so the frequency response of the phototransistor is further reduced. The phototransistor, however, is a lower-noise device than the avalanche photodiode.

Phototransistors can also be fabricated in heterostructures. The injection efficiency is increased as a result of the bandgap differences, as we discussed in Chapter 11. With the bandgap difference, the lightly doped base restriction no longer applies. A fairly heavily doped, narrow-base device can be fabricated with a high blocking voltage and a high gain.

12.4 | LIGHT-EMITTING DIODES

Objective: Analyze semiconductor light-emitting diodes.

LED

Photodetectors and solar cells convert optical energy into electrical energy—the photons generate excess electrons and holes, which produce an electric current. We might also apply a voltage across a pn junction resulting in a diode current, which in turn can produce photons and a light output. This inverse mechanism is called injection electroluminescence. This device is known as a **l**ight-**e**mitting **d**iode (LED). The spectral output of an LED may have a relatively wide wavelength bandwidth of between 30 and 40 nm. However, this emission spectrum is narrow enough so that a particular color will be observed, provided the output is in the visible range.

12.4.1   Generation of Light

As we discussed previously, photons may be emitted if an electron and hole recombine by a direct band-to-band recombination process in a direct bandgap material. The emission wavelength, from Equation (12.1), is

$$\lambda = \frac{hc}{E_g} = \frac{1.24}{E_g}\mu m \tag{12.37}$$

where E_g is the bandgap energy measured in electron-volts.

When a voltage is applied across a pn junction, electrons and holes are injected across the space charge region, where they become excess minority carriers. These excess minority carriers diffuse into the neutral semiconductor regions, where they recombine with majority carriers. If this recombination process is a direct band-to-band process, photons are emitted. The diode diffusion current is directly proportional to the recombination rate, so the output photon intensity will also be proportional to the ideal diode diffusion current. In gallium arsenide, electroluminescence originates primarily on the p side of the junction because the efficiency for electron injection is higher than that for hole injection.

12.4.2   Internal Quantum Efficiency

Internal quantum efficiency

The *internal quantum efficiency* of an LED is the fraction of diode current that will produce luminescence. The internal quantum efficiency is a function of the injection efficiency and a function of the percentage of radiative recombination events compared with the total number of recombination events.

The three current components in a forward-biased diode are the minority-carrier electron diffusion current, the minority-carrier hole diffusion current, and the space charge recombination current. These current densities can be written, respectively, as

$$J_n = \frac{e D_n n_{p0}}{L_n} \left[\exp\left(\frac{eV}{kT}\right) - 1 \right] \qquad (12.38a)$$

$$J_p = \frac{e D_p p_{n0}}{L_p} \left[\exp\left(\frac{eV}{kT}\right) - 1 \right] \qquad (12.38b)$$

and

$$J_R = \frac{e n_i W}{2\tau_0} \left[\exp\left(\frac{eV}{2kT}\right) - 1 \right] \qquad (12.38c)$$

The recombination of electrons and holes within the space charge region is, in general, through traps near midgap and is a nonradiative process. Since luminescence is due primarily to the recombination of minority-carrier electrons in GaAs, we can define an injection efficiency as the fraction of electron current to total current. Then,

$$\gamma = \frac{J_n}{J_n + J_p + J_R} \qquad (12.39)$$

where γ is the injection efficiency. We can make γ approach unity by using an n$^+$p diode so that J_p is a small fraction of the diode current and by forward biasing the diode sufficiently so that J_R is a small fraction of the total diode current.

Once the electrons are injected into the p region, not all electrons will recombine radiatively. We can define the radiative and nonradiative recombination rates as

$$R_r = \frac{\delta n}{\tau_r} \qquad (12.40a)$$

and

$$R_{nr} = \frac{\delta n}{\tau_{nr}} \qquad (12.40b)$$

where τ_r and τ_{nr} are the radiative and nonradiative recombination lifetimes, respectively, and δn is the excess carrier concentration. The total recombination rate is

$$R = R_r + R_{nr} = \frac{\delta n}{\tau} = \frac{\delta n}{\tau_r} + \frac{\delta n}{\tau_{nr}} \qquad (12.41)$$

where τ is the net excess carrier lifetime.

The radiative efficiency is defined as the fraction of recombinations that are radiative. We can write

Radiative efficiency

$$\eta = \frac{R_r}{R_r + R_{nr}} = \frac{\dfrac{1}{\tau_r}}{\dfrac{1}{\tau_r} + \dfrac{1}{\tau_{nr}}} = \frac{\tau}{\tau_r} \qquad (12.42)$$

where η is the radiative efficiency. The nonradiative recombination rate is proportional to N_t, which is the density of nonradiative trapping sites within the forbidden bandgap. Obviously, the radiative efficiency increases as N_t is reduced.

The internal quantum efficiency is now written as

$$\eta_i = \gamma \eta \qquad (12.43)$$

The radiative recombination rate is proportional to the p-type doping. As the p-type doping increases, the radiative recombination rate increases. However, the injection efficiency decreases as the p-type doping increases; therefore, there is an optimum doping that will maximize the internal quantum efficiency.

12.4.3 External Quantum Efficiency

External quantum efficiency

One very important parameter of the LED is the *external quantum efficiency:* the fraction of generated photons that are actually emitted from the semiconductor. The external quantum efficiency is normally a much smaller number than the internal quantum efficiency. Once a photon has been produced in the semiconductor, there are three loss mechanisms the photon may encounter: photon absorption within the semiconductor, Fresnel loss, and critical angle loss.

Figure 12.22 shows a pn junction LED. Photons can be emitted in any direction. Since the emitted photon energy must be $h\nu \geq E_g$, these emitted photons can be reabsorbed within the semiconductor material. The majority of photons will actually be emitted away from the surface and reabsorbed in the semiconductor.

Photons must be emitted from the semiconductor into air; thus, the photons must be transmitted across a dielectric interface. Figure 12.23 shows the incident, reflected, and transmitted waves. The parameter $\bar{n}_2$ is the index of refraction for the semiconductor and $\bar{n}_1$ is the index of refraction for air. The reflection coefficient is

Reflection coefficient

$$\Gamma = \left(\frac{\bar{n}_2 - \bar{n}_1}{\bar{n}_2 + \bar{n}_1} \right)^2 \qquad (12.44)$$

Fresnel loss

This effect is called Fresnel loss. The reflection coefficient Γ is the fraction of incident photons that are reflected back into the semiconductor.

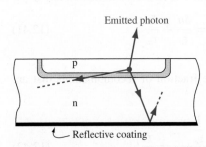

Figure 12.22 | Schematic of photon emission at the pn junction of an LED.

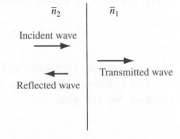

Figure 12.23 | Schematic of incident, reflected, and transmitted photons at a dielectric interface.

EXAMPLE 12.8

OBJECTIVE

To calculate the reflection coefficient at a semiconductor–air interface.

Consider the interface between a GaAs semiconductor and air.

■ Solution

The index of refraction for GaAs is $\bar{n}_2 = 3.66$ and for air is $\bar{n}_1 = 1.0$. The reflection coefficient is

$$\Gamma = \left(\frac{\bar{n}_2 - \bar{n}_1}{\bar{n}_2 + \bar{n}_1}\right)^2 = \left(\frac{3.66 - 1.0}{3.66 + 1.0}\right)^2 = 0.33$$

■ Comment

A reflection coefficient of $\Gamma = 0.33$ means that 33 percent of the photons incident from the gallium arsenide on the gallium arsenide–air interface are reflected back into the semiconductor.

Exercise Problem

EX12.8 Repeat Example 12.8 for a GaP–air interface. Assume $\bar{n}_2 = 3.12$ for GaP.

(Ans. $\Gamma = 0.265$)

Photons incident on the semiconductor–air interface at an angle are refracted as shown in Figure 12.24. If the photons are incident on the interface at an angle greater than the critical angle θ_c, the photons experience total internal reflection. The critical angle is determined from Snell's law and is given by

Snell's law

$$\theta_c = \sin^{-1}\left(\frac{\bar{n}_1}{\bar{n}_2}\right) \tag{12.45}$$

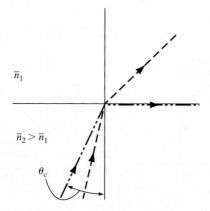

Figure 12.24 | Schematic showing refraction and total internal reflection at the critical angle at a dielectric interface.

EXAMPLE 12.9

OBJECTIVE

To calculate the critical angle at a semiconductor–air interface.

   Consider the interface between GaAs and air.

■ **Solution**

For GaAs, $\bar{n}_2 = 3.66$ and for air, $\bar{n}_1 = 1.0$. The critical angle is

$$\theta_c = \sin^{-1}\left(\frac{\bar{n}_1}{\bar{n}_2}\right) = \sin^{-1}\left(\frac{1.0}{3.66}\right) = 15.9°$$

■ **Comment**

Any photon that is incident at an angle greater than 15.9° will be reflected back into the semiconductor.

Exercise Problem

EX12.9   Repeat Example 12.9 for the interface between GaP and air. Assume $\bar{n}_2 = 3.12$
   for GaP. (Ans. $\theta_c = 18.7°$)

   Figure 12.25a shows the external quantum efficiency plotted as a function of the p-type doping concentration and Figure 12.25b is a plot of the external efficiency as a function of junction depth below the surface. Both figures show that the external quantum efficiency is in the range of 1 to 3 percent.

12.4.4   LED Devices

The wavelength of the output signal of an LED is determined by the bandgap energy of the semiconductor. Gallium arsenide, a direct bandgap material, has a bandgap

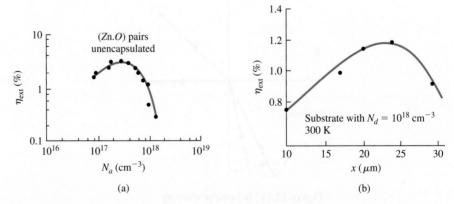

Figure 12.25 | (a) External quantum efficiency of a GaP LED versus acceptor doping.
(b) External quantum efficiency of a GaAs LED versus junction depth.
(From Yang [22].)

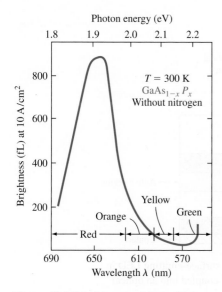

Figure 12.26 | Brightness of GaAsP diodes versus wavelength (or versus bandgap energy).
(From Yang [22].)

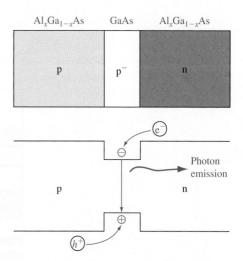

Figure 12.27 | A heterojunction LED with a narrow-gap semiconductor as the active region. The emitted photons pass through the wide-gap layers without being absorbed.

energy of $E_g = 1.42\,\text{eV}$, which yields a wavelength of $\lambda = 0.873\,\mu\text{m}$. Comparing this wavelength to the visible spectrum that was shown in Figure 12.5, the output of a GaAs LED is not in the visible range. For a visible output, the wavelength of the signal should be in the range of 0.4 to $0.72\,\mu\text{m}$. This range of wavelengths corresponds to bandgap energies between approximately 1.7 and 3.1 eV.

GaAs$_{1-x}$P$_x$ is a direct bandgap material for $0 \leq x \leq 0.45$. At $x = 0.40$, the bandgap energy is approximately $E_g = 1.9\,\text{eV}$, which would produce an optical output in the red range. Figure 12.26 shows the brightness of GaAs$_{1-x}$P$_x$ diodes for different values of x. The peak also occurs in the red range. By using planar technology, GaAs$_{0.6}$P$_{0.4}$ monolithic arrays have been fabricated for numeric and alphanumeric displays. When the mole fraction x is greater than 0.45, the material changes to an indirect bandgap semiconductor so that the quantum efficiency is greatly reduced.

Multilayer heterojunctions are commonly used for LEDs. One example is shown in Figure 12.27. The narrow-gap GaAs is the active region. Electrons and holes are injected from the wide-gap n and p regions into the GaAs layer. The emitted photons then pass through the wide-gap top and bottom layers without being absorbed.

A schematic of an LED directly coupled to an optical fiber is shown in Figure 12.28. The active region is again the narrow-gap GaAs layer. The emitted photons pass through the wide-gap AlGaAs layer and are coupled into the fiber.

Multilayer heterojunction LED

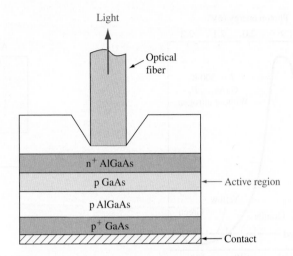

Figure 12.28 | Schematic of a surface-emitting LED in which the photons are directly coupled into an optical fiber.

12.5 | LASER DIODES

Objective: Analyze semiconductor laser diodes.

LASER

The photon output of the LED is due to an electron giving up energy as it makes a transition from the conduction band to the valence band. The LED photon emission is spontaneous in that each band-to-band transition is an independent event. The spontaneous emission process yields a spectral output of the LED with a fairly wide bandwidth. If the structure and operating condition of the LED are modified, the device can operate in a new mode, producing a coherent spectral output with a bandwidth of wavelengths less than 0.1 nm. This new device is a laser diode, where laser stands for **l**ight **a**mplification by **s**timulated **e**mission of **r**adiation. Although there are many different types of lasers, we will be concerned only with the pn junction laser diode.

12.5.1 Stimulated Emission and Population Inversion

Stimulated emission

Figure 12.29a shows the case when an incident photon is absorbed and an electron is elevated from an energy state E_1 to an energy state E_2. This process is known as induced absorption. If the electron spontaneously makes the transition back to the lower energy level with a photon being emitted, we have a spontaneous emission process as indicated in Figure 12.29b. On the other hand, if there is an incident photon at a time when an electron is in the higher energy state as shown in Figure 12.29c, the incident photon can interact with the electron, causing the electron to make a transition downward. The downward transition produces a photon. Since this process was initiated by the incident photon, the process is called *stimulated* or *induced emission*.

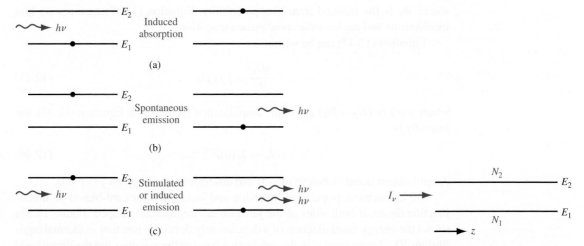

Figure 12.29 | Schematic diagram showing (a) induced absorption, (b) spontaneous emission, and (c) stimulated emission processes.

Figure 12.30 | Light propagating in z direction through a material with two energy levels.

Note that this stimulated emission process has produced two photons; thus, we can have optical gain or amplification. The two emitted photons are in phase so that the spectral output will be coherent.

In thermal equilibrium, the electron distribution in a semiconductor is determined by the Fermi–Dirac statistics. If the Boltzmann approximation applies, then we can write

$$\frac{N_2}{N_1} = \exp\left[\frac{-(E_2 - E_1)}{kT}\right] \tag{12.46}$$

where N_1 and N_2 are the electron concentrations in the energy levels E_1 and E_2, respectively, and where $E_2 > E_1$. In thermal equilibrium, $N_2 < N_1$. The probability of an induced absorption event is exactly the same as that of an induced emission event. The number of photons absorbed is proportional to N_1 and the number of additional photons emitted is proportional to N_2. To achieve optical amplification or for lasing action to occur, we must have $N_2 > N_1$; this is called population inversion. We cannot achieve lasing action at thermal equilibrium.

Population inversion

Figure 12.30 shows the two energy levels with a light wave at an intensity I_ν propagating in the z direction. The change in intensity as a function of z can be written as

$$\frac{dI_\nu}{dz} \propto \frac{\text{\# photons emitted}}{\text{cm}^3} - \frac{\text{\# photons absorbed}}{\text{cm}^3}$$

or

$$\frac{dI_\nu}{dz} = N_2 W_i h\nu - N_1 W_i h\nu \tag{12.47}$$

where W_i is the induced transition probability. Equation (12.47) assumes no loss mechanisms and neglects the spontaneous transitions.

Equation (12.47) can be written as

$$\frac{dI_\nu}{dz} = \gamma(\nu)I_\nu \tag{12.48}$$

where $\gamma(\nu) \propto (N_2 - N_1)$ and is the amplification factor. From Equation (12.48), the intensity is

$$I_\nu = I_\nu(0)e^{\gamma(\nu)z} \tag{12.49}$$

Amplification occurs when $\gamma(\nu) > 0$ and absorption occurs when $\gamma(\nu) < 0$.

We can achieve population inversion and lasing in a forward-biased pn homojunction diode, if both sides of the junction are degenerately doped. Figure 12.31a shows the energy-band diagram of a degenerately doped pn junction in thermal equilibrium. The Fermi level is in the conduction band in the n-region and the Fermi level is in the valence band in the p region. Figure 12.31b shows the energy bands of the pn junction when a forward bias is applied. The gain factor in a pn homojunction diode is given by

$$\gamma(\nu) \propto \left\{ 1 - \exp\left[\frac{h\nu - (E_{Fn} - E_{Fp})}{kT} \right] \right\} \tag{12.50}$$

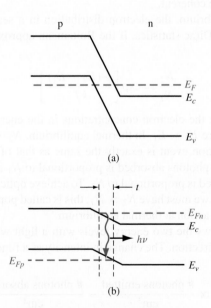

Figure 12.31 | (a) Degenerately doped pn junction at zero bias. (b) Degenerately doped pn junction under forward bias with photon emission.

For $\gamma(\nu) > 1$, we must have $h\nu < (E_{Fn} - E_{Fp})$, which implies that the junction must be degenerately doped since we also have the requirement that $h\nu \geq E_g$. In the vicinity of the junction, there is a region in which population inversion occurs. There are large numbers of electrons in the conduction band directly above a large number of empty states. If band-to-band recombination occurs, photons will be emitted with energies in the range $E_g < h\nu < (E_{Fn} - E_{Fp})$.

12.5.2 Optical Cavity

Population inversion is one requirement for lasing action to occur. Coherent emission output is achieved by using an optical cavity. The cavity will cause a buildup of the optical intensity from positive feedback. A resonant cavity consisting of two parallel mirrors is known as a Fabry–Pérot resonator. The resonant cavity can be fabricated, for example, by cleaving a gallium arsenide crystal along the (110) planes as shown in Figure 12.32. The optical wave propagates through the junction in the z direction, bouncing back and forth between the end mirrors. The mirrors are actually

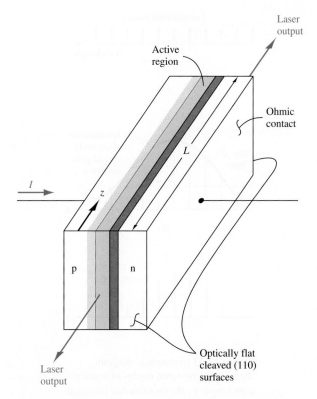

Figure 12.32 | A pn junction laser diode with cleaved (110) planes forming the Fabry–Pérot cavity.
(After Yang [22].)

Fabry–Pérot cavity

only partially reflecting so that a portion of the optical wave will be transmitted out of the junction.

For resonance, the length of the cavity L must be an integral number of half wavelengths, or

$$N\left(\frac{\lambda}{2}\right) = L \tag{12.51}$$

where N is an integer. Since λ is small and L is relatively large, there can be many resonant modes in the cavity. Figure 12.33a shows the resonant modes as a function of wavelength.

When a forward-bias current is applied to the pn junction, spontaneous emission will initially occur. The spontaneous emission spectrum is relatively broadband and is superimposed on the possible lasing modes, as shown in Figure 12.33b. For lasing to be initiated, the spontaneous emission gain must be larger than the optical losses. By positive feedback in the cavity, lasing can occur at several specific wavelengths, as indicated in Figure 12.33c.

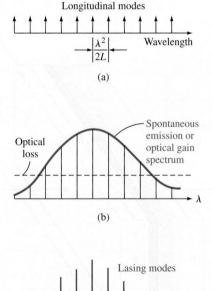

Figure 12.33 | Schematic diagram showing (a) resonant modes of a cavity with length L, (b) spontaneous emission curve, and (c) actual emission modes of a laser diode.
(After Yang [22].)

12.5.3 Threshold Current

The optical intensity in the device can be written from Equation (12.49) as $I_\nu \propto e^{\gamma(\nu)z}$, where $\gamma(\nu)$ is the amplification factor. We have two basic loss mechanisms. The first is the photon absorption in the semiconductor material. We can write

$$I_\nu \propto e^{-\alpha(\nu)z} \tag{12.52}$$

where $\alpha(\nu)$ is the absorption coefficient. The second loss mechanism is due to the partial transmission of the optical signal through the ends, or through the partially reflecting mirrors.

At the onset of lasing, which is known as threshold, the optical loss of one round trip through the cavity is just offset by the optical gain. The threshold condition is then expressed as

$$\Gamma_1 \Gamma_2 \exp\{[2\gamma_t(\nu) - 2\alpha(\nu)]L\} = 1 \tag{12.53}$$

where Γ_1 and Γ_2 are the reflectivity coefficients of the two end mirrors. For the case when the optical mirrors are cleaved (110) surfaces of gallium arsenide, the reflectivity coefficients are given approximately by

$$\Gamma_1 = \Gamma_2 = \left(\frac{\bar{n}_2 - \bar{n}_1}{\bar{n}_2 + \bar{n}_1}\right)^2 \tag{12.54}$$

where $\bar{n}_2$ and $\bar{n}_1$ are the index of refraction parameters for the semiconductor and air, respectively. The parameter $\gamma_t(\nu)$ is the optical gain at threshold.

The optical gain at threshold, $\gamma_t(\nu)$, may be determined from Equation (12.53) as

$$\gamma_t(\nu) = \alpha + \frac{1}{2L} \ln\left(\frac{1}{\Gamma_1 \Gamma_2}\right) \tag{12.55}$$

Since the optical gain is a function of the pn junction current, we can define a threshold current density as

Threshold current

$$J_{th} = \frac{1}{\beta}\left[\alpha + \frac{1}{2L} \ln\left(\frac{1}{\Gamma_1 \Gamma_2}\right)\right] \tag{12.56}$$

where β can be determined theoretically or experimentally. Figure 12.34 shows the threshold current density as a function of the mirror losses. We can note the relatively high threshold current density for a pn junction laser diode.

12.5.4 Device Structures and Characteristics

We have seen that in a homojunction LED, the photons may be emitted in any direction, which lowers the external quantum efficiency. Significant improvement in device characteristics can be made if the emitted photons are confined to a region

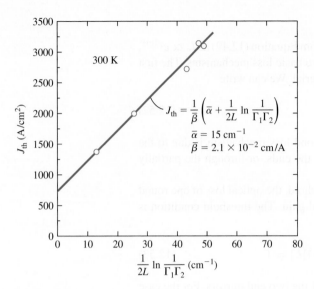

Figure 12.34 | Threshold current density of a laser diode as a function of Fabry-Pérot cavity end losses.
(After Yang [22].)

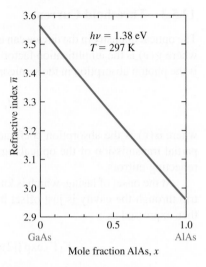

Figure 12.35 | Index of refraction of $Al_xGa_{1-x}As$ as a function of mole fraction x.
(From Sze [18].)

near the junction. This confinement can be achieved by using an optical dielectric waveguide. The first successful lasers used a three-layered, double-heterojunction structure known as a double-heterojunction laser. A requirement for a dielectric waveguide is that the index of refraction of the center material be larger than that of the other two dielectrics. Figure 12.35 shows the index of refraction for the AlGaAs system. We may note that GaAs has the highest index of refraction.

Double-heterojunction laser

An example of a double-heterojunction laser is shown in Figure 12.36a. A thin p-GaAs layer is between P-AlGaAs and N-AlGaAs layers. A simplified energy-band diagram is shown in Figure 12.36b for the forward-biased diode. Electrons are injected from the N-AlGaAs in the p-GaAs. Population inversion is easily obtained since the conduction band potential barrier prevents the electrons from diffusing into the P-AlGaAs region. Radiative recombination is then confined to the p-GaAs region. Since the index of refraction of GaAs is larger than that of AlGaAs, the lightwave is also confined to the GaAs region. An optical cavity can be formed by cleaving the semiconductor perpendicular to the N-AlGaAs–p-GaAs junction.

A disadvantage of the double-heterojunction laser shown in Figure 12.36 is that the laser active region and the waveguide region are one and the same. A more efficient laser would be one in which both the active region and waveguide region were optimized for their particular functions. One such configuration is shown in Figure 12.37. The active region has a width d and may be GaAs. The optical waveguide region has a width w and is a graded composition of $Al_xGa_{1-x}As$. A parabolic grading leads to better waveguiding.

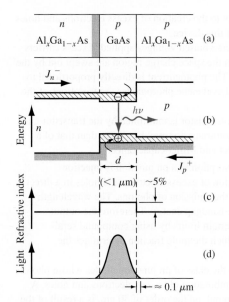

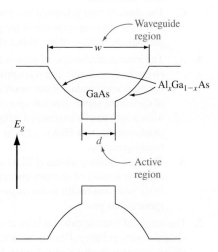

Figure 12.36 | (a) Basic double-heterojunction structure. (b) Energy-band diagram under forward bias. (c) Refractive index change through the structure. (d) Confinement of light in the dielectric waveguide.
(From Yang [22].)

Figure 12.37 | The laser active region width is d and the graded alloy width is w that is the optical waveguide.

12.6 | SUMMARY

1. Optical absorption in a semiconductor was discussed. The optical absorption coefficient as a function of wavelength was considered, and the electron–hole generation rate as a function of incident intensity and wavelength was derived.

2. A. Solar cells convert optical power into electrical power. The simple pn junction solar cell was initially considered. Expressions for short-circuit current and open-circuit voltage were derived. The maximum power was considered.

   B. The conversion efficiency takes into account incident photons with energies less than the bandgap energy that are not absorbed, and also incident photons with energies greater than the bandgap energy whose excess energy produces heat. For these reasons, ideal solar cell conversion efficiencies are typically less than 30 percent.

   C. Heterojunction and amorphous silicon solar cells were also considered. Heterojunction cells can be fabricated that tend to increase conversion efficiency and produce relatively large open-circuit voltages. Amorphous silicon offers the possibility of low-cost, large-area solar cell arrays.

3. A. Semiconductor photodetectors convert optical signals into electrical signals. The photoconductor is perhaps the simplest type of photodetector. The change in

conductivity of the semiconductor due to the creation of excess electrons and holes by the incident photons is the basis of this device.

B. Photodiodes are diodes that have reverse-biased voltages applied. Excess carriers that are created by incident photons in the space charge region are swept out by the electric field creating a photocurrent. The photocurrent is directly proportional to the incident photon intensity. PIN and avalanche photodiodes are variations of the basic photodiode.

C. The photocurrent generated in a phototransistor is multiplied by the transistor gain. However, the time response of the phototransistor may be slower than that of a photodiode because of the Miller effect and Miller capacitance.

4. A. The inverse mechanism of photon absorption in a pn junction is injection electroluminescence. The recombination of excess electrons and holes in a direct bandgap semiconductor can result in the emission of photons. The wavelength of the output signal depends upon the bandgap energy. Therefore the output wavelength can be engineered with certain limits by using compound semiconductors such as $GaAs_{1-x}P_x$, in which the mole fraction determines the bandgap energy.

B. The light-emitting diodes (LEDs) are the class of pn junction diodes whose photon output is a result of spontaneous recombination of excess electrons and holes. A fairly wide bandwidth in the output signal, on the order of 30 nm, is a result of the spontaneous process.

5. The output of a semiconductor laser diode is the result of stimulated emission. An optical cavity, or Fabry–Pérot resonator, is used in conjunction with a diode so that the photon output is in phase, or coherent. Multilayered heterojunction structures can be fabricated to improve the laser diode characteristics.

CHECKPOINT

After studying this chapter, the reader should have the ability to

1. Qualitatively describe optical absorption in a semiconductor as a function of incident wavelength.

2. A. Discuss the basic operation and characteristics of a pn junction solar cell, including the short-circuit current and open-circuit voltage.

B. Discuss the factors that contribute to the solar cell conversion efficiency.

C. Discuss the advantages and disadvantages of heterojunction and amorphous silicon solar cells.

3. A. Discuss the characteristics of a photoconductor, including the concept of the photoconductor gain.

B. Discuss the operation and characteristics of a simple pn junction photodiode.

C. Discuss the advantages of PIN and avalanche photodiodes compared to the simple pn junction photodiode.

D. Discuss the operation and characteristics of the phototransistor.

4. A. Discuss the basic operation of an LED.

B. Discuss the factors that limit the conversion efficiency.

5. A. Discuss the concept of stimulated emission.

B. Discuss the basic operation of a semiconductor laser diode.

REVIEW QUESTIONS

1. A. Sketch the general shape of the optical absorption coefficient in a semiconductor as a function of wavelength.
   B. Sketch the concentration of excess carriers as a function of distance in a semiconductor for two values of optical absorption coefficient.

2. A. Define what is meant by short-circuit current in a pn junction solar cell. Define what is meant by open-circuit voltage in a solar cell. What limits the open-circuit voltage?
   B. Sketch the $I-V$ characteristics of a solar cell. Define what is meant by the maximum power rectangle of a solar cell.

3. A. Write an expression for the steady-state photocurrent in a simple photoconductor.
   B. Sketch the steady-state excess minority-carrier concentrations in a long pn junction photodiode that is being illuminated with photons. Define three components of photocurrent.
   C. Sketch the cross section of a phototransistor, show the currents that are created by incident photons, and explain the current gain mechanism.

4. A. Discuss the concept of spontaneous recombination in an LED.
   B. Explain two factors that limit the number of generated photons from being emitted from an LED.

5. A. Discuss the concept of stimulated emission in a semiconductor laser diode.
   B. Explain the basic operation of a Fabry–Pérot optical resonator.

PROBLEMS

Section 12.1 Optical Absorption

12.1 (*a*) Calculate the maximum wavelength λ of a light source that can generate electron–hole pairs in Ge, Si, and GaAs. (*b*) Two sources generate light at wavelengths of $\lambda = 570$ nm and $\lambda = 700$ nm. What are the corresponding photon energies?

12.2 (*a*) A sample of GaAs is 0.35 μm thick. The sample is illuminated with a light source with $h\nu = 2$ eV. Determine the absorption coefficient and determine the percentage of light that is absorbed in the sample. (*b*) Repeat part (*a*) for silicon.

12.3 A light source with $h\nu = 1.3$ eV and at a power density of 10^{-2} W/cm^2 is incident on a thin slab of silicon. The excess minority-carrier lifetime is 10^{-6} s. Determine the electron–hole generation rate and the steady-state excess carrier concentration. Neglect surface effects.

12.4 Consider an n-type GaAs sample with $\tau_p = 10^{-7}$ s. (*a*) It is desired to generate a steady-state excess carrier concentration of $\delta p = 10^{15}$ cm^{-3} at the surface. The incident photon energy is $h\nu = 1.9$ eV. Determine the incident power density required. (Neglect surface effects.) (*b*) At what distance in the semiconductor does the generation rate drop to 20 percent of that at the surface?

12.5 (*a*) Consider a GaAs semiconductor illuminated with photons at an energy of $h\nu = 1.65$ eV. Determine the thickness of the material so that 75 percent of the energy is absorbed. (*b*) Determine the thickness so that 75 percent of the energy is transmitted.

12.6 If the thickness of a GaAs semiconductor is 1 μm and 50 percent of the incident monochromic photon energy is absorbed, determine the incident photon energy and wavelength.

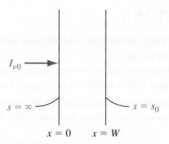

Figure P12.8 | Figure for
Problem 12.8.

*12.7   Consider monochromatic light at an intensity I_{v0} incident on the surface at $x = 0$
of an n-type semiconductor that extends to $x = \infty$. Assume the electric field is zero
in the semiconductor and assume a surface recombination velocity, s. Taking into
account the absorption coefficient, determine the steady-state excess hole concentration as a function of x.

*12.8   Monochromatic light with intensity I_{v0} is incident on a p-type semiconductor as
shown in Figure P12.8. Assume the surface recombination velocity at $x = 0$ is
$s = \infty$ and assume the surface recombination velocity at $x = W$ is $s = s_0$. Derive
the expression for the steady-state excess electron concentration as a function of x.

Section 12.2   Solar Cells

12.9   Consider an ideal long n^+ p junction GaAs solar cell at $T = 300$ K in which excess
carriers are uniformly generated. The parameters of the diode are as follows:

$$N_d = 10^{19} \text{ cm}^{-3} \qquad D_n = 225 \text{ cm}^2/\text{s}$$
$$\tau_{n0} = \tau_{p0} = 5 \times 10^{-8} \text{ s} \qquad D_p = 7 \text{ cm}^2/\text{s}$$

The generated photocurrent density is $J_L = 30$ mA/cm^2. Plot the open-circuit voltage as a function of the acceptor doping concentration for $10^{15} \leq N_a \leq 10^{18}$ cm^{-3}.

12.10   A long silicon pn junction solar cell with an area of 2 cm^2 has the following
parameters:

$$N_d = 10^{19} \text{ cm}^{-3} \qquad N_a = 3 \times 10^{16} \text{ cm}^{-3}$$
$$D_p = 6 \text{ cm}^2/\text{s} \qquad D_n = 18 \text{ cm}^2/\text{s}$$
$$\tau_{p0} = 5 \times 10^{-7} \text{ s} \qquad \tau_{n0} = 5 \times 10^{-6} \text{ s}$$

Assume that excess carriers are uniformly generated in the solar cell and that
$J_L = 25$ mA/cm^2. Let $T = 300$ K. (a) Plot the I–V characteristics of the diode,
(b) determine the maximum power output of the solar cell, and (c) calculate the
external load resistance that will produce the maximum power.

12.11   Consider the solar cell in Problem 12.10. If the solar intensity is increased by a
factor of 10, determine the maximum power output of the solar cell. By what factor
has the power increased from that in Problem 12.10?

*12.12 Consider the pn junction solar cell with nonuniform absorption. Derive the expression for the excess minority-carrier electron concentration for the short-circuit condition and for the case when the p region is very long and the n region is short.

12.13 The absorption coefficient in amorphous silicon is approximately 10^4 cm^{-1} at $hv = 1.7$ eV and 10^5 cm^{-1} at $hv = 2.0$ eV. Determine the amorphous silicon thickness for each case so that 90 percent of the photons are absorbed.

Section 12.3   Photodetectors

12.14 Consider a silicon photoconductor at $T = 300$ K with the following parameters:

$$N_d = 10^{16} \text{ cm}^{-3} \qquad N_a = 10^{15} \text{ cm}^{-3}$$
$$\mu_n = 1000 \text{ cm}^2/\text{V-s} \qquad \mu_p = 430 \text{ cm}^2/\text{V-s}$$
$$\tau_{n0} = 10^{-6} \text{ s} \qquad \tau_{p0} = 10^{-7} \text{ s}$$
$$A = 10^{-3} \text{ cm}^2 \qquad L = 100 \text{ } \mu\text{m}$$

Assume that a voltage of 5 V is applied and assume that excess electrons and holes are uniformly generated at a rate of $G_L = 10^{20}$ cm^{-3}-s^{-1}. Calculate (a) the steady-state excess carrier concentration, (b) the photoconductivity, (c) the steady-state photocurrent, and (d) the photoconductor gain.

12.15 Excess carriers are uniformly generated in a GaAs photoconductor at a rate of $G_L = 10^{21}$ cm^{-3}-s^{-1}. The area is $A = 10^{-4}$ cm^2 and the length is $L = 100$ μm. The other parameters are

$$N_d = 5 \times 10^{16} \text{ cm}^{-3} \qquad N_a = 0$$
$$\mu_n = 8000 \text{ cm}^2/\text{V-s} \qquad \mu_p = 250 \text{ cm}^2/\text{V-s}$$
$$\tau_{n0} = 10^{-7} \text{ s} \qquad \tau_{p0} = 10^{-8} \text{ s}$$

If a voltage of 5 V is applied, calculate (a) the steady-state excess carrier concentration, (b) the photoconductivity, (c) the steady-state photocurrent, and (d) the photoconductor gain.

*12.16 Consider an n-type silicon photoconductor that is 1 μm thick, 50 μm wide, and has an applied electric field in the longitudinal dimension of 50 V/cm. If the incident photon flux is $\Phi_0 = 10^{16}$ cm^{-2}-s^{-1} and the absorption coefficient is $\alpha = 5 \times 10^4$ cm^{-1}, calculate the steady-state photocurrent if $\mu_n = 1200$ cm^2/V-s, $\mu_p = 450$ cm^2/V-s, and $\tau_{p0} = 2 \times 10^{-7}$ s.

12.17 Consider a long silicon pn junction photodiode at $T = 300$ K with the following parameters:

$$N_a = 2 \times 10^{16} \text{ cm}^{-3} \qquad N_d = 10^{18} \text{ cm}^{-3}$$
$$D_n = 25 \text{ cm}^2/\text{s} \qquad D_p = 10 \text{ cm}^2/\text{s}$$
$$\tau_{n0} = 2 \times 10^{-7} \text{ s} \qquad \tau_{p0} = 10^{-7} \text{ s}$$

Assume a reverse-bias voltage of $V_R = 5$ V is applied and assume a uniform generation rate of $G_L = 10^{21}$ cm^{-3}-s^{-1} exists throughout the entire photodiode. Calculate (a) the prompt photocurrent density and (b) the total steady-state photocurrent density.

*12.18 Starting with the ambipolar transport equation for minority carrier holes, derive Equation (12.31) using the geometry shown in Figure 12.17.

12.19   Consider a silicon PIN photodiode at $T = 300$ K. Consider intrinsic layer widths of 1, 10, and 100 μm. If the incident photon flux is $\Phi_0 = 10^{17}$ cm^{-2}-s^{-1} and the absorption coefficient is $\alpha = 3 \times 10^3$ cm^{-1}, calculate the prompt photocurrent density for each diode.

12.20   Consider a silicon PIN photodiode exposed to sunlight. Calculate the intrinsic region width so that at least 90 percent of all photons with wavelengths $\lambda \leq 1$ μm are absorbed in the intrinsic region. Neglect any absorption in the p$^+$ or n$^+$ regions.

Section 12.4   Light-Emitting Diodes

12.21   Consider a pn junction GaAs LED. Assume that photons are generated uniformly in all directions in a plane perpendicular to the junction at a distance of 0.50 μm from the surface. (*a*) Taking into account total internal reflection, calculate the fraction of photons that have the potential of being emitted from the semiconductor. (*b*) Using the results of part (*a*) and including Fresnel loss, determine the fraction of generated photons that will be emitted from the semiconductor into air (neglect absorption losses).

*12.22   In a pn junction LED, consider a point source in the semiconductor at the junction and assume that photons are emitted uniformly in all directions. Show that (neglecting photon absorption) the external quantum efficiency of the LED is given by

$$\eta_{\text{ext}} = \frac{2\bar{n}_1 \bar{n}_2}{(\bar{n}_1 + \bar{n}_2)^2}(1 - \cos\theta_c)$$

where $\bar{n}_1$ and $\bar{n}_2$ are the index of refraction parameters for the air and semiconductor, respectively, and θ_c is the critical angle.

Section 12.5   Laser Diodes

12.23   Consider an optical cavity. If $N \gg 1$, show that the wavelength separation between two adjacent resonant modes is $\Delta\lambda = \lambda^2/2L$.

12.24   If the photon output of a laser diode is equal to the bandgap energy, find the wavelength separation between adjacent resonant modes in a GaAs laser with $L = 75$ μm.

READING LIST

1.   Brennan, K. F. *The Physics of Semiconductors with Applications to Optoelectronic Devices.* New York: Cambridge University Press, 1999.

2.   Carlson, D. E. "Amorphous Silicon Solar Cells." *IEEE Transactions on Electron Devices* ED-24 (April 1977), pp. 449–53.

3.   Fonash, S. J. *Solar Cell Device Physics.* New York: Academic Press, 1981.

4.   Kano, K. *Semiconductor Devices.* Upper Saddle River, NJ: Prentice-Hall, 1998.

5.   Kressel, H. *Semiconductor Devices for Optical Communications: Topics in Applied Physics.* Vol. 39. New York: Springer-Verlag, 1987.

6.   MacMillan, H. F., H. C. Hamaker, G. F. Virshup, and J. G. Werthen. "Multijunction III-V Solar Cells: Recent and Projected Results." *Twentieth IEEE Photovoltaic Specialists Conference* (1988), pp. 48–54.

7. Madan, A. "Amorphous Silicon: From Promise to Practice." *IEEE Spectrum* 23 (September 1986), pp. 38–43.

8. Neamen, D. A. *Semiconductor Physics and Devices: Basic Principles,* 3rd ed. New York: McGraw-Hill, 2003.

9. Pankove, J. I. *Optical Processes in Semiconductors.* New York: Dover Publications, 1971.

10. Pierret, R. F. *Semiconductor Device Fundamentals.* Reading, MA: Addison-Wesley Publishing Co., 1996.

11. Roulston, D. J. *An Introduction to the Physics of Semiconductor Devices.* New York: Oxford University Press, 1999.

12. Roulston, D. J. *Bipolar Semiconductor Devices.* New York: McGraw-Hill, 1990.

13. Shur, M. *Introduction to Electronic Devices.* New York: John Wiley and Sons, 1996.

*14. Shur, M. *Physics of Semiconductor Devices.* Englewood Cliffs, NJ: Prentice-Hall, 1990.

15. Singh, J. *Semiconductor Devices: Basic Principles.* New York: John Wiley and Sons, 2001.

16. Streetman, B. G., and S. Banerjee. *Solid State Electronic Devices.* 5th ed. Upper Saddle River, NJ: Prentice-Hall, 2000.

17. Sze, S. M. *Physics of Semiconductor Devices.* 2nd ed. New York: Wiley, 1981.

18. Sze, S. M. *Semiconductor Devices: Physics and Technology,* 2nd ed. New York: John Wiley and Sons, 2002.

*19. Wang, S. *Fundamentals of Semiconductor Theory and Device Physics.* Englewood Cliffs, NJ: Prentice-Hall, 1989.

20. Wilson, J., and J. F. B. Hawkes. *Optoelectronics: An Introduction.* Englewood Cliffs, NJ: Prentice-Hall, 1983.

*21. Wolfe, C. M, N. Holonyak, Jr., and G. E. Stillman. *Physical Properties of Semiconductors.* Englewood Cliffs, NJ: Prentice-Hall, 1989.

22. Yang, E. S. *Microelectronic Devices.* New York: McGraw-Hill, 1988.

Selected List of Symbols

This list does not include some symbols that are defined and used specifically in only one section. Some symbols have more than one meaning; however, the context in which the symbol is used should make the meaning unambiguous. The usual unit associated with each symbol is given.

a	Unit cell dimension (Å), potential well width, acceleration, gradient of impurity concentration, channel thickness of a one-sided JFET (cm)
a_0	Bohr radius (Å)
c	Speed of light (cm/s)
d	Distance (cm)
e	Electronic charge (magnitude) (C), Napierian base
f	Frequency (Hz)
$f_F(E)$	Fermi–Dirac probability function
f_T	Cutoff frequency (Hz)
g	Generation rate ($cm^{-3}\,s^{-1}$)
g'	Generation rate of excess carriers ($cm^{-3}\,s^{-1}$)
$g(E)$	Density of states function ($cm^{-3}\,eV^{-1}$)
g_c, g_v	Density of states function in the conduction band and valence band ($cm^{-3}\,eV^{-1}$)
g_d	Channel conductance (S), small-signal diffusion conductance (S)
g_m	Transconductance (A/V)
g_n, g_p	Generation rate for electrons and holes ($cm^{-3}\,s^{-1}$)
h	Planck's constant (J-s), induced space charge width in a JFET (cm)

$\hbar$	Modified Planck's constant ($h/2\pi$)
h_f	Small-signal common emitter current gain
j	Imaginary constant, $\sqrt{-1}$
k	Boltzmann's constant (J/K), wavenumber (cm^{-1})
k_n	Conduction parameter (A/V^2)
m	Mass (kg)
m_0	Rest mass of the electron (kg)
m^*	Effective mass (kg)
m_n^*, m_p^*	Effective mass of an electron and hole (kg)
n	Integer
n, l, m, s	Quantum numbers
n, p	Electron and hole concentration (cm^{-3})
$\bar{n}$	Index of refraction
n', p'	Constants related to the trap energy (cm^{-3})
n_{B0}, p_{E0}, p_{C0}	Thermal-equilibrium minority-carrier electron concentration in the base and minority-carrier hole concentration in the emitter and collector (cm^{-3})
n_d	Density of electrons in the donor energy level (cm^{-3})
n_i	Intrinsic concentration of electrons (cm^{-3})
n_0, p_0	Thermal-equilibrium concentration of electrons and holes (cm^{-3})
n_p, p_n	Minority-carrier electron and minority-carrier hole concentration (cm^{-3})
n_{p0}, p_{n0}	Thermal-equilibrium minority-carrier electron and minority-carrier hole concentration (cm^{-3})
n_s	Density of a two-dimensional electron gas (cm^{-2})
p	Momentum
p_a	Density of holes in the acceptor energy level (cm^{-3})
p_i	Intrinsic hole concentration ($= n_i$)(cm^{-3})
q	Charge (C)
r, θ, ϕ	Spherical coordinates
r_d, r_π	Small-signal diffusion resistance (Ω)
r_{ds}	Small-signal drain-to-source resistance (Ω)
s	Surface recombination velocity (cm/s)
t	Time (s)
t_d	Delay time (s)
t_{ox}	Gate oxide thickness (cm or Å)
t_s	Storage time (s)
$u(x)$	Periodic wave function
v	Velocity (cm/s)

v_d	Carrier drift velocity (cm/s)
v_{ds}, v_s, v_{sat}	Carrier saturation drift velocity (cm/s)
x, y, z	Cartesian coordinates
x	Mole fraction in compound semiconductors
x_B, x_E, x_C	Neutral base, emitter, and collector region widths (cm)
x_d	Induced space charge width (cm)
x_{dT}	Maximum space charge width (cm)
x_n, x_p	Depletion width from the metallurgical junction into n-type and p-type semiconductor regions (cm)
A	Area (cm^2)
A^*	Effective Richardson constant (A/K^2/cm^2)
B	Magnetic flux density (Wb/m^2)
B, E, C	Base, emitter, and collector
BV_{CBO}	Breakdown voltage of collector–base junction with emitter open (V)
BV_{CEO}	Breakdown voltage of collector-emitter with base open (V)
C	Capacitance (F)
C'	Capacitance per unit area (F/cm^2)
C_d, C_π	Diffusion capacitance (F)
C_{FB}	Flat-band capacitance (F)
C_{gs}, C_{gd}, C_{ds}	Gate–source, gate–drain, and drain–source capacitance (F)
C_j'	Junction capacitance per unit area (F/cm^2)
C_M	Miller capacitance (F)
C_n, C_p	Constants related to capture rate of electrons and holes
C_{ox}	Gate oxide capacitance per unit area (F/cm^2)
C_μ	Reverse-biased B-C junction capacitance (F)
D, S, G	Drain, source, and gate of an FET
D'	Ambipolar diffusion coefficient (cm^2/s)
D_B, D_E, D_C	Base, emitter, and collector minority-carrier diffusion coefficients (cm^2/s)
D_{it}	Density of interface states (#/eV-cm^3)
D_n, D_p	Minority-carrier electron and minority-carrier hole diffusion coefficient (cm^2/s)
$\mathcal{E}$	Electric field (V/cm)
$\mathcal{E}_H$	Hall electric field (V/cm)
$\mathcal{E}_{crit}$	Critical electric field at breakdown (V/cm)
E	Energy (joule or eV)
E_a	Acceptor energy level (eV)
E_c, E_v	Energy at the bottom edge of the conduction band and top edge of the valence band (eV)

$\Delta E_c, \Delta E_v$	Difference in conduction band energies and valence band energies at a heterojunction (eV)
E_d	Donor energy level (eV)
E_F	Fermi energy (eV)
E_{Fi}	Intrinsic Fermi energy (eV)
E_{Fn}, E_{Fp}	Quasi-Fermi energy levels for electrons and holes (eV)
E_g	Bandgap energy (eV)
ΔE_g	Bandgap narrowing factor (eV), difference in bandgap energies at a heterojunction (eV)
E_t	Trap energy level (eV)
F	Force (N)
F_n^-, F_p^+	Electron and hole particle flux ($\text{cm}^{-2}\,\text{s}^{-1}$)
$F_{1/2}(\eta)$	Fermi–Dirac integral function
G	Generation rate of electron–hole pairs ($\text{cm}^{-3}\,\text{s}^{-1}$)
G_L	Excess carrier generation rate ($\text{cm}^{-3}\,\text{s}^{-1}$)
G_{n0}, G_{p0}	Thermal-equilibrium generation rate for electrons and holes ($\text{cm}^{-3}\,\text{s}^{-1}$)
G_{01}	Conductance (S)
I	Current (A)
I_A	Anode current (A)
I_B, I_E, I_C	Base, emitter, and collector current (A)
I_{CBO}	Reverse-bias collector–base junction current with emitter open (A)
I_{CEO}	Reverse-bias collector–emitter current with base open (A)
I_D	Diode current (A), drain current (A)
$I_D(\text{sat})$	Saturation drain current (A)
I_L	Photocurrent (A)
I_{Pl}	Pinchoff current (A)
I_S	Ideal reverse-bias saturation current (A)
I_{SC}	Short-circuit current (A)
I_ν	Photon intensity (energy/cm^2/s)
J	Electric current density (A/cm^2)
J_{gen}	Generation current density (A/cm^2)
J_L	Photocurrent density (A/cm^2)
J_n, J_p	Electron and hole electric current density (A/cm^2)
J_n^-, J_p^+	Electron and hole particle current density ($\text{cm}^{-2}\,\text{s}^{-1}$)
J_{rec}	Recombination current density (A/cm^2)
J_{r0}	Zero-bias recombination current density (A/cm^2)
J_R	Reverse-bias current density (A/cm^2)
J_S	Ideal reverse-bias saturation current density (A/cm^2)

J_{sT}	Ideal reverse-saturation current density in a Schottky diode (A/cm^2)
L	Length (cm), inductance (H), channel length (cm)
ΔL	Channel length modulation factor (cm)
L_B, L_E, L_C	Minority-carrier diffusion length in the base, emitter, and collector (cm)
L_D	Debye length (cm)
L_n, L_p	Minority-carrier electron and hole diffusion length (cm)
M, M_n	Multiplication constant
N	Number density (cm^{-3})
N_a	Density of acceptor impurity atoms (cm^{-3})
N_B, N_E, N_C	Base, emitter, and collector doping concentrations (cm^{-3})
N_c, N_v	Effective density of states function in the conduction band and valence band (cm^{-3})
N_d	Density of donor impurity atoms (cm^{-3})
N_{it}	Interface state density (cm^{-2})
N_t	Trap density (cm^{-3})
P	Power (W)
$P(r)$	Probability density function
Q	Charge (C)
Q'	Charge per unit area (C/cm^2)
Q_B	Gate-controlled bulk charge (C)
Q'_n	Inversion channel charge density per unit area (C/cm^2)
Q'_{sig}	Signal charge density per unit area (C/cm^2)
$Q'_{SD}(\text{max})$	Maximum space charge density per unit area (C/cm^2)
Q'_{SS}	Equivalent trapped oxide charge per unit area (C/cm^2)
R	Reflection coefficient, recombination rate (cm^{-3} s^{-1}), resistance (Ω)
$R(r)$	Radial wave function
R_c	Specific contact resistance (Ω-cm^2)
R_{cn}, R_{cp}	Capture rate for electrons and holes (cm^{-3} s^{-1})
R_{en}, R_{ep}	Emission rate for electrons and holes (cm^{-3} s^{-1})
R_n, R_p	Recombination rate for electrons and holes (cm^{-3} s^{-1})
R_{n0}, R_{p0}	Thermal-equilibrium recombination rate of electrons and holes (cm^{-3} s^{-1})
T	Temperature (K), kinetic energy (J or eV), transmission coefficient
V	Potential (V), potential energy (J or eV)
V_a	Applied forward-bias voltage (V)
V_A	Early voltage (V), anode voltage (V)

V_{bi}	Built-in potential barrier (V)
V_B	Breakdown voltage (V)
V_{BD}	Breakdown voltage at the drain (V)
V_{BE}, V_{CB}, V_{CE}	Base–emitter, collector–base, and collector–emitter voltage (V)
V_{DS}, V_{GS}	Drain–source and gate–source voltage (V)
$V_{DS}(\text{sat})$	Drain–source saturation voltage (V)
V_{FB}	Flat-band voltage (V)
V_G	Gate voltage (V)
V_H	Hall voltage (V)
V_{oc}	Open-circuit voltage (V)
V_{ox}	Potential difference across an oxide (V)
V_{p0}	Pinchoff voltage (V)
V_{pt}	Punch-through voltage (V)
V_R	Applied reverse-bias voltage (V)
V_{SB}	Source–body voltage (V)
V_t	Thermal voltage (kT/e)
V_T	Threshold voltage (V)
ΔV_T	Threshold voltage shift (V)
W	Total space charge width (cm), channel width (cm)
W_B	Metallurgical base width (cm)
Y	Admittance
α	Photon absorption coefficient (cm^{-1}), ac common-base current gain
α_n, α_p	Electron and hole ionization rates (cm^{-1})
α_0	dc common-base current gain
α_T	Base transport factor
β	Common-emitter current gain
γ	Emitter injection efficiency factor
δ	Recombination factor
$\delta n, \delta p$	Excess electron and hole concentration (cm^{-3})
$\delta n_p, \delta p_n$	Excess minority-carrier electron and excess minority-carrier hole concentration (cm^{-3})
ϵ	Permittivity (F/cm^2)
ϵ_0	Permittivity of free space (F/cm^2)
ϵ_{ox}	Permittivity of an oxide (F/cm^2)
ϵ_r	Relative permittivity or dielectric constant
ϵ_s	Permittivity of a semiconductor (F/cm^2)
λ	Wavelength (cm or μm)

μ	Permeability (H/cm)
μ'	Ambipolar mobility (cm^2/V-s)
μ_n, μ_p	Electron and hole mobility (cm^2/V-s)
μ_0	Permeability of free space (H/cm)
ν	Frequency (Hz)
ρ	Resistivity (Ω-cm), volume charge density (C/cm^3)
σ	Conductivity (Ω^{-1} cm^{-1})
$\Delta\sigma$	Photoconductivity (Ω^{-1} cm^{-1})
σ_i	Intrinsic conductivity (Ω^{-1} cm^{-1})
σ_n, σ_p	Conductivity of n-type and p-type semiconductor (Ω^{-1} cm^{-1})
τ	Lifetime (s)
τ_n, τ_p	Electron and hole lifetime (s)
τ_{n0}, τ_{p0}	Excess minority-carrier electron and hole lifetime (s)
τ_0	Lifetime in space charge region (s)
ϕ	Potential (V)
$\phi(t)$	Time-dependent wave function
$\Delta\phi$	Schottky barrier lowering potential (V)
ϕ_{Bn}	Schottky barrier height (V)
ϕ_{B0}	Ideal Schottky barrier height (V)
ϕ_{fn}, ϕ_{fp}	Potential difference (magnitude) between E_{Fi} and E_F in n-type and p-type semiconductor (V)
ϕ_{Fn}, ϕ_{Fp}	Potential difference (with sign) between E_{Fi} and E_F in n-type and p-type semiconductor (V)
ϕ_m	Metal work function (V)
ϕ'_m	Modified metal work function (V)
ϕ_{ms}	Metal–semiconductor work function difference (V)
ϕ_n, ϕ_p	Potential difference (magnitude) between E_c and E_F in n-type and between E_v and E_F in p-type semiconductor (V)
ϕ_s	Semiconductor work function (V), surface potential (V)
χ	Electron affinity (V)
χ'	Modified electron affinity (V)
$\psi(x)$	Time-independent wave function
ω	Radian frequency (s^{-1})
Γ	Reflection coefficient
$\Theta(\theta)$	Angular wave function
Φ	Photon flux (cm^{-2} s^{-1})
$\Phi(\phi)$	Angular wave function
$\Psi(x, t)$	Total wave function

B

System of Units, Conversion Factors, and General Constants

Table B.1 | International system of units*

Quantity	Unit	Symbol	Dimension
Length	meter	m	
Mass	kilogram	kg	
Time	second	s or sec	
Temperature	kelvin	K	
Current	ampere	A	
Frequency	hertz	Hz	1/s
Force	newton	N	kg-m/s^2
Pressure	pascal	Pa	N/m^2
Energy	joule	J	N-m
Power	watt	W	J/s
Electric charge	coulomb	C	A-s
Potential	volt	V	J/C
Conductance	siemens	S	A/V
Resistance	ohm	Ω	V/A
Capacitance	farad	F	C/V
Magnetic flux	weber	Wb	V-s
Magnetic flux density	tesla	T	Wb/m^2
Inductance	henry	H	Wb/A

*The cm is the common unit of length and the electron-volt is the common unit of energy (see Appendix D) used in the study of semiconductors. However, the joule and in some cases the meter should be used in most formulas.

Table B.2 | Conversion factors

	Prefixes		
1 Å (angstrom) $= 10^{-8}$ cm $= 10^{-10}$ m	10^{-15}	femto-	$= f$
1 μm (micron) $= 10^{-4}$ cm	10^{-12}	pico-	$= p$
1 mil $= 10^{-3}$ in. $= 25.4\ \mu$m	10^{-9}	nano-	$= n$
2.54 cm $= 1$ in.	10^{-6}	micro-	$= \mu$
1 eV $= 1.6 \times 10^{-19}$ J	10^{-3}	milli-	$= m$
1 J $= 10^{7}$ erg	10^{+3}	kilo-	$= k$
	10^{+6}	mega-	$= M$
	10^{+9}	giga-	$= G$
	10^{+12}	tera	$= T$

Table B.3 | Physical constants

Avogadro's number	$N_A = 6.02 \times 10^{+23}$ atoms per gram molecular weight
Boltzmann's constant	$k = 1.38 \times 10^{-23}$ J/K $= 8.62 \times 10^{-5}$ eV/K
Electronic charge (magnitude)	$e = 1.60 \times 10^{-19}$ C
Free electron rest mass	$m_0 = 9.11 \times 10^{-31}$ kg
Permeability of free space	$\mu_0 = 4\pi \times 10^{-7}$ H/m
Permittivity of free space	$\epsilon_0 = 8.85 \times 10^{-14}$ F/cm $= 8.85 \times 10^{-12}$ F/m
Planck's constant	$h = 6.625 \times 10^{-34}$ J-s $= 4.135 \times 10^{-15}$ eV-s $\dfrac{h}{2\pi} = \hbar = 1.054 \times 10^{-34}$ J-s
Proton rest mass	$M = 1.67 \times 10^{-27}$ kg
Speed of light in vacuum	$c = 2.998 \times 10^{10}$ cm/s
Thermal voltage $(T = 300$ K$)$	$V_t = \dfrac{kT}{e} = 0.0259$ V $kT = 0.0259$ eV

Table B.4 | Silicon, gallium arsenide, and germanium properties ($T = 300$ K)

Property	Si	GaAs	Ge
Atoms (cm^{-3})	5.0×10^{22}	4.42×10^{22}	4.42×10^{22}
Atomic weight	28.09	144.63	72.60
Crystal structure	Diamond	Zincblende	Diamond
Density (g/cm^{-3})	2.33	5.32	5.33
Lattice constant (Å)	5.43	5.65	5.65
Melting point (°C)	1415	1238	937
Dielectric constant	11.7	13.1	16.0
Bandgap energy (eV)	1.12	1.42	0.66
Electron affinity, χ (V)	4.01	4.07	4.13
Effective density of states in conduction band, N_c (cm^{-3})	2.8×10^{19}	4.7×10^{17}	1.04×10^{19}
Effective density of states in valence band, N_v (cm^{-3})	1.04×10^{19}	7.0×10^{18}	6.0×10^{18}
Intrinsic carrier concentration (cm^{-3})	1.5×10^{10}	1.8×10^{6}	2.4×10^{13}
Mobility (cm^2/V-s)			
Electron, μ_n	1350	8500	3900
Hole, μ_p	480	400	1900
Effective mass $\left(\dfrac{m^*}{m_0}\right)$			
Electrons	$m_l^* = 0.98$	0.067	1.64
	$m_t^* = 0.19$		0.082
Holes	$m_{lh}^* = 0.16$	0.082	0.044
	$m_{hh}^* = 0.49$	0.45	0.28
Effective mass (density of states)			
Electrons $\left(\dfrac{m_n^*}{m_0}\right)$	1.08	0.067	0.55
Holes $\left(\dfrac{m_p^*}{m_0}\right)$	0.56	0.48	0.37

Table B.5 | Other semiconductor parameters

Material	E_g (eV)	a (Å)	ϵ_r	χ	$\bar{n}$
Aluminum arsenide	2.16	5.66	12.0	3.5	2.97
Gallium phosphide	2.26	5.45	10	4.3	3.37
Aluminum phosphide	2.43	5.46	9.8		3.0
Indium phosphide	1.35	5.87	12.1	4.35	3.37

Table B.6 | Properties of SiO_2 and Si_3N_4 ($T = 300\,\text{K}$)

Property	SiO_2	Si_3N_4
Crystal structure	[Amorphous for most integrated circuit applications]	
Atomic or molecular density (cm^{-3})	2.2×10^{22}	1.48×10^{22}
Density (g-cm^{-3})	2.2	3.4
Energy gap	$\approx 9\,\text{eV}$	$4.7\,\text{eV}$
Dielectric constant	3.9	7.5
Melting point ($^\circ$C)	≈ 1700	≈ 1900

The Periodic Table

Period	Group I a	b	Group II a	b	Group III a	b	Group IV a	b	Group V a	b	Group VI a	b	Group VII a	b	Group VIII a	b
I	1 H 1.0079															2 He 4.003
II	3 Li 6.94		4 Be 9.02		5 B 10.82		6 C 12.01		7 N 14.01		8 O 16.00		9 F 19.00			10 Ne 20.18
III	11 Na 22.99		12 Mg 24.32		13 Al 26.97		14 Si 28.06		15 P 30.98		16 S 32.06		17 Cl 35.45			18 Ar 39.94
IV	19 K 39.09	29 Cu 63.54	20 Ca 40.08	30 Zn 65.38	21 Sc 44.96	31 Ga 69.72	22 Ti 47.90	32 Ge 72.60	23 V 50.95	33 As 74.91	24 Cr 52.01	34 Se 78.96	25 Mn 54.93	35 Br 79.91	26 Fe 55.85 · 27 Co 58.94 · 28 Ni 58.69	36 Kr 83.7
V	37 Rb 85.48	47 Ag 107.88	38 Sr 87.63	48 Cd 112.41	39 Y 88.92	49 In 114.76	40 Zr 91.22	50 Sn 118.70	41 Nb 92.91	51 Sb 121.76	42 Mo 95.95	52 Te 127.61	43 Tc 99	53 I 126.92	44 Ru 101.7 · 45 Rh 102.91 · 46 Pd 106.4	54 Xe 131.3
VI	55 Cs 132.91	79 Au 197.2	56 Ba 137.36	80 Hg 200.61	57–71 Rare earths	81 Tl 204.39	72 Hf 178.6	82 Pb 207.21	73 Ta 180.88	83 Bi 209.00	74 W 183.92	84 Po 210	75 Re 186.31	85 At 211	76 Os 190.2 · 77 Ir 193.1 · 28 Pt 195.2	86 Rn 222
VII	87 Fr 223		88 Ra 226.05		89 Ac 227		90 Th 232.12		91 Pa 231		92 U 238.07 · 93 Np 237 · 94 Pu 239 · 95 Am 241 · 96 Cm 242 · 97 Bk 246 · 98 Ct 249 · 99 Es 254 · 100 Fm 256 · 101 Md 256					

Rare Earths

VI 57-71	57 La 138.92	58 Ce 140.13	59 Pr 140.92	60 Nd 144.27	61 Pm 147	62 Sm 150.43	63 Eu 152.0	64 Gd 156.9	65 Tb 159.2	66 Dy 162.46	67 Ho 164.90	68 Er 167.2	69 Tm 169.4	70 Yb 173.04	71 Lu 174.99

The numbers in front of the symbols of the elements denote the atomic numbers; the numbers underneath are the atomic weights.

APPENDIX

D

Unit of Energy—The Electron-Volt

The electron-volt (eV) is a unit of energy that is used constantly in the study of semiconductor physics and devices. This short discussion may help in "getting a feel" for the electron-volt.

Consider a parallel plate capacitor with an applied voltage, as shown in Figure D.1. Assume that an electron is released at $x = 0$ at time $t = 0$. We can write

$$F = m_0 a = m_0 \frac{d^2x}{dt^2} = e\mathcal{E} \tag{D.1}$$

where e is the magnitude of the electronic charge and $\mathcal{E}$ is the magnitude of the electric field, as shown. On integrating, the velocity and distance versus time are given by

$$v = \frac{e\mathcal{E}t}{m_0} \tag{D.2}$$

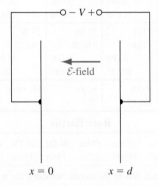

Figure D.1 | Parallel plate capacitor.

and

$$x = \frac{e\mathcal{E}t^2}{2m_0} \tag{D.3}$$

where we have assumed that $v = 0$ at $t = 0$.

Assume that at $t = t_0$ the electron reaches the positive plate of the capacitor so that $x = d$. Then,

$$d = \frac{e\mathcal{E}t_0^2}{2m_0} \tag{D.4a}$$

or

$$t_0 = \sqrt{\frac{2m_0 d}{e\mathcal{E}}} \tag{D.4b}$$

The velocity of the electron when it reaches the positive plate of the capacitor is

$$v(t_0) = \frac{e\mathcal{E}t_0}{m_0} = \sqrt{\frac{2e\mathcal{E}d}{m_0}} \tag{D.5}$$

The kinetic energy of the electron at this time is

$$T = \frac{1}{2}m_0 v(t_0)^2 = \frac{1}{2}m_0 \left(\frac{2e\mathcal{E}d}{m_0}\right) = e\mathcal{E}d \tag{D.6}$$

The electric field is

$$\mathcal{E} = \frac{\text{V}}{d} \tag{D.7}$$

so that the energy is

$$T = e \cdot \text{V} \tag{D.8}$$

If an electron is accelerated through a potential of 1 V, then the energy is

$$T = e \cdot \text{V} = (1.6 \times 10^{-19})(1) = 1.6 \times 10^{-19} \text{ joule} \tag{D.9}$$

The electron-volt (eV) unit of energy is defined as

$$\text{Electron-volt} = \frac{\text{joule}}{e} \tag{D.10}$$

Then, the electron that is accelerated through a potential of 1 V will have an energy of

$$T = 1.6 \times 10^{-19} J = \frac{1.6 \times 10^{-19}}{1.6 \times 10^{-19}}(\text{eV}) \tag{D.11}$$

or 1 eV.

We can note that the magnitude of the potential (1 V) and the magnitude of the electron energy (1 eV) are the same. However, it is important to keep in mind that the unit associated with each number is different.

"Derivation" and Applications of Schrödinger's Wave Equation

The time-independent form of Schrödinger's wave equation was stated in Equation (2.4). This equation can be developed from the classical wave equation. We can think of this development more in terms of a justification of Schrödinger's time-independent wave equation rather than a strict derivation.

E.1 | "DERIVATION"

The time-independent classical wave equation, in terms of voltage, is given as

$$\frac{\partial^2 V(x)}{\partial x^2} + \left(\frac{\omega^2}{v_p^2}\right)V(x) = 0 \tag{E.1}$$

where ω is the radian frequency and v_p is the phase velocity.

If we make a change of variable and let $\psi(x) = V(x)$, then we have

$$\frac{\partial^2 \psi(x)}{\partial x^2} + \left(\frac{\omega^2}{v_p^2}\right)\psi(x) = 0 \tag{E.2}$$

We can write that

$$\frac{\omega^2}{v_p^2} = \left(\frac{2\pi v}{v_p}\right)^2 = \left(\frac{2\pi}{\lambda}\right)^2 \tag{E.3}$$

where v and λ are the wave frequency and wavelength, respectively.

From the wave-particle duality principle, we can relate the wavelength and momentum as

$$\lambda = \frac{h}{p} \tag{E.4}$$

Then

$$\left(\frac{2\pi}{\lambda}\right)^2 = \left(\frac{2\pi}{h}p\right)^2 \tag{E.5}$$

and since $\hbar = \dfrac{h}{2\pi}$, we can write

$$\left(\frac{2\pi}{\lambda}\right)^2 = \left(\frac{p}{\hbar}\right)^2 = \frac{2m}{\hbar^2}\left(\frac{p^2}{2m}\right) \tag{E.6}$$

Now

$$\frac{p^2}{2m} = T = E - V \tag{E.7}$$

where T, E, and V are the kinetic energy, total energy, and potential energy terms, respectively.

We can then write

$$\frac{\omega^2}{v_p^2} = \left(\frac{2\pi}{\lambda}\right)^2 = \frac{2m}{\hbar^2}\left(\frac{p^2}{2m}\right) = \frac{2m}{\hbar^2}(E - V) \tag{E.8}$$

Substituting Equation (E.8) into Equation (E.2), we have

$$\frac{\partial^2 \psi(x)}{\partial x^2} + \frac{2m}{\hbar^2}(E - V)\psi(x) = 0 \tag{E.9}$$

which is the one-dimensional, time-independent Schrödinger's wave equation.

E.2 | APPLICATIONS

We will now apply Schrödinger's wave equation in several examples using various potential functions. The solutions of the wave equation describe the behavior of electrons in solids so the results of these examples will provide an indication of the electron behavior under various conditions.

E.2.1 Electron in Free Space

Consider the motion of an electron in free space. If there is no force acting on the particle, then the potential function $V(x)$ must be a constant and we must have $E > V(x)$. Assume for simplicity that $V(x) = 0$. Schrödinger's wave equation is then given by

$$\frac{\partial^2 \psi(x)}{\partial x^2} + \frac{2mE}{\hbar^2}\psi(x) = 0 \tag{E.10}$$

The solution of Equation (E.10) can be written in the form

$$\psi(x) = A \exp(jKx) + B \exp(-jKx) \tag{E.11}$$

where

$$K = \sqrt{\frac{2mE}{\hbar^2}} \qquad (E.12)$$

The time-dependent portion of the solution is

$$\phi(t) = \exp[-j(E/\hbar)t] \qquad (E.13)$$

Then the total wave solution for the wave function is given by

$$\Psi(x, t) = A \exp\{j[Kx - (E/\hbar)t]\}$$
$$+ B \exp\{-j[Kx + (E/\hbar)t]\} \qquad (E.14)$$

This wave function solution is a traveling wave, which means that a particle moving in free space is represented by a *traveling wave*.

E.2.2 The Infinite Potential Well

The problem of a particle in an infinite potential well is a classic example of a bound particle. A bound electron means that the electron is located within a definite volume of space. The potential $V(x)$ as a function of position for this example is shown in Figure E.1. The particle is assumed to exist in region II so the particle is contained within a finite region of space. The time-independent Schrödinger's wave equation is given by

$$\frac{\partial^2 \psi(x)}{\partial x^2} + \frac{2m}{\hbar^2}[E - V(x)]\psi(x) = 0 \qquad (E.15)$$

where E is the total energy of the electron. If E is finite, the wave function must be zero, or $\psi(x) = 0$, in both regions I and III. A particle cannot penetrate these infinite potential barriers, so the probability of finding the electron in regions I and III is zero.

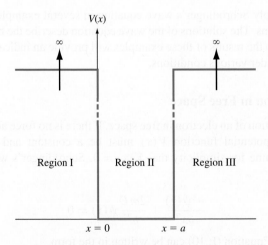

Figure E.1 | Potential function of the infinite potential well.

The time-independent Schrödinger's wave equation in region II, where $V = 0$, becomes

$$\frac{\partial^2 \psi(x)}{\partial x^2} + \frac{2mE}{\hbar^2} \psi(x) = 0 \tag{E.16}$$

A particular form of solution to this equation is given by

$$\psi(x) = A \cos Kx + B \sin Kx \tag{E.17}$$

where

$$K = \sqrt{\frac{2mE}{\hbar^2}} \tag{E.18}$$

One boundary condition is that the wave function $\psi(x)$ must be continuous so that

$$\psi(x = 0) = \psi(x = a) = 0 \tag{E.19}$$

Applying the boundary condition at $x = 0$, we have $A = 0$. Applying the boundary condition at $x = a$, we have

$$\psi(x = a) = 0 = B \sin Ka \tag{E.20}$$

This equation is valid if $Ka = n\pi$, where the parameter n is a positive integer, or $n = 1, 2, 3, \ldots$. We can then write

$$K = \frac{n\pi}{a} \tag{E.21}$$

Combining Equations (E.18) and (E.21), we obtain

$$\frac{2mE}{\hbar^2} = \frac{n^2 \pi^2}{a^2} \tag{E.22}$$

The total energy can then be written as

$$E = E_n = \frac{\hbar^2 n^2 \pi^2}{2ma^2} \tag{E.23}$$

This result shows that the total energy of a bound particle can only take on particular or discrete values. *This result means that the energy of the bound particle is quantized.* The *quantization* of the particle energy is contrary to results from classical physics, which would allow the particle to have continuous energy values.

E.2.3 The Potential Barrier

We now want to consider the potential barrier function, which is shown in Figure E.2. The more interesting problem is for the case when the total energy of an

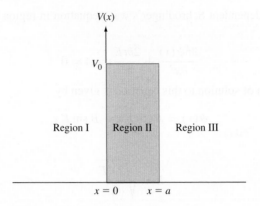

Figure E.2 | The potential barrier function.

incident particle is $E < V_0$. Assume that we have a flux of incident particles originating on the negative x axis traveling in the $+x$ direction. As before, we need to solve Schrödinger's time-independent wave equation in each of the three regions. The solutions of the wave equation in regions I, II, and III are given, respectively, as

$$\psi_1(x) = A_1 \exp(jK_1x) + B_1 \exp(-jK_1x) \qquad \text{(E.24a)}$$

$$\psi_2(x) = A_2 \exp(K_2x) + B_2 \exp(-K_2x) \qquad \text{(E.24b)}$$

$$\psi_3(x) = A_3 \exp(jK_1x) + B_3 \exp(-jK_1x) \qquad \text{(E.24c)}$$

where

$$K_1 = \sqrt{\frac{2mE}{\hbar^2}} \qquad \text{(E.25a)}$$

and

$$K_2 = \sqrt{\frac{2m}{\hbar^2}(V_0 - E)} \qquad \text{(E.25b)}$$

The coefficient B_3 represents a negative traveling wave in region III. However, once a particle gets into region III, there are no potential changes to cause a reflection; therefore, the coefficient B_3 must be zero. We have four boundary relations for the boundaries at $x = 0$ and $x = a$ corresponding to the wave function and its first derivative being continuous.

One particular parameter of interest is the transmission coefficient, in this case defined as the ratio of the transmitted flux in region III to the incident flux in region I. Then the transmission coefficient T is

$$T = \frac{A_3 A_3^*}{A_1 A_1^*} \qquad \text{(E.26)}$$

where A_3^* and A_1^* are the complex conjugates of the coefficients A_3 and A_1, respectively. For the special case when $E \ll V_0$, we find that

$$T \approx 16 \left(\frac{E}{V_0} \right) \left(1 - \frac{E}{V_0} \right) \exp\left(-2K_2 a\right) \qquad \text{(E.27)}$$

Equation (E.27) implies that there is a finite probability that a particle impinging a potential barrier will penetrate the barrier and will appear in region III. This phenomenon is called *tunneling* and it, too, contradicts classical mechanics.

Answers to Selected Problems

Chapter 1

1.1 (a) 4 atoms, (b) 2 atoms, (c) 8 atoms

1.3 4.44×10^{22} cm^{-3}

1.5 $d = 2.45$ Å

1.7 (a) $d = 2.36$ Å, (b) 5×10^{22} cm^{-3},
(c) $\rho = 2.33$ grams/cm^3

1.9 $a_0 = 4.2$ Å, 4.85 Å, 5.94 Å, 9.70 Å

1.11 (a) Density of A and B, 1.01×10^{22} cm^{-3},
(b) same as (a), (c) Same material

1.13 (a) Volume density $= 1/a_0^3$,
surface density $= 1/a_0^2\sqrt{2}$; (b) same as (a)

1.17 (a) $d = 5.25$ Å, (b) $d = 3.71$ Å, (c) $d = 3.03$ Å

1.19 $a_0 = 5.196$ Å; (a) Volume density $=$
1.43×10^{22} cm^{-3}, (b) $d = 3.67$ Å,
(c) Surface density $= 5.24 \times 10^{14}$ cm^{-2}

1.21 1.77×10^{23} cm^{-3}

1.23 $\theta = 109.5°$

1.25 (a) 1.10×10^{-6}, (b) 7.71×10^{-6}

Chapter 2

2.1 Gold: $\lambda = 0.254$ μm, cesium: $\lambda = 0.654$ μm

2.3 $E_{avg} = 0.03885$ eV, $p_{avg} = 1.06 \times 10^{-25}$ kg-m/s,
$\lambda = 62.3$ Å

2.5 (a) $V = 12.4$ kV, (b) $\lambda = 0.11$ Å

2.9 (a) $P = 0.393$, (b) $P = 0.239$, (c) $P = 0.865$

2.11 (a) $E_1 = 0.261$ eV, $E_2 = 1.04$ eV;
(b) $\lambda = 1.59$ μm

2.13 For $a = 10^{-10}$ m, $T = 0.504$; for $a = 10^{-9}$ m,
$T = 7.88 \times 10^{-9}$

2.15 (a) $\psi_1 = B_1 \exp(+K_1 x)$,
$\psi_2 = A_2 \sin K_2 x + B_2 \cos K_2 x, \psi_3 = 0$, where
$$K_1 = \sqrt{\frac{2m(V_0 - E)}{\hbar^2}}, K_2 = \sqrt{\frac{2mE}{\hbar^2}};$$
(b) $B_1 = B_2, K_1 B_1 = K_2 A_2, B_2 = -A_2 \tan K_2 a$

2.17

$T = 100$ K	$E_g = 1.164$ eV
$T = 200$ K	$E_g = 1.147$ eV
$T = 300$ K	$E_g = 1.125$ eV
$T = 400$ K	$E_g = 1.097$ eV
$T = 500$ K	$E_g = 1.066$ eV
$T = 600$ K	$E_g = 1.032$ eV

2.19 (a) $N_0 = 2.12 \times 10^{19}$ cm^{-3},
(b) $N_0 = 3.28 \times 10^{17}$ cm^{-3}

2.21 (a)

E	g_c
$E_c + 0.05$ eV	1.71×10^{21} cm^{-3}eV^{-1}
$E_c + 0.10$ eV	2.41×10^{21}
$E_c + 0.15$ eV	2.96×10^{21}
$E_c + 0.20$ eV	3.41×10^{21}

(b)

E	g_v
$E_v - 0.05$ eV	0.637×10^{21} cm^{-3}eV^{-1}
$E_v - 0.10$ eV	0.901×10^{21}
$E_v - 0.15$ eV	1.10×10^{21}
$E_v - 0.20$ eV	1.27×10^{21}

2.25 (a) $f_F = 0.269$, (b) $f_F = 0.0474$,
(c) $f_F = 2.47 \times 10^{-3}$

2.27 (a)

E	f_F
E_c	6.43×10^{-5}
$E_c + (1/2)kT$	3.90×10^{-5}
$E_c + kT$	2.36×10^{-5}
$E_c + (3/2)kT$	1.43×10^{-5}
$E_c + 2kT$	0.87×10^{-5}

(b)

E	f_F
E_c	7.17×10^{-4}
$E_c + (1/2)kT$	4.35×10^{-4}
$E_c + kT$	2.64×10^{-4}
$E_c + (3/2)kT$	1.60×10^{-4}
$E_c + 2kT$	0.971×10^{-4}

2.29 (a) $E_1 - E_F = 3.91kT$,
(b) $f_F = 1.96 \times 10^{-2}$

2.31 (a) 0.304 percent,
(b) 14.96 percent,
(c) 99.7 percent,
(d) 50 percent

2.33 (a) At $E = E_1$, $f_F(E) = 9.3 \times 10^{-6}$;
at $E = E_2$, $1 - f_F(E) = 1.66 \times 10^{-19}$;
(b) at $E = E_1$, $f_F(E) = 7.88 \times 10^{-18}$;
at $E = E_2$, $1 - f_F(E) = 1.96 \times 10^{-7}$

2.35 (a) Si: $f_F(E) = 2.47 \times 10^{-10}$,
Ge: $f_F(E) = 1.78 \times 10^{-6}$,
GaAs: $f_F(E) = 7.54 \times 10^{-13}$;
(b) Si: $1 - f_F(E) = 2.47 \times 10^{-10}$,
Ge: $1 - f_F(E) = 1.78 \times 10^{-6}$
GaAs: $1 - f_F(E) = 7.54 \times 10^{-13}$

2.37 (a) $\Delta E = 0.1525$ eV,
(b) $\Delta E = 0.254$ eV

Chapter 3

3.1

(a) Silicon

T (K)	kT (eV)	n_i (cm^{-3})
200	0.01727	7.68×10^4
400	0.03453	2.38×10^{12}
600	0.0518	9.74×10^{14}

	(b) Germanium	(c) GaAs
T (K)	n_i (cm^{-3})	n_i (cm^{-3})
200	2.16×10^{10}	1.38
400	8.60×10^{14}	3.28×10^9
600	3.82×10^{16}	5.72×10^{12}

3.3 $T \approx 381$ K

3.5 (a) $E = E_c + kT/2$ (b) $E = E_v - kT/2$

3.7 $\dfrac{n_i(A)}{n_i(B)} = 2.26 \times 10^3$

3.9 (a) (i) $n_0 = 1.24 \times 10^{16}$ cm^{-3}, (ii) 2.61×10^{14},
(iii) 5.49×10^{12};
(b) (i) $p_0 = 4.61 \times 10^{15}$ cm^{-3}, (ii) 9.70×10^{13},
(iii) 2.04×10^{12}

3.11 (a) $E_c - E_F = 0.195$ eV,
(b) $E_F - E_v = 0.198$ eV,
(c) $E_c - E_F = 0.0892$ eV,
(d) $E_F - E_v = 0.188$ eV

3.13 (a) $E_{Fi} - E_{\text{midgap}} = -21.5$ meV,
(b) $E_{Fi} - E_{\text{midgap}} = +51.3$ meV

3.15

T (K)	kT (eV)	$E_{Fi} - E_{\text{midgap}}$
200	0.01727	+23.3 meV
400	0.03453	+46.6
600	0.0518	+69.9

3.19 $r_1 = 104$ Å, $E = 0.0053$ eV

3.21 $p_0 = 2.13 \times 10^{15}$ cm^{-3}, $n_0 = 2.27 \times 10^4$ cm^{-3}

3.23 (a) $p_0 = 19.3$ cm^{-3}, (b) n type,
(c) $E_c - E_F = 0.0999$ eV

3.25 (a) $n_0 = 5.19 \times 10^{14}$ cm^{-3},
$p_0 = 2.08 \times 10^4$ cm^{-3};
(b) $E_c - E_F = 0.176$ eV, $p_0 = 9.67 \times 10^{-3}$ cm^{-3}

3.27 (a) $p_0 = 1.11 \times 10^{16}$ cm^{-3};
(b) $E_{Fi} - E_F = 0.292$ eV;
(c) from (a), $n_0 = 2.03 \times 10^4$ cm^{-3};
from (b), $n_0 = 5.10 \times 10^8$ cm^{-3}

3.29 $F_{1/2}(\eta' = 0) = 0.65$, $p_0 = 7.63 \times 10^{18}$ cm^{-3}

3.31 For the electron concentration,
$E = E_c + (1/2)kT$; for the hole concentration,
$E = E_v - (1/2)kT$

3.33

T (K)	$n_d/(n_d + n_0)$
50	0.972
100	0.0638
200	0.00177

3.35 (a) $\dfrac{n_d}{N_d} = 8.85 \times 10^{-4}$, (b) $f_F(E) = 2.87 \times 10^{-5}$

3.37 (a) $n_0 = 2 \times 10^{15}$ cm^{-3}, $p_0 = 1.62 \times 10^{-3}$ cm^{-3};
(b) $p_0 = 10^{16}$ cm^{-3}, $n_0 = 3.24 \times 10^{-4}$ cm^{-3};
(c) $n_0 = p_0 = n_i = 1.8 \times 10^6$ cm^{-3};
(d) $p_0 = 10^{14}$ cm^{-3}, $n_0 = 1.08 \times 10^5$ cm^{-3}
(e) $n_0 = 10^{14}$ cm^{-3}, $p_0 = 7.90 \times 10^8$ cm^{-3}

3.39 $n_i = 1.72 \times 10^{13}$ cm^{-3} (a) p type
(b) $p_0 = 7 \times 10^{14}$ cm^{-3}, $n_0 = 4.23 \times 10^{11}$ cm^{-3};
(c) $N_I = 2.3 \times 10^{15}$ cm^{-3}

3.41 $n_i = 1.38$ cm^{-3}, $p_0 = 0.617$ cm^{-3},
$n_0 = 3.09$ cm^{-3}, $N_d = 2.47$ cm^{-3}

3.47 (a) $n_0 = 10^{16}$ cm^{-3}, $p_0 = 2.25 \times 10^4$ cm^{-3};
(b) $p_0 = 2.8 \times 10^{16}$ cm^{-3}, $n_0 = 8.04 \times 10^3$ cm^{-3}

3.49 For germanium

T (K)	kT (eV)	n_i(cm^{-3})
200	0.01727	2.16×10^{10}
400	0.03453	8.6×10^{14}
600	0.0518	3.82×10^{16}

T (K)	p_0 (cm^{-3})	$(E_{Fi} - E_F)$ (eV)
200	1.0×10^{15}	0.1855
400	1.49×10^{15}	0.01898
600	3.87×10^{16}	0.000674

3.51 $T \approx 762$ K

3.53 $E_F - E_{Fi} = kT \ln\left(\dfrac{n_o}{n_i}\right)$

N_d(cm^{-3})	$(E_F - E_{Fi})$ (eV)
10^{14}	0.228
10^{16}	0.347
10^{18}	0.467

3.55 $N_d = 1.2 \times 10^{16}$ cm^{-3}

3.57 (a) $E_F - E_{Fi} = 0.2877$ eV;
(b) $E_{Fi} - E_F = 0.2877$ eV;
(c) for (a), $n_0 = 10^{15}$ cm^{-3};
for (b), $n_0 = 2.25 \times 10^5$ cm^{-3}

3.59 (a) $E_F - E_{Fi} = 0.3056$ eV
(b) $E_{Fi} - E_F = 0.3473$ eV (c) $E_F = E_{Fi}$
(d) $E_{Fi} - E_F = 0.1291$ eV
(e) $E_F - E_{Fi} = 0.0024$ eV

3.61 $E_{Fi} - E_F = 0.3294$ eV

Chapter 4

4.1 (a) $n_0 = 5 \times 10^{15}$ cm^{-3}, $p_0 = 4.5 \times 10^4$ cm^{-3},
$\mu_n \approx 1200$ cm^2/V-s, $J_{drf} = 28.8$ A/cm^2;

(b) $p_0 = 5 \times 10^{16}$ cm^{-3}, $n_0 = 4.5 \times 10^3$ cm^{-3},
$\mu_p \approx 380$ cm^2/V-s, $J_{drf} = 91.2$ A/cm^2

4.3 $\mu_n \approx 1100$ cm^2/V-s,
(a) $R = 1.136 \times 10^4$ Ω, $I = 0.44$ mA;
(b) $R = 1.136 \times 10^3$ Ω, $I = 4.4$ mA;
(c) for (a), $\mathcal{E} = 50$ V/cm, $v_d = 5.5 \times 10^4$ cm/s;
for (b), $\mathcal{E} = 500$ V/cm, $v_d = 5.5 \times 10^5$ cm/s

4.5 (a) $\mu_n = 2625$ cm^2/V-s,
(b) $|v_d| = 2.53 \times 10^3$ cm/s

4.7 (a) $\mu_n \approx 1350$ cm^2/V-s, $\mu_p \approx 480$ cm^2/V-s,
then, $\sigma_i = 4.39 \times 10^{-6}$ $(\Omega\text{-cm})^{-1}$;
(b) $\mu_n \approx 200$ cm^2/V-s, $\mu_p \approx 110$ cm^2/V-s,
then, $\sigma_i = 7.44 \times 10^{-7}$ $(\Omega\text{-cm})^{-1}$

4.9 $n_i(300\,\text{K}) = 3.91 \times 10^9$ cm^{-3}, $E_g = 1.122$ eV,
$n_i(500\,\text{K}) = 2.27 \times 10^{13}$ cm^{-3},
$\sigma_i(500\,\text{K}) = 5.81 \times 10^{-3}$ $(\Omega\text{-cm})^{-1}$

4.11 (a) $N_d = 9.26 \times 10^{14}$ cm^{-3}
(b) (i) $T = 200\,\text{K}(-75^\circ\text{C})$, $\mu_n \approx 2500$ cm^2/V-s,
$\rho = 2.7$ Ω-cm; (ii) $T = 400\,\text{K}(125^\circ\text{C})$,
$\mu_n \approx 700$ cm^2/V-s, $\rho = 9.64$ Ω-cm

4.13 (a) $v_d = 2.4 \times 10^4$ cm/s, $E = 1.77 \times 10^{-7}$ eV;
(b) $v_d = 2.4 \times 10^6$ cm/s, $E = 1.77 \times 10^{-3}$ eV

4.17 $\mu = 316$ cm^2/V-s

4.19 $\mu = 167$ cm^2/V-s

4.23 $p(50\,\mu\text{m}) = 2.97 \times 10^{14}$ cm^{-3}

4.25 $I_p = 0.96$ mA

4.27 (a) $J = 16$ A/cm^2; (b) and
(c) same as (a)

4.29 $J_p = 3.41 \exp\left(\dfrac{-x}{22.5}\right)$ (A/cm^2)

4.31 (a) $J_{p,dif} = +1.6 \exp\left(\dfrac{-x}{L}\right)$ (A/cm^2)

(b) $J_{n,drf} = 4.8 - 1.6 \exp\left(\dfrac{-x}{L}\right)$ (A/cm^2)

(c) $\mathcal{E} = \left[3 - 1 \times \exp\left(\dfrac{-x}{L}\right)\right]$ (V/cm)

4.33 (a) $n = n_i \exp\left(\dfrac{0.4 - 2.5 \times 10^2 x}{kT}\right)$
(b) (i) $J_n = -2.95 \times 10^3$ A/cm^2
(ii) $J_n = -23.7$ A/cm^2

4.35 (a) $\mathcal{E} = \alpha(kT/e)$ (b) $V = -(kT/e)$

4.37 $N_d(x) = N_d(0)\exp(-\alpha x)$, where
$\alpha = 3.86 \times 10^4$ cm^{-1}

4.43 $R = 5 \times 10^{19}$ cm^{-3}s^{-1}

4.45 (a) $\tau_n = 8.89 \times 10^6$ s,
(b) and (c) $G_0 = R_0 = 1.125 \times 10^9$ cm^{-3}s^{-1}

4.47 (a) $V_H = 2.19$ mV, (b) $\mathcal{E}_H = 0.219$ V/cm

4.49 (a) p type, (b) $p = 8.08 \times 10^{15}$ cm^{-3},
(c) $\mu_p = 387$ cm^2/V-s

4.51 (a) n type, (b) $n = 8.68 \times 10^{14}$ cm^{-3},
(c) $\mu_n = 8182$ cm^2/V-s,
(d) $\rho = 0.88$ (Ω-cm)

Chapter 5

5.1 (a) For $N_d = 10^{15}$ cm^{-3},

N_a (cm^{-3})	V_{bi} (V)
10^{15}	0.575
10^{16}	0.635
10^{17}	0.695
10^{18}	0.754

5.3 (a)

($N_a = N_d$) (cm^{-3})	V_{bi} (V)
10^{14}	0.456
10^{15}	0.575
10^{16}	0.695
10^{17}	0.814
10^{18}	0.933

5.5 (a) n type, $E_F - E_{Fi} = 0.3294$ eV;
p type, $E_{Fi} - E_F = 0.4070$ eV;
(b) $V_{bi} = 0.3294 + 0.4070 = 0.7364$ eV;
(c) $V_{bi} = 0.7363$ eV; (d) $x_n = 0.426$ μm,
$x_p = 0.0213$ μm, $|\mathcal{E}|_{\max} = 3.29 \times 10^4$ V/cm

5.7 (b) $n_0 = N_d = 8.43 \times 10^{15}$ cm^{-3} (n side),
$p_0 = N_a = 9.97 \times 10^{15}$ cm^{-3} (p side);
(c) $V_{bi} = 0.690$ V

5.9 (a) $V_{bi} = 0.635$ V; (b) $x_n = 0.864$ μm,
$x_p = 0.0864$ μm;
(d) $\mathcal{E}_{\max} = 1.34 \times 10^4$ V/cm

5.11 (a) $V_{bi} = 0.8556$ V, (b) $T_2 = 312$ K

5.13 (a) $V_{bi} = 0.456$ V, (b) $x_n = 2.43 \times 10^{-7}$ cm,
(c) $x_p = 2.43 \times 10^{-3}$ cm,
(d) $\mathcal{E}_{\max} = 3.75 \times 10^2$ V/cm

5.17 (a) $V_{bi} = 0.856$ V; (b) $x_n = 0.251$ μm,
$x_p = 0.0503$ μm; (c) $\mathcal{E}_{\max} = 3.89 \times 10^5$ V/cm;
(d) $C_T = 3.44$ pF

5.19 (a) Factor of 1.414, (b) $\Delta V_{bi} = 17.95$ mV

5.21 (a) $V_R = 72.8$ V, (b) $V_R = 7.18$ V,
(c) $V_R = 0.570$ V

5.23 $V_{R2} = 18.6$ V

5.25 $N_d \approx 3.24 \times 10^{17}$ cm^{-3}

5.27 (a) $V_{bi} = 0.557$ V;
(b) $x_p = 5.32 \times 10^{-6}$ cm, $x_n = 2.66 \times 10^{-4}$ cm;
(c) $V_R = 70.4$ V

5.29 (a) (i) For $V_R = 0$, $C = 1.14$ pF;
(ii) for $V_R = 3$ V, $C = 0.521$ pF;
(iii) for $V_R = 6$ V, $C = 0.389$ pF

5.33 (a) $\mathcal{E}(0) = 7.73 \times 10^4$ V/cm;
(c) $\phi_1 = 3.86$ V, $\phi_i = 15.5$ V, $V_R = 23.2$ V

5.35 (a) $\phi_{B0} = 1.09$ V, (b) $V_{bi} = 0.825$ V,
(c) $W = 1.03 \times 10^{-4}$ cm,
(d) $|\mathcal{E}|_{\max} = 1.59 \times 10^4$ V/cm

5.37 (a) $V_{bi} \approx 0.75$ V, (b) $N_d = 9.89 \times 10^{15}$ cm^{-3},
(c) $\phi_n = 0.10$ V, (d) $\phi_{B0} = 0.85$ V

5.39 (a) $V_D = 0.596$ V, (b) $V_D = 0.667$ V

5.41 $V_D = 1.02$ V

5.43 $A = 1.62 \times 10^{-3}$ cm^2

5.45 (b) $N_d = 1.24 \times 10^{16}$ cm^{-3},
(c) barrier height $= 0.20$ V

Chapter 6

6.1 (a) p type, inversion; (c) p type, accumulation

6.3 (a) $N_d \approx 3.28 \times 10^{14}$ cm^{-3}, so $\phi_{Fn} = 0.2588$ V;
(b) $\phi_s = -2\phi_{Fn} = -0.518$ V

6.5 (a) From Fig. 6.21, $N_d \approx 3 \times 10^{16}$ cm^{-3};
(b) p$^+$ poly gate: impossible;
(c) from Fig. 6.21, $N_d \approx 4 \times 10^{14}$ cm^{-3}

6.7 $Q'_{ss}/e = 1.2 \times 10^{10}$ cm^{-2}

6.9 (a) $\phi_{ms} \approx -0.32$ V, $V_{TP} = -1.18$ V;
(b) $\phi_{ms} \approx -0.47$ V, $V_{TP} = -1.33$ V;
(c) $\phi_{ms} \approx +0.98$ V, $V = +0.12$ V

6.11 By trial and error, $N_a \approx 3.37 \times 10^{16}$ cm^{-3}

6.13 (a) $V_{FB} = -1.52$ V, (b) $V_T = -0.764$ V

6.15 (b) $\phi_{ms} = -1.11$ V,
(c) $V_{TN} = +0.0012$ V

6.19 For $t_{ox} = 20$ Å, $V_{TN} = -0.223$ V;
for $t_{ox} = 500$ Å, $V_{TN} = +0.236$ V

6.21 (a) $C'_{\min} = 0.797 \times 10^{-8}$ F/cm^2,
(b) $C'(\text{inv}) = C_{ox} = 8.63 \times 10^{-8}$ F/cm^2

6.23 (a) $\Delta V_{FB} = -1.74$ V, (b) $\Delta V_{FB} = -0.869$ V,
(c) $\Delta V_{FB} = -1.16$ V

6.27 (a) n type, (b) $t_{ox} = 345$ Å,
(c) $Q'_{ss}/e = 1.875 \times 10^{11}$ cm^{-2},
(d) $C_{FB} = 156$ pF

6.31 (a)

V_{SG} (V)	V_{SD}(sat) (V)	I_D(sat) (mA)
1	0.2	0.00592
2	1.2	0.213
3	2.2	0.716
4	3.2	1.52
5	4.2	2.61

6.35

$V_{DS} = V_{GS}$ (V)	I_D (mA)
0	0
1	0.0133
2	0.48
3	1.61
4	3.41
5	5.87

6.37 $V_T \approx 0.2$ V, $\mu_n = 342$ cm²/V-s

6.39   (a) $W/L = 14.7$, (b) $W/L = 25.7$

6.41   (a) $g_{mL} = 0.148$ mA/V,
(b) $g_{ms} = 0.947$ mA/V

6.43 $V_{BS} = 7.92$ V

6.47   (a) $f_T = 5.17$ GHz,
(b) $f_T = 1.0$ GHz

Chapter 7

7.1   (a) $I_D \Rightarrow \approx k I_D$, (b) $P \Rightarrow k^2 P$

7.3   (a) (i) $I_D = 1.764$ mA, (ii) $I_D = 0.807$ mA;
(b) (i) $P = 8.82$ mW, (ii) $P = 2.42$ mW

7.5   (a) $L = 0.606$ μm, (b) $L = 3.77$ μm

7.9   (a) $r_0 = 59.8$ kΩ, (b) $r_0 = 13.8$ kΩ

7.15 $L = 1.59$ μm

7.21 $\Delta V_T = +0.118$ V

7.25   (a) $V_{BD} = 15$ V, (b) $V_{BD} = 5$ V

7.27 $V_{DS} = 2.08$ V; ideal, $V_{DS} = 4.9$ V

7.29 $L = 1.08$ μm

7.31   (a) $V_T = -3.74$ V,
(b) $D_I = 9.32 \times 10^{11}$ cm^{-2}

7.33

V_{SB} (V)	ΔV_T (V)
1	0.0443
3	0.0987
5	0.138

7.35   Donors, $D_I = 7.55 \times 10^{11}$ cm^{-2}

Chapter 8

8.1 $R' = 5 \times 10^{19}$ cm^{-3}s^{-1}

8.5 $dF_p^+/dx = -2 \times 10^{19}$ cm^{-3}s^{-1}

8.7 $n = 3.6 \times 10^{13}$ cm^{-3}, $p = 1.6 \times 10^{13}$ cm^{-3}, so
$D' = 58.4$ cm²/s, $\mu' = -868$ cm²/V-s, $\tau_n = 54$ μs

8.9 $\sigma = 8 + 0.114[1 - \exp(-t/\tau_{p0})]$ (Ω-cm)$^{-1}$,
where $\tau_{p0} = 10^{-7}$ s

8.11 $I = [54 + 2.20 \exp(-t/\tau_{p0})]$ (mA), where
$\tau_{p0} = 3 \times 10^{-7}$ s

8.13   (a) $R_p'/R_{p0} = 4.44 \times 10^8$, (b) $\tau_{p0} = 2.25 \times 10^{-6}$ s

8.15   (a) For $0 < t < 2 \times 10^{-6}$ s,
$\delta n = 10^{14}[1 - \exp(-t/\tau_{n0})]$; for $t > 2 \times 10^{-6}$ s,
$\delta n = 0.865 \times 10^{14} \exp[-(t - 2 \times 10^{-6})/\tau_{n0}]$

8.17   (a) p type, $p_{p0} = 10^{14}$ cm^{-3},
$n_{p0} = 2.25 \times 10^6$ cm^{-3}
(b) $\delta n(0) = -2.25 \times 10^6$ cm^{-3},
(c) $\delta n = -n_{p0} \exp(-x/L_n)$

8.23   For $-L < x < +L$, $\delta p = \dfrac{G_0'}{2D_p}(5L^2 - x^2)$;

for $L < x < 3L$, $\delta p = \dfrac{G_0' L}{D_p}(3L - x)$;

for $-3L < x < -L$, $\delta p = \dfrac{G_0' L}{D_p}(3L + x)$

8.27 $E_{Fn} - E_{Fi} = 0.3498$ eV,
$E_{Fi} - E_{Fp} = 0.2877$ eV

8.29   (a) $E_{Fn} - E_{Fi} = 0.6253$ eV,
$E_F - E_{Fi} = 0.6228$ eV,
$E_{Fn} - E_F = 0.0025$ eV;
(b) $E_{Fi} - E_{Fp} = 0.5632$ eV

8.31   (a) $\delta p = 5 \times 10^{12}$ cm^{-3}, low injection;
(b) $E_{Fn} - E_{Fi} = 0.1505$ eV

8.33

δn (cm^{-3})	$E_{Fn} - E_F$ (eV)
10^{12}	0.4561
10^{13}	0.5157
10^{14}	0.5754

8.35   (a) $R/\delta n = 1/\tau_{p0} = 10^{+7}$ s^{-1},
(b) $R/\delta n = 1/(\tau_{p0} + \tau_{n0}) = 1.67 \times 10^{+6}$ s^{-1},
(c) $R/\delta n = 1/\tau_{n0} = 2 \times 10^{+6}$ s^{-1}

Chapter 9

9.1   (a) $\Delta V = 59.6$ mV ≈ 60 mV,
(b) $\Delta V = 119.3$ mV ≈ 120 mV

9.5   (a) $\dfrac{J_n}{J_n + J_p} = \dfrac{1}{1 + (2.04)(N_a/N_d)}$,

(b) $\dfrac{J_n}{J_n + J_p} = \dfrac{\sigma_n/\sigma_p}{(\sigma_n/\sigma_p) + 4.90}$

9.7 $\dfrac{N_a}{N_d} = 0.083$

9.9 $I_s = 2.89 \times 10^{-9}$ A, (a) $I = 6.52$ μA,
(b) $I = -2.89$ nA

9.11   (a) $I_{p0} = 4.02 \times 10^{-14}$ A,
(b) $I_{n0} = 6.74 \times 10^{-15}$ A,
(c) $p_n = 3.42 \times 10^{10}$ cm^{-3},
(d) $I_n = 3.43 \times 10^{-9}$ A

9.13   (a) $V_a = 0.253$ V, (b) $V_a = 0.635$ V

9.15 $E_{g2} = 0.769$ eV

9.23 (a) For $I = 1$ mA, $V_a = 0.278$ V;
for $I = 10$ mA, $V_a = 0.338$ V;
for $I = 100$ mA, $V_a = 0.398$ V;
(b) for $I = 1$ mA, $V_a = 0.125$ V;
for $I = 10$ mA, $V_a = 0.204$ V;
for $I = 100$ mA, $V_a = 0.284$ V

9.27 $A = 1.62 \times 10^{-3}$ cm^2

9.29 (a) For the pn junction, $V_a = 0.691$ V;
for the Schottky junction, $V_a = 0.445$ V;
(b) for the pn junction, $I = 120$ mA;
for the Schottky junction, $I = 53.7$ mA

9.31 For $f = 10$ kHz; $Z = 25.9 - j0.0814$;
for $f = 100$ kHz; $Z = 25.9 - j0.814$;
for $f = 1$ MHz; $Z = 23.6 - j7.41$;
for $f = 10$ MHz; $Z = 2.38 - j7.49$

9.33 $\tau_{p0} = 1.3 \times 10^{-7}$ s, at 1 mA, $C_d = 2.5 \times 10^{-9}$ F

9.35 (a) $R_p = 26$ Ω, $R_n = 46.3$ Ω, $R = 72.3$ Ω;
(b) $I = 1.38$ mA

9.37 $I_D = 0.539$ mA, $V_a = 0.443$ V

9.39 $J_s = 8.62 \times 10^{-18}$ A/cm^2,
$J_{gen} = 1.93 \times 10^{-9}$ A/cm^2

9.41 (a) $I_S = 5.75 \times 10^{-22}$ A, $I_{gen} = 6.15 \times 10^{-13}$ A;
ideal diffusion current:
for $V_a = 0.3$ V, $I_D = 6.17 \times 10^{-17}$ A;
for $V_a = 0.5$ V, $I_D = 1.39 \times 10^{-13}$ A;
recombination current:
for $V_a = 0.3$ V, $I_{rec} = 7.97 \times 10^{-11}$ A;
for $V_a = 0.5$ V, $I_{rec} = 3.36 \times 10^{-9}$ A

9.45 $J_{gen} = 1.5 \times 10^{-3}$ A/cm^2

9.47 $N_B = N_d = 1.73 \times 10^{16}$ cm^{-3}

9.49 $V_B \approx 75$ V

9.51 $V_B \approx 95$ V, $x_n(\text{min}) = 4.96$ μm

9.53 (a) $V_R = 4.35$ kV, (b) $V_R = 17.4$ kV; Breakdown is reached first in each case.

9.55 (a) $t_s/\tau_{p0} = 0.956$, (b) $t_s/\tau_{p0} = 0.228$

9.57 $t_s = 1.1 \times 10^{-7}$ s, $C_{avg} = 11.1$ pF,
so $\tau_s = 1.11 \times 10^{-7}$ s;
turn-off time $= t_s + \tau_s = 2.21 \times 10^{-7}$ s

Chapter 10

10.3 (a) $I_S = 3.2 \times 10^{-14}$ A; (b) (i) $i_C = 7.75$ μA,
(ii) $i_C = 0.368$ mA, (iii) $i_C = 17.5$ mA

10.5 (a) $\beta = 85$, $\alpha = 0.9884$, $i_E = 516$ μA;
(b) $\beta = 53$, $\alpha = 0.9815$, $i_E = 2.70$ mA

10.7 (b) $I_C = 4.7$ mA

10.9 (a) $p_{E0} = 4.5 \times 10^2$ cm^{-3},
$n_{B0} = 2.25 \times 10^4$ cm^{-3},
$p_{C0} = 2.25 \times 10^5$ cm^{-3};

(b) $n_B(0) = 6.80 \times 10^{14}$ cm^{-3},
$p_E(0) = 1.36 \times 10^{13}$ cm^{-3}

10.11 (a) 0.9950, (b) 0.648, (c) 9.08×10^{-5}

10.15 (c) For the ideal case, for $x_B \ll L_B$, $\dfrac{J(x_B)}{J(0)} = 1$;
for $x_B = L_B = 10$ μm, $J(0) = -1.68$ A/cm^2
and $J(x_B) = -1.089$ A/cm^2

10.17 (a) $V_{CB} = 0.70$ V, (b) $V_{EC}(\text{sat}) = 0.05$ V,
(c) $Q_{pB}/e = 3.41 \times 10^{11}$ cm^{-2},
(d) $N_{coll} = 8.82 \times 10^{13}$ cm^{-2}

10.19 $V_{CB} = 0.48$ V

10.21 (a) $n_B(0) = 5.45 \times 10^{11}$ cm^{-3}, $I_C = 17.4$ μA;
(b) $\alpha_T = 0.9975$, $\gamma = 0.909$,
$\alpha = 0.9067$, $\beta = 9.72$,
$I_C = 1.36$ mA;
(c) $I_C = 19.4$ μA

10.23 (a) (i) $\dfrac{\gamma(B)}{\gamma(A)} = 1 - \dfrac{N_{B0}}{N_E} \dfrac{D_E}{D_B} \dfrac{x_B}{x_E}$, (ii) $\dfrac{\gamma(C)}{\gamma(A)} = 1$;
(b) (i) $\dfrac{\alpha_T(B)}{\alpha_T(A)} = 1$, (ii) $\dfrac{\alpha_T(C)}{\alpha_T(A)} \approx 1 + \dfrac{x_{B0}}{2L_B}$

10.25 (b) $I_C = 1.19$ mA, $I_E = 0.829$ mA

10.27 (a) $\delta = \dfrac{1}{1 + (15.5)\exp(-V_{BE}/0.0518)}$

(b)

V_{BE} (V)	δ	β
0.20	0.754	3.07
0.40	0.993	142
0.60	0.99986	7142

10.29 (a) $x_B = 0.740$ μm, (b) $\delta = 0.9999994$

10.35 (a) $V_A = 47.8$ V, (b) $V_A = 33.4$ V,
(c) $V_A = 19.0$ V

10.37 (a)

N_E	γ	α	β
10^{17}	0.5	0.495	0.980
10^{18}	0.909	0.8999	8.99
10^{19}	0.990	0.980	49
10^{20}	0.9990	0.989	89.9

(b)

N_E	ΔE_g (meV)	γ	α	β
10^{17}	0	0.5	0.495	0.98
10^{18}	25	0.792	0.784	3.63
10^{19}	80	0.820	0.812	4.32
10^{20}	230	0.122	0.121	0.14

10.39 (a) $R = 893\ \Omega$, (b) $V = 8.93$ mV,

(c) $\dfrac{n_p(S/2)}{n_p(0)} = 70.8$ percent

10.43 $BV_{CB0} = 221$ V, so $N_C \approx 1.5 \times 10^{15}$ cm^{-3}; $x_C = 6.75\ \mu$m

10.45 (a) $V_{pt} = 295$ V, but breakdown voltage is ≈ 70 V.

10.47 (a) $\tau_e = 41.4$ ps, $\tau_b = 98$ ps, $\tau_c = 4.8$ ps, $\tau_d = 20$ ps; (b) $\tau_{ec} = 164.2$ ps, $f_T = 969$ MHz, $f_\beta = 19.4$ MHz

10.49 $\tau_d = 12$ ps, $\tau_c = 1$ ps, $f_T = 1.15$ GHz

Chapter 11

11.1 (a) $V_{p0} = 5.795$ V, $V_p = 4.91$ V; (b) (i) $a - h = 0.215\ \mu$m, (ii) $a - h = 0.0653\ \mu$m, (iii) no undepleted region

11.3 (a) $V_{p0} = 15.5$ V, (b) $V_{GS} = -4.67$ V

11.5 (a) $V_{p0} = 1.863$ V, $V_p = 0.511$ V; (b) (i) $a - h = 4.44 \times 10^{-6}$ cm, (ii) no undepleted region

11.7 (a) $V_{GS} = -1.125$ V, (b) $V_{GS} = -0.125$ V

Chapter 12

12.1 (a) Ge: $\lambda = 1.88\ \mu$m, Si: $\lambda = 1.11\ \mu$m, GaAs: $\lambda = 0.873\ \mu$m;

(b) $\lambda = 570$ nm $\Rightarrow E = 2.18$ eV, $\lambda = 700$ nm $\Rightarrow E = 1.77$ eV

12.3 $g' = 1.44 \times 10^{19}$ cm^{-3}s^{-1}, $\delta n = 1.44 \times 10^{13}$ cm^{-3}

12.5 $\alpha \approx 0.7 \times 10^4$ cm^{-1}, (a) $x = 1.98\ \mu$m, (b) $x = 0.41\ \mu$m

12.9

N_a (cm^{-3})	J_S (A/cm^2)	V_{0C} (V)
10^{15}	3.48×10^{-17}	0.891
10^{16}	3.48×10^{-18}	0.950
10^{17}	3.48×10^{-19}	1.01
10^{18}	3.54×10^{-20}	1.07

12.11 $V_m = 0.577$ V $I_m = 478.3$ mA, $P_m = 276$ mW

12.13 For $h\nu = 1.7$ eV, $\alpha \approx 10^4$ cm^{-1}, so $x = 2.3\ \mu$m; for $h\nu = 2.0$ eV, $\alpha \approx 10^5$ cm^{-1}, so $x = 0.23\ \mu$m

12.15 (a) $\delta p = \delta n = 10^{13}$ cm^{-3}, (b) $\Delta\sigma = 1.32 \times 10^{-2}$ (Ω-cm)$^{-1}$, (c) $I_L = 0.66$ mA, (d) $\Gamma_{ph} = 4.13$

12.17 (a) $J_{L1} = 9.92$ mA/cm^2, (b) $J_L = 0.528$ A/cm^2

12.19 For $W = 1\ \mu$m, $J_L = 4.15$ mA/cm^2; for $W = 10\ \mu$m, $J_L = 15.2$ mA/cm^2; for $W = 100\ \mu$m, $J_L = 16$ mA/cm^2

12.21 (a) 8.81 percent, (b) 5.94 percent

INDEX

Note: Page numbers followed by *f* and *t* refer to figures and tables, respectively.